ENVIRONMENTAL MANAGEMENT IN PRACTICE

Edited by **Elzbieta Broniewicz**

Environmental Management in Practice
Edited by Elzbieta Broniewicz

Published by InTech
Janeza Trdine 9, 51000 Rijeka, Croatia

Publishing Process Manager Davor Vidic

Technical Editor Teodora Smiljanic

Cover Designer InTech Design Team

Additional hard copies can be obtained from orders@intechopen.com

Environmental Management in Practice, Edited by Elzbieta Broniewicz
p. cm.
ISBN 978-953-307-358-3

We are IntechOpen,
the world's leading publisher of
Open Access books
Built by scientists, for scientists

4,000+
Open access books available

116,000+
International authors and editors

120M+
Downloads

Our authors are among the

151
Countries delivered to

Top 1%
most cited scientists

12.2%
Contributors from top 500 universities

WEB OF SCIENCE™

Selection of our books indexed in the Book Citation Index
in Web of Science™ Core Collection (BKCI)

Interested in publishing with us?
Contact book.department@intechopen.com

Numbers displayed above are based on latest data collected.
For more information visit www.intechopen.com

Meet the editor

Dr. Elzbieta Broniewicz is a graduate of environmental engineering on Technical University in Bialystok, Poland. In 1998 she received her PhD in the field of economics. In her teaching and scientific work she combines engineering with economics. The main fields of her interest are: environmental expenditure accounts, environmental goods and services sector, environmental management system and environmental impact assessment.

In recent years the topic of environmental management has become very common. In sustainable development conditions, central and local governments much more often notice the need of acting in ways that diminish negative impact on environment.

Contents

Preface

In recent years the topic of environmental management has become very common. In sustainable development conditions, central and local governments much more often notice the need of acting in ways that diminish negative impact on environment.

Environmental management may take place on many different levels – starting from global level, e.g. climate changes, through national and regional level (environmental policy) and ending on micro level. This publication shows many examples of environmental management.

In the chapters dealing with national and regional level of environmental management, authors have presented many different aspects: communication system, environmental costs, regional development indicators. Case studies from various world regions have also been included.

The second section of the book deals with environmental management in various industries. It presents sustainable business practices in construction industry, pulp and paper industry. Case studies in organizations have been a welcome addition to this section.

The last section focuses on technical aspects of environmental management, mainly on water, waste and wastewater management.

The diversity of presented aspects within environmental management and approaching the subject from the perspective of various countries contributes greatly to the development of environmental management field of research.

I would like to thank all of the authors for presenting high quality chapters, Mr. Vidic for efficient project management and all InTech staff for making this publication possible.

PhD Elzbieta Broniewicz,
Technical University of Bialystok
Poland

Part 1

Environmental Management
at the National and Regional Level

Curbing Climate Change through a National Development of Climate Change Policy

Sumiani Yusoff
University of Malaya
Malaysia

1. Introduction

In the last century, global development trends have tended to favour democratic systems and the capitalist ideology. In turn more equitable, economically secure, technologically advanced and intellectually progressive societies have developed around the world. However, at the same time, the side-effects of these trends have also been the creation of a materialistic society, high energy and resource consuming economy alongside inevitable, irreversible environmental damage and resource plundering. Economic analysis has a special role in contemporary national policy-making, as most of the important decisions fall within the economic domain. A country's development level is principally measured by its GDP or monetary economic growth. Therefore, an economic model that is less materialistic and less energy demanding have to be introduced to achieve sustainable development, especially in the long-run. The development of a sustainable economic model has to recognise the environmental impact as part of the development agenda and finding a viable relationship between the two components. One common idea is to internalise the environmental impact into the economic scene with benefits to society and economy at large. To achieve the sustainable economic model, innovative policy instruments are essential in creating the necessary shifts in economic trends or patterns. A climate change policy plays a role in directing a country towards a sustainable economic development model by regulating the GHGs emission with appropriate sectoral policies in place.

2. Non-renewable energy and carbon emission

With 0.4 per cent of the world's population, Malaysia's 27 million people accounted for 0.6 per cent of the global carbon emissions. As a developing country, Malaysia's carbon emissions growth is one of the fastest; it grew by 221 per cent from 1990 to 2004 (UNDP Human Development Report 2007/2008).[1] Malaysia's rapid rise in its carbon emissions is the result of robust expansion in its industrial and automotive sectors, the over dependence on fossil fuel as its TPES (Total Primary Energy Supply), unsustainable waste management and forest and grassland conversion. With a CO_2 emission intensity of GDP of 1.198 million metric tonne (MT) / USD million (IMF & CDIAC, 2006); Malaysia has one of the highest

---

[1] Source: UNDP Human Development Report 2007/2008.
< http://hdr.undp.org/en/media/HDR_20072008_Summary_English.pdf>

carbon emission intensity of GDP in the world, indicated a low economy output to carbon emission.

Malaysia had announced that it is taking a voluntary reduction of up to 40 per cent carbon emission intensity of GDP by the year 2020 compared to 2005 level at Copenhagen in 2009 (Theseira, 2010). To reach the carbon emission reduction, substantial action has to be taken. This requires first and foremost a viable policy on climate change to achieve this goal.

Country	Annual CO2 emissions (in '000 MT)	GDP (in billions of USD)	CO2 intensity of GDP (million MT / USD billion)
Malaysia	187,865	156.86	1.198
Thailand	272,521	206.99	1.317
Indonesia	333,483	364.35	0.915
Mexico	436,150	952.34	0.458
Argentina	173,536	212.71	0.816
Turkey	269,452	529.19	0.509
Sweden	50,875	393.76	0.129
UK	568,520	2,435.70	0.233
US	5,752,289	13,178.35	0.437
Japan	1,293,409	4,363.63	0.296

Table 1. Comparison of the carbon dioxide emissions intensity of GDP in 2006[2]

A high carbon emission intensity of GDP would normally display the following results in the economy: The major sectors that drive the country's economic growth have high carbon emissions with GDP by sector: Industrial: 42.3 per cent, Services: 47.6 per cent and Agricultural: 10.1 per cent (CIA, 2005). In 2000, the country's total primary energy supply (TPES) was 49.47 million tons of oil equivalents (MTOE). The greatest percentage of the Malaysian fuel mix is petroleum products. In 2006, the TPES increase to 68.33 MTOE and it is projected to grow at a 3.5 per cent per year to 147 MTOE in 2030 because of the increase in demand for coal, oil and gas; with coal demand accounting for the highest growth rate at 9.7 per cent per year through 2030 (IEA, 2008).

Higher energy use per GDP indicates a lower economy output per unit of energy use. Malaysia has one of the highest energy uses (oil equivalent) per unit GDP compared with the developed countries in the comparison lists. Although Malaysia shows a lower value compared with regional developing countries; the fossil fuel consumption in the total energy shares (95.5 per cent) is higher than Thailand (81.2 per cent) and Indonesia (68.8 per cent). This finding can deduce that Malaysia has the highest carbon emission intensity of GDP among the countries of comparison.

---

[2] Sources: GDP data - IMF (International Monetary Fund), 2006 CO2 emission - CDIAC (Carbon Dioxide Information Analysis Center), 2006

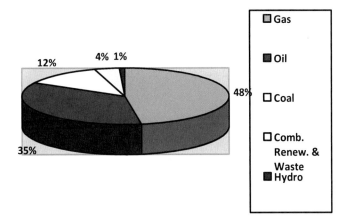

Fig. 1. Malaysia's shares of TPES in 2007[3]

Country	MT of CO2 emission/ capita	Energy use (kg of oil equivalent per capita)	Energy use (kt of oil equivalent)	Energy use / GDP (kt of oil equivalent / USD billion)	Fossil fuel energy consumption (% of total)
Malaysia	7.2	2733	72,589	462.76	95.5
Thailand	4.3	1553	103,991	502.40	81.2
Indonesia	1.5	849	190,647	523.25	68.8
Mexico	4.1	1750	184,262	193.48	89.3
Argentina	4.4	1850	73,065	343.50	89.5
Turkey	3.6	1370	100,005	188.98	90.5
Sweden	5.6	5512	50,422	128.05	32.9
UK	9.4	3464	211,308	86.76	89.6
US	19	7766	2,339,942	177.56	85.6
Japan	10.1	4019	513,519	117.68	83.2

*Energy use refers to the TPES
*Fossil fuel refers to coal, oil and natural gas

Table 2. Comparison of energy use and fossil fuel consumption, 2007[4]

3. Unsustainable electricity production

Energy in Malaysia is consumed mainly in the transportation and industrial sectors, 38.2 per cent and 37.8 per cent respectively in 2005, followed by commercial and residential sectors at 12.5 per cent and the non-energy, which consumes 9.7 per cent of the total energy. Electrical energy production increased from 1,622 gigawatt per hour (GWh) in 1963 to 4,971

---

[3] Source: IEA (International Energy Agency), 2008.
<http://www.iea.org/stats/pdf_graphs/MYTPESPI.pdf>
[4] Source: CDIAC, 2006; IEA, 2007; IMF, 2006.

GWh in 1974 and 57,435 GWh in 1998. In 1996, 16 per cent of electrical production was hydro generated, and over 83 per cent was of thermal origin (National Energy Balance, PTM, 2006). In 2007, the country hit a staggering 101325 GWh of total electricity production with only about 6.4 per cent was hydro generated, (coal 29.5 per cent, natural gas 62 per cent and oil 2.1 per cent) according to the statistic shown by IEA in 2010.

Country	Electricity consumption* (TWh)	Electricity Consumption /Population (kWh/capita)	Electricity (production by source) %			
			Fossil fuel*	hydro	nuclear	others
Malaysia	97.39	3668	93.6	6.4	-	-
Thailand	137.68	2157	91.4	5.7	-	2.9
Indonesia	127.17	564	87.1	7.9	-	5.0
Mexico	214.34	2028	81.4	10.6	4.0	4.0
Argentina	104.99	2658	65.8	26.7	6.3	1.2
Turkey	163.35	2210	80.9	18.7	-	0.4
Sweden	139.40	15238	2.4	44.5	45.0	8.1
UK	373.36	6142	77.6	2.3	15.9	4.2
US	4113.07	13616	71.6	6.3	19.2	2.9
Japan	1082.72	8475	66.8	7.4	23.3	2.5

*Gross production + imports - exports - transmission/distribution losses
*Fossil fuel refers to oil, gas and coal

Table 3. Electricity production by source in 2007[5]

The country's electricity consumption per capita is higher than the regional and other developing countries in the comparison list. Furthermore, the share of fossil fuel of the electricity production is the highest among all the countries in comparison. From the brief findings, it can be deduced that the factor contribute to the high carbon emission in any major sectors is the non-renewable energy supply. To reduce the carbon emission in any sector, a fundamental shift in the country's TPES to a higher share of renewable energy is an imperative determinant.

4. Climate change related policies in Malaysia

In general, Malaysia adopts a "precautionary principle" policy with actions to mitigate or adapt to climate change. A National Climate Committee was formed in 1995 with various government agencies, stakeholders from the business and civil society groups. The strategies adopted by the committee include to reduce the heavy reliance on fossil fuel in energy sector, promote renewable energy and energy efficiency, public awareness programme, sustainable forest management, ensure food sufficiency and undertaking coastal vulnerability index (CVI) study that serve as a basis for the development of adaptive

---

[5] Source: IEA, 2010.

measures to mitigate the impact of sea level rise. (Conservation and Environment Management Division, CEMD, 2007)

Existing relevant policies in the country that will, directly or indirectly affect the development of an integrated and coherent climate change policy include:

1. National Policy on the Environment, 2002
2. National Forestry Policy, 1978
3. National Policy on Biological Diversity, 1998
4. National Energy Policy, 1979
5. National Automotive Policy, 2009
6. Third National Agricultural Policy, 1998-2010
7. National Physical Plan, 2006

5. National renewable energy policy 2011

Based on the data below (see Table 4), about 40-50 per cent of the carbon emissions originated from the energy and industrial sector. The emission from the industrial activities is mainly attributed to the energy sector as well. Therefore, the focus has to be on the energy sector in order to achieve any significant reduction goal.

Rank	Sub-sector	GHGs	Emission, CO_2e (mil. MT)	Percentage
1	Emission from energy industries	CO_2	58,486	28.2
2	Transportation	CO_2	35,587	17.2
3	Manufacturing and construction	CO_2	26,104	12.6
4	Landfills	CH_4	24,541	11.8
5	Forest and grassland conversion	CO_2	24,111	11.6
6	Fugitive emissions from fuel	CH_4	21,987	10.60
7	Mineral products	CO_2	9,776	4.7
8	Emission from soil	CO_2	4,638	2.2
9	Commercial	CO_2	2,122	1.0
			207,352	99.9

Table 4. Key sources of GHGs emissions in Malaysia[6]

The key policies guiding energy-related activities in Malaysia consisted of:

- National Petroleum Policy 1975
- National Energy Policy 1979
- National Depletion Policy 1980
- Four Fuel Diversification Policy 1981
- Fifth Fuel Diversification Policy (Eighth Malaysia Plan 2001-2005)

In conjunction with these policies, a number of government supported projects to assist the National Energy Conservation plans, have been identified. Under the guidance and supervision of the Malaysia Energy Centre (PTM), some of the projects introduced are CDM (Clean Development Mechanisms), IRP (Integrated Resource Planning), MEDIS (Malaysia

[6] Source: Abdul Rahim Nik, FRIM (Forest Reserve Institute of Malaysia), 2009.

Energy Database and Information System), MIEEIP (Malaysian Industrial Energy Efficiency Improvement Project), BioGen (biomass power generation and co-generation in palm oil industry), MBIPV (Malaysian Building Integrated Photovoltaic Technology Application Project) and Demand Side Management.

The SREP (Small Renewable Energy Programme) allows Renewable Energy (RE) projects with up to 10 megawatt (MW) of capacity only. The programme was introduced during 8th Malaysia Plan (2001-2005) under the fifth fuel diversification policy which targeted a 5 per cent renewable energy share of total electricity generation; however failed to achieve its target. In 9th Malaysia Plan or 9th MP, (2006-2010), targeted RE capacity to be connected to power utility grid is 300MW in Peninsula Malaysia and 50MW in Sabah with a 1.8 per cent of total power generation mix (65 per cent natural gas, 36 per cent coal, 6 per cent hydro & 0.2 per cent oil). However, RE capacity connected to power utility grid as of 31st December 2009 was 53MW which is barely 15 per cent of 9th MP target. The off grid RE (private palm oil millers and solar hybrids) is more than 430MW (Badriyah, 2010).

The reasons for slow RE development are identified as market failure, absence of legal framework, lack of institutional measures and constraint in financial and technological aspects. A new ministry, Ministry of Energy, Water and Green Technology (KeTTHA) was formed in 2009 following the introduction of Green Technology Policy 2009. The ministry had formulated goals on sustainable use of energy and water. The ministry also provides incentive for the use of green technology. A new policy on renewable energy (National Renewable Energy Policy) will be introduced next year (Loo, 2010). With the new Act, a new feed-in tariff system will be introduced to stimulate the renewable energy sector. The policy statement is "Enhancing the utilization of indigenous renewable energy resources to contribute towards national electricity supply security and sustainable socio-economic development."

6. Potential carbon emission reductions in energy sector

The potential of carbon emissions reduction in energy sectors is discussed in this section. Comparison is made between the existing use of renewable energy and its potential in Malaysia. It is found that Malaysia has a vast potential in renewable energy as compared with the existing utilisation.

Renewable energy	Installed Capacity (MW)	Potential Capacity (MW)
Solar	6.2	6500
Wind	0.2	(low potential)
Municipal Solid Waste	-	400
Hydropower	2225 (year 2000)	22 000
Mini-Hydro	23.8	500
Biomass/Biogas	479	1300 (Palm Oil Waste)

Table 5. Comparison of currently installed and potential capacity of renewable energy[7]

---

[7] Source: Loh, T., Yusoff, S., 2009.

Year	Cumulative RE Capacity	RE Power Mix (vs Peak Demand)	Cumulative CO2 avoided
2010	73 MW	0.5%	0.3 mt
2015	985 MW	6%	11.1 mt
2020	2080 MW	11%	42.2 mt
2030	4000 MW	17%	145.1 mt

*RE capacity achievements are dependent on the size of RE fund
*Assumptions: Feed-in Tariff (FiT) in place & 15.6 per cent compound annual growth rate (CAGR) of RE power capacity from 2011 to 2030

Table 6. National Renewable Energy Target[8]

The current power generation capacity connected to the Malaysia National Grid is 19,023 MW in 2007 (Energy Commission, 2007). Based on the data in Table 4, the potential power generation by renewable energy is 30,700 MW, which is more than the current power generation. Therefore, if the country can reach 40% of the potential renewable energy capacity, 60% of the existing power generation will be from renewable energy. However, less than 10% of the potential renewable energy is utilized currently.

With the implementation of feed-in tariff, the RE power mix is projected to reach 11% in year 2020 (Badriyah, 2010) and the achievement of the 40% reduction of carbon intensity of GDP will be subjected to the country GDP growth. Therefore, the increase of the renewable energy share in the total power generation is a predominant agenda in the development of a climate change policy.

7. Draft national climate change policy

The policy study on climate change was conducted by CEMD under the Ministry of Natural Resource Environment (MNRE) in collaboration with LESTARI (Institute for Environment and Development). The study adopted a three-pronged approach to support the national positions at the UNFCCC and Kyoto Protocol meetings, formulation of a national policy and action plan, and delineation of state level responses to climate change adaptation and mitigation (Figure 2). The first approach is the critical review of several international and local research papers and public documents that was related to post-2012 responses, decision documents of the UNFCCC and Kyoto Protocol, Malaysia's Third Outline Perspective Plan (OPP3), Ninth Malaysia Plan (RMK9), relevant national policies, and Malaysia's Initial National Communication (INC). The second approach involved the comparative studies of national policies or strategies on climate change from selected countries and the third approach focused on stakeholder consultation through national and regional workshops, interviews and surveys which were carried out in a four overlapping phases. The need for a national policy on climate change was articulated in the first and second phase; while in the third and fourth phase, the policy framework including its key actions was supported as a promising tool to mainstream climate change in national development (Tan, et al, 2009).

---

[8] Source: Badriyah, KeTTHA, August 2010.

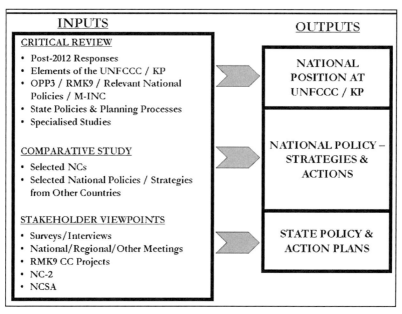

Fig. 2. Climate change policy study approach and expected outputs[9]

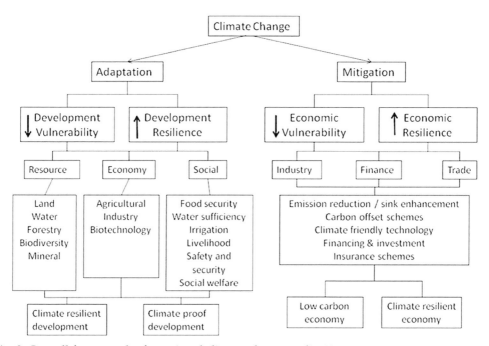

Fig. 3. Overall framework of a national climate change policy[10]

[9] Source: Tan, C. T.; Pereira, J. J. & Koh, F. P. (2009). Stakeholder Consultation in the Development of Climate Change Policy: Malaysia's Approach. Environmental Policy: A multinational conference on policy analysis and teaching methods, KDI School of Public Policy and Management, Seoul, Korea.

Objectives
• Mainstreaming of measures to address climate change challenges through strengthened economic competitiveness, wise management of resources, environmental conservation and enhanced quality of life for sustainable development.   • Integration of responses into national policies, plans and programmes to strengthen the resilience of development from arising impacts of climate change.   • Strengthening of institutional and implementation capacity to better harness opportunities in reducing negative impacts of climate change.
Principles/Strategic Thrusts
Principle 1. Development on a Sustainable Path: Integrate climate change responses in national development plans to fulfil the country's aspiration for sustainable development.   • Strategic Thrust 1. Facilitate the harmonisation of existing policies to address climate change adaptation and mitigation in a balanced manner.   • Strategic Thrust 2. Institute measures to make development climate-resilient through low carbon economy to enhance global competitiveness and attain environmentally sustainable socio-economic growth.   • Strategic Thrust 3. Support climate-resilient industrial development and investment in pursuit of sustainable socio-economic growth.   Principle 2. Sustainability of Environment and Natural Resources: Initiate actions on climate change issues that contribute to environmental conservation and sustainable use of natural resources while enhancing energy efficiency and sufficiency as well as water and food security.   • Strategic Thrust 1. Adopt balanced adaptation and mitigation measures to climate-proof development, strengthen environmental conservation and promote sustainability of natural resources   Principle 3. Integrated Planning and Implementation: Integrate planning and implementation to climate-proof development.   • Strategic Thrust 1. Institute measures to integrate cross-cutting issues in policies, plans, programmes and projects in order to increase resilience to and minimise negative impacts of climate change.   • Strategic Thrust 2. Support knowledge-based decision making through intensive climate related research and development and capacity building of human resources.   Principle 4. Effective Participation: Improve participation of stakeholders and major groups for effective implementation of climate change responses.   • Strategic Thrust 1. Improve collaboration through efficient communication and coordination among all stakeholders for effective implementation of climate change responses.   • Strategic Thrust 2. Increase awareness and public participation to promote behavioural responses to climate change.   Principle 5. Common but Differentiated Responsibility: International involvement on climate change will be based on the principle of common but differentiated responsibility.   • Strategic Thrust 1. Strengthen involvement in international activities on climate change based on the principle of common but differentiated responsibility.

Table 7. The Draft National Policy on Climate Change – Objectives, Principles and Strategic Thrusts[11]

---

[10] *Op. cit.* Tan, et al. (2009).
[11] Source: Pereira, 2008

8. Challenges in the development of climate change policy in Malaysia

8.1 Institutional reformation and policy restructuring

The formation of an institutional framework on climate change issue is the foundation to achieve any result in carbon emission. A clear cut government policy direction on sustainable development has to be established in the quest of achieving goal on carbon emission reduction. The agenda toward low carbon economy requires strong and persistent institutional reformation and political will and direction in a long term basis. A government's primary concerns are the country's economic growth and social welfare. Urgency and priority are the major considerations for the development of any public policy especially for a developing country. Tackling climate change issue or striving towards the sustainable development model is a long term planning process. A country abundant in natural resources may lack urgency in policy planning and implementation in climate change. Coordination and cooperation between various government agencies toward a achieving a common goal on carbon emission reduction is lacking at the moment. In the Malaysian context, political influence is always the prime mover in creating any trends as the decision making power is lacking among the civil servants. Another constraint in policy making process is the conflict in authority and power distribution between federal and state government.[12]

8.2 Lack of expertise in climate change issue

The R&D in climate change is relatively new in the country with concern on the matter is primarily driven by the signing and ratifying of Kyoto Protocol in carbon emission reduction and now more recently, the 40 per cent reduction of carbon emission intensity of GDP as pledged in COP 15. Local expertise on climate change issue especially the trend in the country is important and a proper data management plan needs to be implemented. The country need climate change experts that possess knowledge in climate change globally as well as have a strong understanding on the local socio economic development. Education from primary level is important to instil the understanding of climate change issue to the people since young. With proper education system, the topic can become more pertinent among the people and hopefully will produce more climate change experts.

8.3 Economic status (lack of financial capacity)

State of the art technology and solution to any environmental issue are readily available as solutions. The constraint is in its economic viability (*i.e.* pricing). The economic status does not allow solution for long term environmental issue which typically consume huge amount of money. For example, in waste management sector, the polluter pay principle (PPP) can directly encourage recycling. However it must be equipped with a proper pricing mechanism such as a variable unit based pricing scheme which will serve as a basis of the carrot and stick approach (Munasinghe, 2008). Another example is greywater or sullage that contributes to of 6 per cent of the total river point source pollution (DOE, 2001). The solution to sullage discharge is to retrofit the existing piping back to the sewer line for further treatment. However, the constraint is always related to the cost and priority. The DID (Department of Irrigation and Drainage) had introduced some measures in tackling river

---

[12] Based on the stakeholders discussion session at SLiM 2010 Roundtable: Creating an Institutional Framework for Implementing Sustainable Development (8th July)

pollution such as gross pollutant trap (GPT) and FOG (fat, oil and grease) trap, but these have not been very effective. The most pragmatic solution is sullage pipe retrofitting which is costly and require strong political will to implement it.[13] The same situation happens to renewable energy such as solar, biomass, biogas and the like. The example shows the inadequacy of financial capability in solving a pertinent local environmental issue.

8.4 Public understanding on climate change issue

Public understanding on environmental issue is imperative in the development of the climate change policy as it directly affect the life of an individual. In Malaysia, the understanding of climate change by the public at large is rather insufficient. For example, most of the people are not aware that driving a car or petrol consumption can lead to climate change by carbon emission. Awareness campaigns by the government or NGOs does not take into account the bigger picture provide an understanding of the cause of environmental issues such as climate change. The publicity drive by the government produces only a superficial understanding on the part of the general public so it does not accurately reflect or actually lead to good environmental practices as such. That is to say, the rhetoric is not matched by the reality of an environmentally-friendly situation.

One of the tools to analyse the entire environmental impacts of an issue is LCA (Life Cycle Assessment) which the public in general do not understand. One example is the issue of the banning on the use of plastic bags by certain states in the country. For most, plastic is something "negative" to the environment because of its non-biodegradable nature. Plastic which is beneficial as a "carrier" or for packaging may pose a problem when it comes to "inconsiderate" disposal, especially to any water bodies. However, banning the use of plastic bags will never solve the inconsiderate disposal problem and is myopic, impracticable and counter-productive. The solution has to be proper education and management since plastic bags are still a necessity as its use has yet to be outlasted by environmental concerns. The use of plastic packaging has lesser negative environmental impact if compared with other materials such as paper and metal because of the lower carbon emission in a life cycle perspective. In fact, plastic has reduced the consumption of fossil fuel on transportation and manufacturing. [14]

8.5 Equity in socio-economic development

An important social criterion must be that climate change should not be a hindrance to the development of a more equitable society where no one is made worse off. Thus, environmental policies must leave room for the proper allocation and distribution of resources in the pursuit of socio-economic welfare of the least better off in society. Furthermore, without an equitable society, environmental policies are very difficult to be implemented. For example, solar panel is burdensome for most middle and lower income household without incentives. The total elimination of logging activities will cause the loss of employment among low income workers. However there are also counter-examples: An effective public transport system can bring benefit to the poor as well as reduce carbon emission.

The development of a climate change policy has to include a concern of the poor as the policy may affect their livelihood. In a global perspective, the use of parameters like carbon

---

[13] (Keizrul, 2010, Public Lecture at Faculty of Engineering, University of Malaya, on World Water Day, 22nd March).

[14] Source: MPMA (Malaysian Plastics Manufacturers Association), 2010.

emission per GDP and per capita is questionable in relation to its applicability to all countries with differing levels of economic growth. Developed countries usually have a lower carbon emission per GDP but a higher carbon emission per capita; because of their high economy power. While developing countries usually have comparably higher carbon emission per GDP but lower carbon emission per capita. The measurement of emission with GDP (economy) correlation should be a short term parameter to provide incentive and opportunity for developing countries to boost their economy without much emission liability. However, for developed countries, the focus should be the emission per capita with the strong economy status. Kverndokk (1995)[15] argued that conventional justice and moral principles should favour the equitable allocation of future GHG emission rights on the basis of population, consistent with the UN human rights declaration underlining the equality of all human beings.

9. Discussion

The paper had introduced the existing carbon emission status in the country, two policies (National Renewable Energy and National Climate Change Policy) and identified the challenges of the development and implementation of these policies. To overcome the constraints arise in a viable approach, the climate change impacts have to be embedded into any policy development. Internalization of climate impacts in economic with mixed instruments, establishment of GHGs information centre, adaptation strategy and institutional redesigning and education at all levels are the keys to achieve the carbon reduction target.

9.1 Internalize climate change impact into the economy domain

As an externality in the current economy trend, environmental issue always meets the problem of market failure. To achieve any goal and substantial result in environmental issue, it has to be internalized in the economy domain by putting a price tag on it. When there is a price to pay for any environmental damage caused, people will be able to feel it. For example, climate change issue is something either people can't feel it or due to mere selfishness. Another example is landfill, which most people has never seen before and do not understand its negative impacts. The economic functions of the environment have to be valued for an internalization to happen. Three outlines for the evaluation of the functions are amenity services (natural beauty, recreational, etc), natural resources (minerals and non-minerals, forest, etc) and assimilation of waste products (land, water and air). With this perception of recognizing the economic value of environment, the traditional economic system and the environment will be dynamically interrelated (Munasinghe, 2008).

The entire activity or process of an environmental issue has to be integrated with price mechanism to create a "market based" solution. Market based instrument (MBI) is an economic approach to influence people to include environmental matters in any decision making. Some of the examples are tradable permits, polluter pay principle, green levy, eco-labeling, landfill tax, etc.

The polluter pay principle argues that those who create negative impact to the environment should pay the corresponding costs. The economic rationale is to provide alternatives and

---

[15] Source: Kverndokk, S., 1995. Tradeable CO_2 Emission Permits: Initial Distribution as a Justice Problem, Environmental Value, 4(2), 129-48. <http://www.frisch.uio.no/sammendrag/14_eng.html>

incentive for polluters to reduce their impact or emission to optimal level. This "carrot and stick" approach that incorporated in the principle can be further extended to principle of recompensing victim by using the revenues collected by polluters (Munasinghe, 2008). The approach is important to ensure fairness in the context of social equity. In this method, economic valuation is an important prerequisite. CBA (cost benefit analysis) can be applied to work out the valuation and quantify the damage in a monetary way.

Multi-criteria analysis will be useful for environmental solution that can't be evaluated with single criterion approach like CBA. MBI provides individual or company greater flexibility in their approaches to pollution management. Contrary to the command and control approach which is more prescriptive; MBI provides incentive to innovate and individual at large to make the correct decision. By having a clear and inclusive monetary structure in punishing or rewarding in the context of an environmental issue, the result will be more obvious.

9.2 Mixed instrument: A practical approach in the decoupling of economy growth and environmental impact (carbon emission)

While MBI can be more cost-effective than regulatory instruments it has its own drawbacks. The major weaknesses of MBI are: (Munasinghe, 2008)

- Their effects on environmental quality are not as predictable as those under a traditional regulatory approach as polluters may choose their own solutions.
- In the case of pollution charges, some polluters opt to pollute and to pay a charge if the charge is not set at the appropriate level.
- Require sophisticated institutions to implement and enforce them properly, particularly in the case of charges and tradable permits.

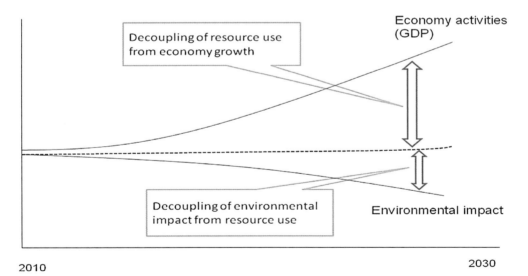

Fig. 4. Decoupling of resource use with economy growth and environmental impact

Internalization of environmental impact in an economic perspective alone can't bring out a comprehensive solution in carbon emission reduction. The most apparent drawback is the rich will pollute more while the poor will pollute less. It doesn't solve the fundamental issue of sustainable consumption and production as the rich countries have the financial capacity to choose whether to increase or decrease their carbon emission. Therefore, both economic and non-economic approaches have to be considered in the internalization process with a flexible mode. Command and control policy such as placing standard, agreement, protocol, etc; is predominantly significance in ensuring a healthy development of MBI. Besides, command and control, as a non-economic approach, may be beneficial as a starting point, when regulators are faced with a significant problem yet have too little information to support a MBI.

In practice, the mixture of both command and control and MBI is more effective. The policy and economy instruments have to be implemented hand in hand to achieve any tangible target in carbon emission reduction. For the example, the readjustment of electricity tariff by TNB (Tenaga National Berhad), the main electricity distributor in Malaysia. With the differential tariff, users that consume less electricity are exempted from the levy which will be exerted on user that exceeds a certain levels of electricity consumption. (Rao, P.K., 2000)

9.3 Establishment of GHGs information management system

GHGs emission shouldn't be merely calculated by the looking at the carbon source. The GHGs sequestration or carbon sink especially by natural sink such as forest has to be taken into account in figuring out the net carbon emission. The net emission data will represent a better overview and bigger picture of the issue in a country context.

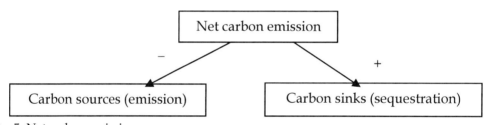

Fig. 5. Net carbon emission

Malaysia with collaboration of the regional countries has to set up a world recognized independent body in the collection and management of data pertaining to carbon emission in the region. Data inconsistency can be an important factor that leads to the failure of the development of an environmental policy. For example, IEA reported that the CO_2 emissions in Malaysia in 2005 was 5.45 MT/capita, UNEP revealed a value of 6.2 MT/capita in 2002, while CDIAC documented a 7.2 MT/capita in 2006; and on the other hand, WRI (World Resource Institute) published a value of 5.4 MT / capita in 2000. The questions are not only the consistency of the volume emissions but also the base year of those data. (Wee et al, 2008).

One reliable GHGs emissions inventory of the country was developed by Malaysia National Steering Committee on Climate Change; which was established following the signing of Kyoto Protocol. The national GHGs emissions inventory was introduced during the preparation of the Initial National Communication (INC) for UNFCCC. In 2000, Malaysia submitted its INC comprising the national GHGs inventory and the assessment of possible impacts of climate change. It detailed the policies and plans in place that represent the national sustainable development agenda of the country. The preparation of Second National Communication (NC2) is a continual step towards further implementation of the UNFCCC at national level which aims to generate a comprehensive report on climate change related issues in Malaysia. (CEMD, 2007)

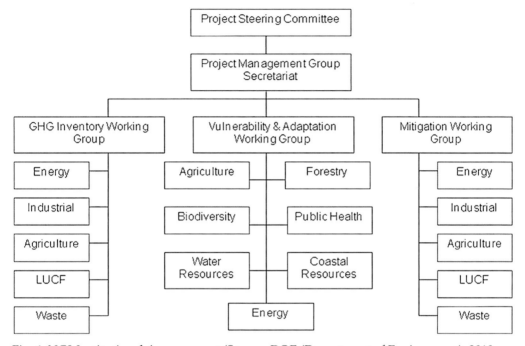

Fig. 6. NC2 Institutional Arrangement (Source: DOE (Department of Environment), 2010

9.4 Adaptation strategy to climate change

Adaptation strategies to climate change are inevitable because of the limited available knowledge. As a global issue, the effects of climate change will happen everywhere around the world. Therefore, adaptation measures have to be taken as well besides the mitigation measures; to ensure the welfare of the society is under control. Adaptation is a shared responsibility between government, community and business entities; that have a stake and role in responding to the climate change impact. Government has to put efforts in studies and research in climate change vulnerability areas and develop the relevant policies. For example, the recent findings revealed in the national coastal vulnerability index (CVI) study conducted by the Drainage and Irrigation Department (DID) in 2006 shows that sea levels off the west coast of Peninsular Malaysia will rise by 10cm to 13cm in the next 100 years and 288.4km or 6% of the peninsula's 4,809km-long coast is being eroded by sea water.

As vulnerability to climate change is a new risk to a country, business and community need to assume the responsibility to manage the risk by factor climate change into everyday decision making. It takes time to adapt and as uncertainty exists in climate change effect, the reasons for taking the relevant action are flexibility and creativity. It is not cost effective for adaptation response measures to prevent all adverse impacts of current and future climate change. Adaptation actions will need to achieve a suitable balance between the risks of acting too early or too late, and to balance the potential benefits of actions with the likely magnitude of impacts. In this context, the government plays a vital role in leading the action by providing information and setting the right conditions for business and community to adapt.

9.5 Institutional framework redesigning

Institution refers to a specific organization or a policy program. Organizations such as a specific government agency, departments, association are a manifestation of institution. For an institution to be changed, organizations are needed. But institutional change is harder to achieve than organizational change. For instance it is easier to restructure the Department of Environment than to transform Malaysia's federal system which is constitutionally defined. Instructive guiding principles are found in Professor Dovers' public lecture delivered in 2009 entitled Implementing Sustainable Development; six generic principles may be adopted and adapted by governments to suit relevant contexts:

1. Factoring in the long term
2. Integrating environment, society and economy in policy
3. Precautionary Principle
4. Global dimensions
5. Innovative policy approaches
6. Community participation

Institutionalizing sustainability by embedding these principles in their institutions is no easy feat for any government. A suggestion in institution reformation is the forming of "Green" ministries clusters typically share matters related to climate change; for example the alliance between Ministry of Natural Resource and Environment, Ministry of Energy, Green Technology and Water, Ministry of Housing and Local Government and Ministry of Science, Technology and Innovation.

9.6 Decision making at all levels

Any decision making related to climate change is fundamentally affected by money and awareness. To look at the micro level in the implementation of the climate change policy, decision making process of all levels are the determining factor. For example, for an individual level, changing to energy saving light bulb can be costly for low income people; however the awareness can drive the individual to take the action. Same for the government level; for instance to embark in renewable energy technology will take tremendous efforts in various agencies; however, with proper planning and collaboration, the positive outcomes of the effort can outweigh the short term unfavorable financial constraint in an entire system outlook. Decision making is always affected by an individual's knowledge, ethic, integrity and mindset. Education is the key toward correct decision making by all levels regarding matters related to climate change. Government had made the move to incorporate environmental issues in science and geography lessons at primary and secondary levels. The question remains is the comprehensiveness and sufficiency of the subject and the qualification and understanding of teachers on the subject.

10. Conclusion

Mainstreaming sustainability has always proven difficult in any country either developed or developing. Nevertheless, the global challenge of climate change will serves as an impetus for the government to set new energy policy that based on clean and renewable energy. With a holistic policy and economy model in place, the achievement of sustainable development is not impossible. However implementation of the policy requires high quality governance and vast pools of expertise with high ethical and integrity. It is time to change the "Business As Usual" attitude and "NATO" (No Action Talk Only) syndrome.

The country politicians, all business sectors and the community at large have to be involve and dwell on the environmental and especially climate change issue as it entails on numerous diverse topics and disciplines. Pending to the formulation of the climate change policy, the planning of the implementation part (enforcement, monitoring, measurement, improvement, etc) has to go concurrently. The introduction of a climate change policy is imperative for any country and in the right timing for the country to act as a strategic trajectory toward sustainable development.

11. References

Mohan Munasinghe, 2008. The sustainomics transdisciplinary meta-framework for marking development more sustainable: Applications to energy issues. In: Pushpam Kumar (eds): Economics of Environment & Development (pp. 11-87). Taylor & Francis Group: CRC Press.

Rao, P.K. 2000. Sustainable development: Economics and policy. Blackwell Publisher.

IEA Statistics, CO_2 emissions from fuel combustion, 2009 edition, International   Energy Agency.

Mohan Munasinghe, 2008. Addressing the sustainable development and climate change challenges together: Applying the sustainomics framework. Procedia social and behavioral science 41 (2010); 6634-6640.

Tan Ching Tiong, Joy Jacqueline Pereira and Koh Fui Pin, 2009. Stakeholder Consultation in the Development of Climate Change Policy: Malaysia's Approach. Environmental Policy: a Multinational Conference on Policy Analysis and Teaching Methods, KDI School of Public Policy and Management - Seoul, South Korea.

Badriyah Abdul Malek, 2010. Ministry of Energy, Green Technology & Water Malaysia. National Renewable Energy Policy & Action Plan. Energy Forum: Securing a Sustainable Energy for Malaysia.

PTM, 2007. Energy sector embracing climate change. National Conference on Climate Change Preparedness towards Policy Changes

Al-Amin, Chamhuri Siwar, Abdul Hamid, Nurul Huda, 2005, Pollution implications of electricity generation in Malaysian economy: An input-output approach.

APEC (Asia-Pacific Economic Cooperation). Energy Demand and Supply Outlook 2006: Malaysia.

Gary W. Theseira, 2010. How can the 40% carbon (intensity) reductions can be achieved? Waste Management 2010 Conference, ENSEARCH.

Loh, T., Yusoff, S., 2009, The clean development mechanism (CDM) as a driver for climate change adaptation in Malaysia.

A. A. Hezri and Mohd. Nordin Hasan, 2006. Towards sustainable development? The evolution of environmental policy in Malaysia. Natural Resources Forum.

A.A. Hezri, 2010. Sustainable Shift: Institutional Challenges for the Environment in Malaysia. EPSM SLiM Roundtable 2010, 'Creating an Institutional Framework for Implementing Sustainable Development'.

National Hydraulic Research Institute Malaysia (NAHRIM). 2006. Study of the impact of climate change on the hydrologic regime and water resources of Peninsular Malaysia – Final Report. Ministry of Natural Resources and Environment.

Energy Commission of Malaysia, 2007. Statistics of interim on the performance of the electricity supply in Malaysia for the first half year of 2007.

Universiti Kebangsaan Malaysia – Institute for Environment and Development (UKM-LESTARI), 2008a. Policy Framework on Climate Change: Stakeholder viewpoints. UKM-LESTARI.

Universiti Kebangsaan Malaysia – Institute for Environment and Development (UKM-LESTARI), 2008b. National Policy on Climate Change (Draft 1: 10 September 2008): Stakeholder viewpoints. UKM-LESTARI.

IPCC. 2005. IPCC Special Report on Carbon Dioxide Capture and Storage Climate Change 2007. Geneva: Working Group III of the Intergovernmental Panel on Climate Change.

IPCC. 2007. Climate Change 2007: The Physical Science Basis. Geneva: Intergovernmental Panel on Climate Change.

Wee Kean Fong, Hiroshi Matsumoto, Chin Siong Ho, Yu Fat Lun, 2008. Energy consumption and carbon dioxide in the urban planning process in Malaysia.

Joy Jacqueline Pereira, Ibrahim Komoo, Tan Ching Tiong, 2010. Climate change and disaster risk reduction, SEADPRI-UKM.

UN. 2007. Sustainable Development Issues. United Nations Division for Sustainable Development. (*http://www.un.org/esa/sustdev/documents/docs_sdissues.htm/*, Retrieved: October 2007)

Anwar Al-Mofleh, Soib Taib, M. Abdul Mujeebu, Wael Salah, 2007. Analysis of sectoral energy conservation in Malaysia. Energy Volume 34, Issue 6, June 2009.

2

Environmental Protection Expenditure in European Union

Elzbieta Broniewicz
Faculty of Management, Technical University of Bialystok
Poland

1. Introduction

Environmental protection expenditure should show the efforts being made to prevent, reduce and eliminate pollution resulting from the production or consumption of goods and services. The chapter presents the basic definitions and survey results of environmental protection expenditure in 25 European Union countries.

Environmental protection expenditure (EPE) is defined as the amount of money spent on all purposeful activities directly aimed at the prevention, reduction and elimination of pollution or nuisances resulting from the production processes (or consumption of goods and services). Data on environmental expenditure are collected from the European countries through the Joint OECD/Eurostat Questionnaire on Environmental Protection Expenditure and Revenues (EPER). The data covers five economic variables:

- investments for environmental protection:
  - pollution treatment investments,
  - pollution prevention investments,
- current expenditure for environmental protection,
- subsidies/transfers given for environmental protection activities.

The Questionnaire EPER contains also the data concerning household's expenditure for environmental protection.

The scope of Environmental Protection is defined according to the Classification of Environmental Protection Activities (CEPA, 2000), which distinguishes nine different environmental domains: protection of ambient air and climate, wastewater management, waste management, protection and remediation of soil, groundwater and surface water, noise and vibration abatement, protection of biodiversity and landscapes, protection against radiation, research and development and other environmental protection activities.

The purpose of the chapter is to provide the information, how vary the environmental protection expenditure in European Union over the years and what are the trends in specific domains of environmental protection. The comparison between the amount of costs in different countries of European Union is very interesting.

Environmental protection is an action or activity (which involves the use of equipment, labour, manufacturing techniques and practices, information networks or products) where the main purpose is to collect, treat, reduce, prevent, or eliminate pollutants and pollution or any other degradation of the environment resulting from the operating activity of the organization.

Environmental protection expenditure is the sum of capital and current expenditure for the undertaking of environmental protection activities.

Investment expenditure refers to financial or material costs, which aim at creating new permanent resources or improving (reconstruction, extension, restoration, adaptation or modernization) the existing objects of permanent property. It also means costs of so called first investment equipment. Presented division of investment costs is developed according to the rules of national accounting system, compliant with the "SNA 1993" recommendations. Investment expenditure can be divided into permanent resources and other costs.

Environmental protection current expenditure includes costs of activity operation and maintenance (technology, process, equipment). Current expenditure is to prevent, reduce, dispose or eliminate pollution and other environmental losses caused by current activities of the entity. They include internal costs (including costs of operation and maintenance of environmental protection installations as well as environmental charges), costs of services provided by external entities, charges for sewage treatment and waste collection; costs of control systems, monitoring, laboratory research, management.

Investment and current environmental expenditure have been divided, according to the property sectors, into:

public sector – government institutions (central public administration, regional and local governments as well as public organizations and institutions mainly classified in NACE, Rev. 1 as 75),

-    business sector – commercial enterprises, financial and insurance institutions as well as non-commercial institutions (all activities except NACE 75),

-    producers specialized in environmental protection (NACE 37 and 90) whose main activity is providing services for environment protection, mainly waste collection disposal and sewage treatment,

-    household sector – there is no clear distribution into investment and current expenditure in this sector; the specificity of household activities combines all the types of expenditure together (SERIEE, 1994).

The latest part of this chapter concerns Polish surveys of environmental protection expenditure in households.

2. Total environmental protection expenditure in UE

Total environmental expenditure in 2007[1] costs European economy around 220 billion euro[2]. The biggest share was contributed by specialized producers – 41,2% of the total environmental expenditure, industry – 31,0% and public sector – 27,8% (Fig. 1 and Table 1).

The basic indicators used to analyse the dynamics of environmental expenditure are:

•   contribution to Gross Domestic Product (GDP),

•   the investment expenditure per inhabitant.

Environmental expenditure in EU25 in 2007 accounted for 1,8% GDP and in 2002 for 1,7% GDP (except household expenditure) are presented in Fig. 2.

---

[1] The latest available data.
[2] Household's expenditure are excluded.

Specification	Time					
	2007	2006	2005	2004	2003	2002
European Union (27 countries)	224 235[e]	205 960[e]	192 387[e]	184 629[e]	179 409[e]	173 353[e]
European Union (25 countries)	219 953[e]	202 686[e]	190 332[e]	182 792[e]	178 206[e]	172 052[e]
European Union (15 countries)	205 186[e]	189 410[e]	179 624[e]	173 023[e]	169 671[e]	163 963[e]
Belgium	:	:	133	6 245	5 963	5 752
Bulgaria	630	546	327	345	297	247
Czech Republic	2 613	2 309	1 449	1 410	1 050	675
Denmark	4 280	3 852	3 860	3 733	3 563	3 652
Estonia	424	399	265	209	121	134
Ireland	:	:	:	:	:	:
Greece	:	:	:	:	12	15
Spain	21 410[e]	19 988	18 744	17 593	16 610	15 190
France	40 893	36 662	34 548	34 175	31 061	30 201
Italy	55 479	52 409	48 690	46 764	41 608	46 005
Cyprus	286[e]	173	128	166	124	37
Latvia	218	180	92	85	87	102
Lithuania	605	572	293	226	178	188
Luxembourg	279	294	280	262	242	239
Hungary	2 002	1 945	2 027	1 780	1 485	1 358
Malta	:	:	:	:	:	:
Netherlands	11 493[e]	7 067	11 493	:	8 620	1 919
Austria	9 463	9 880	8 485	8 266	8 379	7 895
Poland	7 056	6 117	5 186	4 748	4 414	4 558
Portugal	1 773[e]	1 862	1 429	1 519	1 392	1 387
Romania	3 652	2 728	1 728	1 492	905	1 054
Slovenia	785	687	657	614	673	557
Slovakia	777	894	611	532	403	479
Finland	2 076	1 834	1 642	1 693	1 601	1 629
Sweden	2 169	1 989	2 055	1 807	1 776	1 677
United Kingdom	18 551[e]	15 903	14 456	13 224	12 454	11 802

: not available

e) estimated

Table 1. Environmental protection expenditure in European Union, million euro (Eurostat Data Navigation Tree)

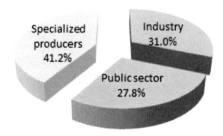

Fig. 1. The structure of environmental expenditure in 25 European Union countries in 2007 (Eurostat Data Navigation Tree)

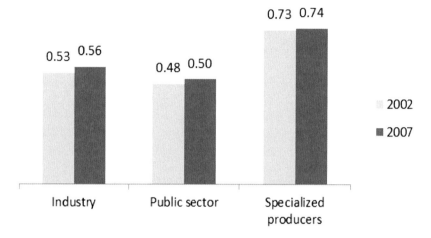

Fig. 2. Environmental protection expenditure in EU25 as % of GDP in 2002 and 2007 – by sectors (Eurostat Data Navigation Tree)

Comparing the share of environmental protection expenditures in GDP in particular countries, it could be noticed, that differences in environmental expenses are huge. Austria is one of the countries with the highest indicator in European Union (Fig. 3). Moreover, that expenditure per inhabitant in Austria is very high – in 2007 it was about 820 euro. In other EU countries this indicator came to 160 – 620 euro per inhabitant (Fig. 4).

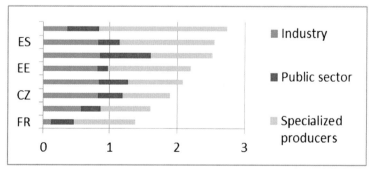

Fig. 3. Environmental protection expenditure in selected countries EU as % of GDP, data from the latest available survey (Eurostat Data Navigation Tree)

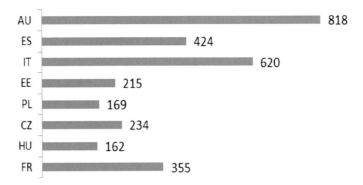

Fig. 4. Environmental protection expenditure in selected countries EU – euro per inhabitant, data from the latest available survey (Eurostat Data Navigation Tree)

Environmental expenditure, according to Classification of Environmental Protection Activities (CEPA), are divided into nine environmental domains:
1. Protection of ambient air and climate
2. Wastewater management
3. Waste management
4. Protection and remediation of soil, groundwater and surface water
5. Noise and vibration abatement
6. Biodiversity and landscapes protection
7. Protection against radiation
8. Research and Development
9. Other environmental protection activities (mainly environmental administration and management, education, training and information, indivisible expenditure and other expenditure not classified elsewhere).

The business sector consists of:
1. agriculture, hunting, fishing, forestry,
2. industry sector:
- mining and quarrying,
- manufacturing,
- electricity, gas and water supply sector,
3. other business.

However, the environmental protection expenditure occur mainly in the industry sector. During the period 2002-2007, the manufacturing sector in EU25, spent around 66% of total environmental protection expenditure, whilst electricity, gas and water supply sector and mining and quarrying sector 27% and 7% respectively. With reference to current expenditure this disproportion is bigger – 79%, 18% and 3% respectively (Georgescu, M.A. & Cabeca J. C., 2010).

In 2007, the leading environmental domain in industry in 25 EU countries was waste management (25,7%). The other important area of environmental expenditure was the wastewater management and protection of ambient air and climate, which accounted for 25,7% and 25,4% of total expenditure. The structure of expenditure by the environmental domains in industry in selected countries in 2007 is shown in Fig. 5.

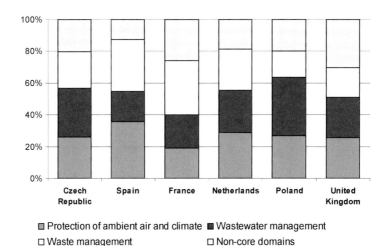

Fig. 5. Structure of environmental expenditure in industry of selected countries in 2007 (Eurostat Data Navigation Tree)

Current expenditure for environmental protection in 25 countries of European Union are higher than investments expenditure. In 2002-2007 current expenditure represented around 81% of total expenditure, whilst investment expenditure – 19% (Fig. 6).

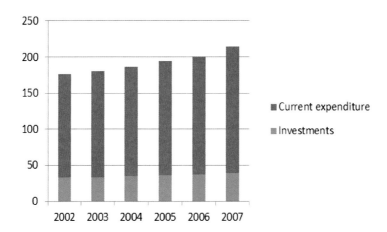

Fig. 6. Investment and current environmental protection expenditure in 25EU in 2002-2007, in million euro (Eurostat Data Navigation Tree)

2. Investment expenditure

Following the methodology applied in European Union (SERIEE, 1994), the investment expenditure includes end-of-pipe and integrated investments:
- the end-of-pipe investments (pollution treatment) – they do not affect in the production process itself (the production may be carried out without this kind of investment), but they reduce and dispose pollutants generated in the production process. The most

investments in the public sector and in specialised producers – according to the methodology recommended by the Office of Statistics of the European Communities EUROSTAT – are entirely rated among end-of-pipe enterprises,

- integrated technology (pollution prevention) – they lead to reduction of generated pollution through the modification of technological processes which makes the production cleaner and more environmentally friendly. When a new production process is introduced, the environmental expenditure refer to the expenditure that outstrip the costs of cheaper and in working order, but less environmentally friendly equipment.

The share of integrated technology in industry in EU25 exceeded the level of 35% in 2001 and in the year 2006 it increased to 43,0% (Georgescu, M.A. & Cabeca J. C., 2010). In 2007 it was 39% (Fig. 7). Companies adjust to the requirements of environmental protection by changing a production technology and implementing the best available productive and environmental solutions. Further changes in the structure of investment expenditure can be expected due to the implementation of a directive concerning integrated prevention and reduction of pollution (a Directive 96/62/EEC on integrated prevention and reduction of pollution – IPPC). Enforcement of the Directive requires establishing standards of pollution emission based on a concept of the Best Available Technique – BAT, that guarantees application of low-waste technologies, economical raw materials and energy use as well as application of the latest scientific and technical achievements.

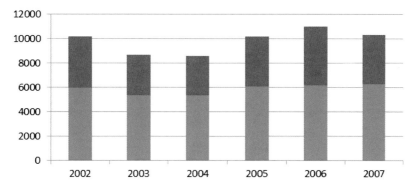

Fig. 7. Industry's environmental protection investments in EU25 in 2002-2007, million euro (Eurostat Data Navigation Tree)

In the industry sector, the environmental domain, which attracted most of capital expenditure for both pollution treatment and pollution prevention investments, was protection of ambient air and climate. The second domain was wastewater management. This tendency is noticed since 2002 (Fig. 8, Fig. 9).

The public sector and specialized producers sector were dominated by end-of-pipe investments, what resulted from the specificity of environmental protection activities. Major expenditure was allocated for building and modernization of wastewater plants, dumping sites and other waste disposal installations.

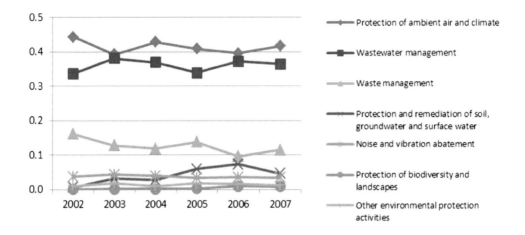

Fig. 8. The structure of industry's pollution treatment investments in EU25 in 2002-2007 by the environmental domains (Eurostat Data Navigation Tree)

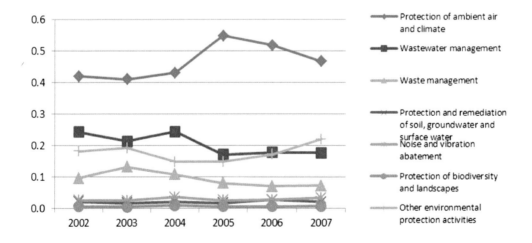

Fig. 9. The structure of industry's integrated technlology in EU25 in 2002-2007 by the environmental domains (Eurostat Data Navigation Tree)

3. Current environmental expenditure

Total current expenditure is the sum of internal current expenditure and fees/purchases.

Internal current expenditure includes the use of energy, material, maintenance and own personnel for measures made by the sector to protect the environment. A large part of internal expenditure is related to operating environmental protection equipment. There are also other internal expenditure such as general administration, education, information, environmental management and certification, research and development. Internal current expenditure includes purchases of connected and adapted non-capital goods[3] such as extra cost for low sulphur fuels. These are sometimes not part of specific surveys but estimated based on existing information e.g. on number of units and unit costs.

Fees/Purchases includes all purchases of environmental protection services, both from public and private producers. These payments are clearly linked with an environmental protection activity done outside the enterprise and should exclude e.g. fines and penalties. The payments include:

- Payments to specialised producers (enterprises) for waste and wastewater collection and treatment and payments to environmental consultants linked e.g. with environmental management and education.
- Payments to Public sector for waste and wastewater collection and treatment (whatever the name of the payments – fees, charges etc) as well as permits and surveillance fees.

Subsidies/Transfers (given or received) include all types of transfers financing Environmental Protection activities in other sectors, including transfers to or from other countries. These constitute expenditure for the paying sector (public sector), and revenue for the receiving sector (business sector and specialised producers sector). Payments of general environmental or green taxes (such as energy taxes) are excluded.

Sometimes Environmental Protection activities produce by-products that have an economic value. These could either be sold and generate revenues, or be used internally and lead to reductions in costs. Examples include energy generated or material recovered, as a result of waste treatment. There should always be a specific Environmental Protection activity (and expenditure) that these receipts stem from. Receipts from by-products is the sum of the sales value and the value of the cost-saving (if used internally) related to these by-products.

Public sector and specialised producers receive the payments for environmental protection services. This is entered as revenues in the respective sector (EPER).

The main environmental domain of current costs in industry sector during the period 2002-2007 was waste management (about 40%) and wastewater management (about 30%). Approximately, 10% concern other environmental protection activities, like general administration, education, information and environmental management – Fig 11.

---

[3] Connected products are products which are used directly and solely for environmental protection (for example septic tanks, filters, waste bags).

Adapted products are products that are less polluting, at the time of their consumption and/or scrapping, than equivalent traditional products. In most cases, such products are more costly, and their production and consumption are usually encouraged by fiscal and other incentives. Products which are cleaner (and therefore more environmentally friendly) when used or disposed of. These products are sometimes also called (environmentally) cleaner products. Only the extra-cost is accounted for in the environmental protection expenditure (Glossary of Environment Statistics, 1997).

Connected products are products which are used directly and solely for environmental protection (for example septic tanks, filters, waste bags).

Current expenditure in public and specialized producers sectors was directed largely towards ensuring a good provision of wastewater treatment and waste management services (Georgescu, M.A. & Cabeca J. C., 2010).

Internal current expenditure						
Related to operating environmental protection equipment						
Protection of ambient air and climate	Wastewater management	Waste management	Protection and remediation of soil, groundwater and surface water	Noise and vibrations abatement	Biodiversity and landscape protection	Protection against radiation
Research and development						
General administration, education, information, environmental management and certification						
(+) plus (-) minus						
Fees/purchases						
(+) plus or (-) minus						
Subsidies/Transfers						
(-) minus						
Receipts from by-products						
= (equals)						
Current expenditure						

Fig. 10. Classification of current expenditure on the environment in industry sector

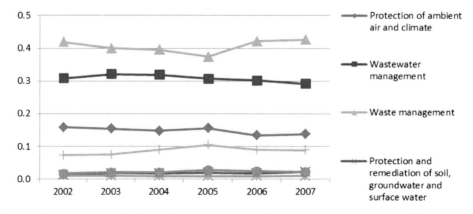

Fig. 11. The structure of industry's current expenditure in EU25 in 2002-2007 by the environmental domains (Eurostat Data Navigation Tree)

4. Environmental expenditure in households

Environmental protection expenditure in households contains of 1) purchases of connected and adapted products and 2) payments and fees for environmental protection services – Fig. 12.

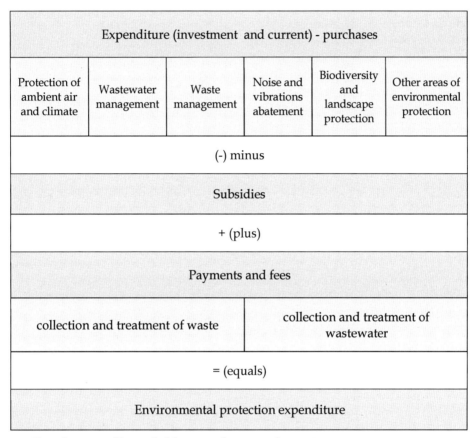

Expenditure (investment and current) - purchases					
Protection of ambient air and climate	Wastewater management	Waste management	Noise and vibrations abatement	Biodiversity and landscape protection	Other areas of environmental protection
(-) minus					
Subsidies					
+ (plus)					
Payments and fees					
collection and treatment of waste			collection and treatment of wastewater		
= (equals)					
Environmental protection expenditure					

Fig. 12. Classification of households expenditure on the environment

Based on Member Countries experience with the collection of data on private households there is no need to make a distinction between investments and current expenditure (EPER). Household purchases are viewed as current, in line with the national accounts. Examples are:

- protection of ambient air and climate:
- heat consumption meters and thermo regulators;
- modernization of central heating systems for the entire building and for a single apartment;
- installation of equipment for the treatment of fuel gases;
- purchase, operation and maintenance of air pollution control devices for motor vehicles e.g. extra costs for use of more environmentally friendly goods such as unleaded petrol, or service costs for proper adjustments of engines,
- purchase and installation of energy-saving windows;
- additional insulation for the building protecting against cold;

- wastewater management:
- connection to the public sewer;
- purchase of sewage treatment facilities such as septic tanks,
- construction of individual wastewater treatment plants;
- waste management:
- purchase of goods used in connection with waste management such as bins, bags, composts etc.;
- biodiversity and landscape protection:
- tree and bush planting;
- house facade repairs;
- noise and vibrations abatement:
- purchase and installation of noise reducing windows;
- fences and live fences, noise and vibrations reducing screens.

Household expenditure for environmental protection includes all payments and fees for services purchased from municipalities and specialised producers of environmental protection services. These include mainly:

- payments for the collection and treatment of waste,
- payments for the collection and treatment of wastewater.

Data of environmental protection expenditures in household is not available in Eurostat. Only a few EU countries conduct surveys in this sector (e.g. Austria, Hungary, Poland). In Poland, environmental protection expenditure in private households are examined from 1998. They are the biggest amount of environmental protection expenditures in Polish economy – during the period 1998-2009 it was approximately the same amount as the sum of expenditure in three sectors: public, business and specialized producers (Results of surveys of environmental protection expenditure conducting in 1998-2010. Ministry of the Environment in Poland).

The surveys are carried out on a representative sample of 1300 Polish households selected randomly by the Central Statistical Office for the purpose of examinating Polish households budgets. The survey covered 6 groups selected in accordance with their social and economic status, namely:

- households of workers – 44,6% of the sample,
- households of farmers with additional source of income – 4,3%,
- households of farmers – 5,7%,
- households of self-employed people – 6,1%,
- households of the retired and pensioners – 35,2%;
- households supported from non-profit sources – 4,1%.

Environmental expenditure of households in 2009 amounted to 5,8 billion euro. The share of purchases, installations and constructions of appliances as well as connected goods accounted for 72,6%, while environmental services 27,4%.

Costs of purchase, installation and construction of environmental devices and products referred mainly to air protection (77,6%), especially purchase and installation of energy-saving windows, houses heat-insulation and heating installation modernization. The majority of expenditure concerning bio-diversity and landscape protection was allocated for renovations of building's elevations and with regard to protection against noise and vibrations – purchase and installation of soundproof windows (Fig. 13).

Among the costs of environmental services, the majority (68,3%) consisted of wastewater collection, treatment and discharge fees. The rest of 33,7% was constituted of waste collection charges.

It should be noted, however, that the rates of fees for the environmental services related to the environmental protection depended on the type of a building. For the purpose of the survey two main groups were defined: a multi-family apartment house (53% households in the sample) and a single-family house (43%). Moreover, in the case of 4% households the delivered information was the total cost of environmental protection products and services for their house (a single-family house), garage, summer house and bungalow. The average services fees for different types of buildings are presented in Fig. 14.

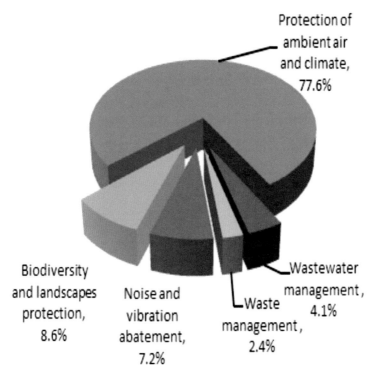

Fig. 13. The structure of expenditure for purchasing connected goods to households in 2009 in Poland (*Environment 2010. Statistical Information and Elaboration*, 2010).

Many owners of single-family houses, mainly in the country, most probably used to discharge their wastewater directly on the farmland and the most popular way of waste disposal was burning them or taking it to an unauthorized dumping ground to avoid the costs of utilization. The amount of charges for the environmental protection services was unrelated to the social and economic status of the members of the household. However, the highest expenditure on the purchase and installation of the equipment and products used directly for the purpose of environmental protection was recorded in households of self-employed people (excluding farmers) – 397 euro in 2009, whereas the lowest – 38 euro in households supported from nonprofit sources. The average expenditure on the environment (services payments excluded) by source of income is presented in Fig. 15.

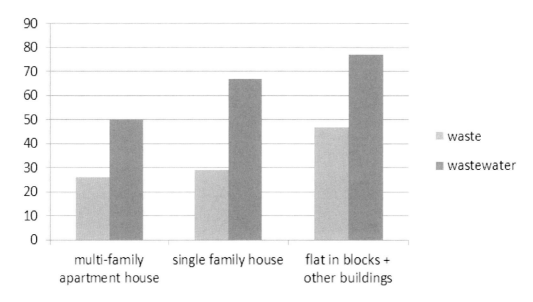

Fig. 14. Cost of environmental protection services for different types of building in Poland in 2009 (in euro).

Fig. 15. The amount of expenditure on the purchase and installation of the equipment and products used directly for the purpose of environmental protection by source of income in all surveyed Polish households in 2009 (in euro).

5. Conclusion

Eurostat works towards systematically collecting environmental statistics for all economic sectors within the EU. These statistics are used to assess the effectiveness of new legislation and policies and to analyse the links between environmental pressures and the structure of the economy.

For many years, European statistical services have collected data on air pollution, energy, water consumption, wastewater, solid waste, and their management. The links between these data and environmental data of an economic nature, such as environmental expenditure enable policymakers to consider the environmental impacts of economic activities, for example on resource consumption, air or water pollution, and waste production, and to assess actions (such as investment and current expenditure) that may be carried out to limit the causes and risks of pollution.

The analysis of spending on environmental protection has a strategic interest and allows an evaluation of environmental policies already in place. A low level of expenditure does not necessarily mean that a country is not effectively protecting its environment. Indeed, information on expenditure tends to emphasise clean-up costs at the expense of cost reductions which may have resulted from lower emissions or more effective protection measures (Georgescu, M.A. & Cabeca J. C., 2010).

6. References

Broniewicz, E. (2001). Expenditure on the Environment by Polish Households in the Year 2000, *Economics and Environment*, ed. by Poskrobko, B., pp. 117-132, Foundation of Environmental and Resource Economists, ISSN 0867-8898, Bialystok, Poland

Broniewicz, E. (2004). Environmental protection expenditure in Poland in comparison with European Union countries, *Proceedings of Business strategy and the environment*, pp. 58-66, Leeds, UK, September 2004

CEPA 2000 – *Classification of Environmental Protection Activities and Expenditure*

Commission Recommendation of 30 May 2001 on the recognition, measurement and disclosure of environmental issues in the annual accounts and annual reports of companies (2001/453/EC). Official Journal of the European Communities

Council Regulation No 58/97 of 20.12.1996 concerning structural business statistics

Environment 2010. Statistical Information and Elaboration (2010). Central Statistical Office, ISSN 0867-3217, Poland, 01-15.03.2011. Available from http://www.stat.gov.pl/gus

EPER – Environmental Protection Expenditure And Revenues. Joint OECD/Eurostat Questionnaire, 2002-2010

Eurostat Data Navigation Tree, 02.01-20.03.2011. Available from http://ec.europa.eu/eurostat

Georgescu, M.A. & Cabeca J. C. (2010). Environmental Protection Expenditure and Revenues in the EU, EFTA and candidate countries 2001-2006, In: *Eurostat. Statistics in Focus*, 31/2010, 12.01.2011. Available from http://ec.europa.eu/eurostat

Glossary of Environment Statistics (1997). Studies in Methods, Series F, No. 67, United Nations, New York, 10.03.2011. Available from http://stats.oecd.org/glossary

Regulation NO 2056/2002 of 5 November 2002 amending Council Regulation NO58/97
        concerning Structural Business Statistics
Results of surveys of environmental protection expenditure conducting in 1998-2010.
        Ministry of the Environment in Poland
SERIEE – European System for the Collection of Economic Information on the Environment,
        Manual, Luxemburg 1994

3

Community Ecology and Capacity: Advancing Environmental Communication Strategies among Diverse Stakeholders

Rosemary M. Caron, Michael E. Rezaee and Danielle Dionne
University of New Hampshire
United States

1. Introduction

Many socioeconomically and geographically diverse communities in the United States have been challenged by occurrences of environmental contamination and the related complex public health issues. The investigations associated with such concerns have traditionally been the responsibility of governmental agencies. Communities facing potential environmental exposures often believe that government-based environmental agencies are not adequately addressing their concerns regarding risk, thus resulting in their misunderstanding and distrust of the regulatory process. A schism develops whereby the community perceives that government is either not doing enough to address their concerns and/or are being influenced by the relevant industry. The governmental agencies involved perceive that the community possesses an inaccurate or irrational perception of the potential risks. As a result, a stressful relationship often arises.

Recommendations for effective risk communication have been developed and published (Covello & Sandman, 2001; Hance *et al.*, 1989; Sandman, 1989). Research has also demonstrated the importance of developing relationships among stakeholders and its impact on information delivery and reception (ATSDR, 2004). Given that stakeholder groups perceive risk differently, it is imperative for each group to appreciate the viewpoints of all involved to engage in effective dialog (Park *et al.*, 2001; Tinker *et al.*, 2001).

Cox (2006) defines environmental communication as "...the pragmatic and constitutive vehicle for our understanding of the environment as well as our relationships to the natural world; it is the symbolic medium that we use in constructing environmental problems and negotiating society's different responses to them." Although opportunities for public participation in environmental assessments have greatly increased, the environmental communication process among key stakeholders needs further evaluation (Charnley & Engelbert, 2005; McKinney & Harmon, 2002). The purpose of this chapter is to describe an evaluative process to develop and propose recommendations that could improve the environmental communication that occurs among diverse stakeholders, such as an environmental regulation and protection agency, waste disposal and energy producing facilities, community activists and the general public. Two case studies will be presented; the first describes the management of environmental permitting decisions in several disparate communities; and the second describes the management and perception of health risks from a single-owner waste-to-energy facility in two distinct communities. To accomplish this goal, this chapter will: 1.) examine how a state environmental agency and waste disposal and energy producing facilities describe their environmental communication experiences regarding various permitting operations and the risk perceptions of the impacted communities; 2.) identify effective communication methods; 3.) discuss the strengths and limitations of these activities; and 4.) propose recommendations for practitioners to advance environmental communication strategies among these key stakeholders.

1.1 Community ecology and capacity

Communities are important determinants in environmental health-related problems for populations. A community's ecology (i.e., its social, cultural, economic, and political composition) can affect how a persistent and/or perceived environmental health problem is addressed. For example, the primary stakeholders in a refugee resettlement community's childhood lead poisoning problem include the residents/resettled refugees in poor quality housing, refugee resettlement agencies, social service agencies, the local city health department, housing agencies, city building inspectors, realtors, property owners/managers, child care providers, health care community, etc. Some stakeholders view the childhood lead poisoning problem in the community as indicative of a larger issue, namely a community that is undergoing growth and diversification due to its refugee and immigrant resettlement status. Hence, others believe they are not able to solve the problem due to its enormity and complexity. As a result, this persistent environmental public health issue propagates in the community with varied efforts (Caron & Serrell, 2009; Wehrly, 2006). Childhood lead poisoning has been described as a wicked persistent environmental public health problem that is multi-factorial in nature and possesses no clear resolution due to the involvement of numerous stakeholders who define the problem differently and who pose uncoordinated solutions. Since wicked problems often possess no definitive solutions, remediation must focus on how to best manage them (Caron & Serrell, 2009). As part of a management practice for complex environmental public health issues, we propose that the community's ecology – its political, ethnic and socioeconomic factors, including zoning laws, housing policies, cultural behavior, and language barriers - is a key determinant in shaping a population's perception of risk and in developing effective communication strategies. In addition, understanding a community's ecology can contribute to building the community's capacity to affect the local management and communication of persistent and/or perceived environmental public health issues.

2. Case study: managing environmental permitting decisions in dissimilar communities

The stakeholders considered in this work include a state environmental agency, facility managers of Title V operating facilities and community residents living near the facilities. Specifically, the New Hampshire Department of Environmental Services, Air Resources Division (NHDES ARD) is responsible for monitoring and regulating air quality that is protective of public health and the natural environment in the State of New Hampshire (ARD, 2010). NHDES ARD accomplishes this goal via numerous programs including a statewide permitting program to assure compliance with the Title V federal mandate. The purpose of the Title V permitting process is to ensure that facilities will not emit hazardous pollutants to a degree which could negatively affect human health. Specifically, the Title V mandate states that facilities which emit over 100 tons of any regulated pollutant, such as carbon monoxide and sulfur oxides; or emit over 50 tons of nitrous oxides; or emit 10 tons of any of the federally regulated hazardous air pollutants need to apply to the state environmental agency for a Title V permit (ARD, 2008).

Table 1 outlines the Title V operating facilities examined in this study: Turnkey Recycling and Environmental Enterprises, a solid waste management facility in operation since 1979 in Rochester, New Hampshire (NH); Mt. Carberry Landfill, historically used as a landfill for pulp and paper byproducts and a solid waste disposal site since 1989 in Berlin, NH; Four Hills Landfill, a solid waste disposal site since 1970 in Nashua, NH; Indeck Energy Services, Inc., a biomass electric generating facility in operation since 1987 in Alexandria, NH; Schiller Station, historically a coal burning facility from 1950 through 2006 and now a woodchip burning operation in Portsmouth, NH; and Wheelabrator Technologies, Inc., a solid waste energy plant in operation since 1987 in Claremont, NH.

Facility Name	Type of Industry	In Operation Since	Location	Population of Community[1]
Turnkey Recycling and Environmental Enterprises	Landfill	1979	Rochester, NH	30,527
Mt. Carberry	Landfill	1989	Berlin, NH	10,109
Four Hills	Landfill	1970	Nashua, NH	86,837
Indeck Energy Services, Inc.	Electricity	1987	Alexandria, NH	1,521
Schiller Station	Electricity	1950	Portsmouth, NH	20,495
Wheelabrator Technologies, Inc.	Incinerator	1987	Claremont, NH	13,097

Table 1. Facility stakeholders involved in the environmental communication of permitting decisions.

The community members living in the midst of these Title V operating facilities represent the final stakeholder group. The demographics of these communities are diverse with three communities considered rural and the remaining considered urban.

3. Methods

Data collection and analysis of the interactions among key stakeholders were conducted using collective case study methodology (Cottrell & McKenzie, 2005). Data was collected from publicly available New Hampshire Department of Environmental Services (NHDES) documents concerning specific Title V operating facilities in the State of New Hampshire. These documents were in the form of written or e-mail correspondence, phone logs and

---

[1] U.S. Census Bureau. *Population Finder*. (http://www.census.gov/)

public hearing audio tapes and written testimonies. A structured questionnaire was applied to each occurrence of communication. Each document was reviewed and information abstracted regarding the date and type of communication; origin of concern; responder; general summary of concern; action requested; response time; total number of complaints per facility; method of ongoing communication; whether feelings of distrust or doubt were expressed by the community with respect to facility operations; the type of organization(s) the community member contacted prior/following to communicating with the state agency or facility; and non-verbal communication (e.g., body language) at public hearings. Abstracted information was first organized in chronological order by facility; duplicate records were removed; and a search for potentially missed documents was conducted. A document summarizing record review information for each site was constructed. Additionally, public inquiries/concerns received about each facility were reviewed and classified into thematic areas.

Semi-structured interviews were conducted, following Institutional Review Board approval from the University of New Hampshire, with NHDES employees involved in the Title V permitting process and Title V operating facility managers. Respondents were asked questions about the public's perception of their work and whether the facility's operations were considered to be contentious or non-contentious; the health and environmental concerns of the impacted community; and who they considered the major stakeholders. Respondents were asked if they had experience conducting and/or attending a public hearing about their facility. Information pertaining to the type and number of concerns communicated by the public was collected, as well as how these issues were addressed. With respect to the environmental management of concerns, the respondents were queried as to whether or not they believed they were proactive in involving the community and if there was a professional at their respective organizations who was responsible for handling the public's concerns. The last series of questions posed to the respondents inquired about whether they thought improving environmental communication among all stakeholders would enhance working relationships; whether an appointed liaison would assist with environmental communication; and what specific recommendations they have to improve the communication of environmental permitting decisions among stakeholders.

The interviews were transcribed and a content analysis, using QSR NVivo (a computer-assisted qualitative data analysis program), was conducted of the structured interview responses to extract and code recurring themes.

4. Results

4.1 Structured questionnaires

Tables 2A-F summarize the correspondence information among stakeholders regarding each facility. In general, public inquiries were fielded by NHDES ARD staff and/or the NHDES Complaint Manager. Inquiries were typically answered in two days or less. The concerns expressed ranged from health concerns (e.g., cancer, respiratory illness) to nuisance complaints (e.g., odor, noise, traffic). The actions most often requested involved scheduling a public hearing, extending the public comment period, conducting air and water quality testing, and initiating an independent investigation of NHDES' administration. In some instances, the community members present at the public hearing called for the closure of the facility. Distrust of NHDES and/or the facility was expressed for the majority of sites. One exception to this sentiment was the Mt. Carberry Landfill.

Common frustrations voiced by citizens included the inability to locate the appropriate representative, either at NHDES or the facility, to communicate their concern(s) and dissatisfaction with the response to their inquiry, thus leading them to contact the Environmental Protection Agency (EPA) or a local official to relay their concerns. Figures 1-6 represent photographs of each facility examined.

Turnkey Recycling and Environmental Enterprises	Correspondence Content	Phone	E-mail	Public Hearing	Written
	Time period of Correspondence	2004, 2005	2003, 2004, 2005	2004	2004
	Total Number	59	7	7	7
	Responder	NHDES ARD; NHDES Complaint Manager	NHDES ARD; Title V Program Manager	NHDES ARD; Title V Permitting Engineer; Facility Manager	None
	Summary of Concern	Odor	Odor	Health (cancer); Odor; Air quality; Water quality	Health (colitis); Odor; Air quality; Water quality
	Response Time	Same day	Same day	Same day	Not applicable
	Action Requested	None	Public hearing	Air and water quality testing; Deny permit; Close facility	Air and water quality testing; Deny permit; Close facility; Investigate NHDES
	Perception of Distrust	Yes	Yes	Yes	Yes
	Ongoing Communication	None	None	None	None
	Other Organizations Contacted	None	Director of Waste Management Services	None	Director of Waste Management Services

Table 2A. Correspondence among stakeholders involved in the environmental communication of permitting decisions for a landfill facility.

Mt. Carberry Landfill	Correspondence Content	Phone	E-mail	Public Hearing	Written
	Time period of Correspondence	2006	No e-mail correspondence	2007	2007
	Total Number	16		1	4
	Responder	NHDES ARD		NHDES ARD and Facility Manager	NHDES and Director of NHDES
	Summary of Concern	Odor		None – in support of facility	Title V permitting process
	Response Time	Same day		Same day	Two days
	Action Requested	None		Extension of public comment period	Public hearing
	Perception of Distrust	No		No	No
	Ongoing Communication	NHDES Follow-up		None	None
	Other Organizations Contacted	No		No	No

Table 2B. Correspondence among stakeholders involved in the environmental communication of permitting decisions for a landfill facility.

Fig. 1. Turnkey Recycling and Environmental Enterprises, Rochester, New Hampshire. Source: http://www.greenrightnow.com/wabc/2009/05/19/unh-first-university-to-use-landfill-gas-as-primary-fuel-source/#more-3818

Fig. 2A. Mt. Carberry Landfill, Berlin, NH.   Fig. 2B. Flare at Mt. Carberry Landfill, Berlin, NH.

Source for both photos: http://www.avrrdd.org/avrrdd-mt-carberry-landfill-berlin-nh.html

Fig. 3. Four Hills Landfill in Nashua, NH.
Source:http://www.gonashua.com/CityGovernment/Departments/PublicWorks/SolidWa
ste/tabid/135/Default.aspx

Four Hills Landfill	Correspondence Content	Phone	E-mail	Public Hearing	Written
	Time period of Correspondence	2007, 2008, 2009	2008	No public hearing	No written correspondence
	Total Number	9	1		
	Responder	NHDES ARD; NHDES Complaint Manager	NHDES Complaint Manager		
	Summary of Concern	Odor; Noise	Odor		
	Response Time	1-2 days	Same day		
	Action Requested	None	None		
	Perception of Distrust	No	No		
	Ongoing Communication	None	Yes (via e-mail)		
	Other Organizations Contacted	EPA; Mayor's office; local health department	No		

Table 2C. Correspondence among stakeholders involved in the environmental communication of permitting decisions for a landfill facility.

Fig. 4. Indeck Energy Services, Inc., Alexandria, NH.
Source: http://www.indeckenergy.com/Alternative_Fuels.php

Indeck Energy Services, Inc.	Correspondence Content	Phone	E-mail	Public Hearing	Written
	Time period of Correspondence	1986, 1991, 2008, 2009	No e-mail correspondence	2000, 2007	1986, 1999, 2007
	Total Number	5		21	7
	Responder	NHDES Complaint Manager		NHDES ARD and Facility Manager	NHDES ARD and NHDES Director
	Summary of Concern	Air quality; Noise		Air quality, In support of permit for economic reasons	Odor; Noise; Traffic; Air quality
	Response Time	Same day		Same day	Two days
	Action Requested	Air quality testing		Air quality testing; more information on facility operations	Information on facility operations and plans; Request a public hearing
	Perception of Distrust	Yes		Yes	Yes
	Ongoing Communication	None		None	None
	Other Organizations Contacted	No		No	No

Table 2D. Correspondence among stakeholders involved in the environmental communication of permitting decisions for an energy (electricity) facility.

Schiller Station	Correspondence Content	Phone	E-mail	Public Hearing	Written
	Time period of Correspondence	2002, 2004, 2007	2003, 2006, 2007	2004	2004
	Total Number	5	3	3	3
	Responder	NHDES ARD; NHDES Complaint Manager	NHDES ARD; NHDES Complaint Manager	NHDES ARD and Facility Manager	NHDES ARD
	Summary of Concern	Coal dust damaged property; Air quality	Health (cancer, allergies); Coal dust damaged property; Air quality	Coal dust damaged property; Air quality	Coal dust damaged property; Air quality
	Response Time	Same day	Same day	Same day	Two days
	Action Requested	None	None	Air quality testing; One organization in support of the facility's operation	Air quality testing of ambient air in homes; Requested a public hearing
	Perception of Distrust	No	No	Yes	Yes
	Ongoing Communication	None	None	None	None
	Other Organizations Contacted	No	No	No	No

Table 2E. Correspondence among stakeholders involved in the environmental communication of permitting decisions for an energy (electricity) facility.

Fig. 5. Schiller Station, Portsmouth, NH.
Source:http://www.unhenergyclub.com/pastevents.php

Fig. 6. Wheelabrator Technologies, Inc., Claremont, NH.
Source: http://www.wheelabratortechnologies.com/index.cfm/our-clean-energy-plants/waste-to-energy-plants/wheelabrator-claremont-company-lp/

Wheelabrator Technologies, Inc.	Correspondence Content	Phone	E-mail	Public Hearing	Written
	Time period of Correspondence	2005, 2006	2007	No public hearing	1995
	Total Number	5	1		11
	Responder	NHDES ARD; NHDES Complaint Manager	NHDES ARD; NHDES Complaint Manager		NHDES ARD; NHDES Director
	Summary of Concern	Health (respiratory illness); Odor; Air quality	Health (respiratory illness); Air quality		General health concerns; Air quality; Water quality; Failure of facility to comply with EPA's emission standards
	Response Time	Same day	Same day		Two days
	Action Requested	Air quality testing	Air quality testing		Facility must engage in smoke stack emission testing; Development of more strict emission standards; Facility must become compliant with emission standards; Deny permit; Facility should communicate with the affected community
	Perception of Distrust	Yes	Yes		Yes
	Ongoing Communication	None	None		None
	Other Organizations Contacted	EPA	EPA		No

Table 2F. Correspondence among stakeholders involved in the environmental communication of permitting decisions for an incineration facility.

4.2 Structured interviews

Both NHDES employees and Title V operating facility managers reported interacting with the public about environmental concerns and agreeing on who the stakeholders were in the environmental permitting process. All respondents believed that the respective facility was viewed positively by the public at the time of the interview. Initially, they may not have been viewed favorably but "Once there was some transparency developed, the public welcomed the facility. They were happy that the facility was going to provide jobs in the area." However, the incinerator was regarded by both NHDES and the facility manager as having a negative public perception. Interestingly, another incinerator, owned by the same parent company, located in a different part of the state is perceived positively by the surrounding community. The next case study examines the differences in environmental communication utilized by this facility in two distinct communities.

One landfill experienced public outcry when it announced that it would be purchasing and re-opening a facility that had been closed for fifteen years. According to NHDES, this facility did not engage the surrounding community in their plans and the community attended the public hearing to obtain an update on the facility's approach. Many of the issues presented at the public hearing could have been addressed beforehand but the facility was not proactive in involving the public. Another landfill facility manager reported that "Hearings have generally been a good experience, especially when the public doesn't show up." The facility manager from a similar site commented that "Our facility does a horrible job reaching out to the public…we are lacking in outreach." In contrast, the Mt. Carberry Landfill held three public meetings. The first two meetings were sponsored by the facility owners and allowed "…the public to voice their concerns…" and served as informational sessions. When the official public hearing was held, all of the issues had been addressed and there was no conflict. The facility manager for Mt. Carberry reported that "We told the public what was going on, how we were going to solve the problem, and we told them that we would keep them involved all along the way – and we did!"

When asked if NHDES and the facility were proactive in involving the public in the permitting process, there were varied responses including "…NHDES and my facility have been reactive instead of proactive" and "We [facility] weren't that involved actually" and "I think it's been a combination of both."

When asked if improving environmental communication would benefit the environmental permitting process, the responses varied. NHDES stated "Yes, hopefully, ideally. The more ongoing non-regulatory communication, the less issues are able to build up over time…There needs to be a continuous avenue for people to easily voice their concerns." One facility manager stated "We feel that it isn't very practical or efficient to reach out to the community before any kind of permitting decisions are started." Another manager specifically noted that their "…filing for a Title V permit was completely voluntary…We don't meet the guidelines to be considered a major polluting landfill. We applied for a Title V permit to be proactive." The responses were also mixed about whether an appointed liaison would help improve environmental communication. NHDES stated "This depends on who they are affiliated with…If there was a person in this position, it would be helpful if each stakeholder had trust in this person. However, how this trust is built is unclear. It is quite possible that this person could be another barrier in the communication process and act as another layer of litigation." One facility manager stated that "…one person, one contact would be very beneficial in improving environmental communication." In contrast, another facility manager stated that "A person who has this position would get 'beat up' by all the stakeholders involved. I would have to say 'No'."

Table 3 summarizes the recommendations of NHDES and the facility managers to improve the communication with impacted communities regarding environmental permitting decisions. Key recommendations include conducting more informal "conversation" type meetings prior to the public hearing; presenting information at an appropriate educational level; and engaging in public outreach via the Internet, mailings, print media and/or a community liaison; integrating a practice of transparency of information among stakeholders; and creating a uniform meeting setup.

- Hold informal "conversational" type meetings prior to the public hearing for concerns and questions to be addressed (NHDES ARD)
- Alter the meeting room setup for the public hearing so an "Us" versus "Them" scenario is not created (NHDES ARD)
- Keep people informed via web sites, mailings, and newspapers (Landfill facility)
- Community liaison who could share information among stakeholders (Incinerator facility)
- Be transparent with information and the facility's operations (Landfill facility)
- Acknowledge differences in public perception (Electricity generating facility)
- Explain the permitting process and emission standards to the public in an educationally appropriate manner (Landfill facility)
- Facilities need to be more involved in the community (Landfill facility)

Table 3. Summary of recommendations from state agency representatives and facility managers on how to improve environmental communication to the public.

5. Managing environmental permitting decisions in dissimilar communities: discussion

Effective environmental communication among all stakeholders is essential when addressing environmental health risks. Bennett (1999) and McComas (2003) describe how organizations will earn the trust of the community based on the content and delivery of their communication; the willingness for an inclusive, community-based participatory interaction; and their reputation for taking action. There is agreement that environmental communication among stakeholders be an integral component of the working relationship and that resources be allocated to develop public outreach plans that are tailored to the specific community (Brauer et al., 2004; Parkin, 2004).

Given that stakeholder groups perceive risk differently, it is imperative for each group to appreciate the viewpoints of all involved to engage in effective dialog (Park et al, 2001; Tinker et al., 2001). Therefore, we propose that effective and proactive environmental communication that considers the community's ecology (i.e., social, cultural, economic and political composition) among all stakeholders in all types of communities with a regulated industry is essential when addressing perceived health risks to the environmental and population. Based on our systematic examination of the environmental communication that occurred among a state environmental agency, six Title V operating facilities and the public concerning environmental permitting decisions perceived to impact human health, we developed recommendations to facilitate best practices in environmental communication. These recommendations for practitioners are presented in Section 10: Recommendations.

6. Case study: managing perceived health risks from a single-owner waste-to-energy facility in two distinct communities

The perceived health risks and environmental communication from two waste-to-energy facilities operated by the same parent company are examined in this work. Waste

Management, Inc., of Houston, Texas owns Wheelabrator Technologies, Inc. which operates several waste-to-energy facilities across the United States. Wheelabrator operates two such municipal solid waste incinerators in Claremont, New Hampshire (NH) and Concord, NH, respectively. The Claremont, NH facility began operation in 1987 and provides disposal of up to 200 tons of municipal solid waste daily for approximately 70,000 people. This facility can provide electricity to 5,600 homes. The Concord, NH facility began operation in 1989 and provides disposal of up to 500 tons of municipal solid waste daily for approximately 150,000 people. This facility can provide electricity to 17,000 homes (Wheelabrator, 2010).

These facilities use the same waste-to-energy method and are considered Title V operating facilities by the New Hampshire Department of Environmental Services (NHDES). The purpose of the Title V permitting process is to ensure that facilities will not emit hazardous pollutants to a degree which could negatively affect human health. Specifically, facilities which emit over 100 tons of any regulated pollutant, such as carbon monoxide and sulfur oxides; emit over 50 tons of nitrous oxides; or emit 10 tons of any of the federally regulated hazardous air pollutants need to apply to the state environmental agency for a Title V permit (ARD, 2008).

As required by current NHDES permits, the Wheelabrator sites continuously monitor carbon monoxide, sulfur dioxide, particulate matter, as well as other emission indicators such as steam flow and temperature. All monitoring and operational information are maintained in facility records, in accordance with state and federal requirements. "[NH]DES oversees and witnesses the performance of annual relative accuracy tests and audits facility records in order to ensure the accuracy of Wheelabrator's continuous emissions monitoring system. [NH]DES also conducts full Compliance Evaluations at least every two years, witnesses annual compliance stack tests and reviews resultant stack test reports for accuracy" (ATSDR, 2009).

6.1 Two communities: home to the same environmental policy

The demographics of the Claremont and Concord New Hampshire communities are similar with respect to age and sex. Both communities are also classified as cities. However, the demographic information for education, economic and housing characteristics are different. Table 4 outlines selected demographic characteristics of these two communities.

Briefly, Claremont is a city in the western part of New Hampshire with a population of 12,968. It is situated along the Connecticut River in Sullivan County. It is the largest incorporated community in Sullivan County and ranks 22nd in population size among cities and towns in New Hampshire. The majority of the population (97.7%) is White and 78.7% of the population 25 years of age and older have completed high school while 12.8% have a Bachelor's degree. The median household income in 1999 was $34,949 and the median value of a single-family owner-occupied home was $79,800 (Census, 2010).

Concord is the state capital with a population of 42,255. It is situated along the Merrimack River in Merrimack County and ranks 3rd in population size among cities and town in New Hampshire. The majority of the population (95.5%) is White and 88.6% of the population 25 years of age and older have completed high school while 30.7% have a Bachelor's degree. The median household income in 1999 was $42,447 and the median value of a single-family owner-occupied home was $112,300 (Census, 2010).

6.2 Stakeholders in environmental communication

The stakeholders considered in this work include a state environmental agency, community activists living near the facilities and the general public. Specifically, the New Hampshire Department of Environmental Services, Air Resources Division (NHDES ARD) is responsible for monitoring and regulating air quality that is protective of public health and the natural environment in the State of New Hampshire (ARD, 2010). NHDES ARD accomplishes this goal via numerous programs including a statewide permitting program to assure compliance with the Title V federal mandate (ARD, 2008).

Citizens Leading for Environmental Action and Responsibility (CLEAR) is a community activist group that is primarily comprised of Claremont, NH residents. The mission of CLEAR is to "...respect and value the people, the environment, the public health, the political process, and the economics of our community and region;...encourage public participation in the decision-making process to promote the principles of environmental, political, social, and economic health;...commit to an organizational framework that is non-profit, open, democratic, and accountable" (CLEAR, 2010). The general public living or spending time in the communities that house these Title V operating facilities represents the final stakeholder group. Figure 7 represents photographs of the industry examined.

	Claremont, NH	Concord, NH
Total population[2]	12,968	42,255
Race: White	97.7%	95.5%
High school graduate	78.7%	88.6%
Bachelor's degree	12.8%	30.7%
Median household income[3]	$34,949	$42,447
Median value of a single-family owner-occupied home	$79,800	$112,300

Table 4. Demographic characteristics of two communities that host a waste-to-energy facility[4].

[2] Population estimate for 2008, U.S. Census Bureau, *Population Finder*. (http://www.census.gov/)
[3] Median household income for 1999, U.S. Census Bureau, *Population Finder*. (http://www.census.gov/)

Fig. 7. A and B. Wheelabrator Technologies, Inc. in Claremont and Concord, NH, respectively.
Source: http://www.wheelabratortechnologies.com/index.cfm/our-clean-energy-plants/waste-to-energy-plants/wheelabrator-claremont-company-lp/

7. Methods

7.1 Survey instrument

Following Institutional Review Board approval from the University of New Hampshire, a cross-sectional study design was utilized to examine the sources, believability and utility of information and perceptions about environmental health issues among a relevant sample of residents and visitors of the two study communities. Self-report questionnaires utilizing a 4-point Likert scale and multiple choice questions were administered over a five month period at different times and locations (e.g., retail locations and churches of various denominations) in each community. These anonymous surveys were immediately collected from the participants upon completion. Alternatively, participants could choose to mail their completed survey to the University of New Hampshire via self-addressed and stamped envelopes.

All questionnaires had a cover letter attached that explained the purpose of the study and emphasized the anonymity and confidentiality of the results. Participants were told to keep this letter for their records. There were no incentives for participating in this study. Additional open-ended comments from participants were recorded at the end of the survey.

The 19-item questionnaire was designed to determine demographic information, self-reported knowledge about sources and believability of information and perceptions about environmental health issues in the community. Revisions were made during the pilot testing phase of the questionnaire. Ambiguities associated with the survey content were not identified during test trials that were conducted prior to official questionnaire administration.

The survey questions were organized into four sections. First, respondents were asked for demographic information (e.g., length of residence in the community, education level, annual income) and questions pertaining to their interest and level of participation in community issues. Respondents were then asked how often they think about their physical environment

---

[4] Source: U.S. Census Bureau. *Population Finder*. (http://www.census.gov/)

and to choose what environmental health issue in their community concerned them the most from the following list: water quality, land conservation, air pollution, food security and other. This question was followed by an inquiry regarding whether the respondents thought they were well-informed about environmental health issues in their community. Next, respondents were asked to indicate where they would rank their environmental issue of interest relative to other issues (e.g., property taxes) affecting their local community.

In order to determine sources of environmental health information, respondents were asked to choose from the following sources in the next section of the survey: federal agencies (e.g., Environmental Protection Agency, Agency of Toxic Substances and Disease Registry); state agencies (e.g., New Hampshire Department of Environmental Services, New Hampshire Department of Health and Human Services); local government (e.g., city councilor or Mayor); environmental groups (e.g., Greenpeace); academia (university presentations, studies, peer-reviewed literature); media sources (e.g., newspaper, television, radio, Internet); other. Respondents were instructed to circle all that applied to them. Respondents were then asked to rate their believability of the above-mentioned sources of information. Next, in order to determine which media sources were the most useful, respondents were asked to choose from the following sources: television programs, print resources (e.g., pamphlets), newspaper articles or editorials, community meetings, informational websites.

The third series of questions pertained to the respondent's attitude about public meetings. Respondents were asked if they had ever attended a public meeting and whether they believed public meetings were an effective means to communicate environmental health information. Next, respondents were asked if they believed whether their opinion, if voiced at a public meeting, would be taken seriously by officials.

Finally, the last series of survey questions inquired whether or not the respondents believed the status of their personal health is related to the condition of the environment. Respondents were specifically asked if they were familiar with trash incineration and whether or not they believed it to be an effective form of waste disposal.

All data were analyzed using the Statistical Package for Social Sciences. Descriptive analyses were done for each of the participant responses by determining frequencies and proportions. Comparisons of responses were made across both communities by utilizing the chi-square statistic, cross tabulations and independent sample t-tests to assess the statistical significance of these comparisons. For statistical tests, P-values less than 0.05 were considered to be statistically significant. Unknowns were accounted for in all variables.

7.2 Structured interview instrument

Structured interviews were conducted, following Institutional Review Board approval from the University of New Hampshire, with DES employees involved in Title V permitting and environmental health investigations and community activists from CLEAR to examine the experiences that shaped both parties' perceptions of current environmental communication methods.

Participants were asked semi-structured, open-ended questions about the public's perception of their work, whether the facilities' operations were considered to be contentious or non-contentious and the health and environmental concerns regarding the facilities. Participants were asked if they had experience conducting and/or attending a public hearing about the facility. Information pertaining to the type and number of concerns communicated by the public was collected, as well as how these issues were addressed. With respect to the environmental management of concerns, NHDES was queried as to whether or not they believed they were proactive in involving the community and if they employed a professional who was responsible for handling the public's concerns. CLEAR was queried as to their perception in regards of their inclusion, by NHDES, in health investigations concerning the facility and communication efforts from NHDES. The last series of questions posed to the participants inquired about whether they thought improving environmental communication among all stakeholders would enhance working relationships; the usefulness of having an appointed community liaison to assist with environmental communication; and what specific recommendations they have to improve the environmental communication among stakeholders. The interviews were transcribed and a content analysis, using QSR NVivo (a computer-assisted qualitative data analysis program), was conducted of the structured interview responses to extract and code recurring themes.

8. Results

8.1 Two communities: sources, believability and utility of information and perceptions about environmental health issues

One hundred and nine of 250 surveys (44% response rate) were completed and returned by community members and/or visitors to the Claremont and Concord, NH communities. Of the completed 109 surveys, 54 were from the Claremont community and 55 were from the Concord community.

As shown in Table 5, survey results indicate statistically significant differences between the Claremont, NH and Concord, NH survey respondents with respect to demographic

	Claremont, NH	Concord, NH	P-value
College education	53.0%	92.2%	0.000
Annual income $25,000 or greater	55.5%	98.2%	0.000
Lived in the community for ten years or more	51.9%	76.4%	0.008
Active in community issues	42.6%	65.5%	0.017
Ranked the priority of environmental issues higher than other community issues (e.g., property taxes)	38.5%	64.2%	0.008
Familiar with trash incineration as a waste disposal method	75.5%	92.6%	0.015

Table 5. Demographic characteristics of two communities and survey respondents' interest in environmental health issues in their community that hosts a waste-to-energy facility.

characteristics and involvement in environmental health issues. For example, Concord, NH respondents reported higher annual incomes of $25,000 or more (98.2%) compared to Claremont, NH respondents (55.5%). In terms of education level, more Concord, NH respondents completed college education (92.2%) compared to Claremont, NH respondents (53.0%). In addition, Concord, NH respondents were more likely to have lived in their community for more than ten years (76.4%) compared to Claremont, NH respondents (51.9%). Concord, NH respondents were also identified as being more active in community issues (65.5%) compared to Claremont, NH respondents (42.6%). Furthermore, 64.2% of Concord, NH respondents ranked the priority of environmental health issues higher than other community issues (e.g., property taxes) compared to 38.5% of Claremont, NH respondents. Lastly, 92.6% of Concord, NH respondents and 75.5% of Claremont, NH respondents were familiar with trash incineration as a waste disposal effort.

As shown in Table 6, survey results demonstrate statistically significant differences and similarities between these two communities with respect to information sources, believability and usefulness. For instance, Concord, NH respondents were more likely to not only obtain information from state agencies (61.1%), but they were also more likely to believe it (67.3%) compared to Claremont, NH respondents. Also, Concord, NH respondents were more likely to obtain information from environmental groups (50.0%) compared to Claremont, NH respondents (18.5%). Interestingly, both Concord, NH (92.6%) and Claremont, NH (79.6%) respondents were very likely to obtain information from media sources such as newspapers, television, radio and the Internet. However, Claremont, NH respondents were more likely to believe media sources (46.0%) and use (56.6%) the information from the television compared to Concord, NH respondents. Yet, respondents from both the Concord, NH (55.6%) and the Claremont, NH (66.0%) communities reported newspapers to be the most useful source of information.

In terms of having attended public meetings in the past and their effectiveness, both communities were similar in their responses. For example, respondents in the Concord, NH (70.9%) and Claremont, NH (56.6%) communities reported that they had attended a public meeting in the past. Respondents from Concord, NH (52.7%) and Claremont, NH (64.3%) reported that they found such a venue useful for communicating environmental health information. However, respondents from Concord, NH (31.5%) and Claremont, NH (24.5%) reported that if they voiced their opinion in a public meeting, they believed that their comments would not be taken seriously by officials in attendance.

Furthermore, respondents from Concord, NH (63.6%) and Claremont, NH (58.5%) believed that the condition of the environment plays a role in their personal health. Respondents from Concord, NH (92.6%) and Claremont, NH (75.5%) reported that they were familiar with trash incineration but these same respondents did not believe it was an effective means of waste disposal (58.0% and 61.4%, respectively.)

Cross-tabulation analyses indicated several statistically significant relationships (Table 7). For example, respondents with a college education were more likely to use environmental groups (43.4%) and the Internet (43.4%) as a source of environmental health information compared to respondents without a college education. Respondents who did not have a college education reported television (70.8%) as a useful media source for communicating environmental health information. In addition, respondents with a college education were more likely to report ever having attended a public meeting (70.2%), as well as being familiar with trash incineration as a disposal method (89.2%). Similarly, respondents who reported being more active in community issues were also more likely to report ever having attended a public meeting (81.0%), as well as being familiar with trash incineration as a disposal method (91.4%). Lastly, there were also significant relationships identified between living in the community for ten years or more and being well informed about community issues (62.3%).

	Claremont, NH	Concord, NH	P-value
Sources of environmental health information			
State Agencies	24.1%	61.1%	0.000
Environmental Groups	18.5%	50.0%	0.001
Media Sources	79.6%	92.6%	0.051
Believability of sources of environmental health information			
State Agencies	42.3%	67.3%	0.030
Media Sources	46.0%	28.3%	0.042
Useful media sources for obtaining environmental health information			
Television	56.6%	18.5%	0.000
Newspapers	66.0%	55.6%	0.267

Table 6. Survey respondents' sources, believability and usefulness of environmental health information from two communities that host a waste-to-energy facility.

Level of Education	No College Education	College Education	P-value
Environmental groups as source of environmental information	4.0%	43.4%	0.000
Television as useful media source for obtaining environmental information	70.8%	27.7%	0.000
Internet as useful media source for obtaining environmental information	20.8%	43.4%	0.045
Ever attended a public meeting	41.7%	70.2%	0.010
Familiar with trash incineration as a waste disposal method	66.7%	89.2%	0.008
Involvement in Community Issues	Less Active	More Active	P-value
Ever attended a public meeting	44.0%	81.0%	0.000
Familiar with trash incineration as a waste disposal method	75.5%	91.4%	0.025
Length of time lived in community	Less than Ten Years	More than Ten Years	P-value
Active in community issues	38.5%	62.9%	0.014
Well-informed about environmental health issues in the community	39.5%	62.3%	0.023

Table 7. Demographic characteristics and survey respondents' practices about environmental health information and issues from two communities that host a waste-to-energy facility.

8.2 State agency and community activists as stakeholders: perception of environmental communication

Twelve individual structured interviews with NHDES employees involved in Title V permitting and environmental health investigations and community activists from CLEAR were conducted to examine the experiences that shaped their perception of current environmental communication methods.

Through structured interviews with NHDES and a review of publicly available documents (e.g., phone records, e-mail and written correspondence and public hearing recordings) housed at NHDES, it was determined that the public inquiries concerning the Wheelabrator companies were mainly for the facility in Claremont, NH and not Concord, NH, even though they have identical operations. The public inquiries were fielded by NHDES ARD staff and/or the NHDES Complaint Manager. The concerns expressed ranged from health issues (e.g., cancer, respiratory illness) to nuisance complaints (e.g., odor, noise) to environmental issues (e.g., poor air and water quality), all of which were perceived to be due to the operation of the incinerator. The actions most often requested by the public for the Claremont, NH facility included air and water quality testing, compliance evaluations with state and federal emission standards and communication from the facility with the affected community. In some instances, the community members called for the closure of the facility. Distrust of NHDES and/or the facility was expressed in the public documents.

Structured interviews with community activists (n=7) demonstrated that they "feel there is more that should be done regarding this issue (waste-to-energy)." All interviewees discussed this theme in their individual interviews. The activists recommended that state government should further restrict trash incineration. Several interviewees discussed the recent ban on construction and demolition material incineration and pointed out that if this material is outlawed, everything should be banned.

Another theme that emerged was the activists' perception that the state agency pays inadequate attention to the issue of waste incineration in their communities. The activists are also very distrustful of state and industry involvement because many believe the company that owns the two municipal waste incinerators of interest, discusses with NHDES when random emissions testing will occur in advance so the incinerator will burn "cleaner trash" on the testing days. They believe that this skews the data so any emission report released by NHDES is not accurate.

When asked about efforts to improve environmental communication, community activists had mixed reactions. The majority of activists reported that the state agency did a decent job at communicating environmental health information. Beyond typical communication venues, such as newspapers, Internet, and public meetings, activists were hard pressed to suggest anything new. Several community activists mentioned that there was discussion about creating a community panel to review environmental community issues. Decisions regarding the environment (and the incinerator) would go to this panel for review. This idea was met with opposition by the local government and never came to fruition.

Community activists were asked about the effectiveness of having a community liaison located in their community. This individual would gather concerns and questions from the community, relay those concerns and questions to the appropriate state agency and then disseminate information back to the community. Unanimous support among the activists for such a position of this nature was expressed.

Interviews with NHDES regulators and investigators (n=5) revealed their belief that community activists do not acknowledge the state's effort to respond to their concerns. On multiple occasions, requests made by community activists were explored, such as the concern that the Claremont, NH facility was responsible for excessive cancer in that community. As a result, NHDES, in conjunction with the Agency for Toxic Substances and Disease Registry, conducted a community health investigation and analyzed twenty-four major cancer types from 1987-2001. It was determined, from the available data, the cancer rates for the specific types of cancer analyzed were within the expected range (ATSDR, 2006). This was a time-consuming endeavor and utilized many staff and budgetary resources. When results were presented to the community, activists were not pleased with the findings and discredited the initiative. The activists argued that the community health investigation was not done in a way that was inclusive of the community, and that the analysis was unacceptable and the results were inaccurate. As a result, state regulators believed that there was not much that could be done to remedy community activists concerns short of closing the Claremont, NH facility.

Another major theme expressed by NHDES involved community activists' communication with their organization. Direct questions and concerns were reported to be more effective than emotional propaganda from activists. An example expressed multiple times in NHDES interviews was that there were "two types of community activists." There are the community activists that send emotional propaganda, such as hundreds of postcards with dead fish on them to NHDES claiming that the mercury emitted from the Claremont, NH facility is killing all the fish. Other types of emotional propaganda that have been used by this reported "type" of activist include the mailing of pictures of residents who have died from cancer with messages explaining that the negligence of NHDES to shut down the facility was the direct cause of their death. In contrast, the "other type" of community activist sends specific questions and concerns that NHDES can investigate and reply with factual data. This type of communication was preferred and was believed to be more effective.

NHDES regulators and investigators were asked if it would be effective to have a community liaison position in New Hampshire communities where a contentious relationship exists between a community and an industry within the community. The responses were mixed about whether an appointed community liaison would help improve environmental communication. NHDES stated "This depends on who they are affiliated with…If there was a person in this position, it would be helpful if each stakeholder had trust in this person. However, how this trust is built is unclear. It is quite possible that this person could be another barrier in the communication process and act as another layer of litigation."

9. Managing perceived health risks from a single-owner waste-to-snergy facility in two distinct communities: discussion

An ongoing, practical challenge for state agencies involved in investigating community concerns related to an industrial process perceived to impact the environment and human health is how to most effectively communicate with the community as a key stakeholder. We propose that investigators and regulators need to be able to 1.) identify the community's ecology, that is the community's social, cultural, economic and political composition and 2.) understand the community's ecology to engage in effective environmental communication. State agencies frequently describe communities as groups of people living within a certain area, while communities may describe themselves on a more detailed level, such as by their socioeconomic status, religious beliefs, race/ethnicity, etc. (Parkin, 2004). We present the relationships between the demographic characteristics of two communities that host an identical waste-to-energy facility owned by the same parent company, and various communicative structures, such as the sources, believability and utility of environmental health information accessed by these populations, as well as their level of knowledge about trash incineration, the industrial process of concern. We demonstrate that disparate populations that host a similar industry access and believe different sources of environmental health information rank the priority of environmental health issues compared to community health issues differently and have different levels of activity on community issues. Our work suggests that ecological and demographic differences in communities need to be assessed, in order to identify the multidimensional components of the communities' risk perception and to be able to determine the most effective means by which to communicate environmental information.

Interestingly, a review of publicly available documents and structured interviews with community activists and agency stakeholders determined that although two NH communities host an identical municipal waste incinerator, the Claremont community, compared to the Concord community, was more vociferous in regards to their perception that the facility was a risk to the health of the population and their environment. In addition, the Claremont community was hesitant to believe the results of a health consultation and public health assessment conducted by NHDES and the federal Agency of Toxic Substances and Disease Registry that determined "...the Claremont area was in compliance with all National Ambient Air Quality Standards..." for the following criteria pollutants: sulfur dioxide, particulate matter less than 2.5 microns in diameter, ozone and nitrogen dioxide; and that "...cancer rates for 24 major cancer types were all within their expected ranges..." over the fifteen-year period studied (ATSDR, 2006; ATSDR, 2009). We suggest that demographic differences may contribute to the dissimilarity in risk perception of two communities for this industrial process, however, it is not the sole factor. We propose that effective and proactive environmental communicative structures that take into consideration the community's ecology among *all stakeholders* in *all types of communities* with a regulated industry is essential when addressing perceived health risks to the environment and population. Such practices could result in improved relationships with communities and public perception and expectations of community health investigations.

10. Recommendations for practitioners

Both case studies utilized the cultural-experiential model of risk, which requests information regarding the experience and views of impacted populations and their assessment of risk (Cox, 2006). We propose that part of effective environmental communication on the part of practitioners involves not only understanding the community's ecology but also the importance of engaging the public sphere to help build the community's capacity to address the environmental health issue of concern. Cox (2006) defines the public sphere as "The realm of influence created when individuals engage others in communication – through conversation, argument, debate, questions and nonverbal acts – about subjects of shared concern of topics that affect a wider community." The public sphere needs to be the common ground to communicate misunderstandings, knowledge deficits and environmental education. We utilized the cultural-experiential model to better understand the public sphere experienced by dissimilar communities that host different regulated industries, and in one instance, an identical industry.

Based on our systematic examination of the environmental communication preferences and practices among a state environmental agency, Title V operating facilities, community activists and the general public concerning environmental permitting decisions perceived to impact human health, we developed the below recommendations to facilitate best practices in environmental communication:

1. *Initiate communication early with the community:* Proactive communication to potentially affected communities by state agencies and neighboring facilities could facilitate the relationship among stakeholders and serve as the foundation for next steps. This recommendation arose from the experiences of two facilities which were completely different in their public outreach practices. One was not proactive in involving the community during the environmental permitting process and waited until the public hearing to address the community and explain the intent of their facility's operations. In this case, the relationship between the facility and public was strained from the beginning of the permitting process and the situation became the facility *versus* the public, instead of the facility working *with* the public. In contrast, the other facility was proactive in involving the community and held public information sessions prior to the public hearing to address the community's concerns.

2. *Provide seminars to educate facility managers about public engagement:* The state agency could offer seminars designed to educate facility managers on public outreach practices prior to the Title V permitting process. These educational seminars would provide opportunities for facilities to develop an understanding of the concerns typically raised by communities and discuss how to be a "good neighbor" based on best practices.

3. *Require the permit application be accompanied by a public outreach plan:* In order to maintain the neutrality of the official Title V permitting process, yet be proactive in communicating with stakeholders, the state agency could require the facility to include several objective public outreach activities that support public participation. An example could include engaging the community prior to the public hearing, via non-regulatory communication, which would ease the environmental permitting process by providing an opportunity for concerns to be addressed.

4. *Advocate representatives from state government public health and environmental health bureaus be present at public hearings*: The concerns expressed by the public are so varied that no one agency could address them. The inability to answer questions during public hearings led to the community's frustration and increased stress on the communication among the stakeholders. Therefore, representatives from each public health and environmental health state bureau should be represented on the public hearing panel to address a broad array of questions and reduce the feelings of distrust.

5. *Establish citizen advisory committees*: This action could provide an opportunity for citizens to voice their concerns or ask questions about the facility operations on a regular basis. One facility manager explained that this has been a great way for the public to have direct communication with officials about the permitting process and their concerns.

6. *Establishment of a community liaison position:* The community liaison position is a neutral party who would be located in the community and have an established relationship with the community. He/she would gather concerns and questions from the community, relay those

concerns and questions to the appropriate state agency and then disseminate information back to the community. Similar to the community panel mentioned by community activists in Claremont, NH, this action could provide an opportunity for citizens to voice their concerns, ask questions about the facility operations on a regular basis and allow for the community to play a role in policy and program development.

7. Be accountable for communication among stakeholders: State agency(ies) and industry need to understand the best way to communicate with the community. To accommodate the high number of complaints the facility was receiving, one landfill utilized web-based technology for the public to express their concerns. However, it is important that this communication be "two-way." For example, numerous entries stated that many inquiries had been filed online, yet the problems complained about were still in existence and the facility failed to respond to any concerns. Therefore, as part of the routine evaluation of their communication with the public, facilities need to establish processes to assure a timely response to the public's comments. In addition, Claremont, NH respondents (56.6%) reported environmental health information obtained from the television more useful compared to Concord, NH respondents (18.5%). In addition, it is important that this communication be "two-way." Therefore, as part of the routine evaluation of their communication with the public, state agencies and facilities need to establish processes to assure a timely response to the public's comments. A community liaison could be proactive in this practice.

8. Increase state agency awareness: In several instances, the public contacted the EPA because they were unaware of who to contact at state government or the facility. Increasing awareness of the state agency as a stakeholder in the environmental permitting process would help the public understand who to contact concerning environmental issues and facilitate relationship-building between the state and the public. This may be accomplished through state agency and facility-sponsored community events or attendance at existing community events to raise awareness.

9. Use of appropriate information and meeting logistics: Information complexity as a communication barrier for the public was evident in the public hearing audiotapes and interviews with facility managers. For example, the public requested clarification by NHDES ARD concerning emissions and health effects and asked what "all the figures and tables meant." Furthermore, facility managers expressed concern that the information presented by NHDES ARD to the public was too complex, thus leading the public to contact the facility. Taking the time to understand the community's ecology will help state agencies develop appropriate information that is communicated in an effective forum for that community. Hence, this practice will be community-specific.

In addition, the room for public hearings is traditionally organized in a polarized manner where the state agency and the facility are at one end and the community is at the other end. This creates an "us" versus "them" perception, which can inhibit positive communication among stakeholders. It would be optimal for the room to be organized so the stakeholders are interspersed at a roundtable. This format allows each participant to see each other and not feel as though any one viewpoint is valued over another.

10. Provide routine updates to stakeholders: State agency and Title V facilities should provide concerned community members updates about progress made to address their concerns. These updates could be communicated via a list-serve; mass mailings of a newsletter; and updates posted to NHDES' and the facility's web page. This practice would keep the public informed about what the state agency and facilities are doing and can dissuade distrust or contention from developing.

Our recommendations provide a set of communicative structures to help advance effective environmental communication among stakeholders when dealing with regulated industry in different types of communities. Such practices may increase the community's trust in government, as well as their belief in the credibility of community health investigations and their acceptance of the results (Charnley & Engelbert, 2005).

11. Future work

Our future work involves examining how creative partnerships, such as those between academia and the community can further advance environmental communication strategies. Although academic institutions are rich resources for improving the health of the public and the environment, academic partnerships with community organizations can be challenging. Yet, such partnerships have been shown to translate science and best practices into social action and policy change at the local community level (Serrell et al., 2009).

12. Acknowledgments

The authors are grateful to the following: New Hampshire Department of Environmental Services, Air Resources Division; facility managers from Turnkey Recycling and Environmental Enterprises, Mt. Carberry Landfill, Four Hills Landfill, Indeck Energy Services, Inc., Schiller Station, and Wheelabrator Technologies, Inc.; CLEAR NH and the general public and businesses of Claremont, NH and Concord, NH for their participation in this study. In addition, the authors thank Robert J. McGrath, Assistant Professor in the Department of Health Management and Policy, University of New Hampshire for insightful discussions about survey design and analysis; and Holly Tutko, Clinical Assistant Professor, Department of Health Management and Policy, University of New Hampshire for her critical review of this work.

13. References

Agency for Toxic Substances and Disease Registry (ATSDR). (2004). Communicating results to community residents: Lessons from recent ATSDR health investigations. *Journal of Exposure Analysis and Environmental Epidemiology, 14*, 484-491.

Agency for Toxic Substances and Disease Registry (ATSDR). (2006). *Health Consultation for Cancer Incidence: Residents of Claremont, Sullivan County, New Hampshire (Wheelabrator – Claremont Site)* Retrieved December 18, 2010, from: http://www.atsdr.cdc.gov/HAC/pha/WheelabratorClaremont/Wheelabrator-ClaremontHC09.30.06.pdf

Agency for Toxic Substances and Disease Registry (ATSDR). (2009). *Public Health Assessments and Health Consultations.* Retrieved December 18, 2010 from http://www.atsdr.cdc.gov/HAC/PHA/index.asp

Agency for Toxic Substances and Disease Registry (ATSDR). (2009). *Public Health Assessment for Ambient Air Quality in Claremont, Sullivan County, New Hampshire.* Retrieved December 18, 2010, from: http://www.atsdr.cdc.gov/HAC/pha/AmbientAirQualityinClaremontNH/ClaremontInitial-PublicCommentPHA03-02-2009a.pdf

Air Resources Division (ARD), New Hampshire Department of Environmental Services. (n.d.). *Overview*. Retrieved December 15, 2010, from http://des.nh.gov/organization/divisions/air/overview.htm.

Air Resources Division (ARD), New Hampshire Department of Environmental Services. (2008). *Title V Operating Permit Reporting Guidance*. Retrieved December 15, 2010, from: http://des.nh.gov/organization/commissioner/pip/forms/ard/documents/repo rting_guidance.pdf

Bennett, P. (1999). Understanding responses to risk: Some basic findings. In Bennett, P. & Calman, K. (Eds.), *Risk Communication and Public Health*, (pp. 3-19). New York, New York: University Press.

Brauer, M., Hakkinen, P.J., Gehan, B.M., Shirname-More, L. (2004). Communicating exposure and health effects results to study subjects, the community and the public: Strategies and challenges. *Journal of Exposure Analysis and Environmental Epidemiology, 14*, 479-483.

Caron, R.M. & Serrell, N. (2009). Community ecology and capacity: Keys to progressing the environmental communication of wicked problems. *Applied Environmental Education and Communication*, 8(3-4), 195-203.

Charnley, S. & Engelbert, B. (2005). Evaluating public participation in environmental decision-making: EPA's superfund community involvement program. *Journal of Environmental Management, 77*, 165-182.

Citizens Leading for Environmental Action and Responsibility (CLEAR), Claremont, NH (n.d.). *Overview*. Retrieved December 18, 2010, from: http://www.clearnh.org/NewsAction.aspx

Cottrell, R.R. & McKenzie, J.F. (2005). Qualitative research methods. In *Health Promotion & Education Research Methods: Using the Five-Chapter Thesis/Dissertation Model*, (pp. 217-244). Massachusetts: Jones and Bartlett Publishers.

Covello, V. & Sandman, P. (2001). Risk communication: Evolution and revolution. In Wolbarst, A. (Ed.), *Solutions to an Environment in Peril*, (pp.164-178). Baltimore: Johns Hopkins University Press.

Cox, R. (2006). Risk communication: Nonexpert publics and acceptable risk. In *Environmental Communication and the Public Sphere*, (pp.205-240). Thousand Oaks: Sage Publications, Inc.

Hance B.J., Chess C., Sandman P.M. (1989). Setting a context for explaining risk. *Risk Analysis, 9*,113-117.

McComas, K.A. (2003). Citizen Satisfaction with public meetings used for risk communication. *Journal of Applied Communication Research, 31*(2), 164-184.

McKinney, M. & Harmon, W. (2002). Public participation in environmental decision making: Is it working? *National Civic Review, 91*(2), 149-170.

Park, E., Scherer, C.W., Glynn, C.J. (2001). Community involvement and risk perception at personal and societal levels. *Health, Risk & Society*, 3(3), 281-292.

Parkin, R.T. (2004). Communication with research participants and communities: Foundations for best practices. *Journal of Exposure Analysis and Environmental Epidemiology, 14*, 516-523.

Sandman, P. (1989). Hazard versus outrage in the public perception of risk. In Covello V, McCallum D, Pavlova M (Eds.), *Effective risk communication* (pp. 45-49). New York: Plenum Press.

Serrell, N., Caron, R.M., Fleishman, B., Robbins, E.D. (2009). An academic-community outreach partnership: Building relationships and capacity to address childhood lead poisoning. *Progress in Community Health Partnerships: Research, Education, and Action*, 3.1, 53-59.

Tinker, T.L., Zook, E., Chapel, T.J. (2001). Key challenges and concepts in health risk communication: Perspectives of agency practitioners. *Journal of Public Health Management and Practice*, 7, 67-75.

United States Census Bureau (Census). (n.d.). *Population Finder*. Retrieved December 18, 2010 from http://www.census.gov/

Wehrly, R. (2006). Constructing the problem of lead poisoning. Senior thesis (unpublished).

Wheelabrator Technologies, Inc., A waste Management Company. (n.d.) Fact Sheet. Retrieved December 18, 2010, from:

http://www.wheelabratortechnologies.com/index.cfm/our-clean-energy-plants/

4

Regional Issues in Environmental Management

Hiroyuki Taguchi

Policy Research Institute, Ministry of Finance[1]

Japan

1. Introduction

This chapter addresses regional issues in environment management. Economic integration beyond national boundaries has recently made great progress in regional levels as well as in global levels, with the formulations of Free Trade Agreement (FTA) and Economic Partnership Agreement (EPA) as typical examples. This trend in regional economic integration also refocuses attention on regional environmental issues including trans-boundary pollutions, and makes us rethink of what regional cooperation should be in environment management. Based on this context, we herein discuss regional environment issues, with a focus on East Asian region, from the following two perspectives.

The first one is about which effects, i.e. technological spillovers or pollution haven damages, the regional latecomers have dominantly received in environment management under a growing trend in economic integration within East Asia. If the dominance of technological spillovers effect is identified for latecomer's economies, we may have rather optimistic views on the future of environment quality as a whole region, because it implies that latecomers are absorbing the skills and technologies enough to leapfrog the mistakes made by developed economies in the past times. On the other hand, the dominance of pollution haven damages implies the mere relocation of polluters from developed economies towards latecomer's economies, i.e. no decline in pollution as a whole region, thereby making us feel uneasy on regional prospect of environment. Thus, knowing the effects for latecomers seems to be linked with knowing the degree of demand for policy actions as a region. East Asia, in recent decades, has strengthened intra-economic integration in terms of trade and investment flows.[2] At the same time, East Asian economies are still composed of a variety of countries with different stages of development: high-income countries like Japan and Korea, middle-income ones like Malaysia and Thailand, low-income ones such as Cambodia and Myanmar.[3] Since the integration and diversification characterized by East Asian economies make East Asia a typical area with provability of technology spillovers or pollution haven damages, targeting East Asia seems to be meaningful in our analysis.

The second perspective is about what the regional framework of environmental cooperation should be in East Asia. There have been intensive debates on the regional frameworks from

---

[1] The views expressed in this paper are those of the author and not those of the Ministry of Finance or the Policy Research Institute.

[2] Kawai (2009) indicates, for example, that the ratio of intra-regional trade relative to world trade in East Asia has gone up from 35 percent in 1980 towards 54 percent in 2007, which is a little under 57 percent in EU and exceeding 43 percent in NAFTA.

[3] The classification of income classes depends on World Development Indicators of World Bank.

the viewpoints of commitment and compliance, especially in the cases of such trans-boundary issues as long-range air and water pollutions, freshwater resources in international rivers, migratory birds. The frameworks differ in the modality of cooperation: policy dialogue, cooperative environmental monitoring and assessment, implementation of project-based activities, and legal treaties and protocols. There seem to be some contrasts in the approaches towards regional cooperation between East Asia and Europe: Non-binding approaches in East Asia versus binding ones in Europe. The typical example is seen in the framework of the long-ranged trans-boundary air pollution control: East Asia is promoting non-binding agreements on pollution monitoring and other project-based activities, whereas Europe is controlling pollution based on binding agreement in terms of the Convention for the Long-Range Transmission of Air Pollutant in Europe (the LRTAP). Each approach appears to have advantages and disadvantages, and the choice of the approach seems to be linked with the region-specific properties in economical, political, and historical terms. The purpose of this section is, thus, to investigate the reason why East Asia has taken the non-binding approach, and to examine the justification of its choice considering the region-specific properties.

The rest of the paper is structured as follows. Section 2 examines the effects for latecomers in East Asia: technological spillovers versus pollution haven, corresponding to the first perspective above. Section 3 discusses the regional frameworks of environmental cooperation in East Asia, corresponding to the second perspective above.

2. Effects for latecomers: technological spillovers versus pollution haven

The purpose of this section is to examine whether the latecomer's economies in East Asia enjoy technological spillover effects or suffer pollution haven damages in their environment management: in other words, which of latecomer's advantage or latecomer's disadvantage dominates for pollution control in East Asian economies. We focus on environmental indices with data availability: carbon dioxide emissions, consumption of ozone-depleting substances and industrial organic water pollutant (BOD) emissions. The analytical framework of the Environmental Kuznets curve (EK curve) is used to arrive at a conclusion. In the following subsections, we first review previous studies on the EK curve in brief and clarify this article's contribution (Subsection 2.1), present our own empirical study of the effects for latecomers (Subsection 2.2), and end with brief summary (Subsection 2.3).

2.1 Previous studies and our contribution

The environmental Kuznets curve (EK curve) provides an analytical framework to examine how economies deal with environmental issues. The EK curve postulates an inverted-U relationship between pollution and economic development; at early stages of development, environmental quality deteriorates with increases in per capita income, while at higher levels of development, environmental degradation is seen to decrease with further increases in per capita income. Kuznets's name was apparently attached to the curve by Grossman & Krueger (1993), who noted its resemblance to Kuznets inverted-U relationship between income inequality and development. Since the issue of the EK curve was first discussed in the World Bank's 1992 World Development Report, there have been numerous empirical tests and theoretical debates on the EK curve. Until the mid of the 1990s, most of the empirical studies concentrated on validating the EK curve hypothesis and its requirements, using cross-sectional data. Some of evidences on specific pollutants supported the validity of the EK curve (e.g. Grossman & Krueger; 1995, Selden & Song; 1994), while some argue that the EK curve does not hold at all times and for all pollutants (e.g. Shafik; 1994).

Since the late 1990s, the EK curve studies have shifted from cross-sectional analyses to time-series analyses, especially towards the analyses for comparing the EK curves of individual economies in terms of the height and the timing of their peaks, their shapes, etc (e.g. Panayotou; 1997, De Bruyn et al.; 1998).[4] One of the frontiers in this direction of the EK curve studies is to put into empirical tests the two contrasting hypotheses presented by Dasgupta et al. (2002). One is the technological spillover hypothesis that developing societies, by utilizing progressive environmental management and the technologies of more advanced countries, might be able to experience an EK curve that is lower and flatter than what conventional wisdom would suggest. The other is the pollution haven hypothesis that the relatively high environmental standards in high-income economies impose high costs on polluters, and shareholders pressure firms to relocate to low-income countries. This pollution haven scenario may not shift the latecomer's EK curves downward; on the contrary, it may even lift them up. Taguchi & Murofushi (2009), by using the EK curve framework, examined whether developing countries enjoy the latecomer's advantage or suffer the latecomer's disadvantage in the environment management, focusing on sulfur emissions as local air pollutants and carbon emissions as global air pollutants, by using the world-wide samples for the 188 economies from 1960 to 1990 in sulfur emissions and from 1970 to 2003 in carbon emissions. It found contrasting result between sulfur and carbon emissions on the latecomer's effects; sulfur emissions represent the dominance of the latecomer's advantage (the downward shift of latecomer's EK curve), while carbon emissions reveal that of the latecomer's disadvantage (the upward shift of latecomer's EK curve). It interpreted this contrast as the difference of maturity level in the know-how and technology to abate emissions: prevailing desulfurization technology and unrestricted "carbon leakage" (a kind of pollution haven in carbon emissions).

This study aims at testing the two contrasting hypothesis above in East Asia, – the dominance of the latecomer's advantage (technological spillovers) or of the latecomer's disadvantage (pollution haven). The main contribution is to extend the existing literature, mainly of Taguchi (2009), to the following directions. First, our study concentrates on East Asian economies (18 economies). The intra-area of East Asia with the characteristic of economic integration and diversification, as stated in Introduction, can be an experimental area suitable enough to put the hypotheses of technological spillovers and pollution haven into empirical tests. In addition, the evidence on the latecomer's effects in East Asia has been extremely limited in the existing literature. Second, our analysis uses the latest data of the period for 1990-2007 on carbon dioxide emissions, consumption of ozone-depleting substances and industrial organic water pollutant (BOD) emissions. The usage of the latest data enables us to make the EK curve estimation reflect the recent trends of technological progress and policy responses to address environmental issues as well as growing economic interaction of East Asia. Third, our estimation for the EK curve adopts a dynamic panel model by a system of Generalized Method of Moments (GMM). It appears to take some periods for the current level of emissions to adjust toward their equilibrium level – a kind of inertia in the emission level. Most of previous studies for the EK curve have adopted a static

---

[4] Borghesi (1999) criticized the cross-sectional approach by arguing that since environmental degradation is generally increasing in developing countries and decreasing in industrialized ones, the EK curve within the cross-sectional framework might reflect the mere juxtaposition of two opposite trends rather than describe the evolution of a single economy over time.

panel model in terms of ordinary fixed or random estimations. When there is evidence of dynamics in the data, however, the validity of applying a static model might be questioned as being dynamically miss-specified. To our knowledge, it is only Halkos (2003) that constructed a dynamic panel model for the EK curve estimation. This paper adopts the method of Halkos (2003), which allows dynamic adjustments in the level of emissions.

2.2 Empirics

We now turn to the empirical studies using the analytical framework of the EK curve. Our analysis consists of two steps. First, we simply overview the relationships between per capita real income and environmental indices. We then move to a dynamic panel analysis using cross-country panel data to examine the EK curve pattern and to see whether the latecomer's advantage or its disadvantage dominates in the environmental management in East Asian economies.

2.2.1 Data

We collect the data for three environmental indices per capita –carbon dioxide emissions, consumption of ozone-depleting substances and industrial organic water pollutant emissions– and real GDP per capita. All the data come from the Annual Core indicators online database developed by the Statistics Division of the United Nations Economic and Social Commission for Asia and the Pacific (ESCAP).[5] The database covers data from 1990 to 2007, all of which we use as sample periods. The sample economies are the following 18 ones in East Asia: Brunei Darussalam, Cambodia, China, DPR Korea, Hong Kong, Indonesia, Japan, Lao PDR, Macao, Malaysia, Mongolia, Myanmar, Republic of Korea, Singapore, Thailand, the Philippines, Timor-Leste and Viet Nam.

The indicator of "carbon dioxide emissions per capita" that we can obtain from the online database is defined as the quantity of estimated carbon dioxide emissions (tons of carbon dioxide) divided by total population, whose data sources are the United Nations Millennium Development Goals Indicators and the World Population Prospects: the 2006 Revision Population Database. The indicator of "consumption of ozone-depleting substances per capita" is defined as the sum of the national annual consumption in weighted tons of individual substances in the group of ozone-depleting substances multiplied by their ozone-depleting potential (Ozone-depleting substances are any substance containing chlorine or bromine that destroys the stratospheric ozone layer), expressed as ODP kilograms per 1,000 population. Its data sources are the same as those of carbon dioxide emissions per capita. The indicator of "industrial organic water pollutant emissions" is defined as the biochemical oxygen demand, which refers to the amount of oxygen that bacteria in water will consume in breaking down waste, expressed as kilograms per day. Its data source is the United Nations Environment Program, Emission Database for Global Atmospheric Research (EDGAR 3.2). This indicator shows total amount, thereby being divided by population. We can find the other emissions indicators in the online database: nitrous oxide emissions, sulfur dioxide emissions and PM10 concentration in urban area, but do not adopt them for the dynamic estimation later since their data cover only every five years. For the real GDP per capita, the indicator of "GDP per capita on 1990 US dollars base" is obtained from the online database.

---

[5] See the website of http://www.unescap.org/stat/data/syb2008/syb2008_web/index.asp

To sum up, for conducting the dynamic panel estimation later on, we constructed a panel table of the annual data of the 18 economies from 1990 to 2007 on each of per capita environmental indices of carbon dioxide emissions, consumption of ozone-depleting substances and industrial organic water pollutant emissions, and on real GDP per capita.

2.2.2 Overview of the EK curves in sample economies in East Asia
Fiure 1 indicates the time-series relationships between per capita real GDP and three kinds of environmental indices per capita in selected samples of East Asian economies. The rough

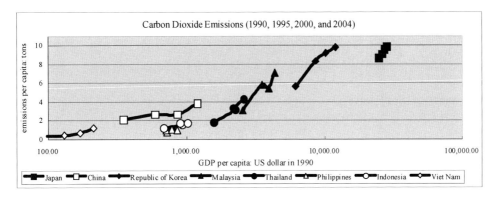

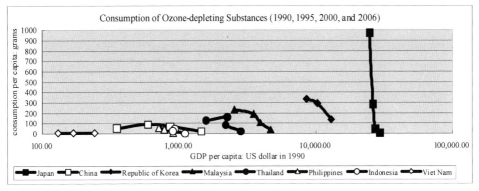

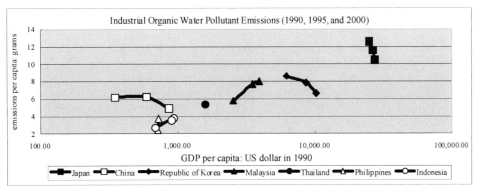

Fig. 1. Overview of the EK curves in selected sample economies

findings are as follows. First, there appears to be no cases where the assembly of the economy's trajectories clearly produces inverted-U shape patterns. The trajectories of carbon dioxide emissions represent an increasing trend whereas their slope seems to be flattened with higher real GDP per capita. The lines of consumption of ozone-depleting substances roughly represent declining slope. The cases of industrial organic water pollutant emissions have no clear trend of trajectories. We might speculate that the carbon dioxide emissions stay at the positively-sloping part of the EK curve, while the consumption of ozone-depleting substances stays at its negatively-sloping part. Second, the locations of the economy's trajectories represent a clear contrast; the upward shifts of trajectories for latecomer's economies are observed in the case of carbon dioxide emissions, while downward shifts are seen in the cases of consumption of ozone-depleting substances. The cases of industrial organic water pollutant emissions have no clear shift of trajectories. The GDP-emissions relationships described above may produce different implications among environmental indices. This point will be statistically tested through dynamic panel estimations in the following section.

2.2.3 Dynamic panel analysis

We'll now move to a dynamic panel analysis using cross-country panel data to examine the EK curve pattern and to see whether the latecomer's advantage or its disadvantage dominates in the environmental management in East Asian economies.

2.2.3.1 Methodology

We first clarify some methodological points related to our analysis. To study the relationship between pollution and growth, there are two possible approaches to model construction. One is to estimate a reduced-form equation that relates the level of pollution to the level of income. The other is to model the structural equations relating environmental regulations, technology, and industrial composition to GDP, and then to link the level of pollution to the regulations, technology, and industrial composition. We here take the reduced-form approach for the following reasons. First, the reduced-form estimates give us the net effect of a nation's income on pollution. If the structural equations were to be estimated first, one would need to solve backward to find the net effect. Moreover, confidence in the implied estimates would depend on the precision and potential biases of the estimates at every stage. Second, the reduced-form approach spares us from having to collect data on pollution regulations and the state of the existent technology, which are not always available. Thus, we think that the reduced-form relationship between pollution and income is an important first step.

We then specify the reduced-form equation by basically following the traditions of the literatures like Grossman and Krueger (1995) and Selden and Son (1994), and adding appropriate variables in accordance with our analytical interests. Our specific concern regarding the EK curve for the sample economies in East Asia is to see whether the EK-curve trajectories for the latecomer's economies have shifted downward or upward, depending on the dominance of either the latecomer's advantage or its disadvantage[6]; in

---

[6] As Dasgupta et al. (2002) showed the revised EK curve that is actually dropping and shifting to the left as growth generates less pollution in the early stages of industrialization and pollution begins falling at lower income levels, the latecomer's effects may not always be tantamount to a simple up- and downward shifts of the EK curve. However, we here simplify the analysis by focusing on up- and downward shift of the EK curve.

other words, the levels of environmental pollution per capita have been affected not only by the level of per capita income following the EK curve, but also by the later degree of development among the economies. If a sample economy with later degree of development among the samples enjoys the lower level of environmental pollution (traces the downward course of the EK curve), we speculate that the economy, not repeating the EK-curve trajectories already experienced by the developed economies, should enjoy the latecomer's advantage by absorbing the progress in environmental know-how, skills, and technology i.e. technological spillover. On the contrary, if the later development in a sample economy is linked with higher pollution, the economy may suffer from the latecomer's disadvantage caused by the "pollution haven" scenario (see Figure 2). Therefore, we will include a term representing the later degree of development among the economies into the equation for the EK curve. The later degree of development of a sample economy in a certain year is specified as the ratio of the GDP per capita of that economy relative to the maximum GDP per capita among sample economies (equivalent to the GDP per capita of Japan) in that year. Another methodological innovation in this study is to adopt a dynamic panel model. Halkos (2003), pointing out that a static model is justified either if adjustment processes are really very fast or if the static equation represents an equilibrium relationship, argued that since the assumption that the data are stationary is incorrect, and we are not expecting a very fast adjustment for estimating the EK curve, a statistically sound approach requires estimating a dynamic model. Following the argument of Halkos (2003), we construct a dynamic panel model by inserting a lagged dependent variable as a regressor into the EK curve equation for materializing a partial adjustment toward equilibrium emissions level.

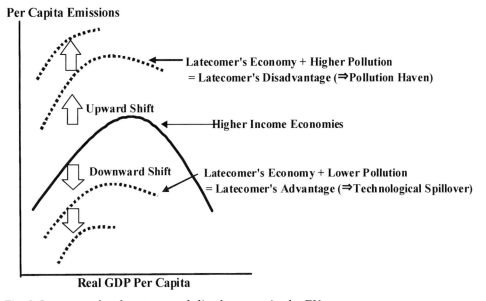

Fig. 2. Latecomer's advantage and disadvantage in the EK curves

Based on analytical interests mentioned above, we specify the modified EK curve model as follows:

$$EMS_{it} = \alpha_0 + \alpha_1 GDP_{it} + \alpha_2 GDP_{it}^2 + \alpha_3 LAC_{it} + \alpha_4 EMS_{it-1} + \alpha_5 f_i + e_{it} \tag{1}$$

where i is the economy's index (country), t is the time index, and e is the error term. The dependent variables EMS is measure of the per capita emissions: carbon dioxide emissions (CDE), consumption of ozone-depleting substances (ODS) and industrial organic water pollutant emissions (BOD). As for the independent variables, GDP is the real GDP per capita. LAC represents the later degree of development, specifically the ratio of the real GDP per capita of a certain economy relative to the maximum real GDP per capita among economies in a certain year (i.e. real GDP per capita of Japan) – the lower LAC means the later development of the economy. The f_i denotes exogenously economy-specific factors that affect emissions; climate, geography, energy resources, etc. The equation does not include period dummy, because its inclusion was rejected significantly by statistical tests in the equation estimate.

To verify the inverted-U shapes of the EK curves, the signs and magnitudes of α_1 and α_2 should be examined. Environmental emissions per capita can be said to exhibit a meaningful EK curve with the real GDP per capita, if $\alpha_1>0$ and $\alpha_2<0$, and if the turning point, $-\alpha_1/2\alpha_2$ is a reasonabe number. Of particular importance is the coefficient of LAC, α_3, which is useful for identifying the dominance of the latecomer's advantage or its disadvantage. The positive sign of α_3, the lower pollution with the later development of the economy that creates the downward shift of the latecomers' trajectories, indicates that the latecomer's advantage surpasses its disadvantage. On the other hand, the negative sign of α_3, the higher pollution with the later development of the economy equivalent to the upward shift of the latecomers' curve, reveals the dominance of the latecomer's disadvantage.

Equation (1) contains the lagged dependent variable among the explanatory variables, thereby the ordinary OLS estimator being inconsistent. Obtaining consistent estimates requires the application of an instrumental variables estimator or Generalized Method of Moments (GMM). We here adopt the system GMM estimator developed by Arellano and Bond (1991) who argues that additional instruments can be obtained in a dynamic model from panel data if we utilize the orthogonality conditions between lagged values of the dependent and the disturbances. The GMM estimator eliminates country effects by first-differencing as well as controls for possible endogeneity of explanatory variables. The first-differenced endogenous variables of EMS with two lagged periods can be valid instruments provided there is no second-order autocorrelation in the idiosyncratic error terms. We also use the first differenced explanatory variables of GDP with one lagged period as an instrumental variable since GDP can possibly be correlated with the error term in case that environmental pollution might aggravates economic growth. We then conduct two step GMM iterations with updating weights once, and adopt White period as GMM weighting matrix. We present the tests for autocorrelations and the Sargan test of over-identifying restrictions in the table that follow.

2.2.3.2 Estimation results and interpretations

Table 1 lists the results of the GMM estimation per capita on carbon dioxide emissions (CDE), consumption of ozone-depleting substances (ODS) and industrial organic water pollutant emissions (BOD). All the cases indicate that the inclusion of the lagged dependent variable of the emissions per capita proved to be positively discernable, thus imply inertia in the level of the emissions and justify forming the dynamic panel model. The Sargan tests do not suggest rejection of the instrumental validity at conventional levels for any cases estimated. As for the test results for autocorrelations, all the AR(2) test statistics reveal absence of second-order serial correlation in the first-differenced errors and thus that the instruments are valid.

We first verify the shape of the EK curve of each emission index. There are no cases that reveal the meaningful EK curve with the inverted-U shape. The linear CDE estimation indicates upward sloping with real GDP per capita at significant level. The quadratic CDE estimation has the significant coefficients, α_1 and α_2 with correct signs of the inverted-U shape. Its turning point of 26,800 US dollars is, however, falling into the edge of the samples, i.e. only within the sample of Japan with the highest real GDP per capita. Almost all of the trajectories are within the monotonic increasing trend, i.e. the positively-sloping part of the EK curve. The ODS estimation indicates that the trajectories are in the monotonic decreasing trend regardless of the linear or quadratic equation forms. Although the quadratic estimation's coefficients, α_1 and α_2, suggest not inverted-U but U shape, the turning point of 116,000 US dollars is far higher from the range of the samples. The BOD represents only monotonic downward sloping in its estimation, since the coefficient of the square of GDP, α_2, is insignificant. We speculate that it is due to the shortage of sample data backward from 1990 that the ODS and BOD do not prove to form the inverted-U shape curve in their estimation.

We next see if the latecomer's EK trajectories show a downward shift or an upward shift, namely whether the latecomer's advantage or its disadvantage dominate in the environmental management of latecomer's economies. The CDE estimate has significantly negative α_3, coefficient of LAC, thereby representing the upward shift of the latecomer's trajectories and the dominance of the latecomer's disadvantage. On the other hand, the ODS and BOD estimates have significantly positive α_3, showing the downward shift of the latecomer's trajectories, the dominance of the latecomer's advantage.

	CDE		ODS		BOD	
GDP	$4.43*10^{-4}$ ***	$2.57*10^{-3}$ ***	$-2.33*10^{-2}$ ***	$-2.98*10^{-2}$ ***	$-1.38*10^{-4}$ ***	$-3.41*10^{-4}$ **
	(978.87)	(33.96)	(-68204.89)	(-6078.09)	(-6.97)	(-2.25)
GDP^2		$-4.78*10^{-8}$ ***		$1.28*10^{-7}$ ***		$3.53*10^{-9}$
		(-21.42)		(1150.38)		(1.25)
LAC	$-2.21*10$ ***	$-5.18*10$ ***	$1.56*10^{2}$ ***	$2.39*10^{2}$ ***	1.22 *	4.61 **
	(-2980.99)	(-291.37)	(14700.19)	(3125.34)	(1.72)	(2.12)
$(EMS)_{t-1}$	$4.96*10^{-1}$ ***	$4.53*10^{-1}$ ***	$5.66*10^{-1}$ ***	$5.65*10^{-1}$ ***	$6.11*10^{-1}$ ***	$5.76*10^{-1}$ ***
	(11958.02)	(106.46)	(517030.9)	(171680.4)	(19.48)	(10.00)
Tuning Point		$2.68*10^{4}$		$1.16*10^{5}$		$4.83*10^{4}$
Sargan test	0.60	0.85	0.71	0.75	0.88	0.91
AR(1)	0.00	0.01	0.07	0.07	0.01	0.01
AR(2)	0.21	0.24	0.74	0.75	0.86	0.81
No. of obs.	222	222	192	192	93	93

(Notes)
i) The t-value are in parentheses. ***, **, and * indicate rejection at the 1 percent, 5 percent, and 10 percent significance levels.
ii) "Sargan test" denotes the p-value of a Sargan-Hansen test of overidentifying restrictions.
iii) AR(k) is the p-value of a test that the average autocovariance in residuals of order k is zero.

Table 1. Results of dynamic panel estimation by GMM

There seem to be some contrasts of estimation results in terms of both the trajectory's shape and location between CDE and the other indices of ODS and BOD. These contrasts appear to be interpreted as follows. The first contrast is concerned with the shape of the EK trajectories. The ODS and BOD mainly come from manufacturing production activities, thereby being subject to regulation due to their localized impact. In fact, the pollution controls on the ODS and BOD have intensively been promoted by East Asian countries. The ozone-depleting substances have been strictly regulated since the 1987's signature of the Montreal Protocol, i.e. an international treaty designed to protect the ozone layer by phasing out the production of a number of substances believed to be responsible for ozone depletion. All of East Asian countries have had a commitment to the treaty or its amendments in terms of ratification, accession or acceptance. The issues of water pollution as well as air pollution have also been addressed with technological progress over a broad area of East Asia since the 1970-80s, when ASEAN countries formulated comprehensive environmental protection laws (the Philippines in 1977, Malaysia in 1974, Thailand in 1975, and Indonesia in 1982). These factual backgrounds seem to make the EK trajectories of ODS and BOD slope downward i.e. create downward sloping part of the inverted-U shaped EK curve. On the other hands, the CDE is producing an opposite pattern of its trajectories, a positively-sloping part of the EK curve. It seems to be because carbon dioxide emissions arise from not only production but also from consumption such as automobile use and the burning of fossil fuels for the generation of electricity, thereby being easily externalized and thus not subject to regulation. The reality is that it is only after the Kyoto Protocol was approved in 1997 that regulatory frameworks on Greenhouse Gas have come to be set about domestically and internationally. The contrasting outcomes on the shape of the EK trajectories in this study appear to be consistent with those of previous works, which Nahman & Antrobus (2005) summarize by stating that the levels of the pollutants with local impacts fall with per capita income whilst the levels of easily externalized pollutants continue to rise with per capita income.

The second contrast – downward shift of the latecomer's trajectories on the ODS and BOD versus upward shift on the CDE – can be explained by the degree of maturity in the know-how and technology to abate those emissions in East Asia. More or less, the concentration of manufacturing industrial activities have tended to shift from advanced economies to developing economies since wealthy consumers in advanced economies demand a cleaner environment and stringent environmental regulations. Thus, the pollution haven effects can not help being avoided for latecomer's economies. The question is, then, whether the technological spillover effects overcome the pollution haven effects for latecomer's economies i.e. the dominance of latecomer's advantage or disadvantage. The cases with downward shift of the latecomer's trajectories on ODS and BOD can be interpreted in such a way that the policy efforts, know-how and technology to abate those emissions are mature and feasible enough to be transferred to latecomer's economies and to exceed their suffering pollution haven effects in the area of East Asia. Especially, as Kofi Annan, the Former Secretary General of the United Nations, stated "perhaps the single most successful international agreement to date has been the Montreal Protocol",[7] the widespread adoption and implementation of the international framework to protect the ozone layer seems to be effective enough for developing economies in East Asia to enjoy the latecomer's advantage. On the contrary, the case with upward shift of the latecomer's trajectories on CDE may be

---

[7] See the website: http://www.theozonehole.com/montreal.htm

explained in such a way that the regulatory framework and technology to mitigate the emissions coming from both production and consumption are too immature to be transferred and disseminated to latecomer's economies (Yaguchi et al. 2007). Thus, only the pollution haven effect seems to remain for latecomer's economies. This phenomenon on carbon dioxide emissions might be regarded as what we call "carbon leakage" in the context of the Greenhouse Gas reduction at global level: the effect that there is an increase in carbon emissions in one country as a result of an emission reduction by a second country with a strict climate policy.

2.3 Summary

In this section, we set out to examine, using the analytical framework of the environmental Kuznets curve, whether the latecomer's economies in East Asia enjoy technological spillover effects or suffer pollution haven damages in their environmental pollution management, in other words, which of latecomer's advantage or latecomer's disadvantage for pollution control dominates in East Asian economies. For this purpose, we carried out dynamic panel estimation by a system of Generalized Method of Moments (GMM), using the panel data with 18 economies for the period from 1990 to 2007 on environmental indices of carbon dioxide emissions, consumption of ozone-depleting substances and industrial organic water pollutant emissions.

Through this analysis, we found two contrasting results among the environmental indices: 1) per capita consumption of ozone-depleting substances and industrial organic water pollutant emissions indicate monotonic decreasing trends with per capita real GDP while per capita carbon dioxide emissions show monotonic increasing trend, and 2) consumption of ozone-depleting substances and industrial organic water pollutant emissions represent the dominance of the latecomer's advantage while carbon dioxide emissions reveal that of the latecomer's disadvantage. We speculate that the contrast in the trends comes from the difference in the origin of emissions: consumption of ozone-depleting substances and industrial organic water pollutant emissions come mainly from production (easily regulated on the local level), and carbon dioxide emissions come from both production and consumption (easily externalized and not easily subject to regulation). We also presume that the contrast in the latecomer's effects lies in the degree of maturity in regulatory framework and technology that offset pollution haven effect: good governance for controlling ozone-depleting substances and water pollutants, versus unrestricted "carbon leakage" for latecomer's economies.

The result implying "carbon leakage", suggests the urgent necessity to facilitate the technological progress such as the development of technology on carbon dioxide capture and storage, and the internalization of external diseconomy through such methods as emissions charge and greenhouse taxes. For latecomer's economies in East Asia, which appear to face a trade-off between environmental quality and productive activities and to strengthen regional economic integration, it can be expected that the spillover effects from technological progress and the consolidated regulatory framework should overcome "carbon leakage".

3. Regional framework of environmental cooperation

In the previous section, we argued that the technological spillovers, offsetting the pollution haven damages, take an important role in environment management, especially in East Asia with the characteristic of economic integration and diversification. The significance of the technological spillovers reminds us of the necessities of international cooperation in environment management in terms of regional framework as well as global and bilateral ones. The regional framework of environmental cooperation is, at the same time, crucial in addressing trans-boundary pollutions in specific region's air and water. This section discusses the regional framework of environment cooperation, with a focus on the non-binding approach taken by East Asia. In the following subsections, we first review major trans-boundary environmental issues in East Asia (Subsection 3.1), represent the regional frameworks to address the trans-boundary issues (Subsection 3.2), and finally discuss the background and justification of the non-binding approach characterized by East Asia.

3.1 Trans-boundary issues in East Asia
We herein pick up major trans-boundary environmental issues in East Asia: acid deposition, marine pollution, haze pollution, and sand and dust storms.

3.1.1 Acid deposition[8]
Acid deposition originates from such pollutants as sulfur oxides (SOx) and nitrogen oxides (NOx), generated mainly by combustion of fossil fuels. Acid deposition appears in various forms of precipitation, such as rain, fog, mist, snow, etc. Its impacts are: affecting fishes due to the acidification of inland waters, threatening forests due to soil acidification, accelerating the decay of cultural monuments, and so forth. Since the substances causing acid deposition are transported over long distance, its influence diffuses to not only inside of the country but also to outside of the country. In East Asia, the rapid growth, accompanying the increasing energy consumption, has threatened to aggravate acid deposition since the 1990s. Some researches show that the trans-boundary acid rain in Northeast Asia is linked primarily to China's coal consumption which accounts for two thirds of the country's primary energy source (Yoon; 2007).

Addressing the trans-boundary acid deposition in East Asia, was motivated by the Agenda 21 adopted by the United Nations Conference on Environment and Development in 1992, "the programs (in Europe and North America) need to be continued and enhanced, and their experience needs to be shared with other regions of the world". Since 2001, the Acid Deposition Monitoring Network in East Asia (EANET) under 13 countries participation has been running as a regional cooperative initiative for monitoring acid deposition. As a related cooperative framework, the Northeast Asian Sub-regional Programme of Environmental Cooperation (NEASPEC) is promoting the several projects for mitigation of trans-boundary air pollution from coal-fired power plants in North-east Asia.

3.1.2 Marine pollution[9]
The Northwest Pacific sea region is specifically composed of the Yellow Sea, surrounded by China and the two Koreas, and the Sea of Japan/the East Sea, encircled by Japan, the two Koreas, and Russia. The region features coastal and island ecosystems with spectacular marine life and commercially important fishing resources. The region has, however, been getting enormous pressures and demands on its environment through coastal area

---

[8] Most of the description is based on
http://www.env.go.jp/en/earth, http://www.eanet.cc/index.html, and http://www.neaspec.org.
[9] Most of the description is based on http://www.nowpap.org/index.php.

development, river pollution flowing into the seas, and marine dumping. Marine contamination occurs also by such accidents as heavy oil spills from troubled tankers, e.g. the "Oil disaster of Nakhodka Accidents" in Japanese coastal sea by the Sea of Japan (the East Sea) in 1997.

As a regional framework for monitoring and assessing marine pollution, the Action Plan for the Protection, Management and Development of the Marine and Coastal Environment of the Northwest Pacific Region (NOWPAP) was adopted in September 1994 as a part of the Regional Seas Programme of the United Nations Environment Programme (UNEP). The participants of this plan are the countries bordering the sea region: China, Japan, Korea, and Russia (North Korea still reserves the option to become a regular member).

3.1.3 Haze pollution[10]

Haze is an atmospheric phenomenon where dust, smoke and other dry particles obscure the clarity of the sky. In the 1990s, haze pollution spreading across national boundaries was getting obvious in Southeast Asia. It originated from widespread land clearance through open forest burning, with the most well-known hotspots being in Sumatra, Borneo and the Malay Peninsula. Most of the smoke came from oil palm plantations which used burning instead of heavy equipment to clear land. The year 1997 was particularly noted for the raging forest fires in Indonesia which produced a pall of small particle pollution over the region for several weeks. Due to the prevalent monsoon winds, Malaysia, Singapore, Thailand and Brunei were seriously suffering from haze pollution.

In light of the haze disaster, environmental ministers of the Association of Southeast Asian Nations (ASEAN) agreed on the Regional Haze Action Plan (RHAP) in 1997. As a further step, the ASEAN reached a legal agreement in 2002, which entered into force for the ratifying countries in 2003. The agreement contains provisions for monitoring, assessment and prevention, technical cooperation, scientific research, mechanisms for coordination and lines of communication, etc. for addressing trans-boundary haze pollution. Due to Indonesia's current decision not to ratify and implement the agreement, however, the provisions of the agreement are not legally binding for the country which is perceived as being by far the greatest contributor to haze in Southeast Asia.

3.1.4 Sand and dust storms[11]

The dust and sand storms (DSS) is a phenomenon of wind carrying dust, which originate in the arid and semi-arid regions of northern China and Mongolia, and arrive at Japan and Korea across national boundaries in the spring due to the region's prevailing seasonal winds. DSS has recently been worsening in terms of their frequency and intensity because of China's rapid desertification, soil degradation, and forest reduction. It causes problems in human health (e.g., sore eyes and respiratory infections), agricultural products, dust-sensitive industries (such as semi-conductor manufacturing), and transportation.

The Tripartite Environmental Ministers Meeting (TEMM) among China, Japan, and Korea, in its forth meeting in 2002, sharing their concern about the DSS problem, agreed to strengthen monitoring capacity to combat sandstorms, and stressed the importance of

---

[10] Most of the description is based on UNEP (2010).

[11] Most of the description is based on http://www.env.go.jp/en/earth/dss/pamph/02.html, http://www.env.go.jp/earth/coop/temm/introduction_j.html, and http://www.neaspec.org.

extensive engagement of national environmental administrations in the region and international organizations in the efforts to cope with the DSS challenges. In 2003, the Global Environment Facility (GEF) launched the joint projects including those of improving monitoring and developing early warning network systems for DSS, in collaboration with the UNEP, the ADB, the UNESCAP, the United Nation Convention to Combat Desertification (UNCCD), and four countries (China, Japan, Korea and Mongolia). The NEASPEC is also promoting a demonstration project focusing on the prevention of dust and sandstorms at source areas in China and Mongolia.

3.2 Modalities of regional frameworks in East Asia

The fore-mentioned trans-boundary environmental issues in East Asia have urged the countries in the region to make efforts to promote regional cooperation to address these issues. In this subsection, we pick up regional frameworks focusing on those for coping with trans-boundary environmental issues in East Asia, and examine their modalities in comparison with that in Europe.

When we see the ongoing cases of regional frameworks for environmental cooperation in the world, we can find a variety of their modalities (e.g. IGES; 2001, Takahashi; 2003). We herein attempt to classify the modalities from the viewpoint of the consolidation of regional governance for cooperation as follows: a) Policy dialogue for sharing views and information on common environmental issues, b) Monitoring and assessment on trans-boundary environmental pollution by common methodologies, c) Project-based joint activities for mitigating pollution by utilizing permanent financial resources, d) Treaty and protocol for imposing common regulations on trans-boundary environmental pollution.

Table 2 reports the existing regional frameworks for environmental cooperation to address trans-boundary environmental issues. If we simply follow the modality classification above, the TEMM is classified into a)-type (policy dialogue); the EANET and the NOWPAP into b)-type (monitoring and assessment); the NEASPEC into c)-type (project-based joint activities); the ASEAN Agreement on Trans-boundary Haze Pollution into d)-type (treaty and protocol). It should be noted that the ASEAN Agreement on Trans-boundary Haze Pollution has problem in its implementation because of the lack of enforcement and liability clauses in the agreement in addition to Indonesia's current decision not to ratify and implement the agreement as mentioned above (UNEP; 2010).

Europe, though having various modalities in regional frameworks for environmental cooperation, appears to depend more on legal frameworks backed by the EU organization than East Asia does. Some clear contrasts can be seen in the framework to address trans-boundary acid deposition and marine pollution. The acid deposition problem first came to trans-boundary attention in Europe in the 1970s. In the first place, the OECD responded to a request from Scandinavian countries to inaugurate a multilateral monitoring program of acid rain in 1972. And it was taken over by the United Nations Economic Commission for Europe in 1977. Subsequently, the Convention for the Long-Range Transmission of Air Pollutant in Europe (the LRTAP) was agreed upon in 1979, and the protocols on 30% reduction of sulfur emission and on NOx emission control were adopted in the 1980s. For trans-boundary marine pollution, for instance, the Convention for the Protection of the Mediterranean Sea Against Pollution (the Barcelona Convention) was concluded in 1975, followed by the protocols on marine dumping, emergency oil pollution, land based pollution source, and so forth in 1975 and 1980. These conventions and protocols are definitely classified into d)-type in the classification above, whereas East Asian frameworks for trans-boundary acid deposition and marine pollution mainly fall into a), b), or c)-type of modalities.

Acid Deposition Monitoring Network in East Asia (EANET)	
Staring year:	2001
Area:	East Asia: 13 countries
Issues:	Acid Deposition
Secretariat:	UNEP
Modality:	Joint monitoring and assessment
Northwest Pacific Action Plan (NOWPAP)	
Staring year:	1994
Area:	Northeast Asia: China, Japan, Korea (South), and Russia
Issues:	Marine Pollution
Secretariat:	UNEP
Modality:	Joint monitoring and assessment
ASEAN Agreement on Transboundary Haze Pollution	
Staring year:	2002
Area:	ASEAN
Issues:	Haze Pollution
Secretariat:	ASEAN
Modality:	Legal agreement
Tripartite Environmental Ministers Meeting (TEMM)	
Staring year:	1999
Area:	China, Japan, and South Korea
Issues:	Comprehensive
Secretariat:	Rotation
Modality:	Policy dialogue
North-east Asian Subregional Programme of Environmental Cooperation (NEASPEC)	
Staring year:	1993
Area:	Northeast Asia: China, Japan, Korea (North), Korea (South), Mongolia, and Russia
Issues:	Comprehensive
Secretariat:	UN/ESCAP (Interim)
Modality:	Project-based activities

Table 2. Regional frameworks for environmental cooperation

3.3 Discussion on non-binding approach in East Asia

The modality of regional frameworks for environmental cooperation has recently been discussed in terms of binding and non-binding approaches (e.g. Yoon; 2007, Köppel; 2009). Yoon (2007) argued that the environmental cooperation in Northeast Asia has evolved through non-binding agreements which do not contain official commitments on compliance or legal restrictions for non-compliance, whereas that in Europe has followed binding agreements by concluding with conventions and working through a series of protocols for solid compliance. This view is consistent with our comparative analysis on the modalities for environmental cooperation between in East Asia and Europe in the previous section. Then, why East Asia has taken the non-binding approach for environmental cooperation is the question in this section.

Köppel (2009) explained theoretically the advantages of both binding and nonbinding agreements as follows. A nonbinding agreement is easier and faster to achieve, allows states to tackle a problem collectively at a time they otherwise might not due to economic or political reasons, and enables governments to formulate their commitments in a more precise and ambitious form than they would be possible in a binding treaty. Seeking deeper cooperation like a smaller club of "like-minded enthusiasts", and facilitating learning processes or learning by doing, can be further benefits of nonbinding agreements. On the other hand, binding agreements strengthen the credibility of a commitment, increase compliance with the commitment, and reduce intergovernmental transaction costs.

Considering this theoretical viewpoint, we can interpret East Asian choice of non-binding approach in such a way that East Asia is getting or trying to get the non-binding advantages whereas facing the difficulties for getting the binding advantages. In fact, the progress in the trans-boundary on-going projects under the frameworks of EANET, NOWPAP, NEASPEC, etc., appears to be reflecting East Asian stances to pursue the "easier", "faster" and "deeper" advantages of non-binding approach. On the other hand, the difficulties for binding approach in East Asia seem to come from the following economical, political and historical backgrounds. First, a lack of economic and political homogeneity is making it difficult for East Asia to reach binding agreements. As mentioned in Introduction, East Asian countries are composed of a variety of countries with different stages of development and with different political system. In addition, there is no regional organizations equivalent to the EU in East Asia except for ASEAN. The typical contrast can be shown in the LRTAP Convention, which was created by homogenous advanced European nations and has well been maintained by strong links to EU policies and aid programs. Second, the environmental cooperation in East Asian region is too immature to lead to legal agreements. It was only after the Rio Earth Summit in 1992 that East Asian countries initiated environmental cooperation as an official diplomatic issue as shown in Table 2. We can also see a contrast in monitoring trans-boundary acid deposition: East Asian started its system in 2001 as the EANET, while Europe inaugurated it about thirty years earlier, in 1972. Finally, more importantly, political sentiments among East Asian nations are placing obstacles on the road toward binding agreements (see Yoon; 2007). The historical experiences of World War Two are making East Asian nations suspicious of Japanese initiatives on regional affairs. And China tends to prefer bilateral cooperation to supranational institutions, because bilateral negotiations do not place the country in the diplomatically unfavourable situation of being the main source of regional, trans-boundary pollution. The bilateral environmental cooperation promoted by Japan through official development assistant (ODA) may also have attenuated the need for binding agreements at multilateral level.

To sum up, considering the region-specific properties in economical, political, and historical terms, non-binding approach as regional framework of environmental cooperation may be an optimal choice for East Asia, in the sense that it provides the "easier", "faster" and "deeper" framework regardless of economical, political, and historical constraints.

5. References

Arellano, M. & Bond, S.R. (1991). Some tests of specification of panel data: Monte Carlo evidence and an application to employment equations. *Review of Economic Studies*, Vol.58, No.2, (April 1991), pp. 277–297, ISSN: 00346527

Borghesi, S. (1999). The Environmental Kuznets Curve: a survey of the literature. *FEEM (Fondazione ENi Enrico Mattei) Working Paper*, No. 85–99

Dasgupta, S.; Laplante, B.; Wang, H. & Wheeler, D. (2002). Confronting the Environmental Kuznets Curve. *Journal of Economic Perspectives*, Vol.16, No.1, (Winter 2002), pp. 147-168, ISSN 08953309

De Bruyn, S.M.; Van den Bergh, J.C.J.M. & Opschoor, J.B. (1998). Economic Growth and Emissions: Reconsidering the Empirical Basis of 166 Journal of Economic Perspectives Environmental Kuznets Curves. *Ecological Economics*, Vol.25, No.2, (May 1998), pp. 161-175, ISSN 09218009

Grossman, G. & Krueger, A. (1993). Environmental Impacts of the North American Free Trade Agreement, In: *The U.S.-Mexico Free Trade Agreement*, P. Garber, (Ed.), 13-56, MIT Press, ISBN 0-262-07152-5, Cambridge

Grossman, G. & Krueger, A. (1995). Economic Growth and the Environment. *Quarterly Journal of Economics*, Vol.112, No.2, (May 1995), pp. 353–377, ISSN 00335533

Halkos, G.E. (2003). Environmental Kuznets Curve for sulfur: evidence using GMM estimation and random coefficient panel data models. *Environment and Development Economics*, Vol.8, No.4, (October 2003), pp. 581-601, ISSN 1355770X

Institute for Global Environmental Strategies (IGES) (2001). *Regional/Subregional Environmental Cooperation in Asia*, IGES, Japan

Kawai, M. (2009). International exchange and monetary system in East Asia. *Financial Review*, Vol.93, No.1, (March 2009), pp. 176-194, ISBN 978-4-9904174-4-4 (Japanese)

Köppel, M. (2009). Explaining the Effectiveness of Binding and Nonbinding Agreements: Tentative Lessons from Transboundary Water Pollution. *Paper prepared for the 2009 Amsterdam Conference on the Human Dimensions of Global Environmental Change, 2-4 Dec 2009*, Available from

http://www.earthsystemgovernance.org/ac2009/papers/AC2009-0283.pdf

Panayotou, T. (1997). Demystifying the Environmental Kuznets Curve: Turning a Black Box into a Policy Tool. *Environment and Development Economics*, Vol.2, No.4, (October 1997), pp. 465-484, ISSN 1355770X

Nahman, A. & Antrobus, G. (2005). The Environmental Kuznets Curve: A Literature Survey. *South African Journal of Economics*, Vol.73, No.1, (March 2005), pp.105–120, ISSN 00382280

Selden, T.M. & Song, D. (1994). Environmental Quality and Development: Is There a Kuznets Curve for Air Pollution Emissions? *Journal of Environmental Economics and Management*, Vol. 27, No.2, (September 1994), pp. 147-162, ISSN 00950696

Shafik, N. (1994). Economic Development and Environmental Quality: An Econometric Analysis. *Oxford Economic Papers*, Vol.46, (Supplement, October 1994), pp. 757-773, ISSN 00307653

Takahashi, W. (2003). Historical Development of Regional Cooperative Framworks on Environment of Europe. Paper Series of Utsunomiya University, No.17, (March 2003), pp.13-31, (Japanese)

Taguchi, H. & Murofushi, H. (2009). Environmental Latecomer's Effects in Developing Countries – The Case of SO2 and CO2 Emissions. *Journal of Developing Areas*, Vol.44, No.2, (Spring 2011), pp. 143-164, ISSN 0022-037X

UNEP (2010). *Air Pollution : promoting regional cooperation*, UNEP, ISBN 978-92-807-3093-7

Yaguchi, Y. ; Sonobe, T. & Otsuka, K. (2007). Beyond the Environmental Kuznets Curve: A Comparative Study of SO2 and CO2 Emissions Between Japan and China.

Environment and Development Economics, Vol.12, No.3, (June 2007), pp. 445-470, ISSN
    1355770X

Yoon, E. (2007). Cooperation for Transboundary Pollution in Northeast Asia: Non-binding
    Agreements and Regional Countries' Policy Interests. *Pacific Focus*, Vol. XXII, No. 2
    (Fall 2007), pp. 77-112, ISSN 1976-5118

5

Geo-environmental Terrain Assessments Based on Remote Sensing Tools: A Review of Applications to Hazard Mapping and Control

Paulo Cesar Fernandes[1] da Silva and John Canning Cripps[2]
[1]*Geological Institute - São Paulo State Secretariat of Environment,*
[2]*Department of Civil and Structural Engineering,*
University of Sheffield,
[1]*Brazil*
[2]*United Kingdom*

1. Introduction

The responses of public authorities to natural or induced geological hazards, such as land instability and flooding, vary according to different factors including frequency of occurrence, severity of damage, magnitude of hazardous processes, awareness, predictability, political willingness and availability of financial and technological resources. The responses will also depend upon whether the hazard is 1) known to be already present thus giving rise to risk situations involving people and/or economic loss; or 2) there is a latent or potential hazard that is not yet present so that development and land uses need to be controlled in order to avoid creating risk situations. In this regard, geo-environmental management can take the form of either planning responses and mid- to long-term public policy based territorial zoning tools, or immediate interventions that may involve a number of approaches including preventative and mitigation works, civil defence actions such as hazard warnings, community preparedness, and implementation of contingency and emergency programmes.

In most of cases, regional- and local-scale terrain assessments and classification accompanied by susceptibility and/or hazard maps delineating potential problem areas will be used as practical instruments in efforts to tackle problems and their consequences. In terms of planning, such assessments usually provide advice about the types of development that would be acceptable in certain areas but should be precluded in others. Standards for new construction and the upgrading of existing buildings may also be implemented through legally enforceable building codes based on the risks associated with the particular terrain assessment or classification.

The response of public authorities also varies depending upon the information available to make decisions. In some areas sufficient geological information and knowledge about the causes of a hazard may be available to enable an area likely to be susceptible to hazardous processes to be predicted with reasonable certainty. In other places a lack of suitable data may result in considerable uncertainty.

In this chapter, a number of case studies are presented to demonstrate the methodological as well as the predictive and preventative aspects of geo-environmental management, with a particular view to regional- and semi-detailed scale, satellite image based terrain classification. If available, information on the geology, geomorphology, covering material characteristics and land uses may be used with remotely sensed data to enhance these terrain classification outputs. In addition, examples provided in this chapter demonstrate the identification and delineation of zones or terrain units in terms of the likelihood and consequences of land instability and flooding hazards in different situations. Further applications of these methods include the ranking of abandoned and/or derelict mined sites and other despoiled areas in support of land reclamation and socio-economic regeneration policies.

The discussion extends into policy formulation, implementation of environmental management strategies and enforcement regulations.

2. Use of remote densing tools for terrain assessments and territorial zoning

Engineering and geo-environmental terrain assessments began to play an important role in the planning process as a consequence of changing demands for larger urban areas and related infra-structure, especially housing, industrial development and the services network. In this regard, the inadequacy of conventional agriculturally-orientated land mapping methods prompted the development of terrain classification systems completely based on the properties and characteristics of the land that provide data useful to engineers and urban planners. Such schemes were then adopted and widely used to provide territorial zoning for general and specific purposes.

The process of dividing a country or region into area parcels or zones, is generally called land or terrain classification. Such a scheme is illustrated in Table 1. The zones should possess a certain homogeneity of characteristics, properties, and in some cases, conditions and expected behaviour in response to human activities. What is meant by homogeneous will depend on the purpose of the exercise, but generally each zone will contain a mixture of environmental elements such as rocks, soils, relief, vegetation, and other features. The feasibility and practicability of delineating land areas with similar attributes have been demonstrated throughout the world over a long period of time (e.g. Bowman, 1911; Bourne, 1931; Christian, 1958; Mabbutt, 1968; amongst others), and encompass a wide range of specialisms such as earth, biological and agricultural sciences; hydrology and water resources management; military activities; urban and rural planning; civil engineering; nature and wildlife conservation; and even archaeology.

According to Cendrero et al. (1979) and Bennett and Doyle (1997), there are two main approaches to geo-environmental terrain assessments and territorial zoning, as follows. 1) The analytical or parametric approach deals with environmental features or components individually. The terrain units usually result from the intersection or cartographic summation of several layers of information [thus expressing the probability limits of findings] and their extent may not corresponding directly with ground features. Examples of the parametric approach for urban planning, hazard mapping and engineering purposes are given by Kiefer (1967), Porcher & Guillope (1979), Alonso Herrero et al. (1990), and Dai et al. (2001). 2) In the synthetic approach, also termed integrated, landscape or physiographic approach, the form and spatial distribution of ground features are analysed in an integrated manner relating recurrent landscape patterns expressed by an interaction of

Terrain unit	Definition	Soil unit	Vegetation unit	Mapping scale (approx.)	Remote sensing platform
Land zone	Major climatic region	Order	-	< 1:50,000,000	
Land division	Gross continental structure	Suborder	Plant panformation to Ecological zone	1:20,000,000 to 1:50,000,000	Meteorological satellites
Land province	Second-order structure or large lithological association	Great group	-	1:20,000,000 to 1:50,000,000	
Land region	Lithological unit or association having undergone comparable geomorphic evolution	Subgroup	Sub-province	1:1,000,000 to 1:5,000,000	Landsat SPOT ERS
Land system *	Recurrent pattern of genetically linked land facets	Family	Ecological region	1: 200,000 to 1:1,000,000	Landsat SPOT, ERS, and small scale aerial photographs
Land catena	Major repetitive component of a land system	Association	Ecological sector	1:80,000 to 1:200,000	
Land facet	Reasonably homogeneous tract of landscape distinct from surrounding areas and containing a practical grouping of land elements	Series	Sub-formation; Ecological station	1:10,000 to 1: 80,000	Medium scale aerial photographs, Landsat, and SPOT in some cases
Land clump	A patterned repetition of two or more land elements too contrasting to be a land facet	Complex	Sub-formation; Ecological station	1:10,000 to 1: 80,000	
Land subfacet	Constituent part of a land facet where the main formative processes give material or form subdivisions	Type	-	Not mapped	Large-scale aerial photographs
Land element	Simplest homogeneous part of the landscape, indivisible in form	Pedon	Ecological station element		

Table 1. Hierarchical classification of terrain, soil and ecological units [after Mitchell, 1991]

environmental components thus allowing the partitioning of the land into units. Since the advent of airborne and orbital sensors, the integrated analysis is based in the first instance, on the interpretation of remotely sensed images and/or aerial photography. In most cases, the content and spatial boundaries of terrain units would directly correspond with ground features. Assumptions that units possessing similar recurrent landscape patterns may be expected to be similar in character are required for valid predictions to be made by extrapolation from known areas.   Thus, terrain classification schemes offer rational means of correlating known and unknown areas so that the ground conditions and potential uses of unknown areas can be reasonably predicted (Finlayson, 1984; Bell, 1993). Examples of the applications of the landscape or physiographic approach include ones given by Christian & Stewart (1952, 1968), Vinogradov et al. (1962), Beckett & Webster (1969); Meijerink (1988), and Miliaresis (2001).

Griffiths and Edwards (2001) refer to Land Surface Evaluation as a procedure of providing data relevant to the assessment of the sites of proposed engineering work. The sources of data include remotely sensed data and data acquired by the mapping of geomorphological features. Although originally viewed as a process usually undertaken at the reconnaissance or feasibility stages of projects, the authors point out its utility at the constructional and post-construction stages of certain projects and also that it is commonly applied during the planning of engineering development. They also explain that although more reliance on this methodology for deriving the conceptual or predictive ground model on which engineering design and construction are based, was anticipated in the early 1980s, in fact the use of the methods has been more limited.

Geo-environmental terrain assessments and territorial zoning generally involve three main stages (IG/SMA 2003; Fernandes da Silva et al. 2005b, 2010): 1) delimitation of terrain units; 2) characterisation of units (e.g. in bio-geographical, engineering geological or geotechnical terms); and 3) evaluation and classification of units. The delimitation stage consists of dividing the territory into zones according to a set of pre-determined physical and environmental characteristics and properties. Regions, zones or units are regarded as distinguishable entities depending upon their internal homogeneity or the internal interrelationships of their parts. The characterisation stage consists of attributing appropriate properties and characteristics to terrain components. Such properties and characterisitics are designed to reflect the ground conditions relevant to the particular application. The characterisation of the units can be achieved either directly or indirectly, for instance by means of: (a) ground observations and measurements, including in-situ tests (e.g. boring, sampling, infiltration tests etc); (b) laboratory tests (e.g. grain size, strength, porosity, permeability etc); (c) inferences derived from existing correlations between relevant parameters and other data such as those obtained from previous mapping, remote sensing, geophysical surveys and geochemical records. The final stage (evaluation and classification) consists of evaluating and classifying the terrain units in a manner relevant to the purposes of the particular application (e.g. regional planning, transportation, hazard mapping). This is based on the analysis and interpretation of properties and characteristics of terrain - identified as relevant - and their potential effects in terms of ground behaviour, particularly in response to human activities.

A key issue to be considered is sourcing suitable data on which to base the characterisation, as in many cases derivation by standard mapping techniques may not be feasible. The large size of areas and lack of accessibility, in particular, may pose major technical, operational, and economic constraints. Furthermore, as indicated by Nedovic-Budic (2000), data collection and integration into useful databases are liable to be costly and time-consuming operations. Such problems are particularly prevalent in developing countries in which suitably trained staff, and scarce organizational resources can inhibit public authorities from properly benefiting from geo-environmental terrain assessment outputs in planning and environmental management instruments. In this regard, consideration has been given to increased reliance on remote sensing tools, particularly satellite imagery. The advantages include: (a) the generation of new data in areas where existing data are sparse, discontinuous or non-existent, and (b) the economical coverage of large areas, availability of a variety of spatial resolutions, relatively frequent and periodic updating of images

Geo-environmental Terrain Assessments Based on Remote
Sensing Tools: A Review of Applications to Hazard Mapping and Control

89

(Lillesand and Kiefer 2000; Latifovic et al. 2005; Akiwumi and Butler 2008). It has also been proposed that developing countries should ensure that options for using low-cost technology, methods and products that fit their specific needs and capabilities are properly considered (Barton et al. 2002, Câmara and Fonseca 2007). Some examples are provided here to demonstrate the feasibility of a low-cost technique based on the analysis of texture of satellite imagery that can be used for delimitation of terrain units. The delimited units may be further analysed for different purposes such as regional and urban planning, hazard mapping, and land reclamation.

The physiographic compartmentalisation technique (Vedovello 1993, 2000) utilises the spatial information contained in images and the principles of convergence of evidence (see Sabins 1987) in a systematic deductive process of image interpretation. The technique evolved from engineering applications of the synthetic land classification approach (e.g. Grant, 1968, 1974, 1975; TRRL 1978), by incorporating and advancing the logic and procedures of geological-geomorphological photo-interpretation (see Guy 1966, Howard 1967, Soares and Fiori 1976), which were then converted to monoscopic imagery (as elucidated by Beaumont and Beaven 1977; Verstappen 1977; Soares et al. 1981; Beaumont, 1985; and others). Image interpretation is performed by identifying and delineating textural zones on images according to properties that take into account coarseness, roughness, direction and regularity of texture elements (Table 2). The key assumption proposed by Vedovello (1993, 2000) is that zones with relatively homogeneous textural characteristics in satellite images (or air-photos) correspond with specific combinations of geo-environmental components (such as bedrock, topography and landforms, soils and covering materials) which share a common tectonic history and land surface evolution. The particular combinations of geo-environmental components are expected to be associated with specific ground responses to engineering and other land-use actions. The process of image interpretation (whether or not supported by additional information) leads to a cartographic product in which textural zones constitute comprehensive terrain units delimited by fixed spatial boundaries. The latter correspond with ground features. The units are referred to as physiographic compartments or basic compartmentalisation units (BCUs), which are the smallest units for analysis of geo-environmental components at the chosen cartographic scale (Vedovello and Mattos 1998). The spatial resolution of the satellite image or air-photos being used for the analysis and interpretation is assumed to govern the correlation between image texture and terrain characteristics. This correlation is expressed at different scales and levels of compartmentalisation. Figure 1 presents an example of the identification of basic compartmentalisation units (BCUs) based on textural differences on Landsat TM5 images. In this case the features on images are expressions of differences in the distribution and spatial organisation of textural elements related to drainage network and relief. The example shows the contrast between drainage networks of areas consisting of crystalline rocks with those formed on areas of sedimentary rocks, and the resulting BCUs.

3. Terrain susceptibility maps: applications to regional and urban planning

Terrain susceptibility maps are designed to depict ground characteristics (e.g. slope steepness, landforms) and observed and potential geodynamic phenomena, such as erosion, instability and flooding, which may entail hazard and potential damage. These maps are useful for a number of applications including development and land use planning, environmental protection, watershed management as well as in initial stages of hazard mapping applications.

Textural entities and properties	Description
Image texture element	The smallest continuous and uniform surface liable to be distinguishable in terms of shape and dimensions, and likely to be repetitive throughout an image. Usual types of image texture elements taken for analysis include: segments of drainage or relief (e.g. crestlines, slope breaks) and grey tones.
Texture density	The quantity of textural elements occurring within an area on image. Texture density is defined as the inverse of the mean distance between texture elements. Although it reflects a quantitative property, textural density is frequently described in qualitative and relative terms such as high, moderate, low etc. Size of texture elements combined with texture density determine features such as coarseness and roughness.
Textural arrangement	The form (ordered or not) by which textural elements occur and are spatially distributed on an image. Texture elements of similar characteristics may be contiguous thus defining alignments or linear features on the image. The spatial distribution may be repetitive and it is usually expressed by 'patterns' that tend to be recurrent (regularity). For example, forms defined by texture elements due to drainage expressed in rectangular, dendritic, or radial patterns.
Structuring (Degree of spatial organisation)	The greater or lesser organisation underlying the spatial distribution of textural elements and defined by repetition of texture elements within a certain rule of placement. Such organisation is usually expressed in terms of regular or systematic spatial relations, such as length, angularity, asymmetry, and especially prevailing orientations (tropy or directionality). Tropy reflects the anisotropic (existence of one, two, or three preferred directions), or the isotropic (multi-directional or no predominant direction) character of textural features. Asymmetry refers to length and angularity of linear features (rows of contiguous texture elements) in relation to a main feature identified on image. The degree of organisation can also be expressed by qualitative terms such as high, moderate, low, or yet as well- or poorly-defined.
Structuring order	Complexity in the organisation of textural elements, mainly reflecting superposition of image structuring. For example, a regional directional trend of textural elements that can be extremely pervasive, distinctive and superimposed on other orientations also observed on imagery. Another example is drainage networks that display different orders with respect to main stream lines and tributaries (1st, 2nd, 3rd orders)

Table 2. Description of elements and properties used for recognition and delineation of distinctive textural zones on satellite imagery [after Vedovello 1993, 2000].

Early multipurpose and comprehensive terrain susceptibility maps include examples by Dearman & Matula, (1977), Matula (1979), and Matula & Letko (1980). These authors described the application of engineering geology zoning methods to the urban planning process in the former Republic of Czechoslovakia. The studies in this and other countries focused on engineering geology problems related to geomorphology and geodynamic processes, seismicity, hydrogeology, and foundation conditions.

Culshaw and Price (2011) point out that in the UK, a major initiative on urban geology began in the mid-1970s with obtaining geological information relevant to aggregates and other industrial minerals together with investigations relating to the planning of the proposed 3rd London Airport. In the latter case, a very wide range of map types was produced, including one that could be viewed in 3D, using green and red anaglyph spectacles. Of particular interest was the summary "Engineering Planning Map which showed areas that were generally suitable for different types of construction and, also, detailed suggested site investigation procedures (Culshaw and Northmore 2002).

As Griffiths and Hearn (2001) explain, subsequently about 50 experimental 'environmental geological mapping, 'thematic'geological mapping' and 'applied geological mapping' projects were carried out between 1980 and 1996. Culshaw and Price (2011) explain that this was to investigate the best means of collecting, collating, interpreting and presenting geological data that would be of direct applicability in land-use planning (Brook and Marker 1987). Maps of a variety of geological and terrain types, including industrially despoiled and potentially unstable areas, with mapping at scales between 1:2500 and 1:25000 were produced. The derivation and potential applications of these sets of maps and reports are described by Culshaw et al. (1990) who explain that they include basic data maps, derived maps and environmental potential maps. Typically such thematic map reports comprise a series of maps showing the bedrock and superficial geology, thickness of superficial deposits, groundwater conditions and areas of mining, fill, compressible, or other forms of potentially unstable ground. Maps showing factual information include the positions of boreholes or the positions of known mine workings. Derived maps include areas in which geological and / or environmental information has been deduced, and therefore is subject to some uncertainty. The thematic sets include planning advice maps showing the constraints on, and potential for, development and mineral extraction. Culshaw et al. (1990) also explained that these thematic maps were intended to assist with the formulation of both local (town or city), regional (metropolis or county) structure plans and policies, provide a context for the consideration of development proposals and facilitate access to relevant geological data by engineers and geologists. It was also recognised that these is a need for national (or state) policies and planning to be properly informed about geological conditions, not least to provide a sound basis for planning legislation and the issuing of advice and circulars. Examples of such advice include planning guidance notes concerning the granting of planning permission for development on potentially unstable land which were published (DOE, 1990, 1995) by the UK government. A further series of reports which were intended to assist planners and promote the consideration of geological information in land-use planning decision making were compiled between 1994 and 1998 by consultants on behalf of the UK government. Griffiths (2001) provides details of a selection of land evaluation techniques and relevant case studies. These covered the following themes:

- Environmental Geology in Land Use Planning: Advice for planners and developers (Thompson et al., 1998a)
- Environmental Geology in Land Use Planning: A guide to good practice (Thompson et al., 1998b)
- Environmental Geology in Land Use Planning: Emerging issues (Thompson et al., 1998c)
- Environmental Geology in Land Use Planning: Guide to the sources of earth science information for planning and development (Ellsion and Smith, 1998)

For an extensive review of world-wide examples of geological data outputs intended to assist with urban geology interpretation, land-use planning and utilisation and geological hazard avoidance, reference should be made to Culshaw and Price (2001).

Three examples of terrain susceptibility mapping are briefly described and presented in this Section. The physiographic compartmentalisation technique for regional terrain evaluation was explored in these cases, and then terrain units were further characterised in geo-environmental terms.

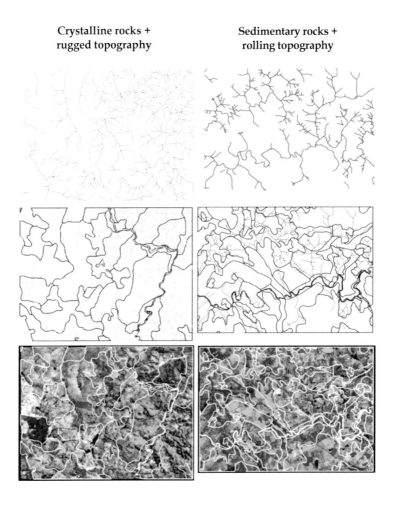

Fig. 1. Identification of basic compartmentalisation units (BCUs) based on textural differences on image. The image for crystalline rocks with rugged topography contrasts with sedimentary rocks with rolling topography. Top: Drainage network. Mid Row: Drainage network and delineated BCUs. Bottom: Composite Landsat TM5 image and delineated BCUs [after Fernandes da Silva et al. 2005b, 2010]

3.1 Multipurpose planning

The first example concerns the production of a geohazard prevention map for the City of São Sebastião (IG/SMA 1996), where urban and industrial expansion in the mountainous coastal zone of São Paulo State, Southeast Brazil (Figure 2) led to conflicts in land use as well as to high risks to life and property. Particular land use conflicts arose from the combinations of landscape and economic characteristics of the region, in which a large nature and wildlife park co-exists with popular tourist and leisure encroached bays and beaches, a busy harbour with major oil storage facilities and associated pipelines that cross the area. Physiographic compartmentalisation was utilised to provide a regional terrain classification of the area, and then interpretations were applied in two ways: (i) to provide a territorial zoning based on terrain susceptibility in order to enable mid- to long-term land use planning; and (ii) to identify areas for semi-detailed hazard mapping and risk assessment (Fernandes da Silva et al. 1997a, Vedovello et al., 1997; Cripps et al., 2002). Figure 2 presents the main stages of the study undertaken in response to regional and urban planning needs of local authorities.

In the Land Susceptibility Map, the units were qualitatively ranked in terms of ground evidence and estimated susceptibility to geodynamic processes including gravitational mass movements, erosion, and flooding.

Criteria for terrain unit classification in relation to erosion and mass movements (landslides, creep, slab failure, rock fall, block tilt and glide, mud and debris flow) were the following: a) soil weathering profile (thickness, textural and mineral constituency); b) hillslope profile; c) slope steepness; and d) bedrock structures (fracturing and discontinuities in general). Criteria in relation to flooding included: a) type of sediments; b) slope steepness; and c) hydrography (density and morphology of water courses). The resulting classes of terrain susceptibility can be summarised as follows:

Low susceptibility: Areas where mass movements are unlikely. Low restrictions to excavations and man-made cuttings. Some units may not be suitable for deep foundations or other engineering works due to possible high soil compressibility and presence of geological structures. In flat areas, such as coastal plains, flooding and river erosion are unlikely.

Moderate susceptibility: Areas of moderate to high steep slope (10 to 30%) with little evidence of land instability (small-scale erosional processes may be present) but with potential for occurrence of mass movements. In lowland areas, reported flooding events were associated with the main drainage stream in relevant zones. Terrain units would possess moderate restrictions for land-use with minor engineering solutions and protection measures needed to reduce or avoid potential risks.

High susceptibility: Areas of moderate (10 to 20%) and high steep slope (20 to 30%) situated in escarpment and footslope sectors, respectively, with evidence of one or more active land instability phenomena (e.g. erosion + rock falls + landslide) of moderate magnitude. Unfavourable zones for construction work wherein engineering projects would require accurate studies of structural stability, and consequently higher costs. In lowland sectors, recurrent flooding events were reported at intervals of 5 to 10 yrs, associated with main drainage streams and tributaries. Most zones then in use required immediate remedial action including major engineering solutions and protection measures.

Very high susceptibility: Areas of steeper slopes (> 30%) situated in the escarpment and footslope sectors that mainly comprised colluvium and talus deposits. There was evidence of one or more land instability phenomena of significant magnitude requiring full restriction on construction work. In lowland sectors, widespread and frequent flooding events at intervals of less than 5 years were reported and most land-used needed to be avoided in these zones.

Units or areas identified as having a moderate to high susceptibility to geodynamic phenomena, and potential conflicts in land use, were selected for detailed engineering geological mapping in a subsequent stage of the study. The outcomes of the further stage of hazard mapping are described and discussed in Section 4.

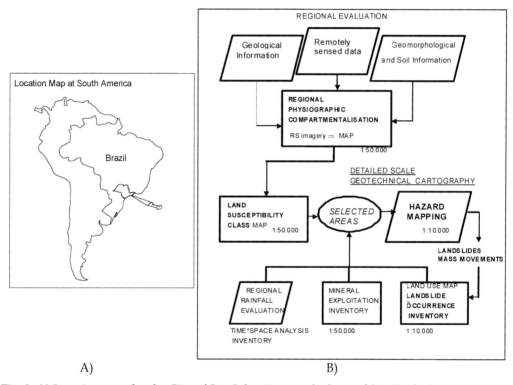

A)   B)

Fig. 2. A) Location map for the City of São Sebastião, north shore of São Paulo State, Southeast Brazil. B) Schematic flow diagram for the derivation of the geohazard prevention chart and structural plan (after IG/SMA, 1996).

3.2 Watershed planning and waste disposal

The physiographic compartmentalisation technique was also applied in combination with GIS tools in support of watershed planning in the Metropolitan District of Campinas, central-eastern São Paulo State (Figure 3). This regional screening study was performed at 1:50,000 scale to indicate fragilities, restrictions and potentialities of the area for siting waste disposal facilities (IG/SMA, 1999). A set of common characteristics and properties (also referred to as attributes) facilitated the assessment of each BCU (or terrain unit) in terms of susceptibility to the occurrence of geodynamic phenomena (soil erosion and land instability) and the potential for soil and groundwater contamination.

As described by Brollo et al. (2000), the terrain units were mostly derived on the basis of qualitative and semi-quantitative inferences from satellite and air-photo images in conjunction with existing information (maps and well logs – digital and papers records) and field checks. The set of attributes included: (1) bedrock lithology; (2) density of lineaments (surrogate expression of underlying fractures and terrain discontinuities); (3) angular relation between rock structures and hillslope; (4) geometry and shape of hillslope (plan view and profile); (5) soil and covering material: type, thickness, profile; (6) water table depth; and (7) estimated permeability. These attributes were cross-referenced with other specific factors, including hydrogeological (groundwater production, number of wells per unit area), climatic (rainfall, prevailing winds), and socio-political data (land use, environmental restrictions). These data were considered to be significant in terms of the selection of potential sites for waste disposal.

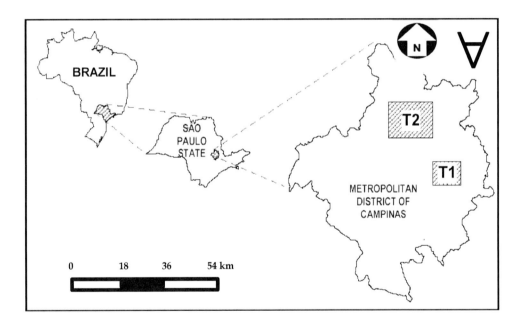

Fig. 3. Location map of the Metropolitan District of Campinas (MDC), central-eastern São Paulo State, Southeast Brazil (see Section 3.2). Detail map depicts Test Areas T1 and T2 within the MDC (see Section 3.3). Scale bar applies to detail map.

Figure 4 displays the study area in detail together with BCUs, and an example of a pop-up window (text box) containing key attribute information, as follows: 1st row - BCU code (COC1), 2nd - bedrock lithology, 3rd - relief (landforms), 4th – textural soil profile constituency, 5th - soil thickness, 6th - water table depth (not show in the example), 7th - bedrock structures in terms of density of fracturing and directionality), 8th - morphometry (degree of dissection of terrain). The BCU coding scheme expresses three levels of compartmentalisation, as follows: 1st letter – major physiographic or landscape domain, 2nd– predominant bedrock lithology, 3rd - predominant landforms, 4th– differential characteristics of the unit such as estimated soil profile and underlying structures. Using the example given in Figure 4, COC1 means: C = crystalline rock basement, O = equigranular gneiss, C = undulating and rolling hills, 1 = estimated soil profile (3 textural horizons and thickness of 5 to 10 m), underlying structures (low to moderate degree of fracturing, multi-directional). In terms of general interpretations for the intended purposes of the study, certain ground characteristics, such as broad valleys filled with alluvial sediments potentially indicate the presence water table level at less than 5 m below ground surface. Flood plains or concave hillside slopes that may indicate convergent surface water flows leading to potentially high susceptibility to erosion, were considered as restrictive factors for the siting of waste disposal facilities (Vedovello et al. 1998).

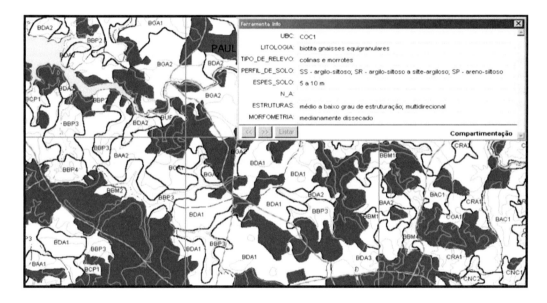

Fig. 4. Basic compartmentalisation units (BCUs) and pop-up window showing key attribute information relevant to BCUs. See text for details. [Not to scale] [after IG/SMA, 1999]

3.3 Regional development planning

The third example is a territorial zoning exercise, in which terrain units delimited through physiographic compartmentalisation were further assessed in terms of susceptibility to land instability processes and groundwater vulnerability (Fernandes da Silva et al. 2005b). The study was conducted in two test areas situated in the Metropolitan District of Campinas (Figure 3) in order to assist State of São Paulo authorities in the formulation of regional development policies. It incorporated procedures for inferring the presence and characteristics of underlying geological structures, such as fractures and other discontinuities, then evaluating potential implications to ground stability and the flow of groundwater.

Details of image interpretation procedures for the delimitation of BCUs are described by Fernandes da Silva et al. (2010). The main image properties and image feature characteristics considered were as follows: (a) density of texture elements related to drainage and relief lines; (b) spatial arrangement of drainage and relief lines in terms of form and degree of organisation (direction, regularity and pattern); (c) length of lines and their angular relationships, (d) linearity of mainstream channel and asymmetry of tributaries, (e) density of interfluves, (f) hillside length, and (g) slope forms. These factors were mostly derived by visual interpretation of images, but external ancillary data were also used to assist with the determination of relief-related characteristics, such as slope forms and interfluve dimensions. The example given in Figure 1 shows sub-set images (Landsat TM5) and the basic compartmentalisation units (BCUs) delineated for Test Areas T1 and T2.

Based on the principle that image texture correlates with properties and characteristics of the imaged target, deductions can be made about geotechnical-engineering aspects of the terrain (Beaumont and Beaven 1977, Beaumont 1985). The following attributes were firstly considered in the geo-environmental characterisation of BCUs: (a) bedrock lithology and respective weathered materials, (b) tectonic discontinuities (generically referred to as fracturing), (c) soil profile (thickness, texture and mineralogy), (d) slope steepness (as an expression of local topography), and (e) water table depth (estimated). Terrain attributes such as degree of fracturing, bedrock lithology and presence and type of weathered materials were also investigated as indicators of ground properties. For instance, the mineralogy, grain size and fabric of the bedrock and related weathered materials would control properties such as shear strength, pore water suction, infiltration capacity and natural attenuation of contaminants (Vrba and Civita 1994, Hudec 1998, Hill and Rosenbaum 1998, Thornton et al. 2001, Fernandes 2003). Geological structures, such as faults and joints within the rock mass, as well as relict structures in saprolitic soils, are also liable to exert significant influences on shear strength and hydraulic properties of geomaterials (Aydin 2002, Pine and Harrison 2003). In this particular case study, analysis of lineaments extracted from satellite images combined with tectonic modelling underpinned inferences about major and small-scale faults and joints. The approach followed studies by Fernandes and Rudolph (2001) and Fernandes da Silva et al. (2005b) who asserted that empirical models of tectonic history, based on outcrop scale palaeostress regime determinations, can be integrated with lineament analysis to identify areas: i) of greater density and interconnectivity of fractures; and ii) greater probability of open fractures; also to iii) deduce angular relationships between rock structures (strike and dip) and between these and hill slope directions. These procedures facilitated 3-dimensional interpretations and up-scaling from regional up to semi-detailed assessments which were particularly useful for assessments of local ground stability and groundwater flow.

The BCUs were then classified into four classes (very high, high, moderate, and low) in terms of susceptibility to land instability and groundwater vulnerability according to qualitative and semi-quantitative rules devised from a mixture of empirical knowledge and statistical approaches. A spreadsheet-based approach that used nominal, interval and numerical average values assigned in attribute tables was used for this. A two-step procedure was adopted to produce the required estimates where, at stage one, selected attributes were analysed and grouped into three score categories (A - high, M - moderate, B - low B) according to their potential influence on groundwater vulnerability and land instability processes. In the second step, all attributes were considered to have the same relative influence and the final classification for each BCU was the sum of the scores A, B, M. The possible combinations of these are illustrated in Table 3. Figure 5 shows overall terrain classifications for susceptibility to land instability.

Combinations of scores	Classification
AAAA	Very high
AAAM, AAAB, AAMM	High
AAMB, AABB, AMMM, AMMB, MMMM	Medium
AMBB, ABBB, MMMB, MMBB, MBBB, BBBB	Low

Table 3. Possible combinations of scores "A" (high), "M" (moderate), and "B" (low) respective to the four attributes (bedrock lithology and weathered materials, fracturing, soil type, and slope steepness) used for classification of units (BCUs) in terms of susceptibility to land instability and groundwater vulnerability.

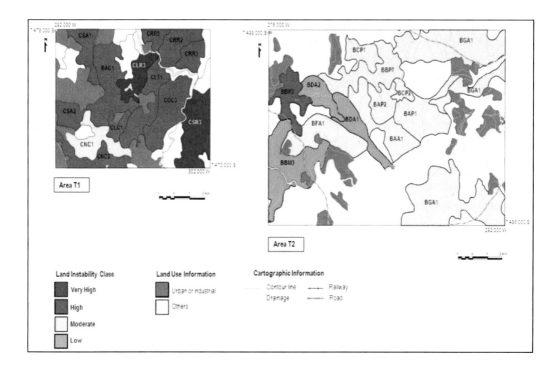

Fig. 5. Maps of susceptibility to land instability processes. Test Areas T1 and T2. UTM projection and coordinates [After Fernandes da Silva et al., 2010].

4. Hazard mapping: Land instability and flooding

In order to prevent damage to structures and facilities, disruption to production, injury and loss of life, public authorities have a responsibility to assess hazard mitigation and controls that may require remedial engineering work, or emergency and contingency actions. In order to accommodate these different demands, information about the nature of the hazard, and the consequences and likelihood of occurrence, are needed. Hazard maps aim to reduce adverse environmental impacts, prevent disasters, as well as to reconcile conflicting influences on land use. The examples given in this Section demonstrate the identification and zonation in terms of the likelihood and consequences of land instability and flooding hazards. There are several reasons for undertaking such work, for instance to provide public authorities with data on which to base structural plans and building codes as well as civil defence and emergency response programmes.

4.1 Application to local structural plans

As indicated in Section 3.1, the BCUs (terrain units) classified as having a moderate to high susceptibility to geodynamic processes (mass movements and flood) were selected for further detailed engineering geological mapping. This was to provide data and supporting information to the structure plan of the City of São Sebastião. The attributes of the selected units were cross-referenced with other data sets, such as regional rainfall distribution, land-use inventory, and mineral exploitation records to estimate the magnitude and frequency of hazards and adverse impacts. Risk assessment was based on the estimated probability of failure occurrence and the potential damage thus caused (security of life, destruction of property, disruption of production). Both the triggering and the predisposing factors were investigated, and, so far as was possible, identified. It is worth noting the great need to consider socio-economic factors in hazard mapping and risk analysis. For instance, areas of consolidated housing and building according to construction patterns and reasonable economic standards were distinguished from areas of unconsolidated/expanding urban occupation. Temporal analysis of imagery and aerial photos, such as densities of vegetation and exposed soil in non-built-up areas, were utilised to supplement the land use inventory. The mineral exploration inventory included the locations of active and abandoned mineral exploitation sites (quarries and open pit mining for aggregates) and certain geotechnical conditions. Besides slope steepness and inappropriate occupancy and land use, the presence of major and minor geological structures was considered to be one of the main predisposing factors to land instability in the region studied.

Figure 6 depicts a detail of the hazard map for the City of São Sebastião. Zones of land instability were delimited and identified by code letters that correspond with geodynamic processes as follows: A - landslides, B - creep, C - block tilt/glide, and D - slab failure/rock fall. Within these zones, landsliding and other mass movement hazards were further differentiated according to structural geological predisposing factors as follows: r – occurrence of major tectonic features such as regional faults or brittle-ductile shear zones; f – coincidence of spatial orientations between rock foliation, hillslope, and man-made cuttings; t – high density of fracturing (particularly jointing) in combination with coincidence of spatial orientations between fracture and foliation planes, hillslope, and man-made cuttings (Moura-Fujimoto et al., 1996; Fernandes da Silva et al. 1997b).

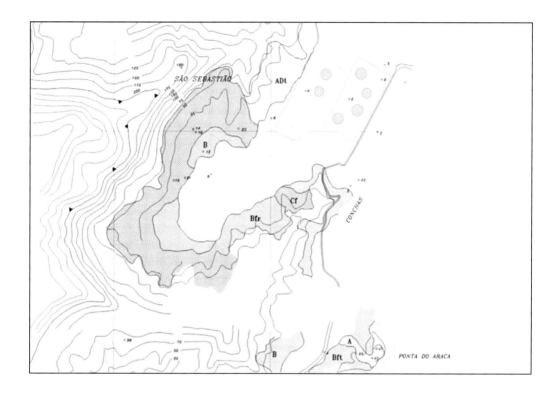

Fig. 6. Example of hazard map from the City of São Sebastião, north shore of São Paulo State, Southeast Brazil. Key for unit classification: Light red = very high susceptibility; Blue = high susceptibility; Light orange = moderate susceptibility; Yellow = low susceptibility. See Section 4.1 for code letters on geodynamic processes and predisposing factors. [after Fernandes da Silva et al. 1997b] (not to scale).

4.2 Application to civil defence and emergency response programmes

Methods of hazard mapping can be grouped into three main approaches: empirical, probabilistic, and deterministic (Savage et al. 2004, as cited in Tominaga, 2009b). Empirical approaches are based on terrain characteristics and previous occurrence of geodynamic phenomena in order to estimate both the potential for, and the spatial and temporal distribution of, future phenomena and their effects. Probabilistic approaches employ statistical methods to reduce subjectivity of interpretations. However, the outcomes depend very much on measured patterns defined through site tests and observations, but it is not always feasible to perform this acquisition of data in developing regions and countries. Deterministic approaches focus on mathematical modelling that aims quantitatively to describe certain parameters and rules thought to control physical processes such as slope

Geo-environmental Terrain Assessments Based on Remote
Sensing Tools: A Review of Applications to Hazard Mapping and Control
101

stability and surface water flow. Their application tends to be restricted to small areas and detailed studies.

In the State of Sao Paulo (Southeast Brazil), high rates of population influx and poorly planned land occupation have led to concentration of dwellings in unsuitable areas, thus leading to increasing exposure of the community to risk and impact of hazard events. In addition, over the last 20 years, landsliding and flooding events have been affecting an increasingly large geographical area, so bringing about damage to people and properties (Tominaga et al. 2009a). To deal with this situation, Civil Defence actions including preventive, mitigation, contingency (preparedness), and emergency response programmes have been implemented. The assessment of the potential for the occurrence of landslides, floods and other geodynamic processes, besides the identification and management of associated risks in urban areas has played a key role in Civil Defence programmes. To date, systematic hazard mapping has covered 61 cities in the State of São Paulo, and nine other cities are currently being mapped (Pressinotti et al., 2009).

Examples that mix empirical and probabilistic approaches are briefly presented in this Section. The concepts of hazard mapping and risk analysis adopted for these studies followed definitions provided in Varnes (1984) and UN-ISDR (2004), who described risk as an interaction between natural or human induced hazards and vulnerable conditions. According to Tominaga (2009b), a semi-quantitative assessment of risk, R, can be derived from the product R = [H x (V x D)], where: H is the estimated hazard or likelihood of occurrence of a geodynamic and potentially hazardous phenomenon; V is the vulnerability determined by a number of physical, environmental, and socio-economic factors that expose a community and/or facilities to adverse impacts; and D is the potential damage that includes people, properties, and economic activities to be affected. The resulting risk, R, attempts to rate the damage to structures and facilities, injury and loss of lives, and disruption to production.

The first example relates to hazard mapping and risk zoning applied to housing urban areas in the City of Diadema (Marchiori-Faria et al. 2006), a densely populated region (around 12,000 inhab. per km²) of only 31.8 km², situated within the Metropolitan Region of the State Capital – São Paulo (Figure 7). The approach combined the use of high-resolution satellite imagery (Ikonos sensor) and ortho-rectified aerial photographs with ground checks. The aim was to provide civil defence authorities and decision-makers with information about land occupation and ground conditions as well as technical advice on the potential magnitude of instability and flooding, severity of damage, likelihood of hazard, and possible mitigating and remedial measures. Driving factors included the need to produce outcomes in an updateable and reliable manner, and in suitable formats to be conveyed to non-specialists. The outcomes needed to meet preventive and contingency requirements, including terrain accessibility, linear infrastructure conditions (roads and railways in particular), as well as estimations of the number of people who would need to be removed from risk areas and logistics for these actions. Risk zones were firstly identified through field work guided by local authorities. Site observations concentrated on relevant terrain characteristics and ground conditions that included: slope steepness and hillslope geometry, type of slope (natural, cut or fill), soil weathering profile, groundwater and surface water conditions, and land instability features (e.g. erosion rills, landslide scars, river undercutting). In addition, information about periodicity, magnitude, and effects of previous landsliding and flooding events as well as perceptions of potential and future problems were gathered through interviewing of residents. Satellite images were further used to assist with the identification of buildings and houses liable to be affected and the delineation of risk zone boundaries. Risk assessment was based on a qualitative ranking scheme with four levels of risk: R1 (low); R2 (moderate); R3 (high); R4 (very-high). Low risk (R1) zones, for example, comprised only predisposing factors to instability (e.g. informal housing and cuttings in steep slope areas) or to flooding (e.g. informal housing in lowland areas and close to watercourses but no reported flood within the last 5 years). Very-high risk (R4) zones were characterized by significant evidence of land instability (e.g. presence of cracks in soil and walls, subsidence steps, leaning of trees and electricity poles, erosion rills and ravines, landslide scars) or flooding hazards (e.g. flooding height marks on walls, riverbank erosion, proximity of dwellings to river channel, severe floods reported within the last 5 years).

The outcomes, including basic and derived data and interpretations, were integrated and then presented on a geo-referenced computational system designed to respond the needs of data displaying and information management of the State of São Paulo Civil Defence authorities (CEDEC). As described by Pressinotti et al. (2007), such system and database, called Map-Risk, includes cartographic data, interpretative maps (risk zoning), imagery, and layers of cadastral information (e.g. urban street network). The system also enabled generation and manipulation of outputs in a varied set of text (reports), tabular (tables), and graphic information including photographic inventories for risk zones. The system was fully conceived and implemented at low cost, utilizing commercial software available that were customized in this visualisation system through target-script programming designed to achieve user functionalities (e.g. ESRI/MapObjects, Delphi, Visual Basic, OCX MapObjects). Examples of delineated risk zones for the City of Diadema and a display of the Map-Risk functionalities are presented in Figure 7.

The second example refers to a flooding hazard mapping performed at regional and local scales in the Paraiba do Sul River Watershed, Eastern São Paulo State (Figure 8), in order to provide a rapid and comprehensive understanding of hazard phenomena and their impacts, as well as to enable application of procedures of data integration and mapping in different socio-economic contexts (Andrade et al. 2010). The information was systematised and processed to allow the build-up of a geo-referenced database capable of providing information for both environmental regional planning (economic-ecological zoning) and local scale hazard mapping for civil defence purposes. The regional evaluation covered all the 34 municipalities located in the watershed, and comprised the following stages of work: 1) survey of previous flooding events reported in newspaper and historical archives; 2) data systematisation and consolidation to translate gathered news into useful pieces of technical information; 3) identification of flooding occurrence locations using Google Earth tools; 4) cartographic auditing, geo-referencing and spatial data analysis using a freeware GIS package called SPRING (see Section 5); 5) exploratory statistical analysis of data; 6) preliminary flooding hazard classification on the basis of statistical results. Such preliminary classification used geopolitical (municipality) and hydrographical sub-basin boundaries as units for the analysis.

Geo-environmental Terrain Assessments Based on Remote
Sensing Tools: A Review of Applications to Hazard Mapping and Control
103

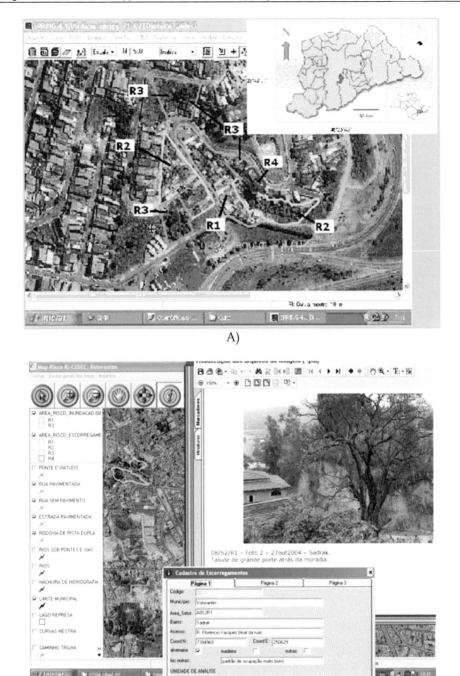

A)

B)

Fig. 7. A) Location of the City of Diadema in the Metropolitan District of São Paulo (State capital), Southeast Brazil and example of delineated risk zones over a high-resolution satellite image (Ikonos). B) Example of Map-Risk system display. See Section 4.2 for details. [after Marchiori-Faria et al., 2006; Pressinotti et al., 2007]

Fig. 8. Location of Paraiba do Sul River Watershed in Eastern São Paulo State and distribution of flooding occurrences. Internal sub-divisions correspond to geopolitical boundaries (municipalities). [After Andrade et al., 2010]

The regional evaluation was followed-up with detailed flooding hazard mapping (1:3,000 scale) in 7 municipalities, which included: a) ground observations - where previous occurrence was reported – to measure and record information on flooding height marks, land occupation, and local terrain, riverbank and water course characteristics; b) geo-referencing and spatial data analysis, with generation of interpolated numerical grids on flooding heights and local topography; c) data interpretation and delimitation of flooding hazard zones; d) cross-referencing of hazard zones with land use and economic information leading to delimitation of flooding risk zones. Numerical scoring schemes were devised for ranking hazard and risk zones, thus allowing relative comparisons between different areas. Hazard zone scores were based on intervals of flooding height (observed and interpolated) and temporal recurrence of flooding events. Flooding risk scores were quantified as follows: $R = [H \times (V \times D)]$, in which potential damage and vulnerability were considered (housing areas, urban infrastructure, facilities and services to be affected) on the basis of image interpretation and cross-referencing with land use maps and information. A detail map (yet unpublished) showing the interpolated grid of flooding heights and delineated hazard zones is presented in Figure 9.

A)

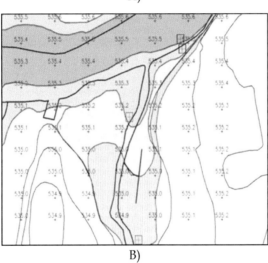

B)

Fig. 9. A) Measurement of maximum flood height for recent flooding event. B) Numerical interpolated grid of flooding heights and delineated flooding hazard zones. Green = Low probability of occurrence, Estimated flooding heights (Efh) < 0.40 m. Yellow = Moderate probability, 0.40 < Efh < 0.80 m. Light Brown = High probability, 0.80 < Efh < 1.20 m. Red = Very high probability, Efh > 1.20 m. Ground observations and measurements: cross and rectangle. Continuous lines: black = topographic contour lines, blue = main river channel boundaries. Not to scale.

5. Geo-environmental assessment: applications to land reclamation policies

Land reclamation of sites of previous mineral exploitation frequently involve actions to minimize environmental damage and aim at re-establish conditions for natural balance and sustainability so reconciling former mined/quarried sites with their surroundings (Brollo et al., 2002). Strategies and programmes for land reclamation need to consider physical and biological characteristics of the local environment as well as socio-economic factors. Socio-environmental regeneration, involves not only revegetation and land stabilisation engineering, but also rehabilitation or introduction of a new function for the area.

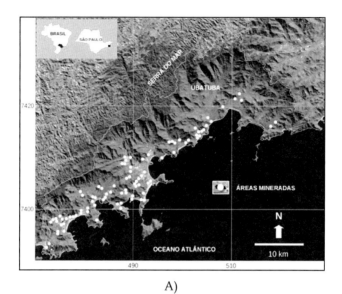

A)

B)

Fig. 10. A) Location map and satellite image of the Municipality of Ubatuba (North Shore São Paulo State, Southeast Brazil). Dots on image represent quarried/mined sites. B) Schematic display of the integrated approach taken to reconcile mineral exploitation management and land reclamation. The scheme shows the three main issues to be addressed (centre) and topics of interest to be studied. [after Ferreira et al., 2006; Ferreira & Fernandes da Silva, 2008]

The case study concerns a GIS-based geo-environmental management scheme to reconcile sustainable mineral exploration of aggregates and construction materials with regeneration of abandoned and/or derelict mined sites in the municipality of Ubatuba (North Shore of São Paulo State, Brazil). Until the early 1990's intensive exploitation of residual soil and ornamental stone (for fill and civil construction) took place in an unplanned and unregulated manner. This led to highly adverse environmental impacts, including the creation of 114 derelict and abandoned sites which resulted in State and Federal authorities enforcing a virtual halt to mining activity in the region. Besides this, the municipality of Ubatuba is highly regarded for its attractive setting and landscape, including encroached coastline with sandy beaches and bays with growing leisure and tourism activities. The area encompasses the Serra do Mar Mountain Range covered by large remnants of Atlantic Forest so that approximately 80% of the municipal territory lies within a nature and wildlife reserve (Figure 10A). As described by Ferreira et al. (2005, 2006), the devised strategy required an integrated approach (Figure 10B) in order to address three key issues: 1) environmental recovery of a number of derelict (abandoned, unsightly) sites; 2) reduction of hazards (land instability, erosion, flooded areas etc), particularly at those sites informally occupied by low income populations; and 3) rational exploitation of materials for local building materials corresponding to local needs. The study was implemented using a freeware GIS and image processing package called SPRING (Câmara et al. 1996, INPE 2009) and ortho-rectified air photos (1-metre resolution, taken in 2001, leading to an approximate scale of 1:3,000).

The key output of the land management strategy was a prioritisation ranking scheme based on a comprehensive site critical condition (ICR) score, which synthesised the significance of each factor or issue to addressed (IG/SMA, 2008; Ferreira et al., 2009). Accordingly, the score system consisted of three numerical indicators: 1) environmental degradation indicator (IDE), 2) mineral potential indicator (IPM), and 3) hazard/risk indicator (IRI). Each indicator was normalised to a scalar range (0 to 1), and the ICR was the sum of the three indicators. The ICR was then used to set up directives and recommendations to advise local and State authorities about the possible measures to be taken, through mid- and long-term policies and/or immediate remedial and mitigating actions.

According to Ferreira et al. (2008), the IDE comprised four component criteria to estimate the degree of adverse environmental impact (or degradation) of the individual mineral extraction sites: erosional features, terrain irregularity, herbaceous and bushy vegetation, and exposed soil. Information on these factors was acquired from imagery and ground checks. Tracing of linear features on images was investigated as an indicator of the frequency and distribution of erosional processes (rills, ravines, piping scars) as well as for terrain irregularity. In the first case, the sum of linear features representative of erosional processes was ratioed by the area of each site to quantify the estimate. Similarly, linear features related to the contour of cutting berms, rill marks, and slope breaks caused by mining/quarrying activity, were also measured to quantify terrain irregularity. The areal extent of herbaceous and bushy vegetation as well as exposed soil were also delimited on images.

The IPM, as described by Ferreira & Fernandes da Silva (2008), was achieved by means of the following procedures: 1) identification and delimitation of quarried/mined sites (polygons) on geo-referenced imagery; 2) derivation of local DEM (digital elevation model) from topographic contour lines to each delimited site; 3) calculation of local volume to material (V1) based on the original geometry of the quarried/mined sites; 4) calculation of volume of material already taken (V2) and exploitable volume of material (V3), so that [V3] = [V1 – V2]; 5) application of classification rules based on legal environmental and land use restrictions. The calculation of volumes of material (residual soil and ornamental stone) was performed by means of GIS operations involving polygons (areas) and numerical grids of topographic heights generated with nearest neighbour interpolator in the SPRING package (Figure 11). The IRI was derived from R = [H x (V x D)] – see Section 4.2 – focussing on mass movement and flood hazards and their consequences to people, property and economic activity. According to Rossini-Penteado (2007) and Tominaga et al. (2008), Hazard, H, was quantified according to the spatial and temporal probability of occurrence of each phenomenon and then weighted in relation to areal distribution of such probabilities (percentage of sq. km). The vulnerability, V, was computed by means of scores assigned to socio-economic aspects such as nature of built structures, spatial regularity of land occupation, presence of urban infrastructure (e.g. water supply, sanitation, health services, refuse collection and disposal method), road/street network, educational and income patterns. Similarly, in order to estimate the extent of potential damage, D, numerical scores were devised and attributed to the estimated number of people and buildings per unit area, and to the proportion of built area in relation to total area of the site.

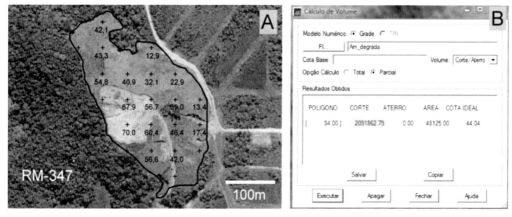

Fig. 11. Example of the mineral potential indicator (IPM) for the Municipality of Ubatuba (North Shore São Paulo State, Southeast Brazil). A) Abandoned/quarried site delimited on image and numerical grid of topographic heights. B) Screen display from GIS-based computation of volumes of exploitable material [after Ferreira & Fernandes da Silva, 2008].

Figure 12 illustrates the application of the ICR scoring scheme to mined/quarried sites in Ubatuba. In summary, 47% of sites were classified as very low priority, 12% as low priority, 19% as moderate priority, 15% as high priority (18 sites), and 7% as very high priority (8 sites). The priorities represent a combination of availability of exploitable volumes of building materials and the need for measures to tackle adverse environmental impacts and high risk situations (Figure 12). Based on the application of the ICR scores and current land use, directives and recommendations for land reclamation and socio-regeneration of mined/quarried sites were consolidated into ten main groups (IG/SMA, 2008; Ferreira et al., 2009). Such directives and recommendations ranged from simple measures such as routine maintenance and cleaning, revegetation with grass and control of water surface flow (including run-off) to the implementation of leisure and multi-purpose public facilities, major land stabilisation projects combined with mineral exploitation, and monitoring.

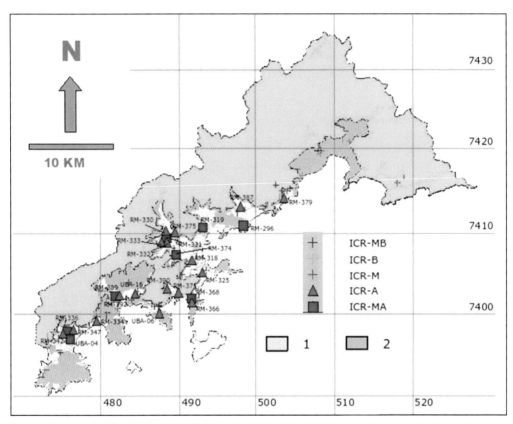

Fig. 12. Spatial distribution of mined/quarried sites classified according to critical condition score scheme (ICR). Sites classified as High (triangles) and Very High (squares) priority are highlighted. Remarks: 1- Serra do Mar Nature and Wildlife State Park, 2- Environmentally sensitive protected areas. ICR-MB = Very Low priority, ICR-B = Low priority, ICR-M = Moderate priority, ICR-A = High priority, ICR-MA = Very high priority [after IG/SMA, 2008].

6. Conclusions

Geo-environmental terrain classification may be used as part of the land-use planning decision making and may also provide the basis of responses to emergency situations. In most examples presented here, classification schemes were based on knowledge of the bedrock geology, topography, landforms, superficial geology (soil and weathered materials), groundwater conditions and land-uses. Information for the classification has been variously derived from remote sensing and fieldwork rather than specific site investigations. A framework for carrying out a terrain classification at different scales has been presented.

In practice, the effectiveness of land zoning system requires the implementation of planning controls. To do this the Local Authority needs adequate resources and an appropriate legal or planning guidance policy framework. Preferably, the control process should be based on the principle that permission will be given unless there is a good reason for refusal. In granting permission, conditions may then be applied to ensure the safety of the development with regard to landsliding, flooding and other potential problems. However it must be recognised that where practical control over development cannot be exercised, other preventive, mitigative or advisory measures may be all that can be used.

Marker (1996) explains that the rate and style of development has a major impact on the information requirements. Without a rigorously enforced planning framework based on accurate information about the ground conditions very rapid urban development will generally lead to construction on areas of less stable land or land which may be subject to hazards such as flooding or pollution. This type of development may also result in the sterilisation of geological resources which it would be expedient to exploit as part of the development process. On the other hand restricting development to designated areas will generally require detailed information about the ground conditions and likelihood and potential impact of hazards to be available at the planning stage. It also assumes existence of the resources and will to enforce the plan. Such models can severely constrain the social and economic development of an area, lead to excessively high population densities and give rise to problems associated with the re-use of previously developed land.

Policy formulation may incorporate incentives (e.g. subsidies and reduced taxes) to be provided by local and state governments to encourage such measures and good practice, which can be viewed as kinds of voluntary or induced control. In some cases financial controls exerted by public funding as well as mortgage and insurance providers are the means by which some types of development may be curtailed but such controls may not prevent informal occupancy of hazardous areas. In this regard, some of the examples presented here, from a regional and local perspective, have also demonstrated environmental management regulations may have little meaning in some urban areas subject to rapid expansion where, because of population influx, informal housing is virtually an inevitable consequence.

Due to the latter hazard mapping updating and post-episode monitoring [failure episodes] are absolutely vital as these procedures facilitate a contemporary understanding of ground conditions and risk circumstances, which can be essential to provide timely and efficient advice for mitigation and control of hazards as well as to design effective contingency actions and engineering solutions.

7. Acknowledgements

The authors are very much indebted to the Sao Paulo State Geological Institute and its staff for most of the examples provided here.

8. References

Akiwumi, F.A., Butler, D.R. (2008). Mining and environmental change in Sierra Leone, West Africa: a remote sensing and hydrogeomorphological study. *Environmental Monitoring Assessment*, 142: 309–318. ISSN 0167-6369

Alonso Herrero, E.; Frances, E., & Cendrero, A. (1990). Environmental geological mapping in Cantabrian Mountains, Spain. In: *Proceedings of the 6th Congress of the Intl.*

Assoc. Engineering Geology and Environment, Amsterdam. Balkema, Rotterdam, 1: 31-35.

Andrade, E.; Danna, L.C.; Santos, M.L., & Fernandes da Silva, P.C. (2010). Survey of flooding occurrence in newspaper records as a support for regional planning and hazard mapping. *Proceedings of 7th Brazilian Symposium on Geotechnical and Geo-environmental Cartography*. ISSN 2178-1834. Maringa, October 2010. 16p. [in Portuguese]

Aydin, F. (2002). Heterogeneity and behaviour of saprolitic slopes. *Proceedings of the 9th International Congress of the Intl. Assoc. Engineering Geology and Environment*, ISBN 0-620-28559-1, Durban, September 2002. p. 846-856.

Barton, J., Alexander, D., Correa, C., Mashelkar, R., Samuels, G., & Thomas S. (2002). Integrating intellectual property rights and development policy. London: UK Department for International Development, Commission on Intellectual Property Rights.

Beaumont, T.E. (1985). An application of satellite imagery for highway maintenance and rehabilitation in Niger. *International Journal of Remote Sensing*, 6 (7): 1263-1267, ISSN 0143-1161.

Beaumont, T.E. & Beaven, P.J. (1977). The use of satellite imagery for highway engineering in overseas countries. (T.R.R.L. - Transport & Road Research Laboratory) England, Supplementary Report 279, 19 p.

Beckett, P.H.T. & Webster, R. (1969). A Review of Studies on Terrain Evaluation by the Oxford-MEXE-Cambridge Group,1960-1969, MEXE Report 1123, Christchurch

Bell, F.G. (1993). *Engineering Geology*. Blackwell, Oxford. 269p.

Bennett, M.R & Doyle, P. (1997). *Environmental Geology*. John Wiley and Sons Ltd, Chicester.

Bourne, R. (1931). Regional Survey and its Relation to Stocktaking of the Agricultural Resources of the British Empire, Oxford Forestry Memoirs No.13.

Bowman, I. (1911). Forest Physiography, Physiography of the US and Principal Soils in Relation to Forestry, John Wiley and Sons, New York.

Brollo M.J., Barbosa, J.M., Rocha, F.T., & Martins, S.E. (2002). Research Programme on Characterisation and Reclamation of Environmentally Degraded Areas. *Proceedings of the 5th Meeting on Environmental Management Research*. São Paulo: CINP/SMA, 2002, p. 74-82. [in Portuguese]

Brollo, M.J., Vedovello, R., Gutjahr, M.R., Hassuda, S., Iritani, M.A., Fernandes da Silva, P.C., & Holl, MC. (2000). Criteria for selection of areas for waste disposal in regional scale (1:100,000). Application area: Metropolitan Region of Campinas, Sao Paulo State, Brazil. *Proceedings of the 8th Congress of the Intl. Assoc. Engineering Geology and Environment*. Vancouver, September 1998, 6: 4281-4286.

Brook D. & Marker B.R. (1987) Thematic geological mapping as an essential tool in land-use planning. In: Culshaw MG, Bell FG, Cripps JC, O'Hara M (eds) *"Planning and Engineering Geology"*, Engineering Geology Special Publication No. 4. Geological Society, London, pp 211–214.

Câmara, G. & Fonseca, F. (2007) Information Policies and Open Source Software in Developing Countries. *Journal of the American Society for Information Science and Technology*, 58(1): 121–132, ISSN 1532-2890.

Câmara, G., Souza, R.C.M., Freitas, U.M., & Garrido, J. (1996). SPRING: Integrating remote sensing and GIS by object-oriented data modelling. *Computers & Graphics*, 20 (3): 395-403, ISSN 0097-8493.

Cendrero, A., Flor, G., Gancedo, R., González-Lastra, J.R., Omenaca, J.S., & Salinas, J.M. (1979). Integrated Assessment and Evaluation of the Coastal Environment of the Province of Vizcaya, Bay of Biscay, Spain. *Environmental Geology*, 2 (6): 321-331, ISSN 0943-0105.

Christian, C.S. (1958). The concepts of land units and land systems. In: *Proceedings of the 9th Pacific Science Congress*. Vol. 20, pp. 74-81.

Christian, C.S. & Stewart, GA. (1952). Summary of general report on Survey of Katherine - Darwin Region. CSIRO Land Research Series No.1

Christian, C.S. & Stewart, GA. (1968). Methodology of integrated surveys. *Proceedings of the Conference on Aerial Surveys and Integrated Studies*. UNESCO, Paris. pp. 233-280

Cripps, J.C., Fernandes Da Silva, P.C., Culshaw, M.G., Bell, F.G., Maud, R.R., & Foster, A. (2002). The planning response to landslide hazard in São Paulo State - Brazil, Durban - South Africa and Antrim - Northern Ireland. *Proceedings of 9th International Congress of the Intl. Assoc. Engineering Geology and Environment*, ISBN 0-620-28559-1, Durban, September 2002. p. 1841-1852.

Culshaw M.G., Foster, A., Cripps, J.C., & Bell FG (1990). Applied maps for land use planning in Great Britain. *Proceedings of the 6th International Congress of the Intl. Assoc. Engineering Geology and Environment*. AA Balkema, Rotterdam, 1: 85-93.

Culshaw M.G., & Northmore K.J. (2002) An engineering geological map for site investigation planning and construction type identification. In: Van Rooy JL, Jermy CA (eds) *Proceedings of the 9th International Association for Engineering Geology and the Environment Congress*, Durban, 423–431. South African Institute of Engineering and Environmental Geologists, Pretoria. On CD-ROM.

Culshaw M.G. & Price S.J. (2011) The 2010 Hans Cloos lecture: the contribution of urban geology to the development, regeneration and conservation of cities. *Bulletin of Engineering Geology and the Environment*, 70, Part 3. [In press]

Dai, F.C., Lee, C.F., & Zhang, X.H. (2001). GIS-based environmental evaluation for urban land-use planning: a case study. *Engineering Geology*, 61 (4): 257 – 271, ISSN 0013-7952.

Dearman, W.R. & Matula, M. (1977). Environmental aspects of engineering geological mapping. *Bulletin of the Intl. Assoc. Engineering Geology and Environment*, 14: 141-146. ISSN 1435-9529.

DOE - Department of the Environment. (1990). Development on unstable ground. Planning Policy Guidance PPG14, HMSO, London.

DOE - Department of the Environment. (1995) Development on unstable ground: Landslides and Planning. Planning Policy Guidance PPG14 Annex 1, HMSO, London.

Ellison, R. & Smith, A. (1998). Environmental Geology in Land Use Planning: Guide to the sources of earth science information for planning and development. Published by British Geological Survey (Nottingham, UK) on behalf of Department of Environment, Transport and the Regions, Great Britain.

Fernandes, A.J. (2003) The influence of Cenozoic Tectonics on the groundwater vulnerability in fractured rocks: a case study in Sao Paulo, Brazil. *Proceedings of the International Conference on Groundwater in Fractured Rocks*, Prague, IAH/UNESCO, p.81-82.

Fernandes, A.J. & Rudolph, D.L. (2001) The influence of Cenozoic tectonics on the groundwater-production capacity of fractured zones: a case study in Sao Paulo, Brazil. *Hydrogeology Journal*, 9: 151-167, ISSN 1431-2174.

Fernandes Da Silva, P.C., Cripps, J.C., & Wise, S.M. (2005a). The use of Remote Sensing techniques and empirical tectonic models for inference of geological structures: bridging from regional to local scales. *Remote Sensing of Environment*, 96 (1): 18 – 36. ISSN 0034-4257.

Fernandes da Silva, P.C., Ferreira, C.J., Fernandes, A.J., Brollo, M.J., Vedovello, R., Tominaga, L.K., Iritani, M.A., & Cripps, J.C. (2005b). Evaluation of land instability and groundwater pollution hazards applying the physiographic compartmentalisation technique: case study in the Metropolitan District of Campinas, Brazil. *Proceedings of the 11th Brazilian Congress on Environmental and Engineering Geology*, ISBN 85-7270-017-X. Florianopolis, November 2005. Pp. 383 – 402. [In Portuguese]

Fernandes da Silva, P.C., Maffra, C.Q.T., Tominaga, L.K., & Vedovello, R. (1997a). Mapping units on São Sebastião Geohazards Prevention Chart, Northshore of São Paulo State, Brazil. In: *Environmental Geology, Proceedings of the 30th International Geological Congress*. Daoxian, Y. (Ed.), 24: 266-281, VSP Scientific Publisher, ISBN 90-6764-239-8. Utrecht.

Fernandes da Silva, P.C., Moura-Fujimoto, N.S.V., Vedovello, R., Holl, M.C., & Maffra, C.Q.T. (1997b). The application of structural geological data in mass movement hazard zoning at the municipality of São Sebastião, Northshore of São Paulo State, Brazil. *Proceedings of the 6th Brazilian Symposium on Tectonic Studies*, Goiania, May 1997. p. 136-138. [in Portuguese]

Fernandes da Silva, P.C., Vedovello, R., Ferreira, C.J., Cripps, J.C., Brollo, M.J., & Fernandes, A.J. (2010) Geo-environmental mapping using physiographic analysis: constraints on the evaluation of land instability and groundwater pollution hazards in the Metropolitan District of Campinas, Brazil. *Environmental Earth Sciences*, 61: 1657-1675. ISSN 1866-6280.

Ferreira, C.J.; Brollo, M.J.; Ummus, M.E.; & Nery, T.D. (2008). Indicators and quantification of environmental degradation in mined sites, Ubatuba (SP). *Revista Brasileira de Geociências*, 38(1): 141-152. ISSN 0375-7536 [In Portuguese]

Ferreira, C.J. & Fernandes da Silva, P.C. (2008). The use of GIS for prioritising mineral exploitation of building materials in derelict sites: the Ubatuba – SP case. *Revista do Instituto Geológico*, 29 (1/2): 19-31. ISSN 0100-929X [In Portuguese]

Ferreira, C.J., Fernandes da Silva, P.C., & Brollo, M.J. (2009). Directives for socio-regeneration of sites affected by mining activity, Ubatuba, Sao Paulo State. *Proceedings of the 11th Southeast Brazil Geological Symposia*, ISSN 2175-697X, São Pedro, November 2009. pp. 123-124.

Ferreira, C.J., Fernandes da Silva, P.C., Brollo, M.J., & Cripps, J.C. (2006). Dereliction problems from exploitation of residual soil and ornamental stone at Sao Paulo

State, Brazil. *Proceedings of the 10th International Congress of the International Association of Engineering Geology and Environment.* Nottingham , September 2006. CD-ROM. 10p.

Ferreira, C.J., Fernandes da Silva, P.C, Furlan, S.A., Brollo, M.J., Tominaga, L.K., Vedovello, R., Guedes, A.C.M., Ferreira, D.F., Cripps, J.C., & Perez, F. (2005). Devising strategies for reclamation of derelict sites due to mining of residual soil (Saibro) at Ubatuba, North coast of Sao Paulo State, Brazil: the views and roles of stakeholders. *Sociedade e Natureza* , Special Issue on Land Degradation, p.643 - 660, ISSN 0103-1570.

Finlayson, A. (1984). Land surface evaluation for engineering practices: Applications of the Australian P.U.C.E. system for terrain analysis. *Quarterly Journal of Engineering Geology*, 17(2): 149-158, ISSN 1470-9236

Grant, K. (1968). A Terrain Evaluation System for Engineering. CSIRO, Div. Soil. Mech. Technical Paper No. 2, Melbourne. 27p.

Grant, K. (1974). The PUCE Programme for Terrain Evaluation System for Engineering Purposes. II. Procedures for Terrain Classification. CSIRO, Div. Soil. Mech. Technical Paper No. 15, Melbourne. 68p.

Grant, K. (1975). The PUCE Programme for Terrain Evaluation System for Engineering Purposes. I. Principles. CSIRO, Div. Soil. Mech. Technical Paper No. 19, Melbourne. 32p.

Griffiths, J.S. & Edwards, R.J.G. (2001). The development of land surface evaluation for engineering practice. In Griffiths, J S (Ed.) Land Surface Evaluation for Engineering Practice. Geological Society, London, Engineering Geological Special Publication, 18, 3 – 9.

Griffiths, J S (Ed.) 2001 Land Surface Evaluation for Engineering Practice. Geological Society, London, Engineering Geological Special Publication, 18.

Guy, M. (1966). Quelques principes et quelques experiences sur la metodhologie de la photointerpretation. *Proceedings of the 2nd International Symposium on Photo-interpretation.* Paris, 1966. v.1: 2-41.

Hill, S.E. & Rosenbaum, M.S. (1998). Assessing the significant factors in a rock weathering system. Quarterly Journal of *Engineering Geology*, 31: 85-94, ISSN 0013-7952.

Howard, A.D. (1967) Drainage analysis in geologic interpretation: a summation. *Bulletin of the American Association of Petroleum Geologists*, 51: 2246-2254, ISSN 0149-1423.

Hudec, P.P. (1998) Rock properties and physical processes of rapid weathering and deterioration. *Proceedings of the 8th International Congress of the Intl. Assoc. Engineering Geology and Environment*, Vancouver, September 1998. p.335-341.

IG/SMA – Instituto Geológico/ São Paulo State Secreariat of Environmet. (1996). São Sebastião Geohazards Prevention Chart, Northshore of São Paulo State, Brazil. São Paulo, Technical Report, 77p. [in Portuguese]

IG/SMA - Instituto Geológico/ São Paulo State Secreariat of Environmet. (1999). Methodology for Selection of Suitable Areas for Treatment and Disposal of Solid Waste: Regional Approach. São Paulo, IG/SMA Technical Report, 98p. [in Portuguese]

IG/SMA - Instituto Geológico/ São Paulo State Secreariat of Environmet. (2003). Evaluation of land instability and groundwater pollution hazards in the Metropolitan District of Campinas, Brazil. São Paulo, Foreign Commonwealth Office Intl. Cooperation Programme. Technical Report, 57p.

IG/SMA - Instituto Geológico/ São Paulo State Secreariat of Environmet. (2008). Directives for Socio-Environmental Regeneration of Derelict Sites Due to Mining of Building Materials, Ubatuba, Northshore of São Paulo State, Brazil. São Paulo, FAPESP – Public Policies Research Programme, Funding Grant n. 03/07182-5. Final Tech. Sci. Report, 168p. [in Portuguese]

INPE - Brazilian National Institute for Space Research (2009) SPRING 5.0. http://www.dpi.inpe.br/spring/english/download.php. Cited in 11 December 2009.

Kiefer, R.W. (1967). Terrain analysis for metropolitan fringe area planning, *Journal of the Urban Planning and Development Division, Proceedings of the American Society of Civil Engineers,* UP4, 93, 119-39.

Latifovic R., Fytas K., Chen J., & Paraszczak J. (2005) Assessing land cover change resulting from large surface mining development. *International Journal of Applied Earth Observation and Geoinformation,* 7: 29–48, ISSN 0303-2434.

Lillesand, T. & Kiefer, R.W. (2000) Remote Sensing and Image Interpretation. 4th Ed., John Wiley, New York.

Mabbut, J.A. 1968. Review of concepts on land classification. In: *Land Evaluation.* Stewart, G.A. (ed.), p. 11-28, Macmillan, Melbourne.

Marchiori-Faria, D.G., Ferreira, C.J., Fernandes da Silva, P.C., Rossini-Pentado, D., & Cripps, J.C. (2006). Hazard mapping as part of Civil Defence preventative and contingency actions: A case study from Diadema, Brazil. *Proceedings of the 10th International Congress of the International Association of Engineering Geology and Environment.* Nottingham , September 2006. CD-ROM. 10p.

Marker, B.R. (1996). Role of the earth sciences in addressing urban resources and constraints In: McCall, G J H ; de Mulder, E F J and Marker, B R (Eds). *Urban Geoscience.* AGID Special Publication Series No 20 in association with Cogeoenvironment. Balkema (Rotterdam), pp 163-180.

Matula, M. (1979). Regional engineering geological evaluation for planning purposes. *Bulletin of the Intl. Assoc. Engineering Geology and Environment,* 18: 18-24. ISSN 1435-9529

Matula, M. & Letko, V. (1980). Engineering geology in planning the metropolitan region of Bratislava. *IAEG Bull.,. Bulletin of the Intl. Assoc. Engineering Geology and Environment,* 19: 47-52. ISSN 1435-9529

Meijerink, A.M. (1988). Data acquisition and data capture through terrain mapping units. *ITC Journal,* International Journal of Applied Earth Observation and Geoinformation 1: 23-44. ISSN 03032434

Miliaresis, G.Ch. (2001). Geomorphometric mapping of Zagros Range at regional scale. *Computer and Geosciences,* 27 (7): 775 – 786. ISSN 0098-3004.

Mitchell, C.W. (1991). *Terrain Evaluation.* 2nd Ed. Longman, Essex. 497p.

Moura-Fujimoto, N.S.V., Holl, M.C., Vedovello, R., Fernandes da Silva, P.C, & Maffra, C.Q.T. (1996). The identification of mass movement hazard zones at the municipality of São Sebastião, Northshore of São Paulo State, Brazil. *Proceedings of the 2nd Brazilian Symposium on Geotechnical Cartography.* São Paulo, November 1996. p. 129-137. [in Portuguese]

Nedovic-Budic, Z. (2000). Geographic Information Science Implications for Urban and Regional Planning. *URISA Journal,* 12(2): 81-93. ISSN 1045-8077.

Pine, R.J. & Harrison, J.P. (2003). Rock mass properties for engineering design. *Quarterly Journal of Engineering Geology and Hydrogeology,* 36: 5–16. ISSN1470-9236.

Porcher, M. & Guillope, P. (1979). Cartographie des risques ZERMOS appliquées a des plans d'occupation des sols en Normandie. Bull. Mason Lab. des Ponts et Chausses, 99.

Pressinotti, M.M.N., Guedes, A.C.M, Fernandes da Silva, P.C, Sultanum, H.J., & Guimarães, R.G. (2007). Automated system for displaying of gravitational mass movement and flooding hazard mapping of São Paulo State. *Proceedings of the 6th Brazilian Symposium on Geotechnical and Geo-environmental Cartography.* Uberlândia, November 2007. p. 324 – 333. [in Portuguese]

Pressinotti, M.M.N, Fernandes da Silva, P.C.; Marchiori-Faria, D.G., & Mendes, R.M. (2009). The experience of the Geological Institute in hazard maping and risk analysis in urban environments. *Proceedings of the 11th Southeast Brazil Geological Symposia.* São Pedro, November 2009. ISSN 2175-697X. P. 156-157. [in Portuguese]

Rossini-Penteado, D., Ferreira, C.J., & Giberti, P.P.C. (2007). Quantification of vulnerability and potential damage applied to hazard mapping and risk analysis, 1:10,000, Ubatuba-SP. *Proceedings of the 2nd Brazilian Symposium on Natural and Technological Disasters.* Santos, December 2007. [in Portuguese]

Sabins Jr., F.F. (1987). *Remote Sensing. Principles and Interpretation.* Freeman, New York.

Soares, P.C. & Fiori, A.P. (1976). Systematic procedures for geological interpretation of aerial photographs. Notícia Geomorlógica 16 (32): 71-104. [In Portuguese]

Soares, P.C., Mattos, J.T., Barcellos, P.E., Meneses, P.R., & Guerra, S.M.S. (1981). Regional morpho-structural analysis on Radar and Landsat images at the Parana Basin. *Proceedings of the 3rd South Brazilian Regional Symposium on Geology,* Curitiba. p. 5-23. [In Portuguese]

Thompson, A., Hine, P.D., Poole J.S. & Greig, J.R. (1998a) Environmental Geology in Land Use Planning: Advice for planners and developers. Published by Symonds Travers Morgan (East Grinstead, UK) on behalf of Department of Environment, Transport and the Regions, Great Britain.

Thompson, A., Hine, P.D., Poole J.S. & Greig, J.R. (1998b) Environmental Geology in Land Use Planning: A guide to good practice. Published by Symonds Travers Morgan (East Grinstead, UK) on behalf of Department of Environment, Transport and the Regions, Great Britain.

Thompson, A., Hine, P.D., Greig, J.R. & Poole J.S. (1998c) Environmental Geology in Land Use Planning: Emerging issues. Published by Symonds Travers Morgan (East Grinstead, UK) on behalf of Department of Environment, Transport and the Regions, Great Britain.

Thornton, S.F., Lerner, D.N., & Banwart, S.A. (2001) Assessing the natural attenuation of organic contaminants in aquifers using plume-scale electron and carbon balances: model development with analysis of uncertainty and parameter sensitivity. *Journal of Contaminant Hydrology*, 53(3-4): 199-232. ISSN 0169-7722.

Tominaga, L.K., Rossini-Penteado, D., Ferreira, C.J., Vedovello, R. & Armani, G. (2008). Landsliding hazard assessment through the analysis of multiple geo-environmental factors. *Proceedings of the 12th Brazilian Congress on Environmental and Engineering Geology*. ABGE, ISBN 978-85-7270-052-8. Porto de Galinhas, November 2008. 15p. [In Portuguese]

Tominaga, L.K. (2009a). Natural Disasters: Why they happen ? In: *Disasters: Knowing to prevent*. Tominaga, L.K., Santoro, J., & Amaral, R (eds). Pp. 147-160, Geological Institute, ISBN 978-85-87235-09-1, São Paulo. [In Portuguese]

Tominaga, L.K. (2009b). Risk Analysis and Mapping. In: *Disasters: Knowing to prevent*. Tominaga, L.K., Santoro, J., & Amaral, R (eds). Pp. 13-23, Geological Institute, ISBN 978-85-87235-09-1, São Paulo. [In Portuguese]

TRRL - Transport & Road Research Laboratory. (1978). Terrain evaluation for highway engineering and transport planning: a technique with particular value for developing countries. TRRL Supplementary Report No. 448, 21p.

UN-ISDR – United Nations – International Strategy for Disaster Reduction. (2004). Living with Risk: A Global Review of Disaster Reduction Initiatives. In: *Inter-Agency Secretariat International Strategy for Disaster Reduction*. Geneve, 152p. Accessed in Aug, 2009. Available at http://www.unisddr.org.

Varnes, D.J. (1984). *Landslide Hazard Zonation: Review of Principles and Practice*. Unesco Press, Paris, 56p.

Vedovello, R. (2000). *Geotechnical Zoning for Environmental Management through Basic Physiographic Units*. (unpublished PhD Thesis, Sao Paulo State University at Rio Claro). [In Portuguese]

Vedovello, R. (1993). *Geotechnical Zoning based on Remote Sensing Techniques for Urban and Regional Planning*. São José dos Campos, 186p. (unpublished M.Sc. Dissertation, National Institute for Space Research) [In Portuguese]

Vedovello, R. & Mattos, J.T. (1998). The use of basic physiographic units for definition of geotechnical units: a remote sensing approach. *Proceedings of the 3rd Brazilian Symposium on Geotechnical Cartography*. São Paulo, November 1998, 11p. [In Portuguese]

Vedovello, R., Brollo, M.J., & Fernandes da Silva, P.C. (1998). Assessment of erosion as a conditioning factor on the selection of sites for industrial waste disposal: an approach based on regional physiographic compartmentalisation obtained from satellite imagery. *Proceedings of the 3rd Brazilian Symposium on Erosion Control*. Presidente Prudente, March 1998. 9p. [In Portuguese]

Vedovello, R., Tominaga, L.K., Moura-Fujimoto, N.S.V., Fernandes da Silva, P.C., Holl, M.C., & Maffra, C.Q.T. (1997). A mass movement hazard analysis approach for public authority responses. In: *Proceedings of the 1st Latin American Forum on Applied Geography*. Curitiba, September 1997. 9p. [In Portuguese]

Verstappen HTh (1977) *Remote Sensing in Geomorphology*. Elsevier Sci. Publ., Amsterdam. 214p.

Vinogradov, B.V., Gerenchuk, K.I., Isachenko, A.G., Raman, K.G., & Teselchuk, Y.N. (1962). Basic principles of landscape mapping, Soviet Geography: Review and Translation, 3 (6), 15-20.

Vrba J. & Civita, M. (1994) Assessment of groundwater vulnerability. In: *Guidebook on Mapping Groundwater Vulnerability*. Vrba, J. & Zaporozec, A. (eds.). 16: 31-48, International Association of Hydrogeologists (IAH).

6

The Implementation of IPPC Directive in the Mediterranean Area

Tiberio Daddi, Maria Rosa De Giacomo, Marco Frey,
Francesco Testa and Fabio Iraldo
Scuola Superiore di Studi Universitari e di Perfezionamento S. Anna, Pisa,
Italy

1. Introduction

In Europe industrial activities are amongst the main causative factors of pollution. Until 1996 European Member States adopted separate regulations and multiple authorizations to address pollution control and prevention, and different laws separately dealt with air, water and soil issues, thus providing only partial solutions to the problem.

The Council Directive 96/61/EC of 24 September 1996, on *Integrated Pollution Prevention and Control* (IPPC Directive[1]) aims at the integrated pollution prevention and control within European Member States (Schoenberger, 2009) starting from the activities listed in the annex I of the Directive (Honkasalo et al., 2005), which consider all environmental aspects (air, water, soil, waste, etc.) as a whole and unique integrated system. According to this approach, the Directive introduces a single authorization (Styles, et al., 2009) - the Integrated Environmental Authorization – the so-called "permit" to regulate the "environmental behaviour" of IPPC-related activities, to determine parameters of environmental aspects and establish measures to avoid or reduce environmental impact.

Thanks to this Directive, European Member States shall correctly manage all aspects of industrial activity likely to generate environmental impacts, under the same administrative procedure in order to be granted the above mentioned permit.

The industrial activities listed in annex I of the law include six main topics: energy production, production and processing of metals, minerals, chemical, waste management and others activities – e.g. pulp and paper, pre-treatment or dyeing of textile fibres or textiles, tanning of hides and skins, intensive pig and poultry farming, surface treatments of substances, objects or products by means of organic solvents -. The Directive is addressed mostly at large installations, and indicates production capacity thresholds that exclude the smallest installations (Samarakoon & Gudmestad, 2011).

This law lays down measures to prevent or, whereas not viable, to reduce emissions in air, water and land from the above-mentioned activities, as well as measures concerning waste, in order to achieve an overall high level of environmental protection (European Commission, 2008). The Directive thus provides an holistic approach to pollution prevention.

---

[1] In order to correct some failures in the application of the Directive, in 2008 the European Commission enacted a new IPPC Directive and many Countries are still implementing it.

The IPPC Directive introduced some important improvements in the form of Best Available Techniques (BATs hereafter), i.e. "the most effective and advanced stage in the development of activities and their methods of operation which indicate the practical suitability of particular techniques for providing in principle the basis for emission limit values designed to prevent and, where that is not practicable, generally to reduce emissions and the impact on the environment as a whole". BATs concerns technologies and organizational measures expected to minimize overall environment pressures at acceptable private costs (Bréchet & Tulkens, 2009). Techniques should be available, so as to allow implementation in relevant industrial sectors, under economically and technically viable conditions, taking into consideration costs and advantages, whether or not the techniques are used or produced within the Member State in question, as long as they are reasonably accessible to the operator. Finally, techniques should be the most effective in achieving a high general degree of environmental protection. In view of that, BAT Reference Documents (BREF), published by the European IPPC Bureau, are the basic tools to implement the requirements of the Directive (Kocabas et al., 2009).

The purpose of this chapter is to present some of the results of the European project MED IPPC NET *("Network for strengthening and improving the implementation of the IPPC Directive regarding the Integrated Pollution Prevention and Control in the Mediterranean")* whose main objective was the evaluation of the implementation of the IPPC Directive in seven European regions.

The chapter proceeds as follows. After a brief literature review about studies on IPPC topic, that will be included in paragraph 2, paragraph 3 illustrates the MED IPPC NET project. Paragraph 4 relates to the research question and the method applied to the study, while paragraphs 5 and 6 include some of the results achieved by the project. Finally, conclusions are included in paragraph 7, and reference list in paragraph 8.

2. The implementation of the IPPC directive

Many studies deal with the evaluation of the IPPC Directive implementation, and most them refer to the application of BAT in the industrial field or in a localized nation or country.

The paper by Kobacas (Kobacas et. al., 2009) illustrates the results of the work derived by the first implementation of the IPPC Directive and the BREF Document within an industrial facility in Turkey *("Adoption of EU's IPPC Directive to a Textile Mill in Turkey: BAT Applications").* In particular, the study focuses on water and energy consumption of a textile mill in Turkey, assessed further to the application of specific BAT aiming to reduce these consumptions.

In their paper Bréchet & Tulkens (Bréchet & Tulkens, 2009) stated that Best Available Techniques should be best not only in term of private aims and interests, but also according to the society's point of view. To this purpose, they present a modeling framework based on methodologies able to satisfy both these two purposes. They conclude that a fair combination of Best Available Techniques should be preferred to one single BAT. In their study they consider a lime factory.

Karavanas et. al. (Karavanas et. al., 2009) presented an integrated methodological approach for the evaluation of the implementation of Best Available Techniques in facilities operating under the IPPC. For the application of the proposed methodology, the authors take into a account the Greek paper manufacturing sector and the relevant environmental performance indicators and indices based on the reports of the European Polluting Emissions Register (EPER), and the application of environmental permits submitted by the Competent Authority for this matter. By means of these data, the authors monitored the progress of BAT implementation through the comparison of indicators and after the normalization with benchmarks from BREF or granted environmental permits. Facilities have been ranked according to their BAT implementation so to provide clear indication about their environmental performance. The methodology proposed by the authors thus provides a useful evaluation of environmental performance in the pursue of IPPC targets.

Barros et. al. (Barros et al., 2009) in their work identified BAT in the seafood industry in the northwest of Spain. In particular, they carried out an analysis about the existing technologies in the mussel canning plant as well as a list of BAT both installed or not. Then BATs have been assessed in order to promote their implementation in a mussel canning facility.

The report "*Assessment of the implementation of the IPPC Directive in the UK*" of January 2008 – commissioned by the Air and Environment Quality Division of the Department for Environment, Food and Rural Affairs (Defra) - aimed to select ten UK-based installations with IPPC permits, and to assess the degree of implementation of IPPC requirements of the Directive by each case study. The survey has focused on the investigation of the procedures applied and the conditions set for selected permits, as also on the assessment of the current installation operation when compared to permit conditions and BAT. In particular, the main objective of this study was to select and analyse some permits issued in UK in order to assess their compliance with the IPPC Directive.

A part of literature deals more specifically with the environmental performance or efficiency of IPPC industries.

About this aspect another study (Honkasalo et. al., 2005) analyses some case studies of British, Finnish and Swedish industries and the corresponding regulatory bodies, to contribute to the discussion on the potentiality of the IPPC Directive as a driver of eco-efficiency in these industries.

Styles et al. (2009) take into account the application of the Environmental Emissions Index (EEI) to reported emissions data about pharmaceutical-manufacturing installations and power stations holding IPPC in Ireland. Results on reported emissions demonstrated environmental performance improvements.

Georgopoulou et al. (Georgopoulou et al., 2008) developed – within the framework of a research project - a decision-support tool for public and private administrators and managers (called "BEAsT", BAT Economic Attractiveness Tool) in order to make possible an assessment of different BATs and their combinations in term of economic costs and environmental benefits deriving from their application. Since the development of this tool initiated by the necessity to provide an action plan for BAT promotion in a Greek region, where main environmental impacts of industrial activities derived from air pollution and liquid waste, the tool was mainly addressed to these two impacts. In practice, BEAsT was used to assess the environmental benefits to be expected from BATs, and to identify which BATs are attractive for end-users in the economic outlook.

The main purpose of the study of Silvo et. al. (Silvo et. al., 2009) was to investigate the impacts of the IPPC Directive on environmental performance of pulp and paper mills in Finland in the period 2001-2006. To do this, the authors compared the Emission Limit Values of the IPPC permits with those of other permits not linked to IPPC.

As outlined in this paragraph, many studies exist in literature on the evaluation of IPPC and the effects that they have generated in some specific activities or sectors that also take into account the different experiences occurred in various different European Member States.

Thanks to the MED IPPC NET project the study carried out represents an added value to the existent studies in literature on about the evaluation of the IPPC. We evaluated the implementation of the IPPC Directive in seven European regions analysing many of its aspects (laws that implemented the Directive, administrative procedure to issuing permits, control system in facilities envisaging permits, content of the permits and the analysis of requirements and prescriptions provided by them). The most important novelty of the study is that it allows a comparison among the regions of many European Member States.

3. The MED IPPC NET project

The MED IPPC NET (*"Network for strengthening and improving the implementation of the IPPC Directive regarding the Integrated Pollution Prevention and Control in the Mediterranean"*) is a 30 month-project co-funded by the European Commission. Its main goal is to identify some crucial aspects in the implementation of the IPPC Directive 96/61/EC of 24 September 1996 concerning Integrated Pollution Prevention and Control within the Mediterranean area. In this area there are significant differences in how European Member States have perceived the importance of the IPPC, and on what kind of supporting or coercive mechanism they have implemented to improve its practical application.

The MED IPPC NET project, by identifying these differences, aims to establish a set of common criteria that should be taken into account by all Mediterranean regions wishing to enhance their implementation. These common criteria will constitute the inputs to develop a common methodology in implementing the IPPC Directives within the Mediterranean area which will help it, in turn, to become a reference for the environmental behaviour of its industrial facilities.

To achieve this goal the seven regions participating in the project, and belonging to four European Member States – Andalusia, Spain (Andalusian Institute of Technology), Piedmont, Italy (Arpa Piemonte), Sicily, Italy (Arpa Sicilia), Slovenia, whole national territory (Scientific Research Centre Bistra Ptuj), Tuscany, Italy (Scuola Superiore Sant'Anna and Eurobic Toscana Sud), Valencia, Spain (Environment, water, town planning and housing Department of Valencian Government), West Macedonia, Greece (Environmental Centre of Kozani) -, carried out in-depth studies in each region about the implementation modalities of the IPPC Directive.

To this purpose the project provided an analytical phase (that constituted a specific task component of the project) in order to study how the seven regions involved in the project implemented the IPPC Directive.

4. Research question and method

In this framework, this chapter aims to answer to some research questions, such as: Has the Directive been implemented with the same approach in the Member States? Do permitting procedure, inspection and control system show differences among Member States?

From June 2009 to May 2010 the seven regions involved in the project collected and analysed information and data on the implementation of the IPPC Directive applying a common research methodology. The results have been later compared building an Interregional Analysis report of the project.

The methodological approach, necessary to evaluate in each region the differences existing in the implementation of the IPPC, has been defined taking into account some existing studies to identify which aspects could be more interesting for the purpose of the project.

On the basis of the final version of the methodology, some operational tools have been applied (e.g. questionnaires, guidelines, etc.) to carry out the Analysis through an homogeneous approach in each region participating to the project.

The methodological approach has included four typologies of Analysis: the Legislative Analysis, the Administrative Analysis, the Control and Inspection System Analysis and the Content of the Authorizations Analysis.

The "*Legislative Analysis*" aimed to analyzing how the IPPC Directive has been implemented in national and local legislative frameworks. In particular, each region collected information and data through the study and the consultation of laws, reports and all documents about the IPPC. Moreover, interviews with Competent Authorities for permit issue have been carried out with the aim to collect information about the typologies of Competent Authorities involved in the issuing of the Integrated Environmental Authorization, the introduction of BAT Reference Documents (BREF) in the national, regional and local contexts, and some information concerning procedures and laws that guarantee the access to information and public participation in the permitting procedure.

The "*Administrative Analysis*" aimed to acknowledge the procedure for the granting of permits in the several regions involved in the project.

Some aspects collected and studied concerned data and documents requested by the procedure on issuing permits, the contents of these documents, the descriptions of simplifications in the permitting procedure for particular categories of enterprises/sectors, the number and the nature of the institutions involved in the permitting procedure, the description of the environmental assessment carried out in the permitting procedure, etc.

The objective of the "*Control and Inspection System Analysis*" is to understand how that System has been implemented in the regions involved. To this purpose, some information has been collected about the nature and the role of Competent Authorities that carry out the inspections, the kinds of non-compliance identified by the Control Authorities, the public fares to pay, etc.

For all above mentioned analyses, each region collected information also through interviews with the Competent Authorities for the granting of permits. Thanks to these interviews it was possible to collect opinions from these Authorities so as to identify strengths and weaknesses – but also best practices - on the IPPC implementation in the Mediterranean regions involved in the project.

The "*Content of Authorizations Analysis*" has been realized by consulting and analysing a sample of permits of some IPPC sectors selected for the project by the activities listed in the annex I of the Directive:

- 1.1: Combustion installation with a rated thermal input exceeding 50 MW;
- 3.5: Installation to manufacturing ceramic products;
- 5.4: Landfills receiving more than 10 tons per day or with a total capacity exceeding 25.000 tons;
- 2.6: installations for surface treatment of metals and plastic materials;
- 6.1; Industrial plants for the production of pulp from timber or other fibrous materials and paper and board with a production capacity exceeding 20 tons per day.

The objective of the Content of Authorization Analysis was to compare the content of permits for the industrial sectors mentioned, and to highlight the differences in the environmental management prescriptions and requirements related to the several environmental aspects. This objective has been performed analyzing a representative sample of permits, as illustrated in the next paragraphs.

5. Result of the analysis phase of the MED IPPC NET project

The Analysis carried out through the MED IPPC NET project has taken into account many aspects of the implementation of the IPPC Directive in the seven regions participating to the project. In this paragraph we highlight some interesting results derived from the Interregional Analysis (the Analysis that has allowed to compare results about the IPPC implementation among the seven regions). In particular, we included some results of the four Analyses which compose the Interregional Analysis report: Legislative, Administrative, Control and Inspection System and Content of Authorizations.

5.1 Legislative analysis

As outlined in paragraph 4, the Legislative Analysis aimed to analyze how the IPPC Directive has been implemented in the legislative framework. In the following paragraph, we consider the results obtained by implementing the Directive regulatory framework in the seven regions, by the Competent Authorities for issuing the Integrated Environmental Authorization, and the modalities to assure the access to information and public participation.

5.1.1 The implementation of the IPPC Directive in the seven regions participating to the project

In the four European Member States involved in the MED IPPC NET project, the IPPC Directive has been implemented by specific national laws. In some regions also regional and local laws regarding specific aspects linked to the IPPC have been enacted.

In Spain the IPPC Directive has been implemented through the national law 16/2002 on Integrated Pollution Prevention and Control. Besides, also two royal decrees have been enacted: the first one (the decree 508/2007) concerned the regulation for the information supply on emissions on Pollutant Release and Transfer Register (PRTR), and the integrated environmental authorizations; the second one (decree 509/2007) deals with the regulation of development and execution of national law 16/2002. The regional law 7/2007 implemented the Spanish national law about IPPC in Andalusia.

The Region of Valencia also applies a regional law (2/2006), enacted by the Generalitat Valenciana, on pollution prevention and environmental quality. In particular, the objective of this law is to define and regulate the instruments of environmental administrative intervention for those activities likely to affect security, health or environment. It established an Annex II for new categories of activities that must also obtain the Integrated Environmental Authorization. Additionally, the regional decree 127/2006, from the Valencia Council, concerns rules about the development and the execution of law 2/2006.

The IPPC Directive was implemented in Italy in August 4th 1999 by the national legislative decree n° 372 that disciplined, for the first time in Italy, the issuing of the Integrated Environmental Authorization according to IPPC criteria. Consequently, the legislative decree 59/2005[2] replaced the first one. There are also other decrees in Italy that discipline

---

[2] On 29th June 2010 the decree n. 59/2005 has been repealed by the legislative decree n. 128/2010. This latter integrates the IPPC within the legislative decree n. 152/2006.

some aspects of the IPPC: the redefinition of the National Competent Authorities on the issuing of the Integrated Environmental Authorization; the technical and administrative documents to submit for the permitting procedure about the issuing of permits; the institution of a national IPPC Commission with the function to supply support to the definition, the updating and the integration of BAT national guidelines; the modalities – also accounting – and the fares to apply in connection with the preliminary inquires and controls provided by the national legislative decree n. 59/05. As regards regional laws, in Piedmont the resolution of the Regional Council (July 29, 2002) confirmed in the provinces the Competent Authorities to grant, renewal and review of IPPC permit[3].

Also in Tuscany the Regional resolution n. 61 adopted in December 22nd 2003 identified as IPPC Competent Authorities the ten Tuscan Provinces (Firenze, Prato, Pistoia, Pisa, Massa Carrara, Livorno, Siena, Arezzo, Grosseto, Lucca), and one Circondario (Circondario Empolese Valdelsa).

In respect to the ministerial decree 24/4/2008[4] on the fares to apply in connection with the preliminary inquires and controls provided by the national legislative decree, both in Piedmont and Tuscany there are more regional resolutions about this matter. They contain a general decrease of national rates, the administrative resolution on the advances of expenses for the preliminary examination on issuing the Integrated Environmental Authorization, the adaptation and the integration of fares to be applied according to the ministerial decree.

In Tuscany other regional resolutions are applied such as, for example, the n. 151 of February 23rd 2004 that sets up the Coordination Technical Committee and the decree n. 1285 of March 10th 2004 concerning the appointment of the Coordination Technical Committee members.

In Sicily a "Guideline" document to drafting, monitor and control a plan to set up IPPC tools has been prepared (reference document with the minimum information to be included into the Control and Monitoring Plan[5]), jointly with the ARTA Sicily Decree 12/08/2004 (GURS 36/04) approving the procedures for the application of the permit.

In West Macedonia the IPPC Directive has been implemented at national level by law 3010/2002 that amended the basic Environmental Greek Law (L.1650/1986) to be harmonized with the European Directives 96/61 and 97/11. Moreover, two ministerial decisions have been adopted (CMD.15393/2332/2002 and CMD 11014/703/Φ104/2003). The subject of these two decisions is the adjustment of the environmental authorization procedure of activities included in the Annex I of the Directive. Besides, these activities are being categorized in relation of their impact on the environment.

Finally, Slovenia has implemented the IPPC Directive with two acts: the Environmental Protection Act (ZVO-1; Official Gazette of the RS, no. 41/04), and the decree on activities and installations causing large-scale environmental pollution (IPPC Decree, Official Gazette of the RS, no. 97/04). We shall also consider the following regulations: the two Decrees amending the Decree on activities and installations causing large-scale environmental pollution (Official Gazette of the RS, n. 71/07 and n. 122/07), and two additional regulations on reporting to the European Pollutant Release and Transfer Register (PRTR).

---

[3] Once the operator of the installation presented an application to obtain the permit the Competent Authority issues the permit.

[4] Since the national decree n. 59/05 has been repelled by the legislative decree n. 128/2010, also the decree 24/4/2008 will be repelled in next months with a new one.

[5] This document should be filled in by the operator of the installation and should be presented jointly with the application to obtain the permit.

The table below indicates the kind of legislation that implemented the IPPC Directive in each of the participant regions.

IMPLEMENTATION OF THE IPPC DIRECTIVE IN THE SEVEN REGIONS								
State	Spain		Slovenia	Greece	Italy			
Region	Andalucía	Valencia	Slovenia	West Macedonia	Piedmont	Sicily	Tuscany	**Total**
National laws and/or other national regulations/acts	X	X	X	X	X	X	X	7
Regional law and/or other local laws	X	X	-	-	X	X	X	5

Table 1. Implementation of the IPPC Directive in the seven regions.

5.1.2 Competent authorities in the granting of the integrated environmental authorization

Another main aspect analysed is the type of Competent Authorities in charge of issuing the Integrated Environmental Authorization. In particular, the Analysis revealed that in some of the seven regions involved in the project these Authorities are provincial or regional, while in others they are ministerial or national ones.

In the case of the Region of Andalusia, the Competent Authorities are Provincial Delegations of the Department of Environment (Provincial Delegations are in Seville, Huelva, Cádiz, Córdoba, Málaga, Granada, Jaén y Almería). The territorial jurisdiction is determined by the location of the plant. When the plant serves more than one province, the competent Directorate General for Environmental Prevention and Control within the Department of Environment, will instruct and follow through with the proceedings, except when it delegates such competencies to one of the Provincial Delegations.

In Tuscany and Piedmont the regional governments have delegated to provinces the competence for permit issue. The ten Tuscan Provinces are: Firenze, Prato, Pistoia, Pisa, Massa Carrara, Livorno, Siena, Arezzo, Grosseto and Lucca, besides the Circondario Empolese Valdelsa has also been appointed as Competent Authority. In Piedmont the eight provinces are: Alessandria, Asti, Biella, Cuneo, Novara, Torino, Verbano-Cusio-Ossola, Vercelli. For both regions (and also in Sicily), the Ministry of Environment is the Competent Authority in the place of provinces (or instead of the Region in the case of Sicily) when provided by the national law that implemented the IPPC Directive. In fact, in Sicily the whole process of permit release is under the responsibility of the Service II SEA-IEA (Regional Department of Territory and Environment). The Italian Regional Agencies for the Environmental Protection (ARPA) are involved in permit process, particularly in respect to the evaluation of the control and monitoring plan (PMC), included in every Integrated Environmental Authorization's application.

In Valencia, the Competent Authorities in charge of permit processing depend upon the type of activities performed. For those activities included in the Annex I of the regional law[6] (Annex I of the IPPC Directive) the CA is the Environment, Water, Town Planning and Housing Department of the Valencian Government (Conselleria de Medio Ambiente, Agua,

---

[6] Regional law n. 2/2006

Urbanismo y Vivienda de la Generalitat Valenciana), through its General Office of Climate Change (Dirección General para el Cambio Climático). For those activities included in the Annex II of the same regional law, the Competent Authorities are the provincial Offices (Direcciones Territoriales for the 3 provinces: Alicante, Castellón, Valencia) of Environment, Water, Town Planning and Housing Department of the Valencian Government. The activities included in this latter Annex II are similar to those included in the Annex I of the law, but with lower production capacity.

In the case of West Macedonia the law establishes that the Competent Authorities are the Ministry of Environment Energy and Climate Change and the Direction of Environment and Development, Department of Environment and Land-Planning of the Region of West Macedonia (Prefectures of Kozani, Kastoria, Grevena and Florina). In reality, the permits examined within the scope of the project have all been issued by the Ministry because the region did not authorise any IPPC plant at the time of the analysis. The jurisdiction between Ministry and Region is determined by the production ability of the installation[7].

In Slovenia the Competent Authorities are national: the Ministry of Environment and Spatial Planning, and the Environmental Agency of the Republic of Slovenia (ARSO). ARSO performs professional, analytical, regulatory and administrative tasks in the field of environment nationally, it contributes to solving environmental problems as far as possible with the implementation of environmental legislation and keeps records of emissions, manages and monitors the implementation of remedial programs and seeks comprehensive solutions to the problems regarding climate change. Particularly, ARSO pays attention to raising public awareness on the environment and on environmental issues. Likewise, Slovenia set up a nation-wide special expert group established under the IPPC Directive, consisting of acting inspectors depending on the technological processes. The Environmental Agency of the Republic of Slovenia (ARSO) cooperates with the Inspectorate of the Republic of Slovenia for Environment and Spatial Planning (IRSOP) in the field of control of administrative decisions, since the IRSOP is responsible to supervise all environmental legislation adopted by the Parliament, the Government or the Ministry.

We summarized in the following table the Competent Authorities for the Integrated Environmental Authorizations:

COMPETENT AUTHORITY/IES FOR THE PERMITTING PROCEDURE OF THE INTEGRATED ENVIRONMENTAL AUTHORIZATION								
State	Spain		Slovenia	Greece	Italy			
Region	Andalucía	Valencia	Slovenia	West Macedonia	Piedmont	Sicily	Tuscany	Total
National Competent Authority			X	X	X	X	X	5
Regional Competent Authority		X		X		X		3
Provincial Competent Authority	X	X			X		X	4

Table 2. Competent Authority/ies for the permitting procedure of the Integrated Environmental Authorization.

---

[7] CMD 15393/2332/2002 and CMD11014/703/Φ104/2003.

5.1.3 The modalities to assure access to information and public participation in the permitting procedure for issuing the Integrated Environmental Authorization

The primary method to ensure access to information and public participation in the permitting procedure in all regions is represented by the publication of some information (e.g. in newspapers, bulletins, etc.).

In Italy, according to the national decree that implemented the IPPC Directive, the Competent Authority identifies the offices where to record the proceedings for public consultation. Moreover, it provides that the operator publishes an advertisement for the public in a provincial, regional or national newspaper. Anyone can have access to a copy of the issued IPPC permits, and to any relating document in a public office, as determined by the Competent Authorities. The Competent Authority shall make available to the public the data provided by the operator relating to emission controls required by integrated environmental authorization. The results of the monitoring of emissions, required by permit conditions and held by the Competent Authority, should be available to the public. The legislative decree n. 195 adopted on 19th August 2005 – implementing the European Directive 2003/4/CE - disciplines public access to environmental information. On the one hand, this decree establishes terms, fundamental conditions and modalities to exert public access; on the other hand, it guarantees that the environmental information is at public disposal and it is disseminated accordingly. Moreover, when the Competent Authority informs a business company about the beginning date of the procedure, the operator should publish an announcement containing information on the plant at provincial, regional or national media outlets.

In Valencia the Competent Authority submits the permit application along with the required documentation for public information procedure, within a minimum period of 30 days, by publishing it in the Official Diary of the Valencian Government, as well as in the relevant City Hall bulletin board. Its public dissemination (notification to neighbours, record of submitted documentation in CA offices) is therefore allowed, except for that data considered to be confidential. At the end of the procedure it also publishes the resolution of the permit, to which it is possible to make objections within a period of 30 days. In compliance with the principle of access to information relating to the environment, citizens can consult the emissions of specific pollutants of IPPC installations in the PRTR, and the content of the permit issued.

In Andalusia the procedure of information and public participation for the Integrated Environmental Authorization falls at national level under the jurisdiction of the Autonomous Communities establishing only a minimum period of public information (30 days) - as in the case of Valencia -. Once the competent body verifies the project compatibility to the environmental regulations, it renders the Integrated Environmental Authorization available for public consultation and formulation of the relevant declarations, by including its advertisement in the Official Bulletin of the Government of Andalusia (Oficial de la Junta de Andalucía) (for 45 days), and through personal notification to the immediate neighbourhoods of the place where the activity is located (for 30 days). Following these terms, the competent body will remit all annexes and comments received to the requesting entity in charge of the Integrated Environmental Authorization, to the State body responsible for granting public permits in the field of maritime-terrestrial competences, and to the regional body responsible for granting the substantive permit, that can be declared within 15 days.

In West Macedonia the competent Service of Environment of the Ministry of Environment Energy and Climate Change or the Region that has been granted the study, prior to approving the environmental procedure, conveys a copy to the Prefectural Council within a ten days period. Subsequently, the Prefectural Council has five days to publish the study in at least one local newspaper, and to disseminate it publicly (within 30 days) for information, to allow the public opinion to share objections on its content.

In Slovenia the national legislation guarantees the access to information and public participation in the permitting procedure through many tools, as for example: an IPPC website, by organizing training cycles, seminars, workshops for operators of installations, specialized publications, public debates and round tables, public presentations to explaining the procedures for issuing the permit (application form, etc.).

The table below includes the main modalities adopted by each participating region to assure the access to information and public participation in the permitting procedure.

MAIN MODALITIES ADOPTED TO ASSURE THE ACCESS TO INFORMATION AND PUBLIC PARTICIPATION IN THE PERMITTING PROCEDURE								
State	Spain		Slovenia	Greece	Italy			
Region	Andalucía	Valencia	Slovenia	West Macedonia	Piedmont	Sicily	Tuscany	Total
Record of document in specific offices		X			X	X	X	4
Advertisement publication in newspaper/ other publication about IPPC matter				X	X	X	X	4
Publication of permit and other documents in the Official Diary of Government and/or in City/Government bulletin	X	X						2
Publication of emissions of specific pollutants of IPPC installations in the Pollutant Release and Transfer Register		X						1
Personal notification to neighbors	X	X						2
Publication of statement in the Table of Statements of the Prefecture				X				1
IPPC portal on website		X	X					2
Training/ seminars/workshops for operators of installations and Public debates and round tables		X	X					2

Table 3. Main modalities adopted by regions to assure the access to information and public participation in the permitting procedure.

5.2 Administrative analysis

The *"Administrative Analysis"* focuses essentially on the procedure for granting the permit in the seven regions of the project. As previously assessed for the legislative analysis, also in this case we identify some of the resulting elements, such as the nature of the institutions involved in the first issuing for new and existing installations, the content of documents to be submitted within the Integrated Environmental Authorizations, the time envisaged for the issuing of the Integrated Environmental Authorization, and the simplified rules and regulations within the permitting procedure for particular categories of enterprises.

5.2.1 Institutions involved in the first issue for new and existing installations

The institutions involved in the permitting procedure for the permit issuing are more similar among the seven regions, in regards to content and object of the documents. However, in most of them are some institutions always participate in the permitting procedure, while some are present only in some cases.

In Tuscany and in Piedmont, for example, the institutions involved in the permitting procedure are: the Municipality, the Local Health Authority and the Environmental Protection Regional Agency, while the Regional Administration, the waters managers, the Basin Authority[8] and the fire department are sometimes present. In both regions the waste and sewage system competent authorities, the ATO[9], the Basin Authority and, in the case of permit that should be issued for landfills, the superintendent can also be part of the process. In the case of Piedmont, public stakeholders can be part of it. In Tuscany the opinions of the above-mentioned institutions are generally not binding, but in the permitting procedure these latter tend to comply to them. In Piedmont the opinions of the municipality and the province are always binding, those of the regional administration is binding only for some sectors, while the opinions of the other institutions are not binding.

In Sicily the opinion of the municipality, province, regional administration, local health authority, of the Provincial Committee for Environmental Protection (CPTA) and of the Ministry of Environment and Protection of territory (or in case of national Integrated Environmental Authorization process, the Ministry of Environment) are binding. On the contrary, for the following involved institutions the opinion is not binding: Regional Agencies for Environmental Protection, Regional Agencies for waste and water, the waste management ATO, Departments responsible for water, air, etc. In Andalusia the institutions participating in the permitting procedure are: the Municipality, the Regional Department of Environment, the State Environmental Body, the Water Basin Entity. Their opinions are binding. In Valencia the Environment, Water, Town Planning and Housing Department of the Valencia Government (EWTPH) has set up the Integrated Environmental Analysis Commission, a body whose representatives are one from each administration/institution involved in the permitting procedure. The institutions and organisations that are always involved in this Commission are: the IPPC Service of EWTPH, the Waste Service of EWTPH, the Environmental impact Service of EWTPH, the Air Service of EWTPH, the Water Service of EWTPH, the Basin authority, the Clean Technologies Centre of EWTPH. This

---

[8] The Basin Authority is an institution aiming to safeguard the whole catchment basins. It was established by the national law n. 183/1999.
[9] The ATO is an institution of control and guidance, competent for the management of the water service, sewerage and waste. It was established by the national law n. 36/1994.

Commission is similar to the Italian one (called "Meeting of Public Services") in its composition and activities. As in the case of Tuscany and Valencia also for West Macedonia there are some institutions that are always involved in the permitting procedure, and others that are present from time to time. The Special Service of Environment of the Ministry of Environment Energy and Climate Change, the Direction of Planning of the Ministry of Environment Energy and Climate Change, the Department of Environment of the Ministry of Environment Energy and Climate Change and the Region, the Prefectural Department of Environment, the Prefect and the Council for Public Information, belong to the first category. The Relative to the Investment Ministries, the Regional Department of Forests, the Regional Department of Waters, the Revenue of Antiquities, the Prefectural Departments of Agriculture and of Health belong to the second one. The opinions of all institutions are binding but not defined by law, the Competent Authority has the final decision but in almost all the cases it takes into account the remarks of the authorities involved.

In Slovenia there is a sole institution involved in the permitting procedure is the Ministry of Environment and Spatial Planning, Environmental Agency of the Republic of Slovenia. Its opinion is binding.

The table 4 indicates the institutions involved in the first issue of the permit for new and existing installations, in the seven regions of the project.

MAIN INSTITUTIONS INVOLVED IN THE PERMITTING PROCEDURE								
State	Spain		Slovenia	Greece	Italy			Total
Region	Andalucía	Valencia	Slovenia	West Macedonia	Piedmont	Sicily	Tuscany	
National institution	X		X	X	X*	X*	X*	6
Regional institution		X		X	X	X	X	5
Local institution	X	X			X	X	X	5
Specific public institution (e.g. basin authority)	X	X		X	X	X	X	6
Other technical public departments (e.g. fireman)	X	X		X	X		X	5
Public health and safety authority		X			X	X	X	4
Bearers of collective interests		X			X			2

* In Italian regions the national institution is involved when Ministry is the Competent Authority for the permit issue.

Table 4. Main institutions involved in the permitting procedure

5.2.2 Time forecast to issuing the Integrated Environmental Authorization

In Italy the time frame to issuing the permitting procedure for new and existing installations is established by the legislative decree 152/2006. In particular, within 30 days from the application for permit receipt, the Competent Authority communicates to the operator the starting date of the proceeding. Within 15 days from the receipt of communication, the operator publishes an announcement on the plant features. Further, within 30 days from the publication of the announcement, the interested parties can present observations. Subsequently, if there is compliance with the requirements of the decree 152/2006, the Competent Authorities may issue the permit within 150 days from the application; or in the case of no-compliance they deny the permit. However, in case of particular/relevant environmental impacts and of the complexity and/or national interest of a plant, specific agreements can be concluded. In this case, the 150 days timeframe is replaced with a 300 days timeframe. In Andalusia the deadline for granting the permit is of 10 months from the submission of the application. After this period without receiving the notification of any special resolution, the application can be rejected. In this case, the proceedings under the Integrated Environmental Authorization shall not become the subject neither of Municipal License, nor of substantive authorizations. In Valencia the permitting procedure begins with a public information phase, followed by a sector-based report to the concerned competent administrations and institutions requested by the Competent Authority that calls the IPPC operator for an audience. Closer to the end of the procedure, the Competent Authority carries out an environmental assessment of the IPPC activity which will take into account all factors involved in it, therefore completing the process by issuing a resolution containing all the constraints that the activity must comply for their exploitation. The resolution is then notified to the operator and published in the Official Diary of the Government of Valencia. As it happens in Andalusia, also in Valencia the maximum period for completing the permitting procedure is 10 months. This deadline is valid for the activities included in the Annex I of the regional law. For those activities included in the Annex II of the regional law, the deadline is 8 months. In Slovenia once a company has presented all the required documents, the Environmental Agency of the Republic of Slovenia may require further clarification. The presentation of them allows the Environmental Agency to prepare of a consensus and the public presentation of application, leading to the issuing of the permit. For the issuing of new permits, the deadline is set in 7 months, while for the existing installations the term of the permitting procedure is not determined. However, in the case of West Macedonia, once the Competent Authority judges that the documents presented are complete, it transmits them to the relevant consultative authorities within 10 days that can request additional data and clarifications of the investor in the following 15 days. Within 5 days from the interval of 15 days, the Competent Authority approves or denies the Pro-EIA. In West Macedonia first of all is realised an initially study called Pro-EIA where interested submits application to the responsible authority that is accompanied by file which contains 6 copies of the study with technical and administrative information. The approval and the Pro-EIA documents are transmitted to the Prefectural Council for public information, and within 30 days it is possible to formulate opinions and objections regarding the project. In order to receive the Environmental authorization, the investor submits a documented application accompanied by the 6 copies of EIA, including the approval of Pro-EIA. In case the competent authority judges the documents incomplete, it can ask for additional supporting information within 10 days, otherwise it transmits it within 10 days to the competent consultative authorities, jointly with the prefectural observations. These latter should provide a final recommendation within 35 days, following this period of time, the Competent Authority has 15 days to approve or deny the EIA. Finally, the EIA approval is transmitted to the Prefectural Council for public information. If the entire documentation is complete the authorisation is granted within a maximum period of 90 days. This interval can be extended for another 90 days for peculiar cases. The table below indicates times for Integrated Environmental Authorization issuing.

TIMES FOR THE FIRST ISSUING FOR INTEGRATED ENVIRONMENTAL AUTHORIZATION NEW AND EXISTING INSTALLATIONS								
State	Spain		Slovenia	Greece	Italy			Total
Region	Andalucía	Valencia	Slovenia	West Macedonia	Piedmont	Sicily	Tuscany	
From 5 to 10 months				X	X	X	X	4
7 months			X**					1
8 months		X*						1
10 months	X	X*						2

* Times depend by activity typology
** for new installations

Table 5. Times for the first Integrated Environmental Authorization issuing for new and existing installations

5.2.3 The simplifications in the permitting procedure for particular categories of enterprises

In most regions (Andalusia, Valencia, Tuscany, Piedmont and Sicily), laws provide simplified permit procedures for particular categories of enterprises.

In Spain the royal decree 509/2007 provided a simplified procedure to apply for an IPPC Permit for Farming Installations, as referred to in category 9.3 of the Law 16/2002 (paragraph 6.6 of the Directive 96/61/EC) for the documentation[10] to be included in the basic project that accompanies the request of Integrated Environmental Authorization. Additionally, this decree grants Autonomous Regions the permission to establish measures simplifying the mechanisms used to verify the fulfilment of the conditions envisaged by the IPPC permit for those facilities that apply an Environmental Management System (as per the requirements established by International Standard UNE-EN ISO 14001 - International Organization for Standardization- and/or Regulation EMAS- Eco-Management and Audit Scheme -).

In Valencia the regional decree 127/2006 establishes that for the renewal of the Integrated Environmental Authorization, jointly to the application the owner shall submit a certificate stating the environmental assessment adequacy of the facility to the existing environmental legislation. This adequacy will be certified by an Environmental Quality Collaborating Entity. Given that the EMAS register requires a yearly assessment/audit of compliance with the environmental legislation, if an IPPC company adhered to EMAS it is not necessary to submit the certificate for the renewal of the application. By consequence, the facility or activity will be in accordance to the current environmental constraints/legislation.

---

[10] Annex II of the Royal Decree 509/2007.

In Piedmont, in Sicily and in Tuscany some of the provided simplifications are laid out by the legislative decree n. 59/05:

- If at the moment of issuing the permit a plant is registered according to the CE Regulation n. 1221/2009 (EMAS), the renewal of the Integrated Environmental Authorization is filled in every eight years (usually, it is a five years renewal). If the registration according to the CE Regulation n. 1221/2009 (EMAS) comply to the authorization, the renewal is carried out every eight years starting from the first following renewal.
- If at the moment of issuing the permit a plant is certified according to the Regulation UNI EN ISO 14001, the renewal of the Integrated Environmental Authorization is filled in every six years. If the certification according to the Regulation UNI EN ISO 14001 comply to the authorization, the renewal is carried out every six years starting from the first following renewal.

MAIN SIMPLIFICATIONS IN THE PERMITTING PROCEDURE FOR PARTICULAR CATEGORIES OF ENTERPRISES								
State	Spain		Slovenia	Greece	Italy			
Region	Andalucía	Valencia	Slovenia	West Macedonia	Piedmont	Sicily	Tuscany	Total
Any simplification			X	X				2
Simplification of documents to submit in order to obtain permit for farming installations	X	X						2
Simplification about documents to submit for installations registered EMAS		X						1
Simplification in inspection control activities in facilities registered EMAS or certified ISO 14001	X	X						2
Longer validity of permit enterprises registered EMAS or certified ISO 14001					X	X	X	3
Reduction of fares for enterprises registered EMAS or certified ISO 14001					X	X	X	3

Table 6. Main simplifications in the permitting procedure for particular categories of enterprises.

According to article 5 of the decree n. 59/05, if the information and the descriptions provided comply to the Regulation UNI EN ISO 14001, or the data provided for the registered sites comply to the Regulation CE n. 1221/2009 (EMAS), and if any other information is in compliance with the overall rules, particularly with one or more of the requirements set in the Integrated Environmental Authorization application, these can be applied for the registration of the Integrated Environmental Authorization application.

The Italian ministerial decree adopted in April 24th 2008 (decree about fares) provided other simplifications: one reads that the installations registered according to the CE Regulation n. 1221/2009 (EMAS), can be granted reduced fares between 1.000 up to 8.000 euro; whilst another provides that for the installations certified according to the Regulation UNI EN ISO 14001, the reduction is granted between 500 and 5.000 euro.

Slovenia and West Macedonia do not provide for simplifications in the permitting procedure for particular categories of enterprises.

The Table 6 summarizes main simplifications in the permitting procedure for particular categories of enterprises.

5.3 Control and inspection system analysis

The primary scope of this Analysis is to assess the system of Control and Inspection carried out in those facilities applying an Integrated Environmental Authorization. In the following paragraphs some of the elements resulting from this analysis are outlined.

5.3.1 The Competent Authorities appointed for the inspections and control procedures in the regions

The Competent Authorities for inspections and controls are regional for the most regions, while are national in few cases.

In Andalusia the General Direction of Environmental Prevention and Quality of the Regional Government for Environment of Andalusia, is competent for drafting various Sector Plans on Environmental Inspections. In Valencia the Competent Authorities for control and inspection are: the IPPC Service - belonging to the Environment, Water, Town Planning and Housing Department of the Government of Valencia -, and the Environmental Quality Collaborating Entities (EQCE) duly authorized and recognized in the IPPC industry. Their technical competences are certified by the Spanish Accreditation Entity, and they are registered in the Valencia Register of EQCE (managed by the Clean Technologies Centre). There are 10 accredited EQCE in Valencia. In most of the installations, the inspections are being carried out by the EQCE. In Italy the legislative decree n. 59/05 states that the Agency for Environmental Protection and Technical Services (ISPRA), for facilities under State jurisdiction, or the regional and provincial environmental protection agencies, are the Competent Authorities for controls and inspections. In Italy for example there is a regional agency in each region (Environmental Protection Regional Agency), but in each province there is also a local department having a supervisory role. In this way the provincial departments guarantees the knowledge of the local reality although there is a risk to overlapping or of differing approaches. In Sicily, in the case of landfills, the Competent Authority for the release of permits (Service II SEA-IEA, Regional Department of Territory and Environment), let the agency ARPA make a testing visit coordinated with the Provinces, to value the compliance to the permit requirements. In West Macedonia and Slovenia the situation is different from the previous regions. In the former region there are several Authorities involved in controls, in the latter one the Control Authority is national. Specifically, in West Macedonia the Competent Authorities responsible for the inspection procedure can be divided into those who inspect the enterprises during the permitting procedure, and those tasked of the ongoing renewal of permits. In Slovenia the inspections are carried out by the inspection service under the control program adopted for three years. The table-summary indicates the main Competent Authorities for the control and inspection procedure.

MAIN COMPETENT AUTHORITIES DESIGNATED FOR THE CONTROL AND INSPECTION PROCEDURE								
State	Spain		Slovenia	Greece	Italy			Total
Region	Andalucía	Valencia	Slovenia	West Macedonia	Piedmont	Sicily	Tuscany	
National Competent Authorities	X		X	X				3
Regional Competent Authorities	X	X	-	X	X	X	X	6

Table 7. Main Competent Authorities designated for the control and inspection procedure.

5.3.2 Most frequently non-compliances identified

The most non-compliances identified during the inspections in the seven regions are indicated below:

THE MOST FREQUENTLY NON-COMPLIANCES IDENTIFIED								
State	Spain		Slovenia	Greece	Italy			Total
Region	Andalucía	Valencia	Slovenia	West Macedonia	Piedmont	Sicily	Tuscany	
Non compliance ELVs				X	X		X	3
Non regular data transmission	X			X	X		X	4
Non compliance with requirements contained in permit	X	X	X	X	X	X		6
Dissimilarity from the management of measuring instruments (incorrect positioning, operation, calibration, maintenance of instruments)		X		X		X	X	4

Table 8. The most frequently non-compliances identified

In most of the regions, the main non-compliance characteristics that have emerged when monitoring deal with the requirements contained in the permit, while the non conformity with Emission Limit Values has been indicated by a lower number of regions.

5.4 Content of authorization analysis

The Content of authorizations analysis was made possible by the study of a sample of IPPC Integrated Environmental Authorizations of four IPPC sectors, according to the activities listed in the annex I of the IPPC Directive:

- 1.1: Combustion installation with a rated thermal input exceeding 50 MW;
- 3.5: Installation for the manufacture of ceramic products;
- 5.4: Landfills receiving more than 10 tonnes per day or with a total capacity exceeding 25.000 tonnes;
- 2.6: Installations for surface treatment of metals and plastic materials;
- 6.1: Industrial plants for the production of pulp from timber or other fibrous materials and paper and board with a production capacity exceeding 20 tonnes per day.

The aim of the Content of Authorization analysis was the comparison of Integrated Environmental Authorizations within the industrial sectors of the seven regions involved in the project, to highlight differences as to the management of environmental prescriptions and requirements. The sample of Integrated Environmental Authorizations analysed for the MED IPPC NET project, with the indication of the number of permits analysed by each region for each IPPC sector, is indicated in the following table:

Region	Number of IPPC permits analyzed					
	Combustion plants (1.1)	Ceramics (3.5)	Landfills (5.4)	Surface treatment of metals and plastic materials (2.6)	Paper production (6.1)	TOTAL
Andalusia	8	8	8	8	0	32
Valencia	4	8	7	8	0	27
Slovenia	7	8	1	8	0	24
West Macedonia	2	2	3	1	0	8
Piedmont	19	24	21	0	15	79
Sicily	1	0	6	1	0	8
Tuscany	5	13	16	0	13	47
TOTAL	46	63	62	26	28	225

Table 9. Sample of Integrated Environmental Authorizations analysed in the "Content of Authorizations Analysis".

Every partner has collected a high number of Integrated Environmental Authorizations. In any case it is important to highlight the work carried out by Piedmont, which collected 79 permits, i.e. about 80% of the total permits issued in its region in the four sectors covered by the project.

About 60% of the sample is represented by permits from Italy, followed by the Spanish regions with about 27% of analysed permits.

As to targets, the methodology envisages three fixed sectors: "combustion plants", "ceramics", "landfills". All partners had to analyze these three sectors. For the fourth sector each partner was allowed to choose between "Surface treatment of metals and plastic materials" or "Paper production". The partners from Tuscany and Piedmont chose the "paper production" sector due to its relevance in the two regions, while the other partners selected the sector "Surface treatment of metals and plastic materials".

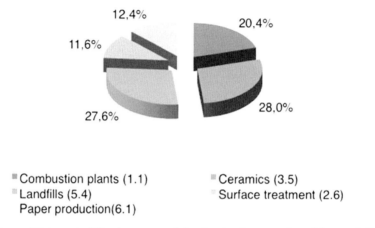

Fig. 1. Percentage of Integrated Environmental Authorizations analysed for each IPPC sector of the project.

Ceramics and landfills are the IPPC sectors most represented in the Analysis. The highest number of Authorisations for these two sectors was collected in Tuscany and Piedmont. The three fixed sectors (combustion plants, ceramics, landfills) are fully represented by permits of each region, which means that at least one permit was collected in each region involved in the project.

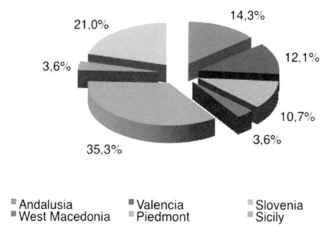

Fig. 2. Percentage of Integrated Environmental Authorizations analysed by regions.

5.4.1 The requirements and conditions indicated in the permits to protect from contamination of soil and groundwater

The permits require the highest possible frequency of controls and prescribe the protection of contamination of soil and groundwater, by means of measures for the storage of chemicals. In many cases the permits require a containment basin for the storage or prescribe a spillage kit.

Being an expensive activity, the requirement about monitoring the quality of groundwater is particularly significant, and as can be expected it is imposed most of all to landfills.

Requirements about protection of contamination of soil and groundwater							
State	Spain		Slovenia	Greece	Italy		
Region	Andalusia	Valencia	Slovenia	West Macedonia	Piedmont	Sicily	Tuscany
Preliminary Report on the soil	43,8%	0,0%	58,3%	0,0%	0,0%	0,0%	0,0%
Storage of chemical products	37,5%	92,6%	100,0%	100,0%	54,4%	12,5%	19,1%
Spill walls	15,6%	3,7%	0,0%	100,0%	0,0%	0,0%	0,0%
Draining and collection system	15,6%	0,0%	100,0%	100,0%	54,4%	12,5%	8,5%
Proofs of leakage detection and watertight	12,5%	3,7%	100,0%	0,0%	5,1%	0,0%	0,0%
Communication/information of some aspects	0,0%	14,8%	100,0%	0,0%	0,0%	0,0%	6,4%
Control/analysis/monitoring of groundwater	3,1%	18,5%	0,0%	100,0%	25,3%	62,5%	14,9%
Monitoring of ground-water level	3,1%	0,0%	0,0%	100,0%	25,3%	0,0%	10,6%

Table 10. Requirements indicated in the permits about protection of contamination of soil and groundwater (disaggregate data for regions).

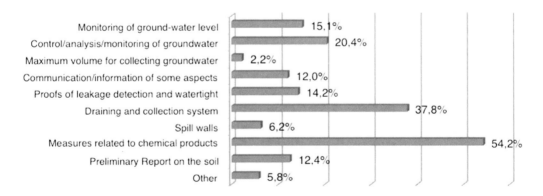

Fig. 3. Requirements and conditions to protect from contamination of soil and groundwater (aggregate data for regions).

Another relevant requirement is related to the draining and collection system contained in 37,8% of permits.

In the table 10 the same requirements are classified according to an interregional perspective.

The measures related to the monitoring of groundwater are mostly contained in the permits of Piedmont and West Macedonia. The need to submit a preliminary report on the soil is only required in Andalusia and Slovenia. The "measures related to the storage of chemical products" is the only requirement identified in at least 1 permit of each region. The other requirements show at least one region without frequency.

5.4.2 The emission limit values related to water emissions

The table below indicates the Emission Limit Values in the four IPPC sectors analyzed (Ceramics -3.5-, Landfills -5.4-, Surface treatment of metals and plastic materials -2.6-, Paper production -6.1-) for which the destinations of industrial water emissions are the same (surface water and sewer), to compare limits among the seven regions of the project.

Emission Limit Values related to industrial water emissions for Ceramics (3.5), Landfills (5.4), Surface treatment of metals and plastic materials (2.6), Paper production (6.1) (with data of number of permits)						
Destination	Surface water			Sewer		
Pollutants (mg/l)	COD	TSS	Sulphates	COD	TSS	Sulphates
Andalusia	n.a. (not available)	n.a.	n.a.	160 (2) 1550 (2)	30 (2) 35 (1) 42,5 (1) 800 (2)	400 (1) 800 (3)
Valencia	125 (2)	60 (2)	250 (1) 400 (1)	1000 (1)	500 (2)	n.a.
Slovenia	100 (3) 120 (2) 150 (2) 500 (1) 268 (1)	80 (9)	3000 (3) 1900 (1) 1187 (1)	n.a.	80 (2) 100 (1) 400 (1) 300 (1) 350 (1)	600 (2) 900 (1) 500 (1)
West Macedonia	125 (3)	25 (3)	250 (3)	n.a.	n.a.	n.a.
Piedmont	160 (20)	80 (20)	1000 (20)	500 (7) 700 (1)	200 (7) 700 (1)	1000 (8)
Sicily	160 (6)	80 (6)	1000 (6)	500 (6)	200 (6)	1000 (6)
Tuscany	160 (14)	80 (14)	1000 (14)	500 (7) 3000 (1)	200 (8)	1000 (8)

Table 11. Emission limit values related to industrial water emissions for all sectors

As for emissions flowing in surface water, Slovenia presents a high variability in the limits imposed for COD. West Macedonia and Valencia have the same limit, lower than the limit required by the permits of the Italian Regions. For TSS the permits show one limit applied in each region. Slovenia and the Italian regions have the highest one (80 mg/l), while West Macedonia applies the strictest one. The permits of West Macedonia confirm the lowest level also for the Sulphates with a value of 250 mg/l applied in three permits. The permits of companies from Slovenia include the highest limits for the same parameter achieving until a limit of 3000 mg/l imposed in three Authorisations. For the water emissions in sewer the limits change very much in the same region and among regions. One of the reasons could be the presence of a purification plant at the end of the industrial sewer. Often, the company responsible for the management of the purification plant can set the limits to be applied to companies that are connected to the sewerage. These limits are often decided by taking into account the characteristics of the purification plant and the number of connected companies. Thus each Management Body of purification plant could apply different limits.

6. Strengths and weaknesses identified in the analysis

The Analysis carried out within the project, enhanced some strengths and some weaknesses of the IPPC matter, most of which reflecting the opinions of the Competent Authorities that issue the permits. One of the strengths of the Legislative Analysis, identified in Andalusia and Piedmont, is represented by the introduction - through national laws that implemented the IPPC Directive - of a single environmental permit which brings together all environmental-related permits. According to the Competent Authorities, in Piedmont the IPPC implementation has been a significant phase of reorganization and the introduction of the company's monitoring and control plan is very important. In Tuscany a strength highlighted by the Legislative Analysis is that the environment is perceived as global and unique system that makes an integrated vision on enterprises activities possible. Another strength identified in Tuscany is that the IPPC Directive makes enterprises more motivated to achieve better work and activity levels also taking into account the environment preservation. The coordination among the Competent Authorities for issuing the permits is considered by West Macedonia, Sicily and Andalusia as a strength of the Legislative aspect of the IPPC Directive.

As regards weaknesses, the Tuscan partners identified the considerable difference between the IPPC Directive principles and the real environment of enterprises applying for IPPC permit. So often the law adaptation to the firms and to the different situations is very difficult. Moreover, according to the Tuscan partners, the enforcement of the Directive does not take into account the complexity and the large number of environmental aspects to manage. One strength emerging in Piedmont from the Administrative Analysis is that the IPPC Directive enables companies to focus on the planning of future activities of environmental improvement. Tuscany identified as a strength the new and different conception of environmental authorizations that the Directive caused to companies and public administration. In West Macedonia and Sicily, the existence of one single authority responsible for administrative issues is considered a strength.

Finally, simplifications in the authorization procedure for livestock categories and companies with environmental management systems are considered a positive factor in the Valencia region. As regards weaknesses linked to the administrative permit procedure, all regions see a problem in some delays in permit issue caused by several reasons. Delays are due to late application of regulations (Slovenia); to failure to meet deadlines of the Integrated Environmental Authorizations granting (West Macedonia and Andalusia); to the increased workload due to the need for the permit itself (Piedmont); to the absence of a deadline agenda for permit issuing (Tuscany); to the lack of human resources in the

Competent Authority organization, to the poor quality of the IPPC activity projects submitted by the operators; to the administrations and institutions that sometimes fail to meet deadlines in elaborating their reports (Valencia), and to the lack of authorities involved in the conference cycle (Sicily). Linked to the above aspect, the lack of preparation of the personnel of Competent Authorities, is a drawback for West Macedonia and Tuscany. There are no training activities and insufficient personnel in the Competent Authorities. Another weakness indicated by West Macedonia is the lack of exceptions or simplifications for enterprises certified according to EMAS or ISO 14001:04.

Some strengths and weaknesses have been identified for the Control and Inspection System Analysis as well. One positive aspect identified both by Andalusia and West Macedonia is the existence of clear and detailed definitions in the guidelines for operational and monitoring control and the measurement of environmental aspects in the Control and Monitoring Plans of the Integrated Environmental Authorization. Moreover, some aspects linked to the Competent Authorities in charge of controls and inspections are considered as strengths by some regions. Valencia indicates as a positive element the technical competence and the independence of the Environmental Quality Collaborating Entities, one of the Control Competent Authorities in Valencia, while Andalusia identifies as a positive aspect the appointment of a specific service to carry out the monitoring and inspection activities defined in the Environmental Control and Monitoring Plans. Still on this aspect, Sicily considers the existence of ARPA Provincial Department for each province a positive element. In Piedmont the punctual and systematic control of all environmental components is a positive aspect of the control system, but the difficulty in interpreting and understanding the rules about IPPC is considered by this region as a weakness. In Andalusia it is difficult to meet deadlines for the control and inspection activities listed in the Control and Monitoring Plans of the Integrated Environmental Authorizations. For West Macedonia a problem is the lack of specialized IPPC personnel and inspectors in control authorities. The latter is a weakness also indicated by Piedmont.

7. Conclusion

According to European law, "the directive binds the Member State only about the results to obtain and leaves to its competence the way and the tools". Also, according to the subsidiarity principle (art. 3 B Maastricht Treaty) the European Directives can bring some differences in the implementation among the Member States. This Analysis aimed at investigating how the IPPC Directive has been implemented and if the differences are able to affect cost-related competitiveness of firms subjected to the IPPC Directive and located in different Member States. Although this chapter only included a few results, it investigates the differences in permit procedures and contents, control and inspection systems included in the national and local legislative framework of the involved regions, in order to identify methodologies and approaches to reduce these differences as a top priority for the next phases of the MED IPPC NET Project.

To this aim, the results obtained from the Analysis phase of the project were elaborated and assessed. As for the institutional analysis (legislative, administrative, control and inspection and content of authorisations analysis), significant differences emerged in the different regions. Among the most relevant issues, some concern the disparity of Competent Authorities for the permit issue (national, regional or provincial Authority) or the main modalities adopted by each region to assure the access to information and public participation in the permit issuing procedure. The deadline for issuing the permit, as well as the type of simplifications in the issuing procedure provided for specific categories of enterprises, also vary among the seven regions involved in the project, and time is a crucial factor for competitiveness. Most regions (and Countries) chose to enact some forms of simplifications to favour companies that developed and certified an environmental management system. One of the suggestions (that also relates to the duration of the permit), is to try and standardize at least the favourable conditions granted to EMAS-registered companies at the EU level. Many indications on the approach followed by the different Competent Authorities were provided also by the analysis of the permits. This also provided some insights on the differences among the investigated regions.

For example, the detailed analysis of specific requirements of different environmental aspects outline a great distance between the approach chosen by the different Competent Authorities, especially as to the "typologies" of requirements. From the Analysis of all these aspects it is possible to specify some recommendations to improve the IPPC implementation within Europe.

One of the most important is that the European Commission should promote national and regional actions concerning activities oriented to harmonize contents and approaches wherever there are many different Competent Authorities. It would be particularly useful to create a permanent forum for the monitoring and the comparison of different implementation modalities of the IPPC Directive, as it has been experimented within the MED IPPC NET project. In this way, it could be possible to provide timely feedback and suggestions to improve the whole system whenever these differences may cause excessive problems for some of the member states or a failure in achieving the Directive's goals.

Furthermore, to prevent disparities a "standard model" might be created at the European level, in order to coordinate contents among different Competent Authorities and Member States.

Another recommendation could attain the setting up and the promotion of more specific and in-depth competences by training the personnel of competent and control authorities: the IPPC requires a holistic vision and wide qualification in many different environmental aspects to reach an integrated vision of environmental problems.

8. References

Barros., M.C., Magán, A., Valiño, S., Bello, M.P., Casares, J.J. & Blanco, J.M. (2009). Identification of Best Available Techniques in the seafood industry: case study. *Journal of Cleaner Production*, Vol. 17, No. 3 , (February 2009), pp. 391-399.

Bréchet, T. & Tulkens, H. (2009). Beyond BAT. Selecting optimal combinations of available techniques, with an example from the limestone industry. *Journal of Environmental Management*, Vol. 90, No. 5 , (April 2009), pp. 1790-1801.

Entek UK Limites, (January 2008). Assessment of the implementation of the IPPC Directive in UK. Department for Environment, Food and Rural Affairs, Available from http://www.defra.gov.uk/environment/quality/pollution/ppc/background/doc uments/implementation-study.pdf

European Commission (2008). Council Directive 2008/1/EC of 15 January 2008 Concerning Integrated Pollution Prevention and Control, Brussles.

Georgopoulou, E., Hontou, V., Gakis, N., Sarafidis, Y., Mirasgedis, S., Lalas, D.P., Loukatos, A., Gargoulas, Mentzis, A., Economidis, D., Triantafilopoulos, T. & Korizi, K.

(2008). BEAsT: a decision-support tool for assessing the environmental benefits and the economic attractiveness of best available techniques in industry. *Journal of Cleaner Production, Vol. 16, No.3* (February 2008), pp. 359-373.

Honkasalo, N., Rodhe, H., & Dalhammar, C. (2005). Environmental permitting as a driver for eco-efficiency in the dairy industry: A closer look at the IPPC directive. *Journal of Cleaner Production,* Vol. 13, No. 10-11, (August-September 2005), pp. 1049-1060.

Karavanas, A., Chaloulakou, N. & Spyrellis, N. (2009). *Journal of Cleaner Production*, Vol. 17, No. 4 , (March 2009), pp. 480-486.

Kocabas, A.M., Yukseler, H., Dilek, F.B. & Yetis, U. (2009). Adoption of European Union's IPPD Directive to a textile mill: analysis of water and energy consumption. *Journal of Environmental Management*, Vol. 91, No. 1, (October 2009), pp. 102-113.

Samarakoon, S.M.K. & Gudmestad, O.T. (2011). The IPPC directive and technique qualification at offshore oil and gas installations. *Journal of cleaner production,* Vol. 19 , No. 1 , (January 2011), pp. 13-20.

Schoenberger, H. (2009). Integrated pollution prevention and control in large industrial installations on the basis of best available techniques – The Sevilla Process. *Journal of Cleaner Production,* Vol. 17, No. 16, (November 2009), pp. 1526-1529.

Silvo, K., Jouttijärvi, T. & Melanen, M. (2009). Implications of regulation based on the IPPC Directive – A review on the Finnish pulp and paper industry. *Journal of cleaner production,* Vol. 17, No. 8, (May 2009), pp. 713-723.

Styles, D., O'Brien, K., & Jones, M. (2009). A quantitative integrated assessment of pollution prevention achieved by Integrated Pollution Prevention Control licensing. *Environment International*, Vol. 35, No. 8, (November 2009), pp. 1177-1187.

7

Contaminated Sites and Public Policies in São Paulo State, Brazil

Ana Luiza Silva Spínola and Arlindo Philippi Jr.
School of Public Health, University of São Paulo
Brazil

1. Introduction

The existence of contaminated sites is an environmental issue that has been increasingly detected by environmental authorities in Brazil, most specifically in the State of São Paulo. The state government is in charge of the environmental management of contaminated sites through its environmental agency, the Environmental Company of the State of São Paulo [CETESB][1]. Since the beginning of the 90's the agency carries out the systematic management of these sites.

The environmental agency has pursued its own structuring to meet this growing demand, enabling its effective action and finding solutions for this serious environmental problem. Thus, since the beginning of the nineties, due to the German expertise and know-how regarding this subject, a technical cooperation was established with the German government, through its Technical Cooperation Society (Deutsche Gesellschaft für Technische Zusammenarbeit, GTZ), which encompasses both technical and financial support. This cooperation allowed the development of a specific project in order to build the capacity of the state agency for the management of contaminated sites (CETESB, 2011a).

The origin of contaminated sites is related to a lack of knowledge, back in time, about safe procedures for the handling of hazardous substances, to the disrespect of such procedures and to accidents or spillings during the development of production processes, transportation or storage of raw materials and products (CETESB, 2011b).

According to CETESB (2011a) "the soil and underground water contamination have been the focus of great concern for the last three decades in the industrialized countries, mainly in the USA and Europe. This environmental problem becomes more serious in urban industrial centres such as the Metropolitan Region of São Paulo".

The State of São Paulo has 3.675 contaminated confirmed sites (CETESB, 2011b). This inventory has been published since the year of 2002.

Table 1 shows the distribution of contaminated sites registered in São Paulo by region and activity, regarding the last data published by CETESB on December 2010.

Cunha (1997) considers that it is the inactive industries which more critically affect the environment and the population, among the contaminating sources in total.

---

[1] CETESB is the institution that by law is in charge, among other assignments, of enforcing administrative policies for environmental issues throughout the entire State of São Paulo, as established by Laws no. 118/73 and no. 997/76.

In addition, according to Sánchez (2001), it is possible to relate this issue to the life cycle of factories that had their doors shut for various motives: either because they had lost economic competitiveness or because their location became less advantageous. This means that there is the need for modernization and re-use, including potential interim uses up to the point of a potential industrial or other re-use. Cases such as these are part of urban dynamics and deserve special attention. Nowadays those are one of the main urban conflicts to be solved in cities worldwide.

Region	Activities					
	Commercial	Industrial	Residues	Gas Stations	Accidents	Total
São Paulo	39	114	28	1.004	5	1.190
São Paulo Metropolitan Region - others	29	125	20	419	6	599
Country Side	60	158	40	1.105	12	1.375
Coastal Area	15	40	21	223	1	300
Paraíba Valey	4	34	1	171	1	211
Total	147	471	110	2.922	25	3.675

Table 1. Contaminated sites in São Paulo State, Brazil – December 2010

The existence of a contaminated site becomes the generator of many problems, such as the threat to superficial and underground water sources, the devaluation of properties, besides the threats to public health.

Brazil does not have yet a national public policy, approved by law, about contaminated sites or brownfield redevelopment[2]. Therefore many contaminated sites have been reused for new commercial or housing purposes without any type of control from municipal public authorities – potentially ticking time bombs, entailing possibly serious health and environmental risks in the near future.

As the appearance of contaminated sites is daily increasing, being a considerable problem mainly in the industrial cities, the State of São Paulo, breaking new ground, has approved on July 2009 a public policy, by which main regulatory aspects and legal framework on the issue are established, setting the tone for new legislation on this matter by the other states of the Brazilian Union.

---

[2] From the conceptual point of view, it is important to highlight that the term "Brownfield" corresponds to a site degraded by previous use, which was abandoned or is under-utilized. It may or may not have real or perceptive contamination problems. Most are located in urbanized areas and require some type of intervention for a potential re-use as defined in the "Sustainable Brownfield Regeneration: CABERNET Network Report" (CABERNET, 2006, p. 26). Up until now the term "Brownfield" has not been translated into Portuguese. Sánchez (2001, p. 29) suggests the translation into Portuguese as "dysfunctional real estate/property", for there is no possibility that the sites hold a new function without some type of treatment. Thus, the contaminated site (degraded site by contamination) is a type of Brownfield as described above.

A National Environmental Council Resolution has also been approved, on a federal basis, establishing guidelines values for soil and underground water, as well as environmental directions for contamination management.

The objective of this paper is to comment the management of contaminated sites carried out by the State of São Paulo and to present its new legislation.

2. Methodology

The information and data collection methods combined literature and documental research. The literature research included bibliographies on contaminated sites management. The documental research included basically official documents published by CETESB, some federal legislation and the new legislation on contaminated sites management approved by the State of São Paulo (Act n. 13.577, of july 8th 2009). Given the newness of the law, there is no literature about it.

3. Results and discussion

3.1 Environmental competences as determined by the constitution

The Brazilian Federal Constitution establishes that "the protection of the environment and fighting pollution in any of its forms" is a common competence of the Union, the States, the Federal District and the Municipalities, according to article 24, I and IV.

The competence to legislate upon the natural resources and soil protection, environment protection and pollution control is concurrent to the Union, the States and the Federal District, according to article 24, VI.

With regard to Municipalities, the Brazilian Federal Constitution attributes competences to "legislate on matters of local interest", "complementation of federal and state laws, when applicable", and "promotion, when applicable, of adequate territorial order, through planning and control of urban land use, parceling and occupation", amongst others (art. 30, paragraphs I, II and VIII respectively).

Although the environmental quality of urban sites depends on State control, the municipalities also have the duty to enforce this control, since their attribution to manage the use and occupation of the land is established by the Constitution.

3.2 Commentaries on the act n 13.577/2009 of the State of Sao Paulo

Even before the approval of the 2009 State Act CETESB had already developed specific procedures to manage contaminated sites based on "Executive Acts" n. 007 and n. 023 initially approved on the year 2000.

On the year 2007 those statutes were revised and updated on a new Executive Act n. 103, which foresees a methodology to manage such sites aiming at their rehabilitation for future use, legal responsibilities for the contaminated site management, technical studies to be made in order to identify and delimit the contamination, emergency actions to be undertaken, remediation techniques, institutional and engineering control measures, monitoring deadlines and communication procedures towards governmental entities (such as the state health department and the municipalities, amongst others).

The State Act is composed of 6 chapters: i) general provisions (including the object, objectives, technical definitions and measures), ii) soil contamination prevention and control, iii) contaminated site (divided in responsibilities, identification and remediation), iv) economical tools, v) infractions and penalties and vi) general provisions.

The object is to protect the soil integrity against harmful contamination alterations, to establish liabilities, identify, register and remediate the contaminated sites in a way to make it safe for present and future use.

As a general objective, it was established the sustainable soil use clause, protecting it from contaminations and preventing alterations on its natural features and functions by means of:

i.   preventive measures, including the protection of soil and underground water natural properties;

ii.   corrective measures including procedures for contaminated sites identification, protection of the health and safety of the population exposed to the contamination; remediation

iii.   incentive measures for the reuse of remediated sites;

iv.   promotion of exchange programs among institutions;

v.   guarantee to information and to participation by the population affected by decisions related with the contaminated areas.

3.2.1 Definitions and tools

As a mainly technical environmental statute, a whole section has being dedicated to the definition of mostly important terms for the soil quality management. Throughout this essay some technical and legal definitions shall be presented.

A number of tools have been determined for the soil quality protection and contaminated sites management, among some of those that follow below:

a) Contaminated sites registration

The database will be composed by detailed information about: i) potentially pollutant activities and enterprises; ii) which, in the past, had promoted activities liable to provoke soil contamination; iii) which are under contamination suspicion iv) any other applicable cases; and will be published in the State of São Paulo Official Gazette and on the State of São Paulo Environment Department website.

As mentioned the environmental agency of São Paulo is already keeping a database of contaminated and reabilitated areas which has been published in its website since 2002.

b) Licenses and enforcement

The licensing and the enforcement activities are important tools both in regards to the preventive and the corrective aspects in the management of contaminated sites.

Environmental licensing is the administrative procedure under which the environmental agency licenses the location, installation, enlargement and operations of undertakings and activities using environmental resources, which are considered effectively or potentially pollutant, or those which, under whatever way, may cause environmental degradation (CONAMA[3], 1997).

The procedure is divided into 3 phases, under which the following documents are issued:

i.   Preliminary License (granted in the undertaking's planning phase, approving its location, conception and environmental viability);

---

[3] National Environmental Council

ii. License for Installation (authorizes the undertaking's installation according to the preliminarily approved specifications); and

iii. License for Operations (authorizes the undertaking's operation, after checking the compliance to previous licenses).

In the State of São Paulo the pollution sources, which depend on environmental licensing, are provided for in the Decree no. 8468/76.

In the process of licensing an industry one should check if the activities performed may contaminate the soil or underground waters. Considering that the great majority of pollution sources depend on the license to operate, the occurrence of contaminated sites may be avoided in advance by including the suitable technical requirements in the undertaking's installation or operation license, such as for example the obligation for adequate disposal of chemicals stored or of waste generated in the production process. Otherwise, from the correction stand point, it is possible that the undertaking's operation license renewal be linked to the identification or remediation actions.

c) Deactivation Plan

The Act establishes that the entities legally responsible for undertakings, which are subject to environmental licensing and potential contamination generators, about to be totally or partially deactivated or disoccupied, must communicate the suspension or closing of activities to the competent state agency.

At this moment a Deactivation Plan should be presented, contemplating the existing environmental condition, especially regarding the existence of contamination, and should contain, when applicable, information about the remediation measures to be taken.

Sánchez (2005) highlights the deactivation planning importance. Shutting down is a stage of the industrial activities cycle of life in which the environmental damages accumulated throughout the previous enterprise stages should be repaired, to avoid conveying the reparation cost to either third parties or society.

Since year 2002, in the State of São Paulo, the obligation to present a deactivation plan for the termination of activities subject to environmental licensing is already in force (according to Decree n. 47.400/2002).

d) City master plan and land use and occupation legislation

This provision is timely to reinforce the need for municipalities to effectively take part in the prevention and management of contaminated sites.

Municipalities have a power-duty to act in the management of contaminated sites under two aspects: i) they hold the common competence with the Union, States and Federal District to protect the environment and fight pollution (since contamination, from the legal stand point, is a type of pollution), and ii) the hold the competence to legislate on matters of local interest and to promote territorial ordering through the planning and control of urban land use.

The Master Plan is the basic instrument for urban development policies. The Act acknowledged the importance of the municipal action in the prevention and management of contaminated sites and has often summoned the municipality to take on its responsibility.

The Master Plans and the legislation regarding land use and occupation should take into account the sites either potentially contaminated or under the suspicion of contamination, and the confirmed contaminated sites. The approval of land parceling and construction projects should guarantee the safe use of such sites.

Vis-à-vis the express determinations provided for in the Act, in practice, municipalities of the State of São Paulo should organize themselves administratively to tackle this issue by creating specific statutes and administrative procedures, providing equipment and technical capacity building of human resources, etc. In addition they are responsible for the land use restriction, in case the contaminated site poses health risks, so to avoid the receptors exposure to the existent contaminants.

During the different phases of the contaminated sites management the local governments should be notified by the competent environmental agency when, e.g., the area is classified as contaminated under investigation, contaminated or remediated for the declared use (art. 18, clause II; art. 24, clause IV; and art. 27, clause III, respectively).

It is therefore not enough that local governments be notified about the presence of contaminated sites, they should know what to do with this information. Questions such as – "What should be done about a contaminated site?" "What are the consequences for urban planning in the presence of contaminated sites?" "Is there a risk to the extent that the land use should be restricted?" "How to restrict the land use?" "Which planning instruments can be created to attract investors to a contaminated site?" – need still to be discussed.

Lazanha (2005) highlights that "the Municipality, as a federative entity holding the competence of territorial ordering, should be held accountable for corrective and pro-active measures in these sites, thus avoiding the spreading of further damages to society with the construction of housing and other buildings in contaminated sites" (p. 116).

In this context, Marker (2003) highlights the importance of assessing – within the Brazilian context – which are the pre-requisites to "identify and mark the degraded sites in master plans and land use, to make diagnoses and develop strategies for their revitalization" (p.40). In São Paulo, despite the action of the state agency, there is urgent need to involve the municipalities on this issue. At the municipal level, however, there are neither instruments nor any kind of action to enforce the intervention on contaminated sites. In the State of São Paulo an exception is the municipality of São Paulo where urban planning provides the control of contaminated sites.

e) "Bank collaterals" and "environmental insurance"

Such tools, which still need to be regulated, were provided to ensure the fulfillment of the remediation plan and should reach the minimum value of 125% of the Plan's estimated cost. In case of non-compliance there is a provision for the possibility that the environmental agency execute the collaterals aiming at covering the remediation measures complementary costs.

f) Quality criteria for soil and underground waters

In regards to the control of air and superficial waters pollution, the environmental legislation established standards of emission and quality, while the soil quality control is conducted through the use of "guideline values".

"The adoption of guideline value lists has been the usual practice in countries with a tradition in soil and underground waters quality monitoring and in contaminated sites' control" (CETESB, 2001, p. 10). "In a distinct manner there is no standardized international approach – regarding soil pollution – because of its complex and variable nature, and the soil is a privately owned economic asset" (CETESB, 2001, p.14).

These "guideline values" are determining tools for the soil and underground waters quality management, since they are the fundamentals for making important decisions both preventive, and of pollution control in sites under the suspicion of contamination, as well as corrective, since they are indispensable for the area to be considered contaminated legally. This will eventually deploy a series of actions from the legally responsible agency and the Public Power.

After specific studies which took into account the natural quality of the State of São Paulo soil, in 2001, CETESB published the "Report for the establishment of Guideline Values for Soils and Underground Waters in the State of São Paulo". This report shows the approach of the USA, Germany and Holland in regards to the subject and it also reports the methodology adopted by the State of São Paulo for the establishment of its own values. The values published in 2001 were revised and nowadays those approved by the CETESB Executive Act n. 195/2005/E are ruling.

g) Fund

As it occurs in countries such as the USA, a specific Fund for contaminated sites can be used in cases where the site is considered *"orphan"*, i.e., where the responsible entity is not identified or localized.

The Act provided for the creation of the State Fund for the Prevention and Remediation of Contaminated Sites, which is an investment fund linked to the Environment Department of the State of São Paulo and aimed at soil protection and contaminated sites' identification and remediation.

Different sources of revenue were considered, among which resources resulting from international aid and cooperation and from intergovernmental agreements; donations; environmental compensations resulting from potentially contaminating activities; 30% of the amount collected with fines applied based on the Act; reimbursement of State expenditures, etc.

h) Environmental compensation

The environmental compensation was regulated by the State of Sao Paulo Decree no. 54.544/2009. In the environmental licensing of enterprises, potentially generating contaminated sites (to be defined by an executive act of the Environment Secretary), the entrepreneur will collect a value – to be determined by the competent agency – as a means of compensation to the Fund.

3.2.2 Legally responsible entities for the identification and remediation of contaminated sites

The Act established the following subjects as legally, and solidarily, responsible for the prevention, identification and remediation of a contaminated site: the one that caused the contamination and its successors; the owner of the area; the "the holder of the right of surface use"[4], the holder of the actual possession; whoever benefits directly or indirectly from it.

---

[4] The Act defines "the holder of the right of surface use" as the "holder of the right to the surface of a land lot, for a determined or undetermined period of time, through a public deed registered in the Property Registry Office, in the terms of the Federal Law no. 10257, July 9th, 2001. According to this law of 2001 (named Statute of the City, that establishes the general guidelines of the urban policy) the right to the surface encompasses the right to use the ground, the underground or the land related aerial space, in the form established in the respective contract, meeting the urbanistic legislation (paragraph 1st of art. 21).

Solidarity is a legal concept provided for in the civil law[5], and in the case of contaminated sites it is possible to demand total obligation (e.g. of remediation) from all the responsible listed above.

The responsibility of the contaminated site's owner is transmitted to the next owner in the case, e.g., of the sale of the contaminated land. The jurisprudence related to the matter has been understanding that a real estate environmental obligation (e.g. that of maintaining the green areas and the permanent preservation areas) is transmitted to the new acquirer.

It is worth mentioning a recent decision held by the Brazilian Superior Court of Justice on an appeal reported by Justice Herman Benjamin: "the obligations derived from the illegal dumping of waste or residues on the land are of *propter rem* nature, meaning that they adhere to the title and are transferred to the future owner (...) regardless any discussion about the good or bad faith of the acquirer, for one is not in the condition of subjective responsibility based on the establishment of a personal guilt"[6].

3.2.3 Contaminated sites preventive actions

As a general rule the Act provided that any individual or legal entity that may contaminate the soil should adopt the measures for not to allow the occurrence of changes that are significant and damaging to the functions of the soil.

The functions of the soil were listed as: 1- sustainability of the life and "habitat" for humans, animals, plants and soil organisms; 2 – maintenance of the water cycle and its nutrients; 3 – protection of underground water; 4 – maintenance of the historical, natural and cultural heritage; 5 – conservation of the reserves of minerals and raw-materials; 6 – food production; 7 – means for the maintenance of social-economic activity.

Environmental agencies were then obliged to act preventively and correctively with the purpose of preventing significant changes in the functions of the soil. As a parameter for actions, the use of the following guideline values (already cited above) was provided for:

- quality reference value is the "concentration of a determined substance in the soil and in the underground water that defines a soil as clean, or the natural quality of underground water". These are to be used to guide the soil functions prevention and control policy.

- prevention value is the "concentration of a determined substance above which harmful changes to the quality of soil and underground water may occur." They shall be used to discipline the introduction of substances in the soil. In case they are surpassed there will be the need of monitoring resulting impacts.

- intervention value is the "concentration of a determined substance in the soil and in the underground water, above which there are potential direct and indirect risks to human health, considering a generic exposure scenario". These will be used to stop the continuous introduction of polluting loads in the soil.

3.2.4 Identification of contaminated sites

In the initial phase of contaminated sites identification, two concepts are important: i) "contamination potential area": area, land, location, facility, construction or improvement

---

[5] Article 264 of the Civil Code (Law no. 10.406/2002) establishes that "there is solidarity when in the same obligation more than one creditor or more than one debtor concur, each one with the right, or obliged to the whole debt".

[6] RESP n. 650.728 – SC

where activities, are or were developed and that due to their characteristics may accumulate amounts or concentrations of materials in such conditions which render it contaminated; and ii) "area under the suspicion of contamination": site, land, location facility, construction or improvement with traces of being a contaminated site.

The Act foresees that when detecting traces or suspicions that a site is contaminated, the legally responsible entity should immediately communicate such fact to the competent environment and health agencies.

The technical study that is to be conducted is the "preliminary assessment", which has the purpose of clarifying if the contamination suspicion proceeds or not. This assessment was defined as an "initial assessment, based on available information, to fundament the suspicion of contamination in a site".

In case there is a fundamented suspicion of contamination one should start the "confirming investigation", which "aims at proving the existence of a contaminated site". This investigation is basically composed of the capturing and chemical analyses of samples and the interpretation of the results. The results are to be compared with the intervention values for soils and underground waters established by the CETESB.

In case the concentrations observed *in loco* are above these values the site will be classified as "contaminated site under investigation", which has been defined as the "contaminated site on which procedures are taking place to determine the extension of the contamination and the affected receptors".

In this management phase obligations were established for the environmental agency – such as, for example, carrying out the preliminary assessment at the site or request the entity responsible to adopt measures, demand confirmatory investigation – once significant changes harmful to the soil functions are detected.

In addition, the environmental agency must notify the State agencies involved (especially the organization in charge of granting the right of use of underground waters, the Municipalities, the Municipal Environmental Boards and other stakeholders), as well as determine the legally entity in charge that may start emergency action procedures.

The environment and health agencies shall implement a program that guarantees the affected population, through its representatives, the access to available information and participation in the site assessment and remediation process.

3.2.5 Rehabilitation and remediation of contaminated sites

The site rehabilitation process main objective is to "rehabilitate the site for a pre-established purpose". The remediation goals to be achieved should be defined based on the scenario of the soil future occupation.

After the site is classified as "contaminated under investigation", new studies are to be carried out to detail the amplitude of the contamination.

The legally responsible entity shall carry out a "detailed investigation" to establish a knowledge around the total extension of the contamination and the identification of all the receptors under risk. This investigation was legally defined as a "process of field data acquisition and interpretation which allows the understanding of the dynamics of the contamination plumes in each one of the physical means affected".

In case a water supply source is compromised, the entity responsible for the contamination shall provide an alternative drinking water source to supply the affected population.

It is important to clarify that typically a contaminated site may be remediated focusing one between two possible future situations: that the soil be compatible with **one** previously determined **use** ("fitness for use approach"), or with **all** possible **uses** ("multifunctionality of soil approach"):

- Fitness for use clause: a health risk assessment is conducted and takes necessarily into account the scenario of future use of the land and ways through which people are (or may be) exposed to existing contaminants. The risk is **minimized** so it is possible to maintain the contaminants within the site, as long as this risk is manageable and maintained at an acceptable level. The site remediation is made as far as necessary to allow its use for the previously established purpose. Such decision is fundamented on "guideline values" for soils and underground waters (explained ahead) which vary according to each exposure scenario. In this case the site is **rehabilitated** for a determined purpose.

- Multifunctionality of soil clause: the risk is **eliminated** by the removal or total destruction of the polluting substances. The site is **recovered** to its natural conditions (i.e., concentrations prior to contamination), and may be used for whichever purposes. In this case, remediation costs may be infinitely higher than in the previous hypothesis, even causing the non feasibility of site intervention.

One starts from the premise that "certain soil uses require it to have excellent quality – such as for housing and recreation – while other uses are less demanding, such as for industrial purposes or paved parking lots" (Sánchez, 2001, p. 131).

Regarding the history of contaminated sites management in 16 European countries, Ferguson (1999, p. 33) mentions that "twenty or so years ago land contamination was usually perceived in terms of relatively rare incidents, with poorly known but possibly catastrophic consequences for human health and the environment. (...) As a result politicians responded by seeking maximum risk control: pollution should be removed or contained completely".

However it is now widely recognized that drastic risk control, for example cleaning up all sites to background concentrations or to levels suitable for the most sensitive land use, is neither technically nor economically feasible" (Ferguson, 1999, p. 33).

To give an example, according to Ferguson (1999, p. 33) "in 1981 about 350 sites in the Netherlands were thought to be contaminated and possibly in need of remedial action. By 1995 the number had grown to 300,000 sites with and estimated clean-up cost of 13 billion ECU[7]. Similar circumstances exist in most other industrialized countries. Consequently, although the need for policies to protect soil and groundwater is recognized, strategies for managing contaminated land have moved towards *fitness for use*".

The article written by Ferguson (1999) allows us to conclude that the management of contaminated sites in the 16 European countries studied is fundamentally based on the assessment of risk, be it to human health or to the environment. Most of the countries adopt the "fitness for use approach" (or *function oriented approach, suitable for use approach, cost-effective approach*), i.e., the future use of the land is taken into account to define the remediation goals to be achieved. This is of great importance for remediation to be successful and efficient both from the technical and the economic point of view.

Furthermore, guideline values are adopted for different land use scenarios as a means to assess the risk of a determined area and based on which the objectives of remediation will be defined. Eventually, the need and tendency to take into account the economic aspect to

---

[7] European Currency Unit

find solutions for a contaminated site stood out, and today managing sites aiming at the multifunctionality of soil approach is an exception.

In this respect Cunha (1997) underlines that a point in common to all countries which elaborated contaminated sites management programs, was the high number of sites and the amount of resources necessary to their remedial. There is thus the need of evaluating the real need of remediating a contaminated site, considering the existing levels of contamination and the potential to cause harm to the health of the population. "Such procedure is generically known as health risk assessment and has been adopted in some countries as a way to determine the real need for a site remediation, as well as in the definition of the remediation system to be put in place" (p.09).

Following the trend of countries that have a tradition in managing contaminated sites, the State of São Paulo adopted the "fitness for use" approach, finally putting an end to the issue related to how extensively a site should be remediated. The Act established the risk assessment as a subsidy for making decisions regarding interventions for remediation purposes to take place in a contaminated site.

"Risk assessment" was legally defined as "the process through which risks to human health, to the environment and to other assets to be protected are identified, evaluated and quantified". When the values defined for acceptable risk are surpassed, the site will be classified as "contaminated site" and its remediation is to be provided.

The expression "contaminated site" was defined as "area, land, location, facility, building or improvement that contains **amounts or concentrations of materials** in such conditions that cause or may eventually cause harm to the human health, to the environment or to any other asset that is to be protected"[8]. Thus the legal concept of contaminated site is not precise and unequivocally limited, but it derives from the surpassing of acceptable risk values, that will be analyzed, in the concrete case, by means of a specific "risk assessment".

The site remediation will include the "adoption of measures for the elimination or reduction of risks to acceptable levels for the declared use", according to definition established by the Act.

After the site is classified as contaminated, the environmental agency shall inform the health agencies, when there is risk to human health, notify other public agencies involved, start the remediation procedures in tune with the ongoing emergency actions and demand the presentation of a remediation plan from the legally responsible entity.

During this phase of the site management it is an attribution of the environmental agency to determine to the legally responsible entity the contaminated site status recording on the real state registration. Such imposition has been widely discussed about due to a possible conflict with article 22, clause XXV, of the Brazilian Constitution that says that "the Union has exclusive legislative competence on public recordings issues".

However, even before the arrival of the State Act n. 13.577/2009, record on contaminated sites real state registration was already a procedure adopted by CETESB in respect to the Executive Act n. 167/2005 rendered by the Judiciary General Corrective Office, published on the State of Sao Paulo Official Gazzete on June 12th 2006.

---

[8] The legal definition of contaminated site was provided for the first time in the Brazilian legislation, by the State of São Paulo Solid Residues Policy for (Law no. 12300, March 16th, 2006), and it is identical to the definition brought by the Act now discussed.

With all that, any possible acquirer could have available any information about past or present contamination related events on the real state.

When an acceptable risk level is reestablished for the declared use, the site will be classified as "remediated site for declared use", which is defined as "area, land, location, facility, building or improvement previously contaminated, which, after being submitted to remediation, has reestablished the level of risk acceptable to human health, considering the declared use".

Thus, besides information about the contamination ("Contaminated Site Term") CETESB also emits the "Rehabilitation of the Site for Declared Use Term" which includes the kind of use the site is specifically rehabilitated for, that will also be recorded on the real state registration.

3.2.6 Infractions and penalties

The actions or omissions contrary to the Act are considered administrative infractions and will be punished with written warnings, fines, embargo, demolition or suspension of funding and of tax benefits.

A limit was imposed to the fine penalty, ranging from 4 to 4,000,000 times the value of the Fiscal Unit of the State of São Paulo – UFESP (currently calculated at approximately R$ 17,45), and may not surpass the value of R$ 50,000,000 (fifty million reais).

4. Conclusions

The Act n. 13.577/2009 constitutes the first public policy issued in Brazil about contaminated sites management. It came to fulfill a great legal, as well as technical gap. It brought to the Brazilian Environmental Law important definitions on technical terms, it established the legal entities responsible for the contaminated site remediation and it determined the management stages to be followed.

It also adopted the risk assessment as an important decision making tool as far as the site intervention will be developed on the terms of the "fitness for use" approach.

The Fund created by the Act, following a tendency on countries with a established tradition on contaminated sites management, will specially contribute to an effective management of certain "orphan" and abandoned sites as it habilitates and financially enable the State`s action.

Under the institutional aspect the Act established an "exchange among institutions" as one of many ways of reaching its goal. On the various management phases it will be necessary for the involved public bodies to communicate with each other imposing an effective and efficient information exchange in a way that each entity, in its particular area of competence, establishes the necessary procedures on it administrative routine. That was exactly the objective of the article 50 that states that "the State Environment Secretary and Health Secretary should establish common procedures and routines for any joint campaigns aiming the prevention or formation of contaminated sites as well as the identification and remediation of existing ones". We point out that the municipalities also should be inserted in such a process in a way to specially consider the adoption of this issue in its urban and environmental planning.

Under the important aspect of publicity the Act has institutionalized the contaminated sites registration database, imposing the publication of such information on the State

Environment Secretary website as well as on the State Official Gazzete. On an innovative fashion, meaning an important move to make the information available to the general public, it determined the record of contamination site status and of rehabilitated site status on the real state registration.

Some important issues still need to be regulated, for example: the way the participation of the affected population will take place on decisions regarding a site intervention; specification of "bank collaterals" and "environmental insurances" as financing tools to guarantee the site remediation; and effective creation of tax and crediting incentives.

This innovative Act will probably set a national tendency in a way that other states of Brazil will probably create their own public policies on contaminated sites regarding regional particularities. A national public policy would be welcome as to establish directives and general clauses on the concurrent legislative competence of the Union, States and Federal District on environmental protection and pollution control issues. A national policy would also fulfill legal gaps for any state that hasn`t developed its own legislation, which can also be subject of future researches.

5. References

CABERNET. (2006). *Sustainable Brownfield Regeneration: CABERNET Network Report,* University of Nottingham, ISBN: 0-9547474-5-3, Nottingham, United Kingdom.

CETESB. (2001). *Relatório de estabelecimento de valores orientadores para solos e águas subterrâneas no Estado de São Paulo,* CETESB, São Paulo, Brazil.

CETESB. (2011a). O que são áreas contaminadas, In: *CETESB,* 03.02.2011, Available from: <http://www.cetesb.sp.gov.br/areas-contaminadas/O-que-s%E3o-%E1%81reas-Contaminadas/1->

CETESB. (2011b). O gerenciamento de áreas contaminadas no Estado de São Paulo, In: CETESB, 03.02.2011, Available from:
<http://www.cetesb.sp.gov.br/userfiles/file/areascontaminadas/texto_explicativo_dez_10.pdf>

Cunha, R. C. de A. (1997). *Avaliação de risco em áreas contaminadas por fontes industriais desativadas – estudo de caso,* Tese (Doutorado em Geociências), Instituto de Geociências, Universidade de São Paulo, São Paulo, Brazil.

Ferguson, C. C. (1999). Assessing risks from contaminated sites: policy and practice in 16 European countries. In: *Land Contamination and Reclamation,* Rupert Hough, (Ed.), 33-54, EPP Publications, Retrieved from
<http://epppublications.com/Documents/07-2-1.pdf>

Lazanha, L. K. S (2005). *Subsídios jurídico-sociais para formulação de políticas públicas: revitalização de áreas degradadas por contaminação no Estado de São Paulo.* Dissertação (Mestrado em Saúde Pública), Faculdade de Saúde Pública, Universidade de São Paulo, São Paulo, Brazil.

Marker, A. (2003). *A revitalização de áreas urbanas degradadas: políticas, instrumentos e incentivos no cenário internacional (Relatório de Consultoria),* GTZ, São Paulo, Brazil.

Sánchez, L. E. (2001). *Desengenharia: o passivo ambiental na desativação de empreendimentos industriais,* Edusp, ISBN: 85-314-0599-8, São Paulo, Brazil.

Sánchez, L. E. (2005). Danos e Passivo Ambiental, In: *Curso Interdisciplinar de Direito Ambiental*, Philippi Jr, A & Alves, A. C. (Ed.), pp. 261-293, Manole, ISBN: 85-204-2187-3, São Paulo, Brazil.

8

Sustainable Management of Muddy Coastlines

Steven Odi-Owei and Itolima Ologhadien
Faculty of Engineering
Rivers State University of Science and Technology, Port Harcourt,
Nigeria

1. Introduction

The Coastal Zone is home to many heavy oil and gas industries, and a significant proportion of the population and wealth generating infrastructure. The coastal zone therefore, provides economic, transport, residential and recreational functions, all of which depend upon its physical characteristics, pleasant landscape, cultural heritage, natural resources and rich marine and terrestrial biodiversity. The United Nations estimated that by 2004, more than 75 percent of the world's population would live within the coastal zone (Reeve *et al.*, 2004). These regions are therefore of critical importance to a majority of humanity and affect an increasing percentage of our economic activities. The pressure on coastal environments is being exacerbated by rapid changes in global climate, overexploitation of fisheries, coastal and marine pollution, coastal erosion and flooding, physical modification and destruction of habitats, etc. For example, the Intergovernmental Panel on Climate Change (IPCC) has predicted a sea level rise of the order of 0.6m over the next century. For Nigeria, it is of the order of 0.83m (Nwaogazie & Ologhadien 2010)

The value of the coastal zone to humanity, and the enormous pressure on it, provides strong incentives for a greater scientific understanding which can ensure effective coastal engineering practice and efficient and sustainable management of coastlines.

2. Muddy coastline

Coastal classification generally falls into two main categories; namely, genetic (nature) and descriptive (based on morphology). Within the descriptive classification, a sub classification in terms of particle size of the beach material have: muddy coasts, sand coast, gavel/shingle coasts and rock coast. Another sub-classification based on typical coastal features have the following: barrier island coasts, delta coasts, dune coasts, cliff coasts, coral reef coasts, mangrove coasts, marsh grass coasts, etc.

While a vast majority of coastlines are made up of sediments ranging from coarse-grained fragments of rocks to fine-grained sand, only a few are muddy coasts. Sediment mixture with a fraction of clay particles (d < 4μm, AGU scale), larger than about 10% have cohesive properties. Mud may be defined as a fluid-sediment mixture consist of (salt) water, sands, silt, clays and organic materials. Muddy coasts fall within the descriptive category of coasts in which classification are based on particle size of the beach material. In a coastal environment, there is a continuous cycle of mud flocs which consists of erosion, settling, deposition, consolidation and erosion. Since mud particles are denser than water and unstable, the continuous agitation of the surf zone by breaking waves transport mud material cross-shore and equilibrium conditions are hardly attained. Thus muddy coastlines hardly form breaches, which offer natural coastal protection systems. Plate 1 shows the action of breaking waves on a muddy coastline.

Plate 1. Wave breaking on a muddy coast at Aiyetoro, Nigeria

3. Coastal processes

The hydraulic and morphological processes in the coastal zone are governed by two primary phenomena; namely, windwaves and astronomical tides. The wind stress on the water surface produces wind-generated waves which are of a relatively short period. The periodic rise and fall of water level is due to the astronomical tides produced by the gravitational field in the presence of the rotating earth, moon and sun. The timescale of tidal oscillations is very much larger than that of the wind-generated waves. Table 1 presents other free surface disturbances.

Phenomena	Generating force	Time scale (period)
Wind generated waves	Shear and wind pressure on sea surface	0-15s
Swell	Long-distance wind wave	0-30$_s$
Surf beats	Grouping of breaking waves	1-5 min
Seiches	Variations of wind speed and atmospheric pressure	1-60 min
Basin resonance	Tsunami, surf beats	1-60 min
Tsunami	Undersea earthquakes	5-60 min
Tide	Moon-sun influences on earth	12-24 hr
Storm surge	Wind shear and atmospheric pressure on sea	1-30 days

Table 1. Free surface disturbances in the coast

The most important hydraulic process in coastal engineering is the wave motion; the understanding of wave motion and of its interaction with structures and coastal hydrography is vital in the estimation of erosion and accretion, sediment transport and coastal morphology. These processes are also important in formulating sustainable management plans.

3.1 Wave motion

The wave profile according to the linear wave theory is

$$\eta = a \cos (kx - \omega t) \tag{1}$$

where η is surface elevation, a is wave amplitude, ω is circular frequency, k is wave number, t is time, and x is positive direction of wave travel. The solution of the velocity potential (ϕ) for the wave profile of Equation 1, must satisfy the Laplace equation, boundary conditions at the sea bed and on the water surface. The resulting solution for ϕ is given by:

$$\phi = -gH \left(\frac{T}{4\pi} \right) \frac{\cosh k(d+z)}{\cosh kd} \sin (kx - \omega t) \tag{2}$$

where g is acceleration due to gravity, H is wave height, T is wave period, k and ω are as previously defined.

The wave celerity (c) and wave dispersion equations are :

$$c = g\omega^{-1} \tanh kd \tag{3}$$

and

$$\omega^2 = gk \tanh kd \tag{4}$$

where $k = \dfrac{2\pi}{L}$ and $\omega = \dfrac{2\pi}{T}$

The particle velocities are derived from Equation 2 using the definition of velocity potential:

$$u = \pi HT^{-1} \frac{\cosh (k(y+d))}{\sinh kd} \cos (kx - \omega t) \tag{5}$$

$$v = \pi HT^{-1} \frac{\sinh (k(y+d))}{\sinh kd} \sin (kx - \omega t) \tag{6}$$

where η is the height of the water surface above stillwater level, u is the horizontal water particle velocity, v is the vertical water particle velocity, d is the still water depth, H is the wave height, L is the wave length and T is the wave period.

For the computation of longshore sediment transport, coastline evolution, design of shore protection works and estimation of wave impact pressures on structures, historic wave data are required. The wave measurement facilities may be situated offshore in relatively deep water. By means of the wave dispersion equations (3 & 4), the wave conditions in the offshore station may be transferred to the coastal zone. Equations 5 and 6 are components of velocity used in estimating the wave forces exerted on structures.

3.2 Sediment transport

Coastal sediment transport consists of two aspects: sediment transport parallel to the shoreline (longshore) and sediment transport transverse to the shoreline (cross–shore). The imbalances in the longshore sediment transport are responsible for the long-term changes in the coastlines, whereas the cross-shore transport is responsible for the short-term variations. The morphological consequences of shore protection works are assessed in terms of quantitative estimates of erosion and accretion. Waves and currents, along with the physical properties of the sediment materials, determine the rate of material transport in the coastal zone. The reliability of sediment transport predictions is strictly dependent upon the accuracy of the semi-empirical equations used to evaluate the sediment transport. Studies have been carried out to establish the validity and reliability of several solid transport formula (White et al. 1973; Gomez and Church 1989; Bathurst et al. 1987). These studies concluded that, there is no solid transport formula valid for all ranges of natural conditions and therefore, the more appropriate formula for each set of particular conditions can be chosen.

A number of longshore transport models have been developed for a number of natural conditions; namely,

3.2.1 Coastal erosion research council (CERC) formula (1963)

In the CERC formula,

$$S = A\, H_o^2 C_o K_{rbr}^2 \sin\phi_{br} \cos\phi_{br} \tag{7}$$

where S is longshore transport due to breaking waves, A is a constant, H_o is deepwater wave height, C_o is deepwater wave celerity, K_{rbr} is wave refraction coefficient at the breaker line, and ϕ_{br} is breaker angle.

The CERC formula does not account for differences in sediment materials often represented by d_{50} (mean size). The formula is often criticized for being only valid for relatively long and straight beaches, where the longshore differences in the breaking wave heights are small. Thirdly, the formula does not account for currents which are not generated by breaking waves, such as tidal currents. When tidal currents are important, another transport formula should be used.

3.2.2 Bijker formula (1967 & 1968)

The Bijker formula is:

$$S_b = b D_{50} \frac{\upsilon}{C} \sqrt{g}\, \exp\left[-\frac{0.27\, \Delta D_{50} C^2}{\pi \upsilon^2 \left\{ 1 + \frac{1}{2}\left(\xi\, \frac{u_b}{\upsilon} \right)^2 \right\}} \right] \tag{8}$$

where S_b is bed load transport, b is a constant (~5), D_{50} is mean grain diameter, υ is current velocity, C is chezy coefficient $= 18\log\left(\dfrac{12h}{\gamma}\right)$, h is water depth, r is bed roughness, g is acceleration due to gravity, Δ is specific density, $\xi = C \left(\dfrac{fw}{2g} \right)^{0.5}$ with $f_w = \exp$

$\left\{ -6.0 + 5.2 \left(\dfrac{a_o}{\gamma} \right) 0.19 \right\}$, a_o is the amplitude of orbital excursion at the bed, μ_b is amplitude of orbital velocity at the bed.

The Bijker longshore shore transport model takes into account the effect of tidal or other types of currents and may be coupled with other models. The Bijker model is unique, because it is adaptable to any current condition.

3.2.3 Kamphius equation (1991)

The Kamphius model was refined using a series of hydraulic model tests, giving

$$Q_k = 2.27 \ H_{sb}^{2.0} T p^{1.5} \ (\tan \beta)^{0.75} \ D_{50}^{-0.25} \ (\sin 2\theta_b)^{0.6} \qquad (9)$$

where H_{sb} is breaker wave height, T_p is peak wave period, β is slope of the beach, D_{50} is medium sediment diameter, θ_b is wave breaker angle. The Kamphius model does not take tidal currents along the coast in account.

4. Coastal morphology

Morphological evolutions are a direct response to changes in sediment transport. The computation of longshore sediment transport rates preceeds prediction of coastal changes due to erosion and accretion. When the sediment transport rate reduces, accretion will occur; conversely, an increase in sediment transport will cause erosion. Consequently, morphological evolutions are indicative of changes in shoreline position, and these changes are often components of the decision making measures against coastal erosion.

In conclusion, the coastline is in a state of dynamic equilibrium, characterized by the local wave climate, currents, and other water level fluctuations summarized in Table 1. In order to manage coasts sustainably, a good data gathering programme comprising: bathymetry/ topography, seabed characteristics/bedform, waterlevels/ waves, etc. is recommended.

5. Data gathering and mathematical modelling

5.1 Mathematical modelling

Most coastal engineering models are non-linear equations, which do not have analytical solution. Therefore, they cannot be applied to problems involving complex boundaries and time-varying boundary conditions. Analytical solution of models of real world will be of little help and one has to resort to numerical techniques. Several types of numerical methods, such as finite differences, finite element, finite volume and boundary element methods have been widely used to coastal engineering problems. Such models are used in investigating coastal processes and the design of coastal engineering schemes.

Experiments using physical models can also be undertaken using controlled conditions, thus allowing investigation of each controlling parameter independently. Physical models are normally smaller scale versions of the real situation. This requires a theoretical framework to relate model measurements to the real (prototype) situation. Unfortunately, the result of this theoretical framework is that scaled physical models are unable to simultaneously replicate all of the physical processes present in the prototype in correct proportion. Thus, we return to nature, by way of field measurements. Such measurements obviously do contain all the real physics, if only we knew what to measure and the appropriate instruments to do so. Such measurement, as are possible, have to be taken in an often hostile environment, at considerable relative cost and under uncontrolled conditions.

5.2 Data gathering

Field investigations are often carried out for major specific coastal defense projects. Basically, measurements are made on waves, tidal currents, water levels and beach profiles. Such measurements are often used to derive the local wave climate, current circulation patterns, extreme still-water levels and beach evolution through the use of numerical models which are calibrated and take their boundary conditions from the measurement.

Mulder *et al.* (2000) described a set of measurement tools considered both comprehensive and informative, comprising descriptions of equipment to measure bathymetry/topography, seabed characteristics/bedforms, water levels/waves, velocities, suspended sediment concentrations, morphodynamics/sediment transport and instrument carrier/frames plat forms.

Table 2 contains some recent tools in measurement equipment taken from Dominic *et al.* (2004). Interested readers are referred to the above texts for guidelines on how to use the tools and examples of results.

In terms of the development of our understanding and the incorporation of that understanding in the management of coastlines, design process, field studies and physical model studies are required to improve both our knowledge of the physics and calibrate and verify our numerical models. These models are key component of the current state-of-the art tools.

5.3 Geographic information system (GIS) tools

Sustainable development and management of natural and economic resources depends on the ability to assess complex relationships between a variety of economic, environmental and social factors across space and time. Lack of Integrated data management tools among the Interrelated and Interwoven dimensions frequently Inhibit the quality of environmental and development planning. Consequently, information management systems are currently receiving growing attention. In this regard, GISs have emerged as a particularly promising approach, enabling users to collect, store, and analyze data that have been referenced to its geographic location.

A Geographic Information System is a system of computer hardware, software, and procedures designed to support the capture, management, manipulation, analysis, and display of spatially referenced data for solving complex planning and management problems.

The advantages of GIS capability can be categorized as long term or short term. The long-term category is where economic and environmental management on a national, regional or local level is called for , in other words, institutional or programmatic applications. The short-term category usually involve specific project situations, for example, Environmental Impact Assessment Studies.

S/No	Name of tool	Brief description
1	Total station leveling for bathymetry/topography	Method of surveying the coast and inter-tidal area, using laser leveling system.
2	Differential global positioning system (GPS)	Method for fixing absolute position (three coordinates), based on calculated distance from at least four geo-stationary satellites.
3	Echo Sounder surveys	Method of surveying the seabed using a standard maritime echo sounder.
4	Van Veen grab for seabed characteristics/bed forms	A method of obtaining samples of subtidal seabed material either for visual analysis or for quantitative particle size distribution analysis.
5	Roxann system	An acoustic system used to produce a map of the near shore and offshore zones of the study area.
6	Digital side-scan sonar	An acoustic system designed to map the bedforms in the offshore and nearshore zones.
7	Pressure transducer (TP) for water levels/waves.	A device for measuring total pressure, when installed underwater, analysis of instantaneous pressures gives measure of wave height/period.
8	Wave pole	A pole or pile driven into the bed, and extending above the highest water level.
9	Directional wave Buoy	A surface buoy for measuring offshore wave conditions, including wave height, period and direction.
10	Wave recording system (WRS)	The wave recording system is an array of 6 pressure transducers used to derive the wave height, period and directional spectra in the nearshore zone.
11	Inshore Wave Climate Monitor (IWCM)	The 5 wave staffs are driven into the beach in a triangular array and are connected to a central data storage/ battery power unit.

Table 2. Names and brief description of measurement tools

The basic equipment, software and human resource skills required may be similar for both long-term and short-term, but the design, implementation and operation implications may be different.

GIS may be particularly useful in cross-sectoral and regional development, for example, in coastal zones, catchments, large urban areas, or multi-purpose development schemes within a given administrative region.

Determining a region's vulnerability to soil erosion for instance, requires the consideration of such factors as soil structure and chemistry, seasonal fluctuations in rainfall volume and intensity, geomorphology, and type of land management regime in practice. Assessing the feasibility of a soil conservation programme in an area requires additional information on the economic status of Inhabitants, the type of crops grown, and the responsiveness to incentives for soil conservation. Then, selecting the appropriate land rehabilitation models requires data on land capability and its suitability for different uses. GIS technologies handle both the spatial and non-spatial properties of data-sets, thus providing an extension to other statistical methods that disregard the spatial nature and variations of environmental data. The advantages of using GIS in environmental assessment include the following:

- It encourages a more systematic approach to environmental data collection;
- It can reduce the overall costs and institutional overlap of environmental data collection and management;
- It increases comparability and compatibility of diverse data sets;
- It makes data used in environmental assessment accessible to a wider range of decision-makers; and,
- It encourages the spatial analysis of environmental impacts that would otherwise be more easily ignored because of analytical difficulty or cost.

Besides Environmental Assessment, GIS provides a powerful set of tools for:

- Supporting Resources Inventories and Baseline Surveys and land-use mapping;
- Impact Assessment and Analysis of Alternatives;

GIS modeling techniques allow complex interrelationships to be evaluated within comprehensive spatially referenced databases. Techniques such as network analysis, digital terrain modeling are routinely applied in coastal engineering to assess the vulnerability of climate change sea-level rise to coastal communities.

Decisions made in GIS application will be useful in designing mitigation measures. Risk assessment applications such as hazard identification, and risk minimization planning are other examples where GIS has been effective.

Environmental Monitoring

When monitoring environmental impacts during and after project completion, databases with multiple attributes must be integrated. GIS can help structure and integrate this diverse information ranging from water quality to soil productivity to habitat data. Specific GIS technologies that are useful in monitoring include remote sensing, which can be applied to monitor, for example, sewage disposal sites, effluent discharges and coastal areas for example.

5.3.1 Available GIS

Geographic information systems are available both in PC/micro computers and mini and main frame computers. Table 3 lists a summary of some commercially available geographic information systems.

5.4 Salt intrusion/gravitational circulation

Sediment-laden flowing water, other natural substances or pollutants move with the water, and therefore are transported by the flow. The flowing water is affected by density differences, causing density induced currents. These currents affect the direction of flow and transport, and may vary over the depth of water. Consequently, density currents are a factor to be considered when studying the sedimentation in estuaries, coast or the transport of pollutants through these systems. Another negative effect of gravitational circulation is the creation of "null points" causing shoaling and sedimentation which interferes with navigation.

System name	Hardware	Geometric Storage	Attribute storage
ARC/INFO	VAX, PRIME IBM, DG	Vector	Relational
DELTAMAP	HP, SUN	Vector	Relational
INFORMAP	VAX	Vector	Relational
INTEGRAPH	VAX	Vector	Network
MAPS	VAX, PRIME	Vector	Relational
SICAD	SIEMENS	Vector	Relational
SYSSCAN	VAX	Vector	Relational
GEOBASED	VAX	Vector	Relational
SYSTEM 600	VAX	Vector	Relational
ARC/INFO	IBM PC/AT SYSTEM 2	Vector	Relational
SPANS	IBM PC/AT SYSTEM 2	Quadtree vector	Relational
INFORMAP II	IBM/AT	Vector	Relational
ERDAS	IBM/AT	Vector	Relational
ILWIS	IBM/AT	Raster vector	Relational
PAMAP	IBM/AT	Raster	Relational
IDRISI	IBM/AT	Raster	Relational

Table 3. GIS in mini and main-frame computers

Management concerns frequently center on the concentration of waterborne indicators, including pollutants and plaktonic organisms. The need to consider the environmental and economic sustainability of present and future coastal management schemes on muddy coasts requires a good understanding of density currents and morpho-dynamics. Aquatic ecosystem sustainability is highly dependent on salinity concentration dynamics and must be studied for the particular environment. Both analytical and mathematical models are currently used to simulate salt intrusion. The models constitute a powerful tool for evaluation of salinity intrusion patterns and as supportive instruments for decision making in coast management. Table 4 contains some widely used coastal engineering models:

Designs	Name	Purpose
1	Genesis	Simulation of coastal processes
2	SBEACH	Coastal Engineering design
3	MODIFIED KRIEBEL	Cross-shore simulation for berm dimensions and hurricane storm events.
4	CEQUALW2	Salinity Intrusion

Table 4. Widely Used Coastal Engineering Models

6. Sustainable management of coastlines

Coastal management plans are designed to provide coastal zone resource development within the framework of:

a. Technical: coastal processes and defense, etc
b. Socio-economic: economic demography, regional planning and
c. Environmental: water quality, biodiversity, etc.
i. Coastal management is continually confronted with conflicting challenges. There are problems of jurisdiction involved in whether the responsibility for running the operation lies with the federal governments, a local government or some regulatory commission, and always there is application of priorities supposedly set by society as a whole. The basic tool is a legal framework to regulate the conflicting activities on the coast. These may include national laws made to meet specific requirements, e.g. National Environmental Policy Acts of 1969 which provides preparation of environmental impact statement, the Water Quality Act of 1970 which addresses oil pollution; international covenants and jurisdictional responsibility.
ii. There is a problem of political process. The political process is such that technical standards will almost always yield to such things as austerity cases, emergency situations, or strong public sentiments. Consequently, decision on coastal environment must have a public input or else the decision will probably not be effective. The manager must be prepared to strike a compromise between the emotional public, individual agencies, both state and federal, often working at cross-purposes.
iii. Arising from (ii), is the need for coordinated approach such that environmental protection, fish and wildlife services, etc, may work together and adopt a consistent approach to survey, mitigation and monitoring. The coordinated approach achieves better results for the environment in terms of a more consolidated, integrated approach and saves on resources and repetition by stakeholders.
iv. The physical characteristics of coastal environment is dictated by the actions of breaking waves and currents on sediment materials. There is need for quality data gathering, both comprehensive and information, comprising bathymethry/topography, seabed characteristics/bedforms, water levels/waves, velocities, suspended sediment concentration.
v. There is need to broaden the emphasis from assessment of physical environment aspects, to assessment of impacts on marine ecological resources, in particular benthic and epibenthic species, habitats.

vi. Application of Hydroinformatics systems: Hydroinforamtics, the use of information and communication technology in hydraulics, encapsulates and integrates engineering methods in software systems. It provides powerful methods to engineers and rational solutions to policy makers. The application of hydroinformatics systems to problem solving in coastal environments requires the availability of databases for calibration and verification of engineered systems. It also calls for adequate instrumentation and experimental methods, and international cooperation for the acquisition and exchange of data. Hydroinformatics systems will have to be built up from proprietary codes and modeling systems that have been constructed, in most cases, for quite other purposes than those of hydroinformatics. Interested readers are referred to Abbot et al., (1988) for full description of hydroinformatics systems.

vii. The need for integrated coastal zone management (ICZM). Integrated coastal zone management has been widely accepted as an effective mechanism for addressing and resolving these types of issues throughout the developed and developing world. ICZM will enable the integration of all issues and emphasize the involvement of all key players in the planning process, coordination between sectoral agencies, and application of cooperative management strategies involving stakeholders.

7. Environmental aspects of coastlines

As a case study, the Nigerian coast and marine areas have been chosen under this heading:

7.1 Wave and tidal characteristics

The Nigerian coast and marine areas are under the influence of moderate oceanographic forcing consisting of semi-diurnal tidal with spring tide ranging between 0.95m in the West to 3.25m in the East. The prevailing South-Westerly waves vary from spilling breaker to plunging waves. The persistence of significant wave height (hs) are in the order of 1.4m – 2.5m. Long shore currents and prevalent in the near shore while the West-East Guinea currents constitute the major ocean current.

The relative importance of diurnal and semidiurnal harmonics can be determined from the ratio, F, given by

$$F = K_1 + O_1 / M_2 + S_2 \qquad (10)$$

where K_1, O_1, M_2 and S_2 denote the amplitudes of the respective tidal constituents. The form of tide (F) found in the Nigerian Atlantic Coast was calculated by substituting the amplitudes for K_1, O_1, M_2 and S_2 into Equation (10). The value of F calculated is 0.1601. Consequently, the tidal behaviour found along the Nigerian Atlantic coast is semi-diurnal, with two high and two low waters of approximately the same height.

7.2 Assessment of climate change

The possible impacts of climate change include higher sea levels altered pattern of rainfall and air temperatures, and increased frequency and intensity of severe storms. Some industries could be directly affected by adverse impacts of climate change. The coastal tourism industry, for example, is vulnerable to both sea-level rise and greater weather extremes. Table 5 shows a comparison of sea-level rise indicator parameters with others (Nwaogazie and Ologhadien 2010).

Parameter	Nigerian Coast	IPCC	Ghana	England	Remarks
Temperature	1.8°C	1.5 – 4.5°C	0.11°C	NA	Per decade
Rainfall	55.2mm	NA	13mm	NA	Per decade
Mean Sea Level	8.3cm	6cm	2.2cm	4cm-6cm	Per decade

NA - Not Available; IPCC – Intergovernmental Panel on Climatic Change

Table 5. Comparison with IPCC and other Predictions

7.3 Sea-break-through inlets

The major environmental concern of the Ondo Coastline in Nigeria is its susceptibility to sea-break through inlets (Odi-Owei and Ologhadien, 2009). The first sea break-through inlet occurred in 1983, when a canal was dredged oblique to the coastline, leaving a vertical head cut. The overhang, coupled with the poor geotechnical characteristics and mechanisms of sediment transport downstream in the channel, initiated an upstream migration at the head cut towards the sea. Over time, the combined actions of the breaking waves, tidal currents and sea wind migration of the head cut eventually opened up the inlet, discharging saline water into the fresh water forest. Consequently, over 20 hectares of fresh water forest resources were destroyed (Plate 2), impacting negatively on the local economy. It also reduced the volume of saw-logs supply to the timber markets in Lagos, Benin, etc. Freshwater resources are extensively exploited for cash or subsistence. The Ondo State coastline is fairly stable except in areas that are exposed to breaking waves.

7.4 Coastal erosion and flooding

The coastline has been subjected to erosion over the years in Nigeria. Scientist from the Nigerian Institute for Oceanography and Marine Research (NIOMR) have reported widespread erosion and flooding of the Barrier Islands and the Niger Delta (Ibe et al., 1984, Awosike 1993) created erosion resulting from deficit of sand due to natural and anthropogenic activities varies. Notable among the natural causes of coastal erosion are vulnerable soil characteristics, topography and occurrence of off-shore canyons. Anthropogenic causes include destruction of coastline dredging and river dams.

The Victoria beach is fastest eroding beach in Nigeria with arrange erosion rate of 20 -30m yearly. Erosion rates range between 18-24m annually at Ugborodo/Escravos; Forcados, 20-22m; 16-19m at Brass; Karamo, 15-20m; Bonny, 20-24m; and Opobo; 10-14m; as reported by Ibe in 1989. Coastal erosion with serious flooding has done widespread damage in many areas along the coastal zone. The beaches along the Nigerian coastline are very susceptible to flooding due to their very low topography. Flooding of the Victoria Island in Lagos State and other low-lying areas of the state are common during the rainy season (June-August). High rainfall in the Niger Delta coupled with poor drainage allow storm waters to collect in the hallows and eventually flood large areas within the Delta.

Plate 2. Dead vegetation around Awoye inlets

Fig. 1. Map showing Canal and Sampling Stations

7.5 Physical modification and festruction of habitats

The coastal zones have undergone wide modifications in the last thirty years. Due to high pressures on coastal resources conflicting exploitation techniques and increasing population leading to loss of biodiversity, in the ecosystem, the value of coastlines has been diminished. The destruction of mangrove ecosystems has been on the increase since exploitation of oil and gas started in the Niger Delta resulting in replacement of mangrove vegetation by new vegetation species like nympa palms.

The Kwale game reserve in the 1950s was rich in biodiversity but due to oil exploration, gas production and poaching elephants and many flora and fauna have disapproved in the Reserve several animal species of conservation interest including Scalter's Guenon, Delta Red Columbus, the Crested Genet, the Pygmy Hippo, Chimpanzee and African Leopard have almost disappeared in the Niger Delta, many plants of medicinal, economic and cultural values such as *Thaumatiococcus daniel* (sweetener) *Fegara sp.* (for sickle cell anemia) and *Rauvolfia vomitoria* (for treatment of high blood pressure and now rare in the Niger Delta).

The major socio-economic problems result from poverty ecosystem modification in the coastal zones include unemployment because the people depend on their tradition mean of livelihood.

7.6 Environmental management plan for coastal communities

The key to effective environmental management plan is adequate monitoring of the projects implementation, predicted impacts and monitoring or implementation of predicted mitigation measures. The environmental issues that will be addressed are;
i.   Over exploitation of Fisheries resources,
ii.   Costal and Marine Pollution
iii.   Oil spills
iv.   Coastal Erosion and Flooding
v.   Physical modification and destruction of habitats
vi.   Climate change and sea-level rise
vii.   Invasive species (exotic species)
viii.   Storm surges.

8. Conclusion

In order to implement the Environmental Management Plan for Coastal Communities, guidelines for dealing with specific environmental issues identified should be developed. As part of the management plan, continuous data collection for bathymetry, topography, waves, tides, surges, wind and salinity need to be carried out.

9. References

Abbot, M.B., (1991), Hydroinformatics; Information Technology and the Aquatic Environment, Avebury Technical, ISBN 1 85628 832 3.

Adnitt, C. and Lewis J. (2004) "The Future of Environmental Impact Assessment for marine aggregate extraction-best practice and emerging issues". *Journal of marine Science and Environment*, No. CI 2004, pp.36-44.

Antonucci, J., GIS: A Guide to the Technology, New York: Von Nostrand Reinhold, 1991.

Bathurst, J.C., Graf, W.H., and Cao, H.H. (1987). "Bed-load Discharge equation for steep mountain rivers" Sediment transport in Gravel-bed rivers, C.R. Thorne, J.C. Bathurst and R.D., Hey, eds., John Wiley and Sons ltd., new York, N.Y.

Bijker, E., "Sedimentation in Channels and Trenches", *Proc. 17th Conf. on Coastal Eng.*, Sydney, Australia, 1980, pp.299-300.

Burrough, P.A., (1986), Principles of GISs for Earth Resources Assessment, Oxford: Clarendon Press.

Christine, A. Coughonowr, Magnus N. Ngolie and Olof Linden (1995); "Coastal Zone Management on Eastern Africa Including the island States: A Review of issues and Initiatives" Ambio Vol.24, No.7-8, pp.448-457.

Dominic Reeve, Andrew Chadwick and Christopher Fleming (2004). *Coastal Engineering: Processes, Theory and Design Practice"*, Spon Press, OX14 4RN.

EA Source Book Update, GISs for Environmental Assessment and review, #3, April, 1993.

Gomez, B., and Church, B. (1989) "An Assessment of bed load Sediment Transport Formulae for Gravel Bed Rivers", J. Water Resources 25(6), 1161-1186.

Hassan, H.M., and C, Hutchinson, Natural Resource and Environmental Information for Decisionmaking, World Bank, 1992.

"Management of the Marine Environment" in Introduction to Marine Pollution Control, Jerome Williams, a Wiley-Interscience Publication. Chap 10.

Mulder, J.P.M., Koningfield, M. Van Owen, M.W. and Rawson, J., 2001. Guidelines on the selection of CZM tools. Report RIKZ/2001.020, Rijkswanterstaat, April 2001.

Nwaogazie I.L, and Ologhadien I. (2010). "Trend Analysis of Climate Change Indicators along the Nigerian Atlantic Coast", Proceedings of the International Conf. on Climate Changes, Nigerian Society of Engineers", Abuja 2010.

Nwilo, P.C. (1997). "Managing the Impacts of Storm Surge on Victoria Island, Lagos, Nigeria" *IAHS*, Publ. No. 239, pp. 325 – 330.

Odi-Owei S. and Ologhadien I. (2009). "Environmental Aspect of Dredging Intra-coastal Navigation Channels in Muddy Coastline: The case of Awoye, Ondo State, Nigeria". *Journal of Food, Agr. & Environ*, Vol. 7(2): 764-768.

Paulson, B., Urban Applications of Satellite Remote Sensing and GIS Analysis, World Bank, 1992.

Rijn, L.C. van "Sediment Transport, Part II: Suspended Load Transport," *Journal of Hydraulic Engineering,* vol. 110, No.11, 1984, pp.1613-1641.

Rijn, L.C. van, "Initiation of Motion, Bed Forms, bed Roughness, Sediment Concentrations and Transport by Currents and Waves", *Report S 487-IV,* Delft Hydraulics Laboratory, Delft, The Netherlands, 1985.

Rijn, L.C. van, "Model for Sedimentation Predictions", *Proc.,* 19th IAHR-Congress, vol.2, New Delhi, India, 1980, pp.321-329.

Rijn, L.C. van, "Sediment Transport, Part I: Bed Load Transport", *Journal of Hydraulic Engineering,* vol.110, No.10, 1984, pp.1431-1456.

Rijn, L.C. van, "Sediment Transport, Part III: Bed Forms and Alluvial Roughness," *Journal of Hydraulic Engineering,* vol.110, No.12, 1984, pp.1733-1754.

Van OS, A.G. (1990). Density currents and salt Intrusion, Lecture Note for the Hydraulic Engineering Course at Unesco-IHE, Delft, The Netherlands.

van Rijn, L.C. (1992) Morphological Processes, Lecture Note for Hydroinformatics Course at Unesco-IHE, Delft, The Wetherlands.

White, W.R., Milli, H., and Crabbe, C. (1973). Sediment Transport: An Appraisal of Available Methods Hydr. Res. Station, Wallingford.

Part 2

Environmental Management in Industry

9

Indicators of Sustainable Business Practices

Hyunkee Bae and Richard S. Smardon
Department of Environmental Studies,
SUNY College of Environmental and Science and Forestry
USA

1. Introduction

Since the end of the 1990s, businesses have started to systematically consider environmental problems in terms of different positions and levels within a firm, such as design, purchase, sale, and disposal (Welford, 2000). The United Kingdom published BS 7750, a standardized specification for an environmental management system in 1994 and the International Organization for Standardization (ISO) published ISO 14001 - an environmental management standard in 1996. The main goal of these standards is to help all kinds of organizations to establish and implement environmental management systems by systematically setting up environmental policies, practices, objectives, and targets. The number of organizations with ISO 14001 certification around the world rapidly increased to 13,368 in December of 1999 to 129,031 in December of 2006 (Corporate Risk Management Company, 2000:2007).

Welford (2000) insisted that Environmental Management Systems (EMSs), such as ISO 14001, are no longer options. However, there are some problems with EMSs. The ISO 14001 standard does not promote the flexibility needed to handle continuously changing environmental issues (Moxen & Strachan, 1998). The ISO 14001 mostly depends on action control and results based on environmental impacts, rather than social and ethical control. Thompson (2002) pointed out three areas of ISO 14001 that should be described: (i) social aspects and impacts and how to control them; (ii) guidelines for a set of widely recognized and accepted environmental performance principles; and (iii) a method to communicate environmental performance information to external stakeholders and decision makers. To address these areas, businesses should go even further than environmental management systems and completely integrate all the components of sustainable development into a new way of doing business (Welford, 2000). In addition, a variety of interested parties, such as governments, "green" consumers, and "green" investors, are also encouraging firms to incorporate their environmental management systems and sustainable development into their decision-making process for sustainable business practices and/or strategies. Companies could implement sustainable business practice to meet these demands for interested parties on sustainable business. To effectively implement sustainable business practices, firms need to know the kinds of indicators that meet the characteristics or concepts of sustainable business practices.

Based on these needs, we aims to identify whether or not firms have applied sustainable business practices based on the Triple Bottom Line (Environmental, economic, and social areas). To accomplish this goal, we conducted two surveys. The first survey identified the trends of indicators in terms of the TBL used to describe sustainable business practices. The second survey assessed the degree to which firms have issued performance reports and what kinds of keywords were used in the titles of these reports.

2. Literature review

2.1 Sustainable business

There is no single definition of sustainable business, as there is for sustainable development (Azapagic, 2003). A lack of a common accepted definition of sustainable business is the most critical problem because the definition is a fundamental tool to carry out new policies and actions. To overcome this, a few institutions have introduced the definition of sustainable business. The Evergreen Group (2008), a business brokerage dedicated to sustainable business, defines that a sustainable business is a business that carries out an environmentally friendly business processes without negative environmental impacts related to their activities, products, and services. Sustinable business.Com[1] (2009) says that sustainable business is "a business that contributes to an equitable and ecologically sustainable economy." Based on these examples of the definitions of sustainable business, sustainable business offers products and services that fulfill society's needs while contributing to the well-being of all earth's inhabitants. Sustainable business is a new, radical paradigm that considers the ecological, social, and economic impacts in a way that will not compromise the needs of future generations (Azapagic & Perdan, 2000; Welford, 2000). Azapagic and Perdan (2000) asserted that firms need a paradigm shift if firms want to integrate sustainable development into their business.

Sustainable business requires effective harmonization of a Triple Bottom Line (TBL), which is the environmental, economic, and social areas. Since the TBL is the key element of sustainable development, firms that carry out sustainable business should not only understand the TBL, but also integrate it into their policies or strategies and decision-making processes (Desimone & Popoff, 1998; WBCSD, 2000).

The environmental area consists of environmental impacts related to an organization's diverse activities, products, and services. These environmental indicators should be identified in all stages of the organization's full life cycle because they are used to track environmental progress, support environmental policy evaluation and inform the public. Examples of environmental indicators are energy and water consumption, air pollution, and solid and hazardous waste produced.

The economic area includes an organization's economic values and performance that are explained by economic indicators. The economy provides solutions and methods to invest in protecting the environment and conservation of natural resources as well as to sustain society. Examples are annual profits and sales, Research & Development investment, fines, capital investment, and share values or annual returns.

The social area is related to wider responsibilities that business has to communities within which it operates and to society in general, including both present and future generations. Since the importance of social and ethical responsibilities of a company is gradually

---

[1] Sustinablebusiness.Com: SustainableBusiness.com is an organization that "provides global news and networking services to help green business grow, covering all sectors: renewable energy, green building, sustainable investing, and organics" http://www.sustainablebusiness.com/

increasing, its social responsibility has become a constituted element within what society expects from business. A few international organizations and institutions, such as the European Commission (EC), have developed and launched a variety of standards relevant to corporate social and ethical responsibility around the world. For instance, the Social Accountability 8000 (SA 8000)[2] focused on social and ethical issues, and on Corporate Social Responsibility (CSR). It is not easy to define and quantify social indicators in terms of physical indicators like economic and environmental indicators. Nevertheless, many firms have set up a realistic goal to continuously measure these indicators in a comparable manner across organizations by using qualitative social indicators. These sets of qualitative social indicators are used to evaluate sustainable business embedded in the concept of sustainable development. Examples of social indicators are: (i) human development and welfare (e.g., education and training and health and safety); (ii) equity (e.g., wages, equal opportunity, and non-discrimination); and (iii) ethical considerations (e.g., human rights and child labor abolition) (Azapagic, 2003).

2.2 Voluntary communication to the public

A firm that would like to apply sustainable business could voluntarily communicate diverse performance of their practices to the public because interested parties want to know information about the firms' sustainable business practices (Adams, Houldrin & Slomp, 1999). Voluntary reporting information about firms' environmental and social performance is becoming a powerful and popular tool to communicate with the public because interested parties can use such information to evaluate firms' activities and performance (Feldman, Soyka, & Ameer, 1996; Sasseville, Willson, & Lawson, 1997). Internal or external reporting systems can have a significant effect on corporate culture for sustainable business because they are designed to support positive behaviors in terms of sustainable development.

Since the early 1990s, a few companies, such as Monsanto and Kodak, have disclosed outcomes of their environmental performance according to their own indicators. However, the lack of credibility and verifiability of the indicators and outcomes disclosed in these reports has become a significant problem (Lin & Wang, 2004; Thompson, 2002).

To overcome these problems, in 2002, the Global Reporting Initiative (GRI) published the 2002 GRI Sustainability Reporting Guidelines based on the concepts of sustainable development (Lin & Wang, 2004 ; Thompson, 2002). The GRI guidelines propose principles and general indicators to report an organization's performance in terms of the TBL: economic, environmental, and social dimensions. After publishing the GRI guidelines, many companies like 3M have integrated their own indicators into the GRI guidelines. SmiXXX (06) said that it used the Global Reporting Initiative's 2002 Sustainability Reporting Guidelines to increase the credibility of its information and reports. In 2002, the European Commission (EC) published "Corporate Social Responsibility (CSR): A business contribution to Sustainable Development". The EC formally defined corporate social responsibility:

---

[2] Social Accountability 8000: Social Accountability 8000 was developed by the Council on Economic Priorities Accreditation Agency in 1997. "SA8000 is promoted as a voluntary, universal standard for companies interested in auditing and certifying labour practices in their facilities and those of their suppliers and vendors. It is designed for independent third party certification" http:// www.mallenbaker.net/csr/CSRfiles/SA8000.html

CSR is a concept whereby companies integrate social and environmental concerns in their business operations and in their interaction with their stakeholders on a voluntary basis. (p. 7)

The Corporate Social Responsibility (CSR) standard includes environmental, financial, and social performance information related to sustainable development. To meet the demands of the public for corporate social responsibility, many companies, such as Kodak and Ford, are annually disclosing the performance reports of their sustainable business practices with different titles, such as "Corporate Social report," and "Sustainability Report" to the public.

2.3 Indicators for sustainable business practices

An indicator is a measurement that shows the status of an environmental, economic, or social system over time (Redefining Progress, Sustainable Seattle, and Tyler Norris Associates, 1997). The goals of indicators are:

- to monitor and evaluate effectiveness and performance of goals and targets of sustainable business (Bennett & James,1999; Parris & Kates, 2003);
- to communicate to diverse stakeholders (Thompson, 2002). Indicators can help stakeholders, including the pubic, decision makers, and managers, to assist in decision-making about sustainable business (Kuhndt & Geibler, 2002); and
- to compare actions and performance of firms that may or may not be implementing sustainable business (Kuhndt & Geibler, 2002).

With these objectives in mind, numerous companies and international organizations, such as the International Organization for Standardization and the Global Reporting Initiatives, have developed a set of indicators to measure progress of environmental performance and sustainable business. Many organizations are using diverse indicators to integrate current environmental management systems into sustainable business.

Indicators for sustainable business practices can be expressed in many different forms (e.g., qualitative or quantitative, general or specific, and absolute or relative), in accordance with objectives and applications of an indicator. Quantitative indicators are measured in terms of mass, volume or number of environmental pollutants or physical materials. Examples of quantitative indicators are total amount of air emissions like CO_2, or total volume of hazardous waste. Not all indicators will be quantitative, and some will have to be expressed qualitatively because they cannot be defined in physical terms (Azapagic & Perdan, 2000). Qualitative indicators are expressed interpretively. Qualitative indicators include social dimensions of a firm's activities, such as changes in cultural values or equity (Azapagic & Perdan, 2000). Sustainable business could be described by both qualitative and quantitative metrics because both are required to explain whether or not an organization's diverse activities consider or meet human needs and social demands (Daly, 1990; Azapagic & Perdan, 2000). Thus, many firms are setting up qualitative indicators as a substantial goal to measure the progress of the firms' policies even though qualitative indicators are difficult to define in physical terms (Azapagic & Perdan, 2000).

Indicators can also be divided into general and specific indicators (Verfaillie & Bidwell, 2000). General indicators are used by businesses across all industries in the world. These general indicators can be used to measure issues that have already been discussed globally, such as an international agreement or consensus: Agenda 21, Montreal Protocol, and Kyoto Protocol (global warming) (Verfaillie & Bidwell, 2000; Muller & Sturm, 2001). General indicators include energy, water and material consumption, greenhouse gas emissions, carbon dioxide, methane, and air emissions per unit product. These indicators can be used to compare one organization's performance against another's. Specific indicators are defined differently and measured in accordance to characteristics of each industry or firm (Verfaillie & Bidwell, 2000). For instance, Chemical Industries Association (2002) established the Responsible Care (RC) program for companies in the chemical industry. RC is the chemical industry's global voluntary initiative program.

Indicators for sustainable business practices can be expressed in absolute or relative forms. Absolute indicators are used to measure a firm's quantitative environmental and social impact related to its activities, products, and services. Thompson (2002) said that absolute indicators are expressed in terms of measured quantities: total amount of energy consumed a year, total amount of water consumed, total amount of wastewater, and total amount of hazardous waste generated. These indicators can provide managers or the pubic with incomplete information relevant to operational levels because these indicators use a single value to represent how much a firm has accomplished towards its goals and targets over time (Bennett & James, 1999). For instance, a firm reduces the total energy consumed this year by 5% compared to last year's total. A manager cannot determine whether or not this reduction is an environmentally positive result since the reduction of energy could be the result of other factors, such as reduction of productivity, rather than actual improvements of environmental activities and technologies. Relative indicators were introduced to address this problem of absolute indicators.

Relative indicators are expressed in terms of a ratio or proportion that compares an absolute indicator with another absolute indicator (Thompson, 2002). Azapagic and Perdan (2000) argue that relative indicators enable firms and interested parties to evaluate improvement from year to year and figure out more sustainable opportunities and practices. Thus, relative indicators could help stakeholders understand whether or not a company truly increases efficiency of emissions by measuring levels of pollutant per unit of production (Bennett & James, 1999). Examples of relative indicators are eco-efficiency indicators, such as carbon dioxide emissions per unit of output, ratio of waste per unit of input material, ratio of total hazardous solid waste per unit of product, etc. These relative indicators can be used to measure the constant economic value of natural capital stocks. However, Bennett and James (1999) mentioned that relative indicators also have a problem because they do not show the total amount of pollutants in terms of absolute values, which could be used as firm to firm benchmarking. To resolve these problems of absolute and relative indicators, many companies choose to use both types of indicators to evaluate and report their performance.

3. Data collection

We conducted two surveys. To conduct the first survey, we collected firms' annual performance reports announced to the public through Internet media. There are two reasons why these performance reports were collected. The first reason is because the changes in the types of indicators for sustainable business practices were described in those performance reports. The second one is that the changes in the performance reports announced through Internet mass media can be used to investigate the extent to which firms have communicated their performance reports to the public.

Sample performance reports for the first survey were collected from January 1999 to December 2006. Since the ISO published ISO 14031 Environmental Performance Evaluation -

guidelines in 1999, firms might have gained interest in reporting their environmental performance beginning in 1999. 2006 is the most current year that firms' performance reports could be collected through firms' Internet homepages.

The announcements that were disclosed the performance reports were identified by using newswire databases; ABI/Inform, Global, Business & Industry, Business & Company Resource Center, and LexisNexis. The key words used to find the announcement events were "Environmental Performance," "Reports," "Sustainability," "Corporate Social Responsibility," and "Citizenship." The following criteria were used to collect sample data:

- Only publicly traded firms on the New York Stock Exchange (NYSE) were considered;
- Companies in the information, finance, and insurance industry were excluded because their businesses did not generate direct environmental pollution; and
- Firms that provide their performance reports (PDF file) were included.

Companies have created and continuously updated their Internet homepages to provide environmental and social performance reports. After identifying firms that announced their performance reports, the performance reports of sample firms were collected through each firm's Internet homepage. The Internet Archive Organization[3] was used to find the performance reports of companies that did not provide previous performance reports directly from the current homepage. The internet archive organization provides archive data of a firm's Internet homepage according to the day that the firm updated the homepage. The North American Industry Classification System (NAICS) was used to classify types of industries A firm's NAICS code categorized by the Wharton Research Data Service (WRDS) was used.

The indicators for sustainable business practices were selected by reviewing diverse environmental and sustainable indicator guidelines, such ISO 14031, GRI guidelines, the Organisation for Economic Co-operation and Development (OECD), Social responsibility, and other researchers.

The second survey was conducted to identify the current trend in the titles of firms' performance reports. The terms used as key words in titles of firms' performance reports could be used to identify the main themes or strategies of the reports (Bruemmer, 2000). Performance reports have been given diverse titles, such as "Environmental Reports," "Environmental, Health, and Safety Report," "Sustainable Reports," "Corporate Social Reports," "Citizenship Report," etc. If a firm used "Environmental" as a key word in the titles of its performance report, it means that the firm did not set up social and economic indicators, which are the fundamental indicators of sustainable business. However, if a firm used the terms, "Social Responsibility," "Corporate Social Responsibility," "Sustainability," and "Citizenship" as key words, it could indicate that the firm has likely incorporated the concepts of sustainable development into its business strategies, which is sustainable business. This is because these terms are evolved from the concept of sustainable development.

For the second survey, we used S&P 500 firms as of December 2006 that reported their performance reports to the public in 2007. Since 2006 performance reports, disclosed in 2007, were the most current reports that could be collected through the Internet, they were chosen as the sample. Thus, the Internet homepages of S&P 500 sample companies were searched to identify annual sustainability or environmental reports for 2006. Among S&P 500 firms, a

---

[3] Internet Archive Organization is "a 501(c)(3) non-profit that was founded to build an Internet library, with the purpose of offering permanent access for researchers, historians, and scholars to historical collections that exist in digital format" http://www.archive.org/index.php

few industries (e.g., Information; Finance and Insurance; Real Estate and Rental and Leasing; Educational Services; and Health Care and Social Assistance) were excluded from the sample because they neither generated environmental pollution nor had heavy environmental burdens.

4. Results and discussion

4.1 Changes in indicators for sustainable business

We found eighty-nine announcements eighty-nine announcements published by 40 companies through Internet media. Approximately eighty-eight percent (78 announcements) of the total sample was taken from the manufacturing industries (NAICS code 31, 32, and 33). The rest of the total samples (21 announcements) was disclosed by firms in other industries: the mining industry (NAICS code 21), the utilities industry (NAICS code 22), the miscellaneous store retailers (NAICS code 45), and the couriers and messengers industry (NAICS code 49). Table 1 presents the distribution of the sampled companies based on the NAICS. Table 2 lists the types of manufacturing industries. Of the

NAICS		Year								Total	
Title (Two digit)	Three digit	'99	'00	'01	'02	'03	'04	'05	'06	Number	%
Mining (21)	212						1	1	1	3	3.4%
Utilities (22)	221							2	2	4	4.5%
Manufacturing (31,32,33)	311							1	3	4	87.6%
	312						1	1	1	3	
	316			1				2	1	4	
	321					1	1	1		3	
	322				1				2	3	
	324			1		2	1	4	3	11	
	325	1		1	1	3	3	2	3	14	
	331				1	2	1	2	2	8	
	333	1					1		2	4	
	334			1		2	1	3	2	9	
	335							1	1	2	
	336		1	1	1		2	5	3	13	
Miscellaneous Store Retailers(45)	453								1	1	1.1%
Couriers and Messengers (49)	492					1		1	1	3	3.4%
Total		2	1	5	4	11	12	26	28	89	

Table 1. Distribution of Sampled Companies Based on the NAICS

NAICS	Type of Manufacturing	Number (%)
311	Food Manufacturing	4 (5%)
312	Beverage and Tobacco Product Manufacturing	3 (4%)
316	Leather and Allied Product Manufacturing	4 (5%)
321	Wood Product Manufacturing	3 (4%)
322	Paper Manufacturing	3 (4%)
324	Petroleum and Coal Products Manufacturing	11 (14%)
325	Chemical Manufacturing	14 (18%)
331	Primary Metal Manufacturing	8 (10%)
333	Machinery Manufacturing	4 (5%)
334	Computer and Electronic Product Manufacturing	9 (12%)
335	Electrical Equipment, Appliance, and Component Manufacturing	2 (3%)
336	Transportation Equipment Manufacturing	13(17%)
Total		78

Table 2. Types of Manufacturing in the Sample Announcements

78 announcements in the manufacturing industries, 55 announcements (71%) are from firms in petroleum and coal products manufacturing, chemical manufacturing, primary metal manufacturing, computer and electronic products manufacturing, and transportation equipment manufacturing. The main reason why firms in these manufacturing industries have disclosed their performance reports more often than in other industries is that firms producing final consumer goods proactively meet needs and avoid potentially adverse stakeholders' reactions (Anton, Deltas & Khanna, 2004). Anton et al. (2004) said that firms that produce consumer goods are pressured by environmental interests more than firms that produce industrial goods. To proactively respond to the increasing environmental pressures and social responsibilities, firms producing consumer goods have actively communicated their environmental and social information to their interested parties.

We could not find many announcements in the mining sector related to the disclosure of environmental or sustainable performance reports during 1999 to 2006. Three announcements were reported by one firm, BXXX Ltd. Other firms in this industry have reported and provided their environmental performance reports on their Internet homepages. For instance, CXXX has reported the performance of a few environmental and social indicators relevant to sustainable development on its Internet homepage. It has monitored the performance of environmental and social indicators since 2005.

Since the utilities industry has to use natural capital to produce their products, such as electric power, natural gas, and fuel, it is one of the critical industries for sustaining society, doing business, and for activities such as the operation of factories and the routine activities of daily life. We found just four announcements in the utilities industry that were reported by. It does not seem that many firms in this industry proactively communicate their performance reports to the public. However, they have started disclosing their performance reports on Internet homepages since 2005 or 2006. For example, SXXX Company began providing its Corporate Responsibility Reports in 2006. To proactively respond to the increasing requirements of firms' performance reports, they might realize that they should disclose their social and environmental performance reports.

OXXX in the miscellaneous store retailers industry announced its performance reports based on the concept of sustainable development and business in 2006. Some firms in this industry have also reported their environmental or sustainability performance reports. For instance, StaXXX Inc. has been reporting its corporate responsibility, which includes a few sustainable business indicators, on its Internet homepage since 2006.

There were three announcements of environmental or sustainable performance reports in the couriers and messengers industry. They were reported by UXXX. UXXX has disclosed its sustainability reports since 2003. Like the utilities industry and the miscellaneous store retailers industry, a few firms like FXXX had provided their environmental or sustainable performance reports on their Internet homepages.

4.1.1 Increasing announcements

Figure 1 shows the trends of the announcements of the disclosure of firms' performance reports during 1999 to 2006. We did not find many firms that announced their performance reports through diverse Internet media even though they began reporting their environmental performance in the early 2000s. This is consistent with previous studies. When Hamilton (1995) studied how media and stock market responded to the disclosure of the Toxic Release Inventory (TRI) data, he used 50 firms that reported TRI data through the media. This indicates that firms did not progressively communicate their environmental information to the public. Firms did not use various communication tools to inform the public about their environmental performance reports. According to Figure 1, the number of announcements of the disclosure of firms' performance reports has been gradually increasing since 2003. Firms that announced performance reports before 2002 were in the manufacturing industry. From 2003, firms in other industries, such as the couriers and messengers, the mining, and the utilities industries, started announcing their performance reports through diverse Internet media. There are two reasons why the number of announcements of firms' performance reports might have increased since 2003.

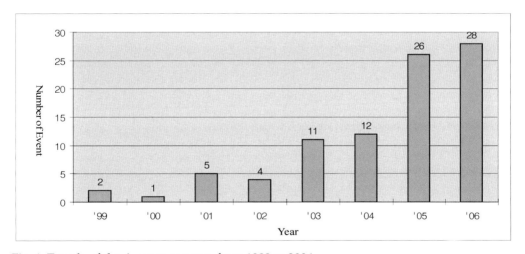

Fig. 1. Trends of the Announcements from 1999 to 2006

The first reason is that after 2003 firms might have recognized that voluntarily announcing their performance reports by using various Internet media is a powerful tool to inform the public of their performance reports (Feldman et al, 1996; Sasseville et al., 1997). Firms can use their socially and environmentally friendly management activities as key information in their marketing strategies because environmental and social information has been gaining significance as a marketing tool since the early 2000s. Another reason is that a few international guidelines relevant to the disclosure of environmental, social, and economic performance reports have been published since 2002, such as the 2002 GRI Sustainability Reporting Guidelines which is the fundamental guidelines of all GRI documents (GRI, 2004). The 2002 GRI guidelines included more detailed performance indicators of three sustainability dimensions (economic, environmental, and social) than the 2000 GRI guidelines first published by the GRI in 2000. Thus, many firms have actively adopted the 2002 GRI guidelines not only to voluntarily implement sustainable business, but also to voluntarily communicate the performance of sustainable business. After publishing the GRI guidelines, many global firms have integrated their own indictors into the GRI guidelines to meet the needs of their interested parties. For example, UXXX announced its first corporate social responsibility report with the title "Operating in Unison UXXX 2002 Corporate Sustainability Report" on Nov 14, 2003. In this report, they mentioned, "We used the Global Reporting Initiative (GRI) as the foundation for writing our first Corporate Sustainability Report."

4.1.2 Identifying sustainable business indicators (SBIs)

After reviewing diverse environmental and sustainable indicator guidelines, such as the GRI guidelines, a total of 90 general indicators were selected. Table 3 shows the list of 90 general indicators. These general indicators were separated into seven categories in order to identify absolute and relative indicators types for sustainable business based on the TBL: 22 Environmental indicators; 14 economic indicators; 16 social indicators; 15 economic and environmental (eco-efficient) indicators; 7 social and environmental (socio-environmental) indicators; 6 social and economic (socio-economic) indicators; and 10 environmental, economic and social (integrated) indicators.

Environmental, economic, and social indicators are absolute indicators. Eco-efficient, socio-environmental, socio-economic, and integrated indicators are relative indicators used to implement sustainable business practices. Socio-environmental indicators are focused on environmental impacts that affect social impacts, and vice versa. Azar, Holmberg, and Lindgren (1996) mentioned that the goal of the socio-environmental indicators is to serve as a tool in planning and decision-making processes at various managerial levels within society. Socio-economic indicators are related to the relationship between a firm's economic activities and social effects. Socio-economic requires firms not only to consider one or more social impacts, but also one or more economic impacts (Etzioni, 2003). Unlike socio-environmental and socio-economic indicators, eco-efficient indicators are more easily understood and quantified than those of the socio-environmental and socio-economic indicators. Eco-efficient indicators incorporated with environmental and economic indicators mean business's activities that increase economic values while decreasing ecological impacts and using natural capital stocks (Desimone & Popoff, 1998). Integrated indicators are comprehensively incorporated with economic, environmental, and social issues of the TBL. They are systematic and fundamental indicators that are built from the concepts of sustainable business as well as supporting the other indicators.

To identify the general indicators for sustainable business, a pilot survey was conducted. This pilot survey was implemented by identifying whether or not each indicator of 90 general indicators was popularly reported in each pilot sample, which is a firm's report. Of the 89 sample firms' reports, 38 performance reports disclosed in 2004 and 2005 were selected as pilot samples in order to select a sample of firms in the industries that significantly affect environmental and social impacts, such as the mining, utilities, and manufacturing industries. Firms in the mining industry started announcing their performance reports in 2004 and firms in the utility industries announced their performance reports in 2005 through Internet media. General indicators that were reported in over 60% of the samples of the pilot survey are defined as sustainable business indicators (SBIs) for this research. Table 3 shows the results of the pilot survey.

Based on Table 3, the distribution of general indicators in each category is as follows: 9 environmental indicators; 5 economic indicators; 10 social indicators: and 5 integrated indicators. We did not find relative indicators, such as socio-environmental and socio-economic indicators that were reported in over 60% of the pilot sample. Based on the results

	Indicators	Reporting (%)	Not Reporting(%)
Environmental	1)Total amount of water used	**34(90%)**	4(10%)
	2)Total amount of materials used to package product	14(37%)	**24(63%)**
	3)Total amount of materials used to produce products	8(21%)	**30(79%)**
	4)Total amount of renewable resources used	7(18%)	**31(82%)**
	5)Total amount of non-renewable resources used	0(0%)	**38(100%)**
	6)Total amount of recycled or reused materials used	15(40%)	23(60%)
	7)Total amount of energy used	**35(92%)**	3(8%)
	8)Total amount of renewable energy used	20(53%)	18(47%)
	9)Total amount of non-renewable energy used (oil)	12(32%)	26(68%)
	10)Concentration of a specific contaminant in tissue of a specific plant species found in the local or regional area	17(45%)	**21 (55%)**
	11)Habitats protected or restored	20(53%)	18(47%)
	12)Strategies, current actions, and future plans for managing impacts on biodiversity	16 (42%)	22(58%)
	13)Total amount of greenhouse gases generated (CO_2)	**38(100%)**	0(0%)
	14)Total amount of emissions of ozone-depleting substances	18(47%)	**20(53%)**
	15)Total amount of Volatile Organic Compound (VOC) generated	**24(63%)**	**14(37%)**
	16)Total amount of air emissions generated (SOx, NOx)	**28(74%)**	**10(26%)**
	17)Total amount of waste recycled or reused	**26(68%)**	**12(32%)**
	18)Total amount of solid waste generated	**32(84%)**	**6(16%)**
	19)Total amount of hazardous waste generated	**31(82%)**	7(18%)
	20)Total number and volume of significant spills and accidents	21(55%)	17 (45%)
	21)Total amount of wastewater	16(42%)	22(58%)
	22)Total number of environmental violations	**30(79%)**	8(21%)
Economic	1)Annual profits	**23(61%)**	15(39.5%)
	2)Annual revenues	18(47%)	20(52.6%)
	3)Annual sales	**30(79%)**	8(21.1%)
	4)Annual operating costs (based on EHS)	14(37%)	24(63.2%)
	5)Costs saving (based on EHS)	8(21%)	30(78.9%)
	6)Capital expenditure (environmental)	11(29%)	27(71%)
	7)Annual productivity	15(40%)	23(60%)
	8)Fines	**28(74%)**	10(26%)
	9)R & D investment (Based on EHS)	8(21%)	**30(79%)**
	10)R & D investment (total)	**24(63%)**	14(37%)
	11)Donations	**37(97%)**	1(3%)
	12)Annual turnover	3(8%)	35(92%)
	13)Value added	0(0%)	**38(100%)**
	14)Stock price/dividends	19(50%)	19(50%)

	Indicators	Reporting (%)	Not Reporting(%)
Social	1)Female, disabled person's rights	**26(68%)**	12(32%)
	2)Abolition of all child labor	21(55%)	17 (45%)
	3)The recruitment of people from ethnic minorities, older workers, women	**26(68%)**	12(32%)
	4)Empowerment of employees	**23(61%)**	15(40%)
	5)Average hours of training per employee	**26(68%)**	12(32%)
	6)Number of employees	**33(87%)**	5 (13%)
	7)Employment creation	20(53%)	18 (47%)
	8)Employment turn over	12(32%)	26(68%)
	9)Recordable Illness rate (RIR)	**27(71%)**	11 (29%)
	10)Lost time Rate (LTR)	**25(66%)**	13(34%)
	11)Total number of work-related fatalities	20(53%)	18(47%)
	12)Whether or not firms implement a broad range of voluntary activities	**35(92%)**	3(8%)
	13)Whether or not firms provide opportunities to communicate internally and externally to interested parties	**31(82%)**	7(18%)
	14)Breakdown of employees in terms of gender, age, and minority group	**27(71%)**	11 (29%)
	15)Ratio of basic salary of men to women by employee category	10(26%)	28(74%)
	16) Whether or not equity was mentioned	7(18%)	31(82%)
Social-Environmental	1)Training time/total amount of solid waste generated	3(8%)	**35(92%)**
	2)Employee's training time /total amount of energy used	2(5%)	**36(95%)**
	3)Total solid waste/employee	5(13%)	33(87%)
	4)Total amount of energy used /employee	3(8%)	**35(92%)**
	5)Voluntary activities/total amount of energy used	0(0%)	38(100%)
	6)Recordable illness rate/total amount of energy used	0(0%)	38 100%)
	7)Lost time rate/total amount of energy used	0(0%)	38(100%)
Social – economic	1)Training time of employee per profit	2(5%)	**36(95%)**
	2)Sales per employee	0(0%)	38 (100%)
	3)Lost time rate per profits	0(0%)	38(100%)
	4)Donations per sales	0(0%)	38(100%)
	5)Donations per profit	0(0%)	38(100%)
	6)Donations per revenue	0(0%)	38(100%)
Eco-efficiency	1)Total amount of material used / sales	1(3%)	**37(97%)**
	2)Total amount of material used /profits	1(3%)	**37(97%)**
	3)Total amount of solid waste /revenue	1(3%)	37 (97%)
	4)Total amount of non-renewable energy used / sales	0(0%)	38 (100%)
	5)Total amount of non-renewable energy used / sales	0(0%)	38 (100%)
	6)Total amount of non-renewable energy used / revenues	0(0%)	38(100%)
	7)Total amount of energy used / sales	21(55%)	**17(45%)**
	8)Total amount of energy used /revenues	1(3%)	**37(97%)**
	9)Total amount of toxic materials generated/sales	2(5%)	36 (95%)
	10)Total amount of toxic materials generated /profits	0(0%)	38 (100%)
	11)Total amount of material recycled and reused/ales	0(0%)	38(100%)
	12)Total amount of material recycled and reused /revenue	0(0%)	38(100%)
	13)Total amount of global warming materials generated/sales	0(0%)	38(100%)
	14)Total amount of global warming materials generated/profits	0(0%)	38(100%)
	15)Total amount of global warming materials generated/ revenue	0(0%)	38(100%)

	Indicators	Reporting (%)	Not Reporting(%)
Integrated	1)Whether or not firms implement voluntary environmental management systems (ISO 14001, LCA, etc)	28(74%)	10(26%)
	2)Whether or not firms implement environmental accounting	2(5%)	36(95%)
	3)Whether or not firms make decisions based on the concept of sustainable business and long-term objective	29(76%)	9(24%)
	4)Whether or not firms enlighten consumers and suppliers for the concept of sustainable business	27(71%)	11(29%)
	5)Whether or not firms deal with the impact on the Third World	16(42%)	22 (58%)
	6)Whether or not being verified their performance reports by third parties	14(37%)	24(63%)
	7)Whether or not firms compare GRI		
	8)Whether or not firms mention culture	25(66%)	13(34%)
	9)Whether or not firms survey in the reports (feedback)	28(74%)	10(26%)
	10)Whether or not firms compare performance based on standard year (total values/relative values)	16(42%)	22(58%)
		21(55%)	17 (45%)

Table 3. The List of 90 General Indicators and the Results of Pilot Survey (Sustainable Business Indicators over 60% of the sample) (N=38)

of the pilot survey, firms were not familiar with relative indicators. Since many firms had already measured and reported absolute indicators, absolute indicators made up a larger proportion of the SBIs than relative indicators such as socio-economic and socio-environmental indicators. With 29 SBIs identified from the pilot survey, a full survey was conducted to identify SBIs in the total sample of 89 firm's reports. Table 4 shows the results of the full survey.

4.1.3 Changes in sustainable business indicators disclosed in performance

Eighty-nine sample companies were separated into two categories, category I (1999 ~ 2002) and category II (2003~2006), to compare the trends of sustainable business indicators over a time period. These two categories were divided based on the year 2003 because the number of firms that announced their performance reports increased beginning in 2003. To compare the trends of sustainable business indicators, we chose firms in the manufacturing industries because all firms in category I were in the manufacturing industries. Among the 89 sample companies, the 78 announcements disclosed by the manufacturing industries were divided into category I (12 firms) and category II (66 firms).

To identify the changes in SBIs used in manufacturing firms, we added four indicators to the previously defined 29 sustainable business indicators; total amount of renewable energy used (solar energy, clean energy); whether or not firms describe environmentally friendly product or process; abolition of all child labor; and whether or not firms use relative indicators (eco-efficiency). Although some of these four indicators were not reported at over 60% in the pilot survey, they are considered necessary by the authors as indicators to evaluate the characteristics of sustainable business. Total amount of renewable energy used and whether or not firms develop or describe environmentally friendly product or process are used to evaluate whether or not firms apply diverse technologies to implement sustainable business; whether or not firms use relative indicators, such as eco-efficiency, is used to identify the consistency of natural capital stocks; and abolition of all child labor is used to evaluate the social performance of sustainable business. Thus, we used a total of 33 SBIs to identify the trends of sustainable business indicators of firms in the manufacturing industries. The trends of sustainable business indicators used in category I and category II is shown in Table 5.

	Indicators	No. of Firms Reporting (%)			No. of Firms Not Reporting (%)
		Quant. indicator	Qual. indicator	Sub-total	
Environmental Indictors	1)Total amount of water used	66	13	79(89%)	10(11%)
	2)Total amount of energy used	69	16	85(96%)	4(4%)
	3)Total amount of greenhouse gases generated (CO_2)	70	17	87(98%)	2(2%)
	4)Total amount of Volatile Organic Compound (VOC) generated	38	16	54(61%)	35(39%)
	5)Total amount of air emissions generate (SOx, NOx)	65	14	79(89%)	10 (11%)
	6)Total amount of waste recycled or reused	51	26	77(87%)	12(13%)
	7)Total amount of solid waste generated	54	28	82(92%)	7(8%)
	8)Total amount of hazardous waste generated	56	19	75(84%)	14 (16%)
	9)Total number of environmental violations	44	24	68(76%)	21(24%)
Economic Indicators	1)Annual profits	44	13	57(64%)	32(36%)
	2)Annual sales	68	12	80(90%)	9(10%)
	3)Fines	49	12	61(69%)	28(31%)
	4)R & D investment (total)	30	22	52(58%)	37(42%)
	5)Donations	52	3	85(96%)	4(4%)
Social Indicators	1)Female, disabled person's rights	0	59	59(66%)	30(34%)
	2)The recruitment of people from ethnic minorities, older workers, women	0	56	56(63%)	33(37%)
	3)Empowerment of employees	0	58	58(65%)	31(35%)
	4)Average hours of training/ employee	4	71	75(84%)	14(16%)
	5)Number of employees	61	20	81(91%)	8(9%)
	6)Recordable illness rate (RIR)	68	2	70(79%)	19(21%)
	7)Lost time rate (LTR)	64	1	65(73%)	24(27%)
	8)Whether or not firms implement a broad range of voluntary activities	0	82	82(92%)	7(8%)
	9)Whether or not firms provide opportunities to communicate internally and externally to interested parties	0	78	78(88%)	11(12%)
	10)Breakdown of employees in terms of gender, age, and minority group	0	55	55(62%)	34 (38%)
Integrated Indicators (reference)	1)Whether or not firms implement voluntary environmental management systems (ISO 14001, LCA, etc)	0	6	68(76%)	21(24%)
	2)Whether or not firms make decisions based on the concept of sustainable business and long-term objective	0	74	74(83%)	15(17%)
	3)Whether or not firms enlighten consumers and suppliers for the concept of sustainable business	0	71	71(80%)	18(20%)
	4)Whether or not firms compare GRI	0	60	60(67%)	29(33%)
	5)Whether or not firms mention Culture	0	71	71(80%)	18 (20%)

Table 4. List of the Sustainable Business Indicators (SBIs) (1999 ~ 2006) (N=89)

No	Indicators	Category I (1999~2002)					Category II (2003~2006)				
		Reporting			Not Reporting (%)	Total	Reporting			Not Reporting (%)	Total
		Quant. (%)	Qual. (%)	Sub-total (%)			Quant. (%)	Qual. (%)	Sub-total (%)		
EN1	Total amount of water used	10 (83%)	2 (17%)	12 (100%)	0 (0%)	12	50 (77%)	15 (23%)	65 (99%)	1 (1%)	66
EN2	Total amount of energy used	8 (67%)	4 (33%)	12 (100%)	0 (0%)	12	53 (80%)	13 (20%)	66 (100%)	0 (0%)	66
EN3	Total amount of greenhouse gases generated (CO_2)	7 (64%)	4 (36%)	11 (92%)	1 (8%)	12	53 (82%)	12 (18%)	65 (99%)	1 (1%)	66
EN4	Total amount of Volatile Organic Compound (VOC) generated	6 (86%)	1 (14%)	7 (58%)	5 (42%)	12	31 (72%)	12 (28%)	43 (65%)	23 (35%)	66
EN5	Total amount of air emissions generated (SOx, NOx)	12 (100%)	0 (0%)	12 (100%)	0 (0%)	12	45 (70%)	19 (30%)	64 (97%)	2 (3%)	66
EN6	Total amount of waste recycled or reused	8 (67%)	4 (33%)	12 (100%)	0 (0%)	12	38 (58%)	28 (42%)	66 (100%)	0 (0%)	66
EN7	Total amount of solid waste generated	6 (50%)	6 (50%)	12 (100%)	0 (0%)	12	41 (66%)	21 (34%)	62 (94%)	4 (6%)	66
EN8	Total amount of hazardous waste generated	8 (73%)	3 (27%)	11 (92%)	1 (8%)	12	39 (68%)	18 (32%)	57 (86%)	9 (14%)	66
EN9	Total number of environmental violations	5 (45%)	6 (55%)	11 (92%)	1 (8%)	12	32 (50%)	32 (50%)	64 (97%)	2 (3%)	66
EN10	Total amount of renewable energy used (clean fuel, solar energy, clean energy)	0 (0%)	3 (100%)	3 (25%)	9 (75%)	12	35 (75%)	12 (25%)	47 (71%)	19 (29%)	66
EN11	Whether or not firms describe environmentally friendly product or process	0 (0%)	9 (100.0%)	9 (75%)	3 (25%)	12	0 (0%)	60 (100%)	60 (91%)	6 (9%)	66
EC1	Annual profits	3 (50%)	3 (50%)	6 (50%)	6 (50%)	12	32 (80%)	8 (20%)	40 (61%)	26 (39%)	66
EC2	Annual sales	7 (64%)	4 (36%)	11 (92%)	1 (8%)	12	54 (89%)	7 (11%)	61 (92%)	5 (8%)	66
EC3	Fines	4 (57%)	3 (43%)	7 (58%)	5 (42%)	12	38 (83%)	8 (17%)	46 (70%)	20 (30%)	66
EC4	R & D investment (total)	4 (80%)	1 (20%)	5 (42%)	7 (58%)	12	23 (55%)	19 (45%)	42 (64%)	24 (36%)	66
EC5	Donations	4 (40%)	6 (60%)	10 (83%)	2 (17%)	12	40 (63%)	24 (37%)	64 (97%)	2 (3%)	66

Table 5. Changes in Sustainable Business Indicators Used in Category I and II

No	Indicators	Category I (1999 ~ 2002)					Category II (2003 ~ 2006)				
		Reporting			Not Reporting (%)	Total	Reporting			Not Reporting (%)	Total
		Quant. (%)	Qual. (%)	Sub-total (%)			Quant. (%)	Qual. (%)	Sub-total (%)		
SO1		0 (0%)	5 (100%)	5 (42%)	7 (58%)	12	0 (0%)	49 (100%)	49 (74%)	17 (26%)	66
SO2	Abolition of all child labor	0 (0%)	2 (100%)	2 (17%)	10 (83%)	12	0 (0%)	41 (100%)	41 (62%)	25 (38%)	66
SO3	The recruitment of people from ethnic minorities, older workers, women	0 (0%)	3 (100%)	3 (25%)	9 (75%)	12	0 (0%)	44 (100%)	44 (67%)	22 (33%)	66
SO4	Empowerment of employees	0 (0%)	1 (100%)	1 (8%)	11 (92%)	12	0 (0%)	41 (100%)	41 (62%)	25 (38%)	66
SO5	Average hours of training/ employee	0 (0%)	12 (100%)	12 (100%)	0 (0%)	12	5 (8%)	61 (92%)	66 (100%)	0 (0%)	66
SO6	Number of employees	7 (58%)	5 (42%)	12 (100%)	0 (0%)	12	48 (76%)	15 (24%)	63 (96%)	3 (4%)	66
SO7	Recordable illness rate (RIR)	8 (100%)	0 (0%)	8 (67%)	4 (33%)	12	52 (95%)	3 (5%)	55 (83%)	11 (17%)	66
SO8	Lost time rate (LTR)	7 (100%)	0 (0%)	7 (58%)	5 (42%)	12	51 (98%)	1 (2%)	52 (79%)	14 (21%)	66
SO9	Whether or not firms implement a broad range of voluntary activities	0 (0%)	10 (100%)	10 (83%)	2 (17%)	12	0 (0%)	64 (100%)	64 (97%)	2 (3%)	66
SO10	Whether or not firms provide opportunities to communicate internally and externally to interested parties	0 (0%)	9 (100%)	9 (75%)	3 (25%)	12	0 (0%)	60 (100%)	60 (91%)	6 (9%)	66
SO11	Breakdown of employees in terms of gender, age, and minority group	0 (0%)	6 (100%)	6 (50%)	6 (50%)	12	0 (0%)	53 (100%)	53 (80%)	13 (20%)	66
I1	Whether or not firms implement voluntary environmental management systems (ISO 14001, LCA, etc)	0 (0%)	6 (100%)	6 (50%)	6 (50%)	12	0 (0%)	53 (100%)	53 (80%)	13 (20%)	66
I2	Whether or not firms make decisions based on the concept of sustainable business and long-term objective	0 (0%)	3 (100%)	3 (25%)	9 (75%)	12	0 (0%)	56 (100%)	56 (85%)	10 (15%)	66

Table 5. Changes in Sustainable Business Indicators Used in Category I and II

No	Indicators	Category I (1999 ~ 2002)					Category II (2003 ~ 2006)				
		Reporting			Not Reporting (%)	Total	Reporting			Not Reporting (%)	Total
		Quant. (%)	Qual. (%)	Sub-total(%)			Quant. (%)	Qual. (%)	Sub-total(%)		
I3	Whether or not firms enlighten consumers and suppliers for the concept of sustainable business	0 (0%)	4 (100%)	4 (33%)	8.0 (67%)	12	0 (0%)	55 (100%)	55 (83%)	11 (17%)	66
I4	Whether or not firms compare GRI	0 (0%)	6 (100%)	6 (50%)	6 (50%)	12	0 (0%)	45 (100%)	45 (68%)	21 (31.8%)	66
I5	Whether or not firms mention culture	0 (0%)	8 (100%)	8 (67%)	4 (33%)	12	0 (0%)	58.00 (100%)	58 (88%)	8 (12.1%)	66
I6	Whether or not firms use relative indicators (eco-efficiency)	3 (100%)	0 (0%)	3 (25%)	9 (75%)	12	56 (100%)	0 (0%)	56 (5%)	10 (15.2%)	66

Table 5. Changes in Sustainable Business Indicators Used in Category I and II

Key Words in the Titles in Category I (1999 ~ 2002)			Key Words in the Titles in Category II (2003 ~ 2006)		
Environmental / Environmental, Health, and Safety	Sustainability	Total	Environmental / Environmental, Health, and Safety	Sustainability	Total
5 (42%)	7 (58%)	12	11 (17%)	55 (83%)	66

Table 6. Changes in Key Words Used in the Title of Performance Reports in Category I and II

Daly (1990) and Azapagic and Perdan (2005) said that sustainable development should be described by qualitative as well as quantitative measurement because it is required to explain whether or not an organization's diverse activities consider or meet human needs and social demands. We also found that firms in category I and II used both qualitative and quantitative indicators in their sustainable business performance reports.

In category II, most social and integrated indicators except for four social indicators and one integrated indicator were qualitative indicators. Two quantitative social indicators, the Recordable Illness Rate (RIR) and the Lost Time Rate (LTR), are used to evaluate firms' occupational safety and health. The recordable illness rate is the number of full-time employees suffering a recordable injury or illness during a given calendar year. The LTR is measured as the number of lost time claims per million hours worked and allows analysis of the number of lost time claims without the distorting effects of the size of the workforce.

4.1.3.1 Consistency of natural capital

The consistency of natural capital stocks can be measured by identifying the changes in the constant physical capital stocks, such as renewable energy and resources. This is because constant physical capital stock is one of the two concepts of the consistency of natural capital stock (Pearce, Barbier, & Markandya, 1990). Accordingly, the amount of renewable energy used in firms is a sustainable business indicator. Examples of renewable energy used in firms' performance reports are wind, solar energy, hydrogen energy, and biogas. Based on Table 5, firms in category I reported the performance of this indicator by 25%, but firms in category II reported it by about 71%. Since 2003, many firms in category II had increased the use of renewable energy while they reduced the use of non-renewable energy. In the Corporate Responsibility Report 2005, STXXX electronics (2006) reported that they increased the use of wind and solar energy from 18.6GWh in 2003 and 30.5GWh in 2004. In the '2004 Sustainability Report' published in 2005, POTXXX Corporate reported that it has started using renewable energy in 2004.

The consistency of the natural capital stock can also be measured by identifying a constant economic value, which is another concept of the consistency of natural capital stock (Pearce et al., 1990). We found firms that disclosed different eco-efficient indicators in their performance reports, such as energy efficiency, the amount of pollution per dollar, etc. Based on Table 5, only 25% of the sample firms in category I disclosed eco-efficient indicators in their performance reports, while about 85% of the sample firms disclosed them in category II. Many firms in category II reported eco-efficient indicators, such as energy efficiency, in their performance reports. This is consistent with what WBCSD (2005) and Desimone and Popoff (1998) stated. They said that firms can integrate sustainable development into their business by applying constant economic values of the natural capital stocks, such as eco-efficient indicators.

By providing the performance of various eco-efficient indicators, firms can help interested parties understand how effectively physical natural capital stocks, such as energy, have been used to retain an appropriate level of natural capital stock. For instance, AnhXXX Company (2006) measured and reported a few eco-efficient indicators, such as energy efficiency in 1,000 gig Joules (gJs) per million dollars Adjusted Net Sales (ANS), and Hazardous waste generated in kg per million dollars ANS. BaXXX Inc. (2005) defined energy efficiency as cumulative % improvement in energy use per unit of production value and reported that energy efficiency increased from 12% in 2002 to 22% in 2004.

Most firms in category I used absolute indicators, such as the total amount of energy consumed, rather than relative indicators, while firms in category II used absolute indicators as well as relative indicators, such as eco-efficient indicators based on their own firms' characteristics. This is because firms in category I did not have diverse and sufficient guidelines for relative indicators. After a few international guidelines, such as the GRI guidelines, were published in 2002, firms had opportunities to use or consider relative indicators, such as various eco-efficient indicators. Those guidelines have introduced and proposed diverse relative indicators, such as eco-efficient indicators. By comparing firms that used eco-efficient indicators in category I and II, we found that firms in category II may have proactively monitored and improved the level of consistency of natural capital stocks by setting up and evaluating eco-efficiency more so than firms in category I.

4.1.3.2 Culture for sustainable business

We found firms that had described their culture for sustainable business practices. This is consistent with what the International Institute for Sustainable Development (IISD) et al. (1992) and what Welford (1995) emphasized. They asserted that a firm should change its corporate culture to implement sustainable business practices. They also proposed some examples of corporate culture: employee participation in decision-making processes, the equitable treatment of women and minority groups, communication with the public, and the impact on the Third World and indigenous populations. We found these examples as SBIs. Table 5 shows the trends of these indicators in category I and II.

We searched the terms, "Empower," "Participation," and "Decision," to identify whether or not firms allow employee participation in the decision making process. Firms in category I and II reported that they involved their employees in their decision making process by empowering employees. While 62% of samples firms in category II reported that they involved their employees in their decision making process by empowering employees, only about 8% of sample firms in category I described the empowerment of employees. For instance, SXXXX Inc. in category II addressed, "Within this culture, employees are empowered and strongly encouraged to use their skills and experience to find better ways of doing business" (Corporate Social Responsibility Report 2005, p. 4). The CoXXX Company in category II also stated that its employees are empowered to keep the highest standards of quality in products, processes and relationships in 2006 Corporate Responsibility Review. STXXX electronics Company in category I did not mention employee empowerment in Corporate Environmental Report and Social Review 2001. However, STXXX electronics Company (2006) in category II stated that employee empowerment is one of the key principles for its sustainable business in their corporate responsibility report.

We found one indicator; breakdown of employees in terms of gender, age group, and minority group membership, as one of the SBIs. This indictor can be used to identify the equitable treatment of women and minority groups which is one aspect of corporate culture that the IISD et al. (1992) proposed. Firms in category II reported this indicator by 80% of the firms, and firms in category I described it 50% of the firms. STXXX electronics Company in category I did not mention diversity and equitable opportunity of women and minority in Corporate Environmental report and Social Review 2001. However, in category II, it reported that it not only ensured diversity and equal opportunity, but also disclosed the changes in percentage of average employee age and seniority, number of nationalities by regions, and gender breakdown by regions in Corporate Responsibility Report 2005 and 2006.

4.1.3.3 Harmonization of the triple bottom line

Table 5 presents the trends of the Triple Bottom Line (TBL) used in firms' performance reports in category I and category II. Sustainable business indicators that were reported in over 60% of sample firms in category I are: 9 environmental indicators (82% of total environmental indicators); 2 economic indicators (40% of total economic indicators); 5social indicators (45% of total social indicators); and one integrated indicator (20% of total integrated indicators). Firms in category I focused more on the environmental indicators, rather than social and economic indicators. On the other hand, many firms in category II described environmental indicators as well as economic and social indicators in their performance reports. Based on Table 5, all sustainable business indicators were reported in over 60% of all sample firms in category II. For example, 17% of firms in category I and 62% of firms in category II reported abolition of child labor. Only about 8% of firms in category I mentioned empowerment of employees in their performance reports, but firms in category II reported it by approximately 65%. Figure 2 shows the harmonization of the TBL used in firms in category I and II. It seems that most firms in category I focused more on environmental indicators and firms in category II tried to harmonize the TBL. Based on Table 6, about 42% of firms in category I used the term, "Environmental," "Environmental, health, and safety" as key words in the titles of their performance reports. While approximately 58% of sample firms in category I used the term "Sustainability" or "Corporate social responsibility" as a key word in the title of their performance reports, about 83% of sample firms in category II used the term. These changes indicate that many firms have shifted the key words in the title of their performance reports from the concept of environmental performance to the concept of sustainable business practices, which is based on the concept of the TBL. For instance, STXXX electronics Company used "Environmental Report" as the title of its performance reports in 2001 and "Social and Environmental Report" in 2003. In 2004, STXXX electronics Company first used the term, "Corporate Responsibility Report 2004" as the title of its performance reports on sustainable business practices.

4.1.3.4 Sustainability enlightenment

Young (2000) insisted that sustainable business enlightens its interested parties, such as investors, customers, and employees, on the concept of sustainable business practices. This is because interested parties have significant roles in changing traditional consumption, purchasing, and investing behaviors toward sustainable business practices. We found firms behaviors that are consistent with Young's (2000) findings. Based on Table 5, 83% of firms in category II and 33% of firms in category I reported that they enlightened their interested parties, such as customers, suppliers, investors, and employees about the concepts of sustainable business. It seems that firms in category II progressively enlightened their

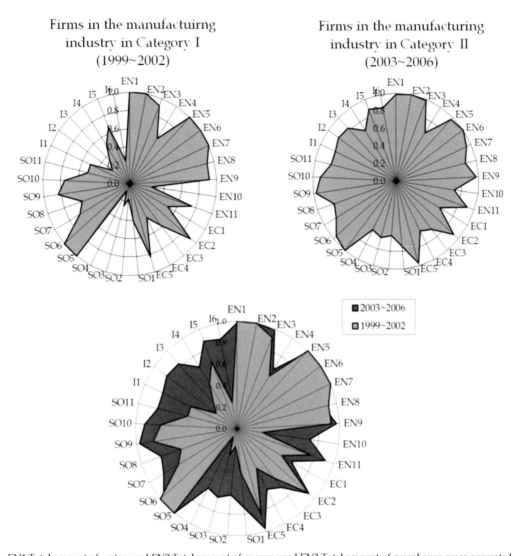

EN1:Total amount of water used;EN2:Total amount of energy used;EN3:Total amount of greenhouse gases generated (CO_2);EN4:Total amount of Volatile Organic Compound (VOC) generated;EN5:Total amount of air emissions generated (SOx, NOx);EN6:Total amount of waste recycled or reused;EN7:Total amount of solid waste generated;EN8:Total amount of hazardous waste generated;EN9:Total number of environmental violations;EN10: Total amount of renewable energy used (clean fuel, solar energy, clean energy);EN11:whether or not firms describe environmentally friendly product or process;EC1:Annual profits;EC2:Annual sales;EC3:Fines;EC4:R&D investment (total);EC5:Donations;SO1:Female, disabled person's rights;SO2: Abolition of all child labor; SO3:The recruitment of people from ethnic minorities, older workers, women;SO4:Empowerment of employees;SO5:Average hours of training per employee;SO6:Number of employees; SO7:Recordable illness rate (RIR);SO8:Lost time rate (LTR);SO9:Whether or not firms implement a broad range of voluntary activities;SO10:Whether or not firms provide opportunities to communicate internally and externally to interested parties;SO11:Breakdown of employees in terms of gender, age, and minority group; I1:Whether or not firms implement voluntary environmental management systems (ISO 14001, LCA, etc);I2:Whether or not firms make decisions based on the concept of sustainable business and long-term objective;I3:Whether or not firms enlighten consumers and suppliers for the concept of sustainable business;I4:Whether or not firms compare GRI;I5:Whether or not firms mention culture;I6:Whether or not firms used relative indicators (eco-efficiency)

Fig. 2. Trend of Sustainable Business Indicators Reported in Category I and II

interested parties on sustainable business practices more so than firms in category I did. For instance, in their 2006 Citizenship Report, GeXXX Electronic Co. reported that it had required their suppliers to consider the concepts of sustainable business since 2002 by complying with laws and regulations governing minimum wage, hours of service, and overtime wages for employees. GeXXX Electronic Co. (2007) introduced *"The Spirit & The Letter"* polices so that GeXXX Electronic Co. could help its interested parties, such as employees, suppliers, and customers, understand the common standards of behaviors required to implement sustainable business practices of GeXXX Electronic Co. In KimXXX's 2005 Sustainability Report, KimXXX Corporation reported that they enlightened and shared tools and technologies with suppliers to meet its social and environmental requirements that are sustainable business practices.

4.1.3.5 Voluntary programs and communication to the public

We identified whether or not a firm implemented diverse voluntary programs as an indicator to evaluate a firm's sustainable business, and found that most of the firms in category I and II have implemented and reported a variety of voluntary programs. This is consistent with Thompson (2002) and Scott (2001). They found that sustainable business should implement diverse voluntary programs to build strong relationships with stakeholders, increase a firm's image and reputation, and consider ethical investment for individual investors and fund managers. In Table 5, about 83% of firms in category I and 97% of firms in category II reported their diverse voluntary programs. In their 2005 Sustainability Report, KimXXX Corporation disclosed that it voluntarily joined the U.S. Environmental Protection Agency's Climate Leaders program in December 2005. GeXXX Company reported that it had implemented various voluntary greenhouse gas management initiatives to mitigate global climate change in their Corporate Responsibility Report of 2004/5. Many firms in category II implemented their voluntary programs especially for people employed in developing countries. AlXX X Inc. and KimXXX Corporation disclosed that they voluntarily implemented HIV/AIDS programs and management systems at places where they operate their facilities in South Africa. The goal of these programs is to help employees and their families undergo voluntary counseling and confidential testing for HIV/AIDS. The increasing number of voluntary HIV/AIDS programs implemented in developing countries is consistent with changes in corporate culture that the IISD et al. (1992) and Welford (1995) suggested in order to implement sustainable business.

Many firms in category II have voluntarily applied to the GRI guidelines to report the performance of their sustainable business practices. AlcXXX Inc. reported that it voluntarily used the GRI guidelines to help its interested parties to understand its sustain able business practices in 2004 Sustainability Report.

4.2 Changes in the key words of the performance titles

Data from a total of 287 firms were collected as sample data among all S&P 500 companies, as of December 2006. The following words were used to codify the results: *Environmental; Report; Environmental, Health, and Safety Report; Sustainability; Corporate Social Responsibility; Corporate Report;* and *Citizenship Report*. The results of these codes are separated into 3 categories; E (environmental report); EHS (environmental, health, and safety reports); Sustainability (sustainability, corporate social responsibility, and sustainable report). Sustainability, corporate social responsibility, corporate report, and sustainable report mean that the firm considered the concept of sustainable business because these words evolved from the concept of sustainable development. Table 7 presents the trends in key word usage

NAICS		Reporting				Not Reporting	Total
Title(2 digit)	Title(3 digit)	E	E, H, S	Sustain ability	Sub-total		
Agriculture, Forestry, Fishing and Hunting (11)	Crop Production (111)	0(0%)	0 (0%)	1 (100%)	1 (100%)	0 (0%)	1
	Forestry and Logging (113)	1 (100%)	0 (0%)	0 (0%)	1 (100%)	0 (0%)	1
	Sub-total	1 (50%)	0 (0%)	1 (50%)	2 (100%)	0 (0%)	2
Mining (21)	Oil and Gas Extraction (211)	0 (0%)	2 (40%)	3 (60%)	5 (62%)	3 (38%)	8
	Mining (except Oil and gas)(212)	1 (33%)	0 (0%)	2 (67%)	3 (75%)	1 (25%)	4
	Support Activities for Mining (213)	0 (0%)	2 (50%)	2 (50%)	4 (57%)	3 (43%)	7
	Sub-total	1 (8%)	4 (33%)	7 (58%)	12 (63%)	7 (37%)	19
Utilities(22)	Utilities (221)	7 (28%)	6 (24%)	12 (48%)	25 (78%)	7 (22%)	32
Construction (23)	Construction of Buildings (236)	0 (0%)	0 (0%)	1 (100%)	1 (20%)	4 (80%)	5
	Heavy and Civil Engineering Construction (237)	0 (0%)	0 (0%)	0 (0%)	0 (0%)	2 (100%)	2
	Sub-total	0 (0%)	0 (0%)	1 (100%)	1 (14%)	6 (86%)	7
Manufacturing (31,32,33)	Food (311)	1 (14%)	2 (29%)	4 (57%)	7 (50%)	7 (50%)	14
	Beverage and Tobacco Product (312)	3 (60%)	0 (0%)	2 (40%)	5 (50%)	5 (50%)	10
	Apparel (315)	0 (0%)	0 (0%)	0 (0%)	0 (0%)	4 (100%)	4
	Leather and Allied Product (316)	0 (0%)	0 (0%)	1 (100%)	1 (50%)	1 (50%)	2
	Wood Product (321)	0 (0%)	0 (0%)	1 (100%)	1 (100%)	0 (0%)	1
	Paper (322)	0 (0%)	1 (25)	3 (75%)	4 (57%)	3 (43%)	7
	Printing and Related Support Activities (323)	0 (0%)	0 (0%)	0 (0%)	0 (0%)	1 (100%)	1
	Petroleum and Coal Product (324)	0 (0%)	3 (43%)	4 (57%)	7 (88%)	1 (12%)	8
	Chemical (325)	0 (0%)	5 (19%)	22 (81%)	27 (64%)	15 (36%)	42
	Plastics and Rubber Product (326)	0 (0%)	1 (33%)	2 (67%)	3 (75%)	1 (25%)	4
	Primary Metal (331)	1 (50%)	0 (0%)	1 (50%)	2 (40%)	3 (60%)	5

NAICS		Reporting				Not Reporting	Total
Title(2 digit)	Title(3 digit)	E	E, H, S	Sustain ability	Sub-total		
	Fabricated Metal Product (332)	0 (0%)	1 (33%)	2 (67%)	3 (60%)	2 (40%)	5
	Machinery (333)	0 (0%)	1 (17%)	5 (83%)	6 (38%)	10 (62%)	16
	Computer and Electronic Product (334)	2 (9%)	3 (14%)	17 (77%)	22 (37%)	37 (63%)	59
	Electrical Equipment, Appliance and Component (335)	0 (0 %)	0 (0%)	2 (100%)	2 (40%)	3 (60%)	5
Manufacturing (31,32,33)	Transportation Equipment (336)	1 (11%)	3 (33%)	5 (56%)	9 (60%)	6 (40%)	15
	Furniture and Related Product (337)	0 (0%)	0 (0%)	1 (100%)	1 (50%)	1 (50%)	2
	Miscellaneous (339)	0 (0%)	0 (0%)	3 (100%)	3 (33%)	6 (67%)	9
	Sub-total	8 (8%)	20 (19%)	75 (73%)	103 (49%)	106 (51%)	209
	Air transportation (481)	0 (0%)	0 (0%)	0 (0%)	0 (0%)	1 (100%)	1
	Rail Transportation (482)	1 (100 %)	0 (0%)	0 (0%)	1 (25%)	3 (75%)	4
Transportation and Warehousing (48,49)	Water Transportation (483)	1 (100%)	0 (0%)	0 (0%)	1 (100%)	0 (0%)	1
	Pipeline Transportation (486)	1 (33%)	2 (67%)	0 (0%)	3 (100%)	0 (0%)	3
	Couriers and Messengers(492)	0 (0%)	0 (0%)	2 (100%)	2 (100%)	0 (0%)	2
	Sub-total	3 (43%)	2 (29%)	2 (28%)	7 (64%)	4 (36%)	11
Accommodation and Food Service (72)	Accommodation (721)	1 (100%)	0 (0%)	0 (0%)	1 (33%)	2 (67%)	3
	Food Services and Drinking Places (722)	0 (0%)	0 (0%)	2 (100%)	2 (50%)	2 (50%)	4
	Sub-total	1 (33%)	0 (0%)	2 (67%)	3 (43%)	4 (57%)	7
Total		21 (14%)	32 (21%)	100 (65%)	153 (53%)	134 (47%)	287

* E: Environment, H: Health, S: Safety

Table 7. Trends of the Key Words Used in the Titles of S&P 500 Firms' Performance Reports in 2006

within the titles of performance reports based on the industry of all 287 sample firms. Of the 287 firms, approximately 53% of the firms (153 firms) reported their performance reports. Performance reports could not be found on the respective Internet homepages for the remaining firms. Of the 153 firms, 65.4% (100 firms) used "sustainability," "sustainable," or "corporate social" as (a) word(s) used in the titles of their performance reports; 20.9% (32 firms) used "environmental, health, and safety" as (a) word(s) for their performance reports; and 13.7% (21 firms) used "environmental" as (a) word(s) for their performance titles. This means that 65.4% of the 153 S&P 500 firms surveyed have reported the performance of sustainable business indicators; 20.9% have disclosed the performance of environmental, health, and safety indicators; and 13.7% have reported only environmental performance.

Fifty-three firms, 18.5% of the total 287 S&P 500 firms surveyed reported that their environmental performance reports used the terms *Environmental reports* or *environmental, health and safety reports* in the title of their performance reports. This result is quite different from that of a previous study. In 1998, the Investor Responsibility Research Center (IRRC) conducted a survey to identify how many S&P 500 firms reported their performance reports to the public. They found that 61% of the 191 S&P 500 companies in 1998 used the term *Environmental* as a keyword in the title of their performance reports (Gozali et al., 2002). This indicates that 61% of the S&P 500 companies surveyed in 1998 focused on the performance of environmental indicators. The use of the term *Environmental* in the title of the performance reports swiftly dropped from 61% in 1998 to18.5% of the total 287 S&P 500 firms (53 firms) in 2006. On the other hand, the IRRC did not find firms that used the term *Sustainability* in the titles of their samples. However, we found 34.8% (100 firms) of 287 S&P 500 companies surveyed in 2006 used the term *Sustainability* as a keyword in the title of their performance reports. Changing the keywords used in the title of a firm's performance reports means that the main strategies of the performance reports have likely changed and that the firm has informed the readers of what they have implemented and evaluated.

4.2.1 Distribution of industries

As of 2006, of the 287 S&P 500 companies surveyed, 19 firms were in the mining industry. 63.2% of these 19 firms (12 firms) provided their performance reports. Of the 12 firms, seven firms (58.3% of 12 firms) used the term, *Sustainability* and five firms (41.7% of 12 firms) used the term *Environmental* and *EHS*. In other words, 58.3% of firms described their performance in accordance with the concept of sustainable development. It could be said that firms in the mining industry have begun to progressively apply sustainable business strategies.

Thirty-two firms in the utilities industry provided their performance reports. Among them, 48.0% of the firms used the term *Sustainability*, and 52% of the firms used the term *Environmental* and *EHS* in the title. Based on these numbers, it appears that many firms had still focused more on environmental management systems than on sustainable business even though international organizations had proposed guidelines, such as the Electric Utilities project proposed by the WBCSD in 2000, to help firms in the utilities industry implement sustainable business practices.

Seventy-five firms (72.8% of 103 firms) in the manufacturing industry used the term *Sustainability*; 8 firms (7.8% of them) used the term *Environmental*; and 20 firms (19.4% of them) used the term *EHS*. It appears that firms in the manufacturing industry have proactively applied sustainable business practices or labels for such practices. Firms in the manufacturing industry have changed from environmental management strategies to sustainable business strategies. This shift was made possible in part because manufacturing firms could easily apply and implement sustainable business aided by the fact that most had already established and implemented several environmental management systems, such as ISO 14001.

The construction industry is a sector where sustainable business practices should be implemented as a business practice for two reasons: it is faced with indispensable challenges posed by "Sustainability"; and the construction industry is generally one of the largest industries in both developed and developing countries in terms of economic, social, and environmental impacts (Zhang, Shen, Love, & Treloar, 2000; Cole, 1998; Spence & Mulligan, 1995). However, we could not find many construction firms among S&P 500 companies in 2006 that reported their environmental or sustainable business performance. Of the seven S&P 500 companies in the construction industry, only one firm published its performance reports with a title that used the term *Sustainability*.

Several international organizations, such as the WBCSD and the Institute of Sustainable Forestry (ISF), have encouraged firms in the agriculture, forestry, fishing, and hunting industry to apply sustainable development by proposing special programs, such as the Sustainable Forest Products Industry project and the Sustainable Forestry Initiatives. This is influenced by the fact that they deal with natural capital stocks. We found only two firms in the S&P 500, as of 2006, in Agriculture, Forestry, Fishing and Hunting. These two firms reported their performance reports and used the terms *Sustainability* and *Environmental* in the title of their performance reports. It is difficult to say whether firms in this industry have applied sustainable business practices because of the small sample.

There are seven firms in the transportation and warehousing industry that published their performance reports. Of the seven firms, two firms (28.6%) used the term *Sustainability* and five firms (71.4%) used the term *Environmental* or *EHS* in their performance titles. It does not seem that firms in the transportation and warehousing industry have implemented sustainable business practices based on the key words used in the title of their performance reports. Of the seven firms, the main products of four firms are the transfer of water and gases through pipelines to their customers. Since transferring water and gases through pipelines has the potential for causing environmental accidents, such as spills and explosion incidents, the focus for these firms may be on the concept of environmental management strategies.

Three firms in the accommodation and food service industry disclosed environmental or sustainability performance reports even though this industry does not produce environmental impact directly. Of the three firms, two firms (66.7% of the 3 firms) used the term *Sustainability* and one report used *Environmental*. This implies that some firms in the accommodation and food service industry have begun to consider the concept of sustainable business.

5. Conclusions

The objective of this research is to identify whether or not firms are applying sustainable business practice based on the Triple Bottom Line (Environmental, economic, and social areas). We found that more companies in the manufacturing industries have measured and disclosed diverse sustainable business indicators based on the Triple Bottom Line so that they have implemented sustainable business practices since 2003. In other words, firms in the manufacturing industries have integrated the concepts of sustainable business practices into their decision-making process and that some firms in other industries have begun incorporating the concepts of sustainable business practices into their business strategies since 2003. We conclude that since 2003 many companies have changed their strategies from environmental management to sustainable business. Although many firms have increasingly disclosed their performance reports to the public as one of their sustainable business practices, in many cases, they have not proactively announced the disclosure of their performance reports to the public through Internet mass media or newspapers.

The results of this research, the distribution and types of sustainable business indicators, could contribute to the existing literature of firms' sustainable business practices and activities. By providing empirical indicators that will be presented to the public, this research can help stakeholders, including "green" investors, "green" consumers, corporate firms, and others, recognize how the surveyed firms have implemented sustainable business practices. This research can also encourage scholars to actively study not only the theoretical methods for evaluating sustainable business practices, but also the theories or methods for the development of sustainable business strategies.

The samples used in this research were not randomly collected, but purposefully sampled. Since the sample for this study is announcements that firms voluntarily disclosed their performance reports, it is not easy to randomly collect samples. Future researchers could conduct case studies to identify the changes in corporate culture and evaluate the benefits of those changes in corporate culture.

6. References

Adams, R., Houldin, M. and Slomp, S. (1999). Toward a Generally Accepted Framework for Environmental Reporting, In: *Sustainable Measures*, Bennett, M. and James, P. (Ed.), 314-321, Greenleaf Publishing Limited, Sheffield, UK

Anton, W. R. Q., Deltas, G. and Khanna, M. (2004). Incentives for environmental self-regulation and implications for environmental performance. *Journal of Environmental Economics and Management*, Vol. 48, pp. 632-654

Azapagic, A. and Perdan, S. (2000). Indicators of sustainable development for industry: A general framework. *Trans IChemE*, Vol. 78, No.B, pp. 243-261

Azapagic, A. (2003). Systems approach to corporate sustainability: A general management framework. *Trans IChemE*, Vol. 81, No.B, pp. 303-316

Azapagic, A. and Perdan, S. (2005). An integrated sustainability decision-support framework part I: Problem structuring. *International Journal of Sustainable Development and World Ecology*, Vol. 12, No. 2, pp. 98-111

Azar, C., Holmberg, J. and Lindgren, K. (1996). Socio-ecological indicators for sustainability. *Ecological Economics*, Vol. 18, No. 2, pp. 89-112

Bennett, M. and James, P. (1999), *Sustainable Measures*, Greenleaf Publishing, Sheffield, UK.

British Standard 7750 (BS7750). (n.d.), 20.09.2008, Available from http://www.quality.co.uk/bs7750. htm

Bruemmer, P. J. (2000). Choose Your Words With Care. 10.01.2008, Available from http://www.clickz.com/831571

Chemical Industries Association. (2002). Responsible Care (RC) program. 01.03.2008, Available from http://www.responsiblecare.org/page.asp?p=6341&l=1

Cole, R. (1998). Emerging trends in building environmental assessment methods. *Building Research and Information*, Vol. 26, No.1, pp.3-16

Corporate Risk Management Company. (2000). The number of ISO 14001/EMAS registration of the world. 01.07.2009, Available from

http://web.archive.org/web/20000305163812/http://www.ecology.or.jp/isoworl
d/english/analy14k.htm

Corporate Risk Management Company. (2007).The number of ISO 14001/EMAS registration
of the world. 01.07.2009, Available from
http://www.ecology.or.jp/isoworld/english/analy14k.html

Council on Economic Priorities Accreditation Agency. (1998). Social accountability 8000.
20.05.2007, Available from
http://www.mallenbaker.net/csr/CSRfiles/SA8000.html

Daly, H. E. (1990). Sustainable development: From concept and theory to operational
principles. *Population and Development Review*, Vol. 16, pp. 25-43

Desimone, L. D. and Popoff, F. (1998). *Eco-efficiency: The business link to sustainable
development*, MIT Press, Cambridge, MA, USA

Evergreen Group. (2008). What is a sustainable business. 10.10.2008, Available from
http://ww w.theevergreengroup.com/sustainable-business.htm

European Commission. (2002). Corporate social responsibility: A business contribution to
sustainable development. 20.06.2008, Available from
http://ec.europa.eu/employment_social/publications/2002/ke4402488_en.pdf

Etzioni, A. (2003). Toward a new socio-economic paradigm. *Socio-Economic Review,* Vol. 1,
pp. 105-134

Feldman, S. J., Soyka, P. A., and Ameer, P. (1996). *Does improving a firm's environmental
management system and environmental performance result in a higher stock price.* ICF
Kaiser Consulting Group. Fairfax, VA, USA

Global Reporting Initiative (GRI). (2002). Sustainability reporting guidelines 2002.
10.06.2007, Available from http://www.rsuniversitaria.org/page6/gri02.pdf

Global Reporting Initiative (GRI). (2004). An abridged version of the 2002 Sustainability
Reporting Guidelines. Integrated with the draft Mining and Metals Sector
Supplement. 20.01.2008, Available from
http://www.wbcsd.org/web/projects/mining/Mining.pdf

Gozali, N. O., How, J. C. Y. and Verhoevern, P. (2002). The economic consequences of
voluntary environmental information disclosure. *The International Environmental
Modelling and Software Society, Lugano, Switzerland, 2002,* Vol. 2, pp. 484-489

Hamilton, J. T. (1995). Pollution as news: Media and stock market reactions to the Toxic
Release Inventory data. *Journal of Environmental Economics and Management*, Vol. 28,
pp. 98-113.

International Institute for Sustainable Development (IISD), Deloitte and Touche, and the
World Business Council for Sustainable Development. (1992). *Business Strategy for
Sustainable Development: Leadership and Accountability for the 90s*, International
Institute for Sustainable Development, Winnipeg, Canada

International Organization for Standardization (ISO). (1999), ISO 14031:1999 (E).
Environmental Management - Environmental evaluation – Guidelines. ISO,
Geneva, Switzerland

Internet Archive Organization (n.d.). 10.06.2008, Available from http://www.archive.org

Kuhndt, M. and Geibler, J. V. (2002). Developing a sectoral sustainability Indicators system
using the COMPASS methodology. *Futura,* Vol. 2 No. 2, pp. 29-44

Lin, L. and Wang, L. (2004). Making sustainability accountable: A valuation model for corporate performance, *Proceedings of the 12th IEEE international Symposium on Electronics and the Environment (ISEE) and the 5th Electronics Recycling Summit, 2004,* pp. 7-12, Scottsdale. AZ, USA, May 10-13,2004

Moxen, J. and Strachan, P. A. (1998). *Managing Green teams,* Greenleaf Publishing, Sheffield, UK.

Muller, K. and Sturm, A. (2001). *Standardized eco-efficiency indicators,* Ellipson AG., Basel, Switzerland

Parris, T. M. and Kates, R. W. (2003). Characterizing and measuring sustainable development. *Annual Review of Environmental and Resources,* Vol. 28, pp. 559-586

Pearce, D. W., Barbier, E. and Markandya, A. (1990). *Sustainable development: Economics and environment in the Third World,* Edward Elgar Publishing, London, UK

Redefining Progress, Sustainable Seattle, and Tyler Norris Associates. (1997). *The Community indicators Handbook: Measuring progress toward healthy and sustainable communities,* Redefining Progress, CA, USA

Sasseville, D. R., Willson, G. W. and Lawson, R. W. (1997). *ISO 14001 Answer book: Environmental management for the world market,* John Wiley & Sons, Inc, New York, USA

Scott, R.W. (2001). *Institutions and Organizations,* Sage, Thousand Oaks, CA, USA

Spence, R., & Mulligan, H. (1995). Sustainable development and construction industry. *Habitat International,* Vol.19, No.3, pp. 279-292

SustainableBusiness.com. (n.d.). Progressive investor. 10.06.2008, Available from http://www.sustainablebusiness.com/index.cfm/go/progressiveinvestor.main/?CFID=19300401&CFTOKEN=27983115

Thompson, D. (2002). *Tools for Environmental Management: A practical Introduction and Guide* New Society, BC VOR, Canada

Verfaillie, H. A. and Bidwell, R.(2000). Measuring eco-efficiency: A guide to reporting company performance. World Business Council for Sustainable Development, Washington, D.C,USA

Welford, R. (1995). *Environmental strategy and sustainable development: The corporate challenge for the 21st century,* Routledge, New York, USA

Welford, R. (2000). *Corporate environmental management 3: Toward sustainable development,* Earthscan Publications Lt, London, UK

Wharton Research Data Service. (n.d), 13.06.2008, Available from http://wrds.wharton.upenn.edu

World Business Council for Sustainable Development (WBCSD). (2000). Sustainability report. 10.08.2008, Available from http://www.sustreport.org/background/definitions.html

World Business Council for Sustainable Development (WBCSD). (2005).Eco-efficiency: Creating more value with less impact. 01.05.2007, Available from http://www.wbcsd.org

Young, C .W. (2000). Towards sustainable production and consumption: From products to services, In: *Corporate Environmental Management 3 Toward Sustainable Development,* Welford, R, 79-108, Earthscan Publications Lt, London, UK

Zhang, Z. H., Shen, L.Y., Love, P. E. D., & Treloar, G. (2000). A framework for implementing ISO 14001 in construction. *Environmental Management and Health,* Vol.11, No.2, pp.139-149

10

Assessment of Industrial Pollution Load in Lagos, Nigeria by Industrial Pollution Projection System (IPPS) versus Effluent Analysis

Adebola Oketola and Oladele Osibanjo
Department of Chemistry, University of Ibadan, Ibadan
Nigeria

1. Introduction

Lagos is the economic capital of Nigeria with over 70% of industries in the country located there. It is also the fastest growing city in Nigeria in terms of development and industrial infrastructure, forecast to be one of the three megacities in the world with population of over 20 million by the year 2025. The rapid growth and haphazard urbanization have led to an increase in waste generation and environmental pollution. The industrial pollution problems faced by Lagos with over 7,000 medium and large scale manufacturing facilities are directly related to the rapid industrial growth and the haphazard industrialization without environmental consideration (Oketola and Osibanjo, 2009a). Pollution abatement technologies are largely absent and the consequence is a gross pollution of natural resources and environmental media. Since effective environmental protection cannot take place in a data vacuum, Industrial Pollution Projection System (IPPS), which is a rapid environmental management tool for pollution load assessment, has been employed in this study to estimate industrial pollution loads and to ascertain the agreement between IPPS models and conventional effluent analysis.

It has been recognized that the developing countries lack the necessary information to set priorities, strategies, and action plans on environmental issues. Plant-level monitoring of air, water and toxic emissions is at best imperfect, monitoring equipment is not available and where available is obsolete; data collection and measurement methodology are questionable, and there is usually lack of trained personnel on industrial sites (Oketola and Osibanjo, 2009b; Hettige et al., 1994). In the absence of reliable pollution monitoring data, the World Bank has created a series of datasets that have given the research community the opportunity to better understand levels of pollution in developing countries, and therefore issue policy advice with more clarity (Aguayo et al., 2001). Hence, the World Bank developed the Industrial Pollution Projection System (IPPS), which is a rapid assessment tool for pollution load estimation towards the development of appropriate policy formulation for industrial pollution control in the developing countries, where insufficient data on industrial pollution proved to be an impediment to setting-up pollution control strategies and prioritization of activities (Faisal, 1991; Arpad et al, 1995).

IPPS is a modeling system, which has been developed to exploit the fact that industrial pollution is heavily affected by the scale of industrial activity, by its sectoral composition, and by the type of process technology used in production. IPPS combines data from industrial activities (such as production and employment) with data on pollution emissions to calculate the pollution intensity factors based on the International Standard Industrial Classification (ISIC) (Hettige et al., 1994). The IPPS has been estimated from massive USA database. This database was created by merging manufacturing census data with USEPA data on air, water, and solid waste emissions. It draws on environmental, economic, and geographic information from about 200,000 US factories. The IPPS covers about 1,500 product categories, all operating technologies, and hundreds of pollutants. It can project air, water, or solid waste emissions, and it incorporates a range of risk factors for human toxic and ecotoxic effects (Hettige et al., 1995).

There are wide ranges of industries and the pollutants introduced largely depends on the type of industry, raw material characteristics, specific process methods, efficacy of facilities, operating techniques, product grades and climatic conditions (Onianwa, 1985). The industrial sectors in Lagos based on the Manufacturer's Association of Nigeria (M.A.N) grouping are food, beverage and tobacco; textile, wearing apparel; pulp and paper products; chemical and pharmaceutical; wood and wood products; nonmetallic mineral products; basic metal; electrical and electronic; motor vehicle and miscellaneous; and domestic and industrial plastics (M.A.N., 1991).The Chemical and pharmaceutical sector is the most polluting industrial sector out of the ten major sectors based on the final ranking of IPPS pollution loads estimated with respect to employment and total value of output while basic metal, domestic and industrial plastics and textile wearing apparel sectors followed suit (Oketola and Osibanjo, 2009a). The chemical manufacturing facilities in the sector range from paint manufacturing industries, soap and detergents, pharmaceuticals, domestic insecticides and aerosol, petroleum products, toiletries and cosmetics, basic industrial chemicals while the basic metal manufacturing facilities are steel manufacturing, metal fabrication, aluminium extrusion etc.

The magnitude of environmental pollution problem is related to the types and quantity of waste generated by industries and the methods of management of the waste. As indicated earlier, there are over 7,000 industries in Lagos state with less than 10% having installed treatment facilities (Onyekwelu et al., 2003). Majority of these industries discharge their partially treated or untreated effluents into the environment and the Lagos Lagoon has gradually become a sink for pollutants from these industries. Industries utilize water for many purposes; these include processing, washing, cooling, boiler use, flushing sanitary/sewage use and general cleaning. Very large amount of water is required for these activities.

Within a given industrial sector, water use correlates with the size of the industry, and also for predicting the rate of generation of wastewater. Water supply requirements of an industry vary from one sector to another. While some industries may only require smaller volumes for cooling and cleaning (as in metal fabrication, cement bagging, etc), some others due to the nature of their processes may require very large volumes of water. Among such industries are breweries, distilleries and soft drinks manufacturing industries where water forms the bulk of the products themselves as a solution. Total consumption is about 205,000 m^3/day, with major users being Breweries, 22%; Textile, 18%; and Industrial chemicals, 16.6% (M.A.N., 2003). Industries utilize a vast array of input in the process of production of goods and services, and generate different forms of waste to varying degrees, which depends on the types and quantity of raw materials inputs, and the process technology employed (Ogungbuyi and Osho, 2005).

This study estimated pollution loads of some industries among the top most polluting sectors in Lagos (i.e., chemical, basic metal, plastics and textile). The selection of the

Assessment of Industrial Pollution Load in Lagos, Nigeria
by Industrial Pollution Projection System (IPPS) versus Effluent Analysis
209

industries was based on data availability and level of cooperation by industries studied. The industries selected are paint manufacturing, industrial gas manufacturing and lubricating oil production under the chemical and pharmaceutical sector while aluminium extrusion, steel manufacturing and glass bottle cap production industries were selected under the basic metal sector. Tyre manufacturing, foam and plastic production; and textile fabric and yarn production industries were selected under the domestic and industrial plastics and textile and wearing apparel sectors, respectively. IPPS pollution loads were estimated with respect to employment and total output, and the results of effluent pollution loads were compared statistically with IPPS pollution loads.

2. Experimental

2.1 Description of the study area

Lagos state has the largest population density of the four most industrialized states in Nigeria (Lagos, Rivers, Kano and Kaduna). It is also the state with the greatest concentration of industries, with well over seven thousand medium and large-scale industrial establishments. It is claimed that about 70-80% of the manufacturing facilities operating within the medium and large-scale industries are located there in. The major industrial estates in Lagos are: Ikeja, Agidingbi, Amuwo Odofin (industrial), Apapa, Gbagada, Iganmu, Ijora, Ilupeju, Matori, Ogba, Oregun, Oshodi/Isolo/Ilasamaja, Surulere (light industrial) and Yaba (Arikawe, 2002; Akinsanya, 2003; Ogungbuyi and Osho, 2005) as shown in Fig. 1.

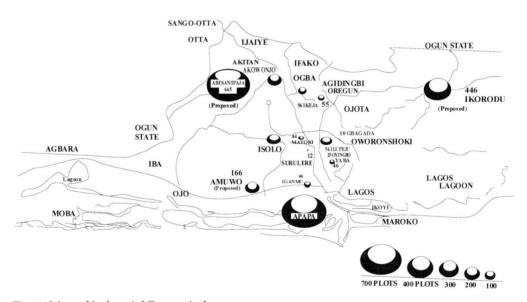

Fig. 1. Map of Industrial Estates in Lagos

2.2 Pollution data estimation methodology

Economic considerations and lack of cooperation from the industries limited the selection of number of industries considered in this study and the number of samples analysed. Hence, two paint manufacturing industries represented as CAP and BGR, domestic insecticides and aerosol production (DIA), and basic industrial gas manufacturing (IGM) were considered under the chemical and pharmaceutical sector; steel manufacturing (UST), aluminium extrusion (AET), aluminium windows and doors production (AWD) and glass bottle cap production (CCP) were selected under the basic metal sector. Industries selected under the domestic and industrial plastics and textile and wearing apparels were tyre, foam and plastic manufacturing industries; and textile and yarn manufacturing industries, respectively.

The total number of employees and average total output in CAP, BGR, LOP, UST, CCM, AWD, AET, FMI, TTP, CLP, WSY, RLT and APT were 225 and 3, 900 ton/yr; 250 and 8,000 ton/yr; 200 and 16.1 ton/yr; 120 and 1,170 ton/yr; 1,025 and 63,200 ton/yr; 370 while total output data was not available; 36 and 222 ton/yr; 200 and 1,800 ton/yr; 710 and 6,650 ton/yr; 1,000 and 9,560 ton/yr; 200 and 960,000 ton/yr; 350 and 12,000 ton/yr; 800 and 3,600 ton/yr; and 375 and 3,750 ton/yr, respectively. Lower Bound (LB) pollution intensities by medium with respect to total value of output and employment were obtained from the literature (Hettige, et al., 1994). The pollution intensities were used to estimate the pollution loads of these manufacturing industries based on the International Standard Industrial Classification (ISIC) code as found in the literature using the formulae:

With respect to total output;

$$\text{Pollution load} = \frac{\text{Pollution intensity factor x Unit of Output}}{2204.6} \qquad (1)$$

With respect to employment;

$$\text{PL} = \frac{\text{PI X TEM}}{1000 \times 2204.6} \qquad (2)$$

Where,

PL   =   Pollution load of a sector in ton/year
PI   =   Pollution intensity per thousand employees per year
TEM   =   Total number of employees in that sector
2204.6 =   Conversion factor from pounds to tonnes

2.3 Effluent sample analysis

Treated and untreated effluent samples were collected from the industries at the point of discharge to the environment and production line, respectively. Effluent samples were analyzed for physico-chemical parameters and heavy metals using standard methods (APHA, 1992; Miroslav and Viadimir, 1999; Taras, 1950). The parameters determined were: temperature, pH, turbidity, conductivity, total suspended solids (TSS), total hardness, acidity, alkalinity, chloride, sulphate, nitrate, chemical oxygen demand (COD), biological oxygen demand (BOD), dissolved oxygen (DO), sodium chloride, calcium, magnesium, and heavy metals (e.g., Fe, Pb, Zn, Cd, Cr, Mn, Ni, Cu, and Co).

2.4 Statistical analysis

The data were validated statistically using t - test at 95% confidence interval (2- tailed) and analysis of variance (ANOVA) to ascertain if there is any significant difference between IPPS pollution loads with respect to employment and total output; and pollution loads from conventional effluent analysis at $p > 0.05$.

Assessment of Industrial Pollution Load in Lagos, Nigeria
by Industrial Pollution Projection System (IPPS) versus Effluent Analysis

211

Industrial Sector	Four ISIC Code	Product Produced	Major Raw Materials	Types of Waste Generated	Mode of Disposal	Effluent Treatment Plant (ETP)/Constrain	General Remarks
CPH	3521 (CAP)	Paints	Pigment, resin, solvent and additives	Effluent Waste solvent	Discharge in drain By contractor off-site	Operational	Discharge treated effluent into the environment
	3521 (BGR)	Paints, wood preservatives, allied products	Dyes, pigment, solvent, extender	Effluent Sludge	Discharge in drain By contractor off-site	Operational	Discharge treated effluent into the environment
	3511 (IGM)	Industrial gases e.g. O$_2$, CO$_2$, acetylene	Caustic soda, soda ash, calcium carbide, ammonium nitrate.	Effluent, Sludge	Discharge in drain, Sludge is disposed by contractor off-site	Not available, installing ETP	Discharge effluent to the environment
	3540 (LOP)	Lubricants, aerosol insecticide etc	Petroleum products	Effluent Solid waste Sludge	Used oil generated is discharged to cement kiln and solid/sludge by contractor off site	Operational	Treat effluent before discharge
DIP	3551 (TTP)	Tyres for cars, trucks and light trucks	Natural and synthetic rubber, ZnO, cobalt stearate, carbon black, mineral oil	Effluent Solid waste	Discharge in drain, By contractor off-site	Not available	Uses effluent as cooling water
	3513 (FMI)	Flexible and rigid foams, adhesives	Polyol, toluene-di-isocyanate (IDI), silicone oil, methylene chloride	Solid waste	Recycled	Not available	Emitting volatile organic compounds into the atmosphere
	3560(CLP)	Plastics	Pigments and mastic batches	Solid waste	Waste oil discharged by contractor off-site	Not Applicable	Do not generate effluent at the production line
TWA	3211 (RLT)	Grey fabrics e.g. suiting, ankara	Yarn, chemicals and dyes	Effluent Solid waste	In drain after treatment By contractor off-site	Operational	Discharge treated effluent into the environment
	3211 (WSY)	Textiles	Dyes, pigment, caustic soda, acetic acid	Effluent Solid waste	Discharge in drain, by contractor off-site	Operational	Discharge treated effluent into the environment
	3219 (APT)	Yarn	Cotton	Solid waste	By contractor off-site	Not applicable	Do not generate effluent.
BML	3720 (AET)	Aluminium profiles	Aluminium billets, H$_2$SO$_4$, NaOH,Tin (II) Sulphate, Chromic acid	Effluent, solid and sludge	Effluent discharged in drain after treatment and sludge by contractor off-site.	ETP operational	Do not discharge effluent that contains hazardous substances into the environment.
	3720 (AWD)	Aluminium windows	Aluminium profile from	Solid waste	Recycle waste	Not applicable	Do not generate effluent at all.

		and doors	aluminium ingot				
	3710 (UST)	Steel bars, refractory bricks and enamelware	Steel scrap, ferrous alloys (Fe-Mn, Fe-Si), NaOH, clay, silica.	Effluent, Slag and Sludge	Discharge in drain By contractor off-site	Not available, installing ETP	Reuse effluent as cooling water
	3720 (CCM)	Paint cans, crown caps and beverage cans	Tin plate, copper wire etc	Solid waste	Molded together and sold off	Not available	Do not generate effluent during production

Table 1. Major raw materials and types of waste generated by the selected industries in Lagos

3. Results and discussion

Emission to air was determined based on emission of total suspended particulate (TSP), fine particulate (FP, PM10), sulphur dioxide (SO_2), nitrogen dioxide (NO_2), carbon monoxide (CO), and volatile organic compounds (VOCs). Emission to water was estimated in terms of biological oxygen demand (BOD) and total suspended solid (TSS) while emission of toxic pollutants was estimated in terms of toxic chemicals and metals released into air, water and land, whose pollution intensities were available in the literature (Hettige, et al., 1994). The major raw materials and the type of waste generated by the selected industries are presented in Table 1 while the total number of employees and total value of output as well as the pollution loads are shown in Tables 2 and 3, respectively. UST have the highest number of employees and second highest total value of output while AWD have the lowest number of employees and LOP the lowest value of output.

3.1 IPPS pollution load assessment
3.1.1 Air pollution load
Air pollution loads for all the selected industries are shown in Tables 2 and 3, respectively for pollution load estimated with respect to employment and total value of output. UST with 1025 employees and 63, 200 ton/yr of total output have the highest emission of all pollutants into environmental media (i.e., air, water, and land). The air pollution load with respect to employment and total value of output are 4,810 tons/yr and 1,860,000 tons/yr, respectively. This was followed by FMI,CCM, LOP, AET, TTP, IGM, RLT, APT, AWD, WSY, BGR, CAP, and CLP, respectively in decreasing order.

In most cases, the higher the number of employees and total output, the higher the air pollution loads. Basic metal, and domestic and industrial plastic (DIP) sectors are the most polluting sector in terms of air pollutant emission. UST ranked first while FMI and CCM ranked second and third, respectively. Total air pollution loads with respect to employment are 2,660 tons/yr and 2050 tons/yr in FMI and CCM, respectively. With respect to total output, air pollution loads are 94,500 ton/yr in FMI. Output data from CCM was not available thus; air pollution load with respect to total output cannot be estimated. Emission of CO and NO_2 was the highest in UST and FMI when pollution load was estimated with respect to the two variables (i.e., employment and total output) while SO_2 emission was the highest in CCM when pollution load was estimated with respect to employment. The trend in air pollution load by pollutant types in these industries are

UST: $CO > SO_2 > NO_2 > FP > TSP > VOC$

$$\text{FMI: } NO_2 > VOC > SO_2 > CO > TSP > FP$$
$$\text{CCM: } SO_2 > CO > TSP > VOC > NO_2 > FP$$

Pollution loads estimated with respect to employment and total output revealed that the most emitted air pollutant from UST was CO. This could be attributed to the fact that in steel making, oxygen reacts with several components in the bath, including Al, Si, Mn, P, C, and Fe, to produce metallic oxides which end up in the slag. It also generates carbon monoxide boil, a phenomenon common to all steel making processes and very important for mixing of the slag. Mixing enhances chemical reaction, purges hydrogen and nitrogen, and improves heat transfer. The CO supplies a less expensive form of energy to the bath, and performs several important refining reactions (Jeremy, 2003; and Bruce and Joseph, 2003). It is also important for foaming and help to bury the arc.

INDUSTRIAL SECTOR/ SECTOR CODE	CHEMICAL & PHARMACEUTICALS (CPH)				BASIC METALS (BML)			
ISIC CODE	3521 (CAP)	3521 (BGR)	3540 (LOP)	3511 (IGM)	3710 (UST)	3720 (CCM)	3720 (AWD)	3720 (AET)
EFFLUENT VOL. (L/day)	1,500	2,000	NA	NA	1MILLON	NA*	NA	10
EFFLUENT TREATMENT PLANT (ETP)	Operational	Operational	Operational	NA	NA	NA*	NA	Operational
NO OF EMPLOYEE	225 (M)	250 (M)	200 (M)	120 (M)	1025 (L)	370 (M)	36 (M)	200 (M)
AIR POLLUTANTS								
SO₂	5.88	6.53	565	200	1320	1,260	122	680
NO₂	5.19	5.77	352	148	575	41.0	3.99	22.2
CO	0.73	0.81	266	115	2060	586	57.0	317
VOC	43.5	48.4	88.3	116	177	45.8	4.46	24.8
FP	1.78	1.98	17.4	6.77	366	11.6	1.13	6.25
TSP	3.49	3.88	217	32.1	307	106	10.3	57.2
TOTAL	60.6	67.3	1,510	617	4810	2,050	199	1,110
WATER POLLUTANTS								
BOD	0.01	0.07	0.59	68.3	0.89	96.5	9.39	52.2
TSS	0.03	0.03	0.73	105.6	14,400	1,400	136	754
TOTAL	0.04	0.10	1.32	174	14,400	1,490	145	806
TOXIC CHEMICALS								
TO AIR	38.8	43.1	10.8	101	73.0	97.3	9.47	52.6
TO LAND	93.1	103	3.17	353	418	258	25.1	140
TO WATER	0.10	0.11	0.32	51.3	25.9	3.78	0.38	2.04
TOTAL	132	147	14.7	505	517	359	35.0	194
TOXIC METALS								
TO AIR	0.33	0.37	0.02	0.50	12.5	6.73	0.66	3.64
TO LAND	2.54	2.82	0.30	15.9	276	223	21.7	121
TO WATER	0.002	0.002	0.01	0.47	1.89	0.13	0.01	0.07
TOTAL	2.89	3.18	0.33	16.9	291	230	22.4	124

NOTE: L = large scale, M = medium scale, S = small scale, NA = not available, NA* = not applicable

Table 2. Pollution loads (ton/yr) with respect to employment

INDUSTRIAL SECTOR/SECTOR CODE	DOMESTIC AND INDUSTRIAL PLASTICS (DIP)			TEXTILE, WEARING APPAREL (TWA)		
ISIC CODE	3560 (CLP)	3513 (FMI)	3551 (TTP)		3219 (APT)	3211 (RLT)
EFFLUENT VOL. (L/day)	NA*	NA*	484,000	160	NA*	720
EFFLUENT TREATMENT PLANT (ETP)	NA	NA	NA	Operational	NA	Operational
NO OF EMPLOYEE	200 (M)	710 (L)	1,000 (L)	350 (M)	375 (M)	800 (L)
AIR POLLUTANTS						
SO2	0.54	441	275	36.0	21.0	82.3
NO2	0.12	1,150	95.1	49.7	8.67	114
CO	0.04	169	11.7	6.67	1.58	15.3
VOC	6.48	838	278	13.6	166	31.2
FP	0.11	0.36	3.93	0.96	0.00	2.20
TSP	0.16	67.3	30.4	6.45	12.5	14.7
TOTAL	7.45	2,660	695	113	210	259
WATER POLLUTANTS						
BOD	4.97	1.89	0.002	1.46	0.00	3.34
TSS	0.11	58.2	0.68	2.27	0.09	5.18
TOTAL	5.08	60.0	0.68	3.73	0.09	8.52
TOXIC CHEMICALS						
TO AIR	18.2	484	9.98	5.22	147	11.9
TO LAND	5.38	401	17.2	4.85	33.2	11.1
TO WATER	0.04	35.4	0.21	2.66	0.01	6.08
TOTAL	23.6	920	27.4	12.7	180	29.1
TOXIC METALS						
TO AIR	0.004	0.13	0.39	0.04	0.03	0.10
TO LAND	0.16	20.9	15.1	0.09	0.01	0.20
TO WATER	0.01	0.44	0.02	0.003	-	0.01
TOTAL	0.18	21.5	15.5	0.13	0.04	0.31

NOTE: L = large scale, M = medium scale, S = small scale, NA = not available, NA* = not applicable

Table 2. Contd. Pollution loads (ton/yr) with respect to employment

INDUSTRIAL SECTOR/ SECTOR CODE	CHEMICAL & PHARMACEUTICALS (CPH)				BASIC METALS (BML)			
ISIC CODE	3521 (CAP)	3521 (BGR)	3540 (LOP)	3511 (IGM)	3710 (UST)	3720(CCM)	3720 (AWD)	3720 (AET)
EFFLUENT VOL. (L/day)	1,500	2,000	NA	NA	1MILLION	NA*	NA	10
EFFLUENT TREATMENT PLANT (ETP)	Operational	Operational	Operational	NA	NA	NA*	NA	Operational
TOTAL VALUE OF OUTPUT (ton/yr)	3,900	8,000	16.1	1,170	63,200	NA	222	1,800
AIR POLLUTANTS								
SO$_2$	435	893	152	6,180	512,000	NA	3,890	31,600
NO$_2$	384	787	94.7	4,590	222,000	NA	127	1,030
CO	54.8	112	71.7	3,550	798,000	NA	1,800	14,700
VOC	3,220	6,600	23.8	3,590	68,600	NA	141	1,150
FP	131	269	4.68	210	142,000	NA	35.7	290
TSP	258	530	58.4	994	119,000	NA	326	2,650
TOTAL	4,480	9,190	405	19,100	1,860,000	NA	6,320	51,300
WATER POLLUTANTS								
BOD	0.46	0.94	0.16	2,120	379	NA	298	2,410
TSS	1.91	0.26	0.20	3,270	5,580,000	NA	4,300	35,000
TOTAL	2.37	1.20	0.36	5,390	5,580,000	NA	4,600	37,400
TOXIC CHEMICALS						NA		
TO AIR	2,870	5,880	2.90	3,140	28,000	NA	300	2,440
TO LAND	6,880	14,100	0.85	10,900	162,000	NA	796	6,470
TO WATER	7.47	15.3	0.09	1,590	10,000	NA	11.7	94.8
TOTAL	9,760	20,000	3.84	15,600	200,000	NA	1,110	9,000
TOXIC METALS								
TO AIR	24.3	49.9	0.01	15.6	4,850	NA	20.8	169
TO LAND	187	385	0.17	493	107,000	NA	689	5,590
TO WATER	0.15	0.32	0.002	14.5	732	NA	0.41	3.36
TOTAL	212	435	0.18	523	112,000	NA	710	5,760

NOTE: NA = not available, NA* = not applicable

Table 3. Pollution loads (ton/yr) with respect to total value of output

INDUSTRIAL SECTOR/ SECTOR CODE	DOMESTIC AND INDUSTRIAL PLASTICS (DIP)			TEXTILE, WEARING APPAREL (TWA)		
ISIC CODE	3560 (CLP)	3513 (FMI)	3551 (TTP)	3211 (WSY)	3211 (RLT)	3219 (APT)
EFFLUENT VOL. (L/day)	NA*	NA*	484,000	160	720	NA*
EFFLUENT TREATMENT PLANT (ETP)	NA	NA	NA	Operational	Operational	NA
TOTAL VALUE OF OUTPUT (ton/yr)	960,000	6,650	9,560	12,000	3,600	3,750
AIR POLLUTANTS						
SO$_2$	24,400	15,600	16,500	13,200	3,950	1,270
NO$_2$	5,230	40,600	5,690	18,300	5,460	526
CO	0.001	6,010	698	2,450	731	95.3
VOC	294,00	30,000	16,700	5,010	1,500	10,100
FP	5,230	12.1	234	355	106	0.00
TSP	7,400	2,390	1,820	2,360	707	757
TOTAL	337,000	94,400	41,600	41,700	12,400	12,800
WATER POLLUTANTS						
BOD	226,000	638	0.09	536	160	0.00
TSS	4,880	2,060	40.9	833	249	5.44
TOTAL	231,000	2,700	41.0	1,370	409	5.44
TOXIC CHEMICALS						
TO AIR	826,000	17.2	598	1,920	573	8,940
TO LAND	245,000	14.2	1,030	1,780	532	2,010
TO WATER	2,020	1.25	12.4	977	292	0.08
TOTAL	1,070,000	32.6	1,640	4,670	1,400	10,900
TOXIC METALS						
TO AIR	192	4.76	23.2	15.8	4.72	1.83
TO LAND	7,400	741.1	903	320	95.5	37.7
TO WATER	416	15.5	1.16	1.07	0.32	0.35
TOTAL	8,010	761	928	336	100.6	39.9

NOTE: NA = not available, NA* = not applicable

Table 3. Contd. Pollution loads (ton/yr) with respect to total value of output

3.1.2 Water pollution load

Of all the industries, UST ranked first in terms of total water pollution load while CCM and AET ranked second and third, respectively. This was due to the fact that emission of TSS from the two industries was more than BOD. Estimated TSS pollution load from these industries are 14,400 and 1,400 ton/yr, respectively while BOD pollution load are 0.89 and 96.5 ton/yr, respectively. The steel industry with the highest number of employees generated the highest water pollution load. Thus, the higher the number of employees, the higher the water pollution loads. Pollution load estimated with respect to total output showed that 5.6 million ton/yr of TSS was generated by UST. Water pollution load estimated with respect to employment and total output revealed that emission of TSS was more than BOD in all the manufacturing facilities under the basic metal sector with UST having the highest water pollution load with respect to the two variables (i.e., employment and total output). This is shown in Tables 2 and 3, respectively. APT and CAP have the lowest water pollution load thus, their contribution to water pollution is insignificant.

3.1.3 Toxic pollution load

Toxic chemical and metal pollution load with respect to employment and total output are presented in Tables 2 and 3, respectively. Total chemical pollution load with respect to employment and total output is more than total metal pollution load in all the facilities. This may be attributed to the nature of the raw materials used by these facilities. Thus, raw material characteristics and product grades are some of the factors affecting pollution load (Oketola and Osibanjo, 2009b).

3.2 Pollution load assessment by effluent analysis

The results of the composite untreated effluent samples collected from the production line of the facilities are presented in Tables 4 and 5, respectively. The result of effluents analysis showed varying concentration of some of the parameters such as heavy metals, COD etc., which are above the permissible limits of Federal Ministry of Environment, (FEPA, 1998) for effluent discharge thus indicating gross pollution. The values of some of the parameters obtained could be attributed to the production processes, raw material characteristics etc.

Industrial Code /Parameters	BGR	CAP	UST[1]	TTP[1]	WSY	LOP	IGM	AET
Sampling time (n)	4	5	2	2	3	2	2	5
Parameters								
Temp0C	30.3±1.7	29.2±1.8	45	33±1.4	46.3±7.8	36±1.4	29.5±0.7	30.5±0.7
pH	7.62±0.5	6.32±0.5	6.75±0.1	5.75±0.1	9.6±1.0	6.85±0.6	11.3±0.0	10.8±0.9
Turbidity (NTU)	4.15±0.3	3.53±0.5	ND	ND	**0.31±0.04**	1,230±360	ND	0.72±0.1
Conductivity (µs/cm)	2210±410	810±85	104±5.7	260±14	0.31±0.04	305±78	2,700±280	3550±780
TSS (mg/L)*	9.65±2.8	1.40±0.8	0.28±0.3	0.05±0.01	0.14±0.1	301±66	1.55±1.3	2.33±1.4

Oil & Grease (mg/L)	3.42±8.8	6.30±1.5	104±5.7	260±14	2,400±400	91.2±30	0.34±0.4	34.3±30
Total Alkalinity (pH 4.3) (mg/L)	863±570	650±270	0.37±0.4	ND	1.0±0.4	32.6±46	505±710	3,730±2,400
Total Acidity (pH 8.3) (mg/L)	813±97	602±120	41.1±6.7	**67.9±10**	7931.0±61	40.5±31	ND	2,070±1,300
Methyl Orange Acidity (pH 3.7) (mg/L)	293±590	ND	34.9±32	ND	147±120	ND	ND	-
Total Hardness (mg/L)	78.7±28	58.8±20	222.6±300	6.27±1.0	376±530	80.5±63	35.9±43	246±350
Cl^- (mg/L)	82.2±38	33.6±10	8.57±4.1	1.79±0.1	36.7±18	9.06±0.5	2.44±1.0	21.1±38
SO_4^{2-} (mg/L)	106±53	855±780	46.1±2.7	1.19±0.1	1,180±680	37.4±49	199±120	717±520
PO_4^{3-} (mg/L)	94.5±20	46.2±17	ND	ND	7.0±6.1	10.5±9.6	12.0±17	47.5±14
NO_3^- (mg/L)	2.12±1.4	ND	ND	ND	0.8±0.7	0.11±0.1	ND	ND
DO (mg/L)	ND	ND	7.50±1.4	6.80±0.1	ND	ND	ND	80±1.8
COD (mg/L)	1700±630	642±390	130±6.4	621±43	783±86	22,160±95	897±7.1	159±130
BOD_5 (mg/L) *	23.4±2.9	20.3±7.7	10.5±3.0	0.48±0.04	4.56±0.4	54.5±18	ND	3.95±1.9
Ca (mg/L)	15.3±5.9	15.6±15	0.34±0.2	1.04±0.02	14.6±15	53.8±65	38.2±19	0.02±0.04
Mg (mg/L)	9.85±9.2	5.77±7.1	53.8±73	0.78±0.1	82.3±140	14.6±15	0.73±1.0	60.0±85
Pb (mg/L)	2.01±4.0	12.4±15	3.07±4.3	ND	**9.07±16**	0.22±0.3	ND	19.0±23
Ni (mg/L)	0.73±0.5	0.52±0.8	0.10±0.1	0.35±0.1	ND	0.1±0.1	0.6±0.8	0.48±0.8
Cd (mg/L)	0.78±1.1	1.77±1.3	0.11±0.2	ND	0.09±0.2	ND	ND	0.44±0.6
Cr (mg/L)	0.53±0.4	0.41±0.3	0.18±0.2	0.05±0.01	0.18±0.1	ND	0.2±0.3	0.19±0.3
Fe (mg/L)	8.80±6.4	4.56±6.4	7.3±10	ND	8.27±7.2	1.40±2.0	4.9±6.9	8.96±12
Mn (mg/L)	2.71±2.2	1.02±0.9	ND	0.23±0.3	ND	0.06±0.1	0.27±0.4	0.98±1.5
Zn (mg/L)	0.15±0.1	0.02±0.04	1.00±1.4	ND	0.01±0.02	0.01±0.01	ND	0.06±0.1
Cu (mg/L)	20.7±14	8.48±7.0	2.70±2.2	0.30±0.1	2.54±0.6	7.8±7.8	4.98±7.0	14.3±6.5
Co (mg/L)	0.29±0.1	0.14±0.1	0.04±0.1	0.02±0.01	0.23±0.2	ND	0.14±0.2	0.25±0.1
TOTAL (mg/L) *	36.7	20.8	14.5	0.95	20.4	9.59	11.1	44.6

Note: * Parameters compared with IPPS pollution load
[1] cooling water

Table 4. Mean concentration and standard deviation of physico-chemical parameters of untreated effluent from the selected industries

Industrial Code/Parameters	BGR (n = 2)	CAP (n = 2)	WSY (n = 2)	LOP (n = 2)	IGM (n = 3)	AET (n = 2)	FMENV LIMIT
Parameters							
Temp^{0}C	30±2.8	28.8±3.2	47.8±1.8	30.8±0.4	35±2	29.5±0.7	
pH	7.3±0.3	8.2±0.0	9.85±0.2	8.45±1.1	9.03±0.3	10.3±0.9	6.5 – 9.0
Turbidity (NTU)	0.05±0.01	0.06±0.01	0.44±0.2	137±52	ND	0.41±0.03	
Conductivity (µs/cm)	545±92	2,300±140	4,500±710	289±150	5,670±610	3,400±570	
TSS (mg/L) *	0.23±0.02	0.32±0.1	0.37±0.2	32.0±9.9	0.44±0.1	1.91±1.3	
Oil & Grease (mg/L)	0.30±0.03	0.03±0.01	19.2±3.8	4.79±1.0	9.19±6.8	3.16±0.4	
Total Alkalinity (pH 4.3) (mg/L)	293±57	572±97	1,350±440	131±56	2,880±170	1,720±1,100	
Total Acidity (pH 8.3) (mg/L)	136±130	60±85	220±75	9.16±1.8	76.1±16	ND	
Total Hardness (mg/L)	118±67	44.5±20	32.1±25	22.0±8.5	207±330	1.57±2.2	
Cl⁻ (mg/L)	31.9±0.2	7.62±8.8	46.4±66	9.34±6.4	127±31	55.1±68	600
SO$_4^{2-}$ (mg/L)	103±16	471±83	303±84	36.4±36	111±32	1,100±890	
PO$_4^{3-}$ (mg/L)	8. 85±5.2	ND	25.5±21	3.14±1.0	8.93±7.7	43.5±30	
DO (mg/L)	3.75±3.5	ND	ND	0.75±1.5	6.5±1.3	1.75±2.5	
COD (mg/L)	1450±92	1,030±250	1,140±510	97.4±6.6	363±260	909±9.9	80.0
BOD$_5$ (mg/L) *	27.0±1.1	16.1±2.7	60.1±11	21.8±8.5	10.2±11	6.55±1.0	30.0
Ca (mg/L)	16.3±16	2.34±0.1	5.31±6.5	10.9±13	2.4±0.4	ND	
Mg (mg/L)	18.7±6.6	9.38±4.8	4.55±2.1	5.38±3.7	48.8±79	0.38±0.5	
Pb (mg/L)	3.27±4.6	4.7±6.7	6.35±9.0	7.0±9.9	0.28±0.4	ND	< 1.0
Ni (mg/L)	2.8±0.6	1.20±0.3	0.90±0.1	ND	0.67±1.2	0.8±1.1	< 1.0
Cd (mg/L)	0.47±0.7	ND	0.97±1.4	ND	1.64±1.6	0.15±0.1	< 1.0

Cr (mg/L)	0.23±0.3	0.14±0.1	0.46±0.1	0.23±0.3	0.1±0.2	0.29±0.4	< 1.0
Fe (mg/L)	10.9±3.3	0.6±0.9	6.5±9.2	4.18±5.7	60.5±66	61.1±61	20.0
Mn (mg/L)	ND	ND	0.08±0.1	0.06±0.1	13±6.7	ND	5.0
Zn (mg/L)	0.11±0.6	0.20±0.3	0.01±0.01	0.12±0.2	0.1±0.1	0.07±0.1	< 1.0
Cu (mg/L)	9.21±7.4	8.03±4.6	3.18±4.5	1.81±2.4	11.5±10	6.85±2.0	< 1.0
Co (mg/L)	0.32±0.4	0.15±0.2	0.16±0.1	ND	0.11±0.2	0.14±0.03	< 1.0
TOTAL (mg/L)*	28.7	16.7	19.3	6.68	87.6	72.7	

Note: * Parameters compared with IPPS pollution load

Table 5. Mean concentration and standard deviation of physico-chemical parameters of effluent discharged to the environment in the selected industries in Lagos

3.3 Results of statistical analysis

IPPS estimated pollution loads with respect to employment and total output in these industries were statistically analysed to ascertain the level of agreement between them. There is no significant difference between the pollution load estimated with respect to the two variables (i.e. employment and total output) at $p > 0.05$ in all the industries except in IGM, WSY, RLT, AWD, and AET. At the 0.05 level, the means are significantly different. IPPS pollution load was also compared with pollution load from conventional effluent analysis. There is no significant difference between them at $p > 0.05$ in CAP, BGR, UST, TTP and AET while there is significant different between IPPS pollution load and pollution load from conventional effluent analysis in WSY. Hence, IPPS compared favourably with effluent analysis in most of the industries.

4. Conclusion

This study estimated pollution loads of some industries in Lagos using IPPS pollution intensities with respect to employment and total output. In most cases, the higher the total number of employees and total output, the higher the estimated pollution loads. There is no significant difference between the pollution loads estimated with respect to the two variables in all the industries except IGM where the two means are significantly different. IPPS pollution loads were also compared with pollution loads from conventional effluent analysis at $p > 0.05$. The two pollution loads compared favourably at this limit.

Application of IPPS in Lagos and most developing countries will no doubt enable the regulatory and monitoring agencies in such countries to focus on the most polluting industries. This will on the long run increase the level of enforcement since more time can be spent on the few polluting industries. This will also enable the policy makers in the developing countries to tackle industrial pollution since IPPS is a cheap means of assessing industrial pollution when compared to running scientific monitoring data gathering, analysis and assessment which is time consuming, expensive and resource intensive.

Detailed information on employment and total output obtained from the fourteen industries studied revealed that in most cases, the higher the total number of employees and output, the higher the pollution loads by pollutant types except in TTP where the higher the total number of employees and total output, the lower the estimated pollution loads. This variation can be attributed to other factors which affect pollution loads. These are types and quantity of raw materials, process technology, product grade, efficacy of facility, and source type etc. Also, pollution load of the fourteen industries estimated with respect to employment and total output were compared statistically using t-test at 95% confidence interval and analysis of variance (ANOVA). At this level, the two means are not significantly different in CAP, BGR, TTP, FMI, UST, LOP, CLP, and APT while there was significant different in AWD, WSY, RLT, IGM, and AET. These can be attributed to the information and data supplied by these industries including process efficiency and efficacy of installed pollution control technology if any. For example, IGM with only 120 employees produced 1,170 ton/yr of total output while LOP with 200 employees have a total production capacity of 16.1 tons/yr which is significantly less than that of IGM.

The results of untreated effluent samples collected from these industries also revealed that most of the industries discharged untreated or partially treated effluent into the environment. Out of the 14 industries which data were available for this study, only 29% have effluent treatment plant which is operational, 36% have no effluent treatment plant while the remaining 36% operate dry process in which Effluent Treatment Plant (ETP) is not applicable. Unavailability of ETP in these industries could be attributed to the high cost of installing and maintaining an ETP, air pollution control devices, and weak enforcement of extant environmental regulations in Lagos.

Pollution load from conventional effluent analysis were compared with IPPS pollution load in these industries. There is no significant difference between them at p > 0.05. IPPS pollution load of the selected industries compared favourably with pollution load from conventional effluent analysis in CAP, BGR, UST, TTP and AET. Enough data was not available from IGM and LOP. The exception was in WSY where there is significant difference between IPPS pollution load with respect to output and pollution load from conventional effluent analysis from effluent collected at the production line. Consequently, there was an agreement between effluent analysis or scientific monitoring and assessment and IPPS. Since IPPS compares favourably with scientific monitoring and analysis in these industries, IPPS therefore offers a cheap management tool for pollution load assessment in these industries; and directional basis for rapid policy intervention by government regulatory agencies in Lagos and other developing countries where pollution abatement technology is absent and level of enforcement is very low. It will enhance industrial pollution control in the developing countries where funding for environmental protection is lacking or grossly inadequate. The effectiveness of the intervening measures would significantly reduce the overall industrial pollution.

5. References

Akinsanya, C.K. (2003). Recent trends in the pollution load on the Lagos Lagoon. – Lagos state perspective. (A paper presented on ecological sustainable industrial development workshop organized by UNIDO).

Aguayo, F., Gallagher, P., and Gohzalez, A. (2001). Dirt is in the eye of the beholder: The World Bank air pollution intensities for Mexico. Global development and environment institute working paper, No. 01-07.

APHA, 1992. Standard methods for the examination of water and wastewater. American Public Health Association, New York. 18th ed.

Arikawe-Akintola. J.O. (2002). The rise of industrialism in the Lagos area. In: Adefuye, A., Agiri, B., and Osuntokun, J. (Eds.).*History of the peoples of Lagos state.* Literamed publications limited, Lagos, Nigeria, pp. 102-116.

Arpad Horvath, Christ T. Hendrickson, Lester B. Lave, Francis C. McMichael, and Tse – Sung Wu (1995). Toxic emissions indices for green design and inventory. *Environ. Sci. Technol.* 29, (2), 8 – 90A.

Bruce Kozak and Joseph Dzierzawski. (2003). Continuous casting of steel: basic principles. American iron and steel institute

Dasgupta, S., Lucas, E.B., and Wheeler, D., 2000. Small plants, pollution and poverty: new evidence from Brazil and Mexico. Policy research working paper, No. 2029.

Faisal, Islam, Rumi Shammiu, and Juhaina Junaid (1991). Industrial pollution in Bangladesh. Retrieved on July 24, 2003, from http://www.worldbank.org/nipr

Federal Ministry of Environment, Housing and Urban Development (FMENV) (1998). Industrial pollution inventory study.

Hettige, H., Martin, P., Singh, M., and Wheeler, D. (1994). The Industrial Pollution Projection System (IPPS) policy research working paper, No. 1431, part 1 and 2.

Hettige, H., Martin, P., Singh, M., and Wheeler, D. (1995). The Industrial Pollution Projection System (IPPS) policy research working paper, No. 1431, Part 3.

Jeremy A.T. Jones (2003). Electric arc furnace steelmaking. American Iron and Steel Institute. Nupro Corporation

Manufacturer's Association of Nigeria (M.A.N.) (1991). Yearly economic review.

Miroslav Radojevic and Viadimir N. Bashkin. (1999). Practical environmental analysis. Royal Society of Chemistry.

Ogungbuyi, O.M. and Osho, Y.B. (2005). Study on Industrial Discharges to the Lagos Lagoon. Report Submitted by United Nations Industrial Development Organization (UNIDO), Country Service Framework Programme under the Ecological Sustainable Industrial Development Programme.

Onianwa, P. C. (1985). Accumulation, exchange and retention of trace heavy metal in mosses from southwest Nigeria. Ph. D. thesis, University of Ibadan, Ibadan, Nigeria.

Onyekwelu, I.U., Junaid, K.A., and Ogungbuyi, O.M. 2003. Recent trends in the pollution load on the Lagos Lagoon – A National perspective. Presented by Federal Ministry of Environment at the Ecological Sustainable Industrial Development Workshop. 2 - 20.

Oketola, A.A., and Osibanjo, O. (2009a). Estimating sectoral pollution load in Lagos by Industrial Pollution Projection System (IPPS): Employment versus Output. *Toxicological & Environmental Chemistry.* 91, (5), 799-818.

Oketola, A.A., and Osibanjo, O. (2009b). Industrial pollution load assessment by Industrial Pollution Projection System (IPPS). *Toxicological & Environmental Chemistry.* 91, (5), 989-997.

Taras J. Michael. (1950). Phenoldisulphonic acid method of determining nitrate in water. *Anal Chem.,* 22, (8), 1020-102

11

Pollution Prevention in the Pulp and Paper Industries

Bahar K. Ince[1], Zeynep Cetecioglu[2] and Orhan Ince[2]

[1]*Bogazici University, Institute of Environmental Science, Istanbul,*
[2]*Istanbul Technical University, Environmental Engineering Department, Istanbul,*
Turkey

1. Introduction

Pulp and paper industry is considered as one of the most polluter industry in the world (Thompson *et al.*, 2001; Sumathi & Hung, 2006). The production process consists two main steps: pulping and bleaching. Pulping is the initial stage and the source of the most pollutant of this industry. In this process, wood chips as raw material are treated to remove lignin and improve fibers for papermaking. Bleaching is the last step of the process, which aims to whiten and brighten the pulp. Whole processes of this industry are very energy and water intensive in terms of the fresh water utilization (Pokhrel & Viraraghavan, 2004). Water consumption changes depending on the production process and it can get as high as 60 m³/ton paper produced in spite of the most modern and best available technologies (Thompson *et al.*, 2001).

The wastewaters generated from production processes of this industry include high concentration of chemicals such as sodium hydroxide, sodium carbonate, sodium sulfide, bisulfites, elemental chlorine or chlorine dioxide, calcium oxide, hydrochloric acid, etc (Sumathi & Hung, 2006). The major problems of the wastewaters are high organic content (20-110 kg COD/air dried ton paper), dark brown coloration, adsorbable organic halide (AOX), toxic pollutants, etc.

The environmental problems of pulp and paper industry are not limited by the high water consumption. Wastewater generation, solid wastes including sludge generating from wastewater treatment plants and air emissions are other problems and effective disposal and treatment approaches are essential. The significant solid wastes such as lime mud, lime slaker grits, green liquor dregs, boiler and furnace ash, scrubber sludges, wood processing residuals and wastewater treatment sludges are generated from different mills. Disposal of these solid wastes cause environmental problems because of high organic content, partitioning of chlorinated organics, pathogens, ash and trace amount of heavy metal content (Monte *et al.*, 2009).

The major air emissions of the industry come from sulfite mills as recovery gurnaces and burnes, sulfur oxides (SOx), from Kraft operation as reduced sulfur gases and odor problems, from wood-chips digestion, spent liquor evaporation and bleaching as volatile organic carbons (VOCs), and from combustion process as nitrogen oxidies (NOx) and SOx. VOCs also include ketone, alcohol and solvents such as carbon disulfide methanol, acetone and chlorofom (Smook, 1992).

Many kinds of the wastes as summarized above are generated from different processes. The amount, type and characteristics of these wastes are important to provide the best treatment technology. Physicochemical and biological treatment technologies are used extensively for the pulp and paper mills. The lab-scale and full-scale studies about sedimentation/floatation, coagulation and precipitation, adsorption, chemical oxidation and membrane filtration were carried out in the literature to examine physico-chemical approach (Pokhrel & Viraraghavan, 2004). Biological treatment both aerobic and anaerobic technologies are preferred for treatment of pulp and paper mills because of wastewater composition consisting of high organic compounds and economical aspects. Additionally, some fungi species are used to remove color and AOX from the effluents (Taseli and Gokcay, 1999). In some countries, tertiary treatment is applied to obtain discharge limits of regulations (Thompson *et al.*, 2001). Finally, the wide application in the full-scale plants for treatment pulp and paper mills is hybrid systems, which is combined physico-chemical and biological treatment alternatives (Pokhrel & Viraraghavan, 2004).

Disposal strategy of solid wastes generated from pulp and paper industry is varied depends on the country and the regulations obeyed. After sorting and handling, dewatering, thermal application such as combustion and anaerobic digestion to obtain energy and deposit in landfills are general applications. However, the solid wastes should be monitored after landfill deposition because of toxic characteristics of the compounds (Monte *et al.*, 2009).

Also gaseous pollutants are other environmental problems generated from pulp and paper industry. To minimize these pollutants, physico-chemical methods such as adsorption to activated coal filters absorption, thermal oxidation, catalytic oxidation and condensation have been widely used (Eweis *et al.*, 1998). In the last decade, low cost and effective trends have been developed to prevent the limitation of physico-chemical applications such as energy cost and generating secondary pollutants (Sumathi & Hung, 2006).

Waste minimization, recycle, reuse, and innovative approaches developed in last 10 years become more than an issue. In this chapter, waste characterization of this industry in terms of type and source with management approaches was discussed. Exemplary applications were presented. Finally 'state of the art' approaches for the environmental problems of this industry were argued.

2. Waste characterization and source

Pulp and paper industry is one of the most water and energy consuming industry in the world. This industry uses the fifth largest energy consumer processes; approximately 4% of total energy is used worldwide. Also during pulp and paper process, the important amount of waste is produced. It has been estimated that 500 million tons of paper and etc. per year will be produced in 2020. Three different raw materials are used in the pulp and paper industry as nonwood fibers and wood materials; soft and hard woods. Waste and wastewaters are generated from both of pulp and bleaching processes. Additionally, 100 million kg of toxic pollutants are released every year from this industry (Cheremisinoff & Rosenfeld, 2010).

2.1 Manufacturing technologies and process description
Pulping process is the first step of the production. The main steps of this part are debarking, wood chipping, chip washing, chip digestion, pulp screening, thickening, and washing. Mechanical and chemical operation processes in pulping are used in the worldwide. While

mechanical processes involve mechanical pressure, disc refiners, heating, and light chemical processes to increase pulping yield; wood chips are cooked in pulping liquors at high temperature and under pressure in the chemical pulping processes. (Sumathi & Hung, 2006). Additionally, mechanical and chemical processes can be combined in some applications. The yield of mechanical processes is higher (90-95%) compared to chemical processes (40-50%). However quality of the pulp obtained from mechanical processes is lower and also the pulp is highly coloured and includes short fibers (Pokhrel & Viraraghavan, 2004). Therefore, chemical pulping carrying out in alkaline or acidic media is mostly preferred. In alkaline media generally referred as Kraft Process, the woodchips are cooked in liquor including sodium hydroxide (NaOH) and sodium sulfide (NaS_2). Mixture of sulphurous acid (H_2SO_3) and bisulfide ions (HSO_3^-) is used in acidic media named as sulfide process.

During the pulp processing, approximately 5-10% of the lignin comes from the raw materials cannot be removed and these are responsible from the dark colour of the end product. The production of white paper (pulp bleaching) includes five or optional six treatment steps with sequentially elemental chlorine (C1), alkali (E1), optional hypochlorite (H) stage, chlorine dioxide (D1), alkali (E2), and chlorine dioxide (D2). The general process steps are given in Figure 1.

2.2 Wastewater

Different pulping processes utilize different amount of water and all of these processes are water intensive. The quality of wastewater generated from pulping and bleaching is significantly distinctive because of the process and chemical types (Billings and Dehaas, 1971). Approximately 200 m³ water are used for per ton of produced pulp and most of them are highly polluted, especially wastewater generated from chemical pulping process (Cecen *et al.*, 1992). Wood preparation, pulping, pulp washing, screening, washing, bleaching, paper machine and coating operations are the most important pollution sources among various process stages. Wastewaters generated from pulping stage include mostly wood debris, soluble wood materials, and also some chemicals from chemical pulping process. Bleaching process wastewater has a different quality. These wastewaters are not higher strength than pulping process wastewater, however they include toxic components.

Process steps and the generated wastewaters from these steps are given in Figure 2.

The wastewater characteristics and their strengths changed depending upon the pulping processing. Kraft process is widely used worldwide approximately 60% within all pulp production includes both mechanical and chemical pulping (Holmberg & Gustavsson, 2007). The regional or geographical distribution of the pulping processes is given in Table 1.

Region	Process Type	Pulp Production (million tons)					
		2004	2005	2006	2007	2008	2009
North America	Chemical wood pulp	59.6	59.1	57.3	55.6	54.8	48.6
	Mechanical wood pulp	16.3	16.2	15.3	14.4	13.6	11.7
	Total Production	75.9	75.3	72.6	70.0	68.4	60.3
Europe	Chemical wood pulp	26.8	25.9	27.5	27.3	32.4	29.5
	Mechanical wood pulp	11.5	11.2	12.4	12.1	14.3	11.9
	Total Production	38.3	37.1	39.9	39.4	46.7	41.4

Table 1. Pulp production in North America and Europe (Food and Agriculture Organization (FAO) Database, 2011)

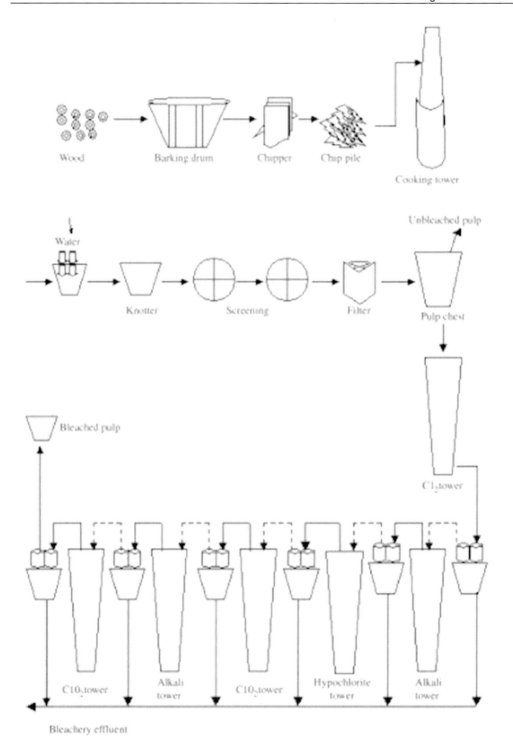

Fig. 1. Process scheme of a conventional pulp and paper industry (Sumathi & Hung, 2006)

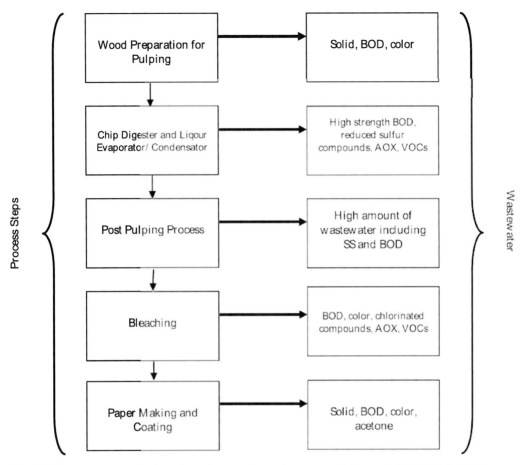

Fig. 2. Wastewater producing steps from pulp and paper mill (Smook, 1992; EPA, 1995)

The wastewaters generated from pulping process consist various wooden compounds such as lignin, carbohydrate and extractives and the treatment of these wastewaters by biologically is difficult. Addition of them, some toxic compounds such as resin acids, unsaturated fatty acids, diterpene alcohols, juvaniones, chlorinated resin acids, and others can exist in the wastewaters subjecting to the process (Pokhrel & Viraraghavan, 2004). The most important reaction in the bleaching step is oxidation of chlorine and the main problem about the wastewater content is chlorinated organic compounds or AOX (Sumathi & Hung, 2006).

The toxic effects of these by-products in the wastewaters on environment have been studied. Various studies reported that fish living in pulp and paper industry wastewaters have toxic/lethal effects on the daphnia, fish, planktons and other bioata in the receiving water bodies (Owens *et al.*, 1994; Hickey and Martin, 1995; Yen *et al.*, 1996; Vass *et al.*, 1996; Liss *et al.*, 1997; Lindstrom-Seppa *et al.*, 1998; Leppanen and Oikari, 1999; Johnsen *et al.*, 1998; Erisction and Larsson, 2000; Schnell *et al.*, 2000b; Kovacs *et al.*, 2002).

2.3 Solid and hazardous wastes

Wastewater and consequently solid wastes are the main environmental problem of the pulp and paper mills because this industry has a very water intensive production processes

(Cabral *et al.*, 1998; Thompson *et al.*, 2001). Solid wastes from pulp and paper industries are mainly treatment sludges, lime mud, lime slaker grits, green liquor dregs, boiler and furnace ash, scrubber sludges, and wood processing residuals. Wastewater treatment sludges have a significant concern for the environment because of including chlorinated compounds (EPA, 2002). The characteristics of all solid waste generated from the pulp and paper mills are organic exception of boiler and furnace ash. The chemicals of the solid wastes are varied depends on the process type. Solid wastes, sources and qualities are given in Table 2.

Source	Waste Type	Waste Characteristic
Wastewater Treatment Plant	Sludge	Organic fraction consistes wood fibers and biosludge.
		Inorganic fraction consists clay, calcium carbonate, and other materials
		20-60% solid content
		pH≈7
Caustic Process	Dregs, muds	Green liquor dregs consisting of non-reactive metals and insoluble materials; lime mud
Power Boiler	Ash	Inorganic compounds
Paper Mill	Sludge	Colour waste and fibre clay including slowly biodegradable organics such as cellulose, wood fibres and lignin

Table 2. Solid waste types and sources from pulp and paper mills (EPA, 2002; Nurmesniemi *et al.*, 2007)

2.4 Gas emissions

Air pollutants and gas emissions are the other concern about the pulp and paper industry. The most important gas emission is water vapours. Additionally, particulates, nitrogen oxides, volatile organic compounds (VOCs), sulfur oxides and total reduced sulfur compounds (TRS). The gas emissions sources and types are given Table 3.

3. Waste management

During the pulp and paper production, high usage of water and energy results in large amount of waste generation like wastewater, solid waste and air emissions. Different types

of waste are produced from different production steps and all these wastes pose important environmental problem. To solve this problem:
- Waste minimization can be done by using new and best available technologies.
- End-of-pipe treatment technologies should be used before the discharge and/or disposal.

Source	Major Pollutants
Chemical Pulping Process	VOCs (terpenes, alcohols, phenols, methanol, acetone, chloroform, methyl ethyl ketone [MEK])
	Reduced sulfur compounds (TRS)
	Organo-chlorine compounds
Bleaching	VOCs (acetone, methylene chloride, chloroform, MEK, chloromethane, trichloroethane)
Wastewater Treatment Plant	VOCs (terpenes, alcohols, phenols, methanol, acetone, chloroform, MEK)
Power Boiler	SO2, Nox, fly ash, coarse particulates
Evaporator	Evaporator noncondensibles (TRS, volatile organic compounds: alcohols, terpenes, phenols)
Recovery Furnace	Fine particulates, TRS, SO2, Nox
Calcining (Lime Kiln)	Fine and coarse particulates

Table 3. Air pollutants types and sources from pulp and paper mills (EPA, 2002)

3.1 Waste minimization

Modern waste minimization approach is by two means. This first way is chemical recovery and recycling. This system especially in chemical pulping process significantly reduces pollutants and additionally economical return is another important aspect. Chemical recovery is necessary because of the basic economic viability of the kraft process. According to EPA, all kraft pulp mills worldwide use chemical recovery systems. However, there is still no recovery system in some sulfite mills. Additionally, scrubber system particulate "baghouses" or electrostatic precipitators (ESPs) are often mill air pollution control components (EPA, 2002).

The second way to minimize waste production from pulp and paper mills is the application of best available techniques (BAT) according to the Integrated Pollution, Prevention and Control (IPPC) Regulation. An effective waste minimization method reduces cost, liability, regulatory burdens of hazardous waste management (Rouleau & Sasseville, 1996; Holland, 1997). Furthermore, hazardous waste generation can be reduced by waste management methods including:
- production, planning and sequencing
- process adjustment and/or modification
- raw material replacement
- housekeepingwaste segregation ans seperation
- recycling

The industries have developed and applied new technologies instead of conventional pulping and bleaching processes. Some examples of these new technologies are given below:

Organic Solvent Pulping: This process is more economical for small and medium scale plants for significant recovery and reuse of chemicals. In this process, organic solvent like ethanol, methanol, etc. are preferred. However, this process is more energy consumer than conventional ones (Sumathi & Hung, 2006).

Acid Pulping: Acetic acid under the high pressure is used for treating of wood chips. The disadvantage of this process is to loss of acid, however recovery is possible (Sumathi & Hung, 2006).

Biopulping: Microorganism or microbial enzymes such as xylanases, pectinases, cellulases, hemicellulases, ligninases, and their combination are used in the pulping process to improve the properties of pulp (Kirk *et al.*, 1996). Biopulping is preferred because:
- To reduce the chemical and energy utilization
- To reduce the pollutants
- To increase the yield and strength properties of pulp.

Elemental Chlorine Free (ECF) and Total Chlorine Free (TCF) Bleaching: Elemental chlorine has been used instead of chlorine dioxide and hypochlorite and oxygen, ozone, caustic soda, and hydrogen peroxide have been applied for TCF bleaching of Kraft pulps to reduce the chlorinated organic wastes (Sumathi & Hung, 2006).

Biobleaching: Fungal cells and or their enzymes are used for pretreatment of pulp. A number of studies showed that application of white rod fungi reduces the chemical dosage of bleaching and enhances the brightness of paper (Kirkpatrick *et al.*, 1990; Reid *et al.*, 1990; Daneult *et al.*, 1994).

Extended Delignification: Enhanced removal of lignin before bleaching step is the main concern of this method (Gullichsen, 1991; McDonough, 1992). It may be achieved by extended cooking, oxygenation, ozonation, and addition of chemical catalysts. Extended delignification positively affect on the bleach effluent quality parameters such as COS, BOD, color and AOX.

3.2 Treatment strategies

Although the best approach is to minimize the waste generation from the pulp and paper mills and to recycle, the treatment applications are still necessary. In this section, up-to date treatment technologies are given.

3.2.1 Wastewater treatment

End of the pipe pollution treatment strategies are necessary to provide the discharge limits. The general flow-chart of a typical wastewater treatment plant is given Figure 3.

The main treatment application for wastewater generated from pulp and paper process is primary and secondary treatment. However, tertiary treatment can be an obligation in future due to possible new legislations. The physicochemical step is rare at present.

Primary Treatment

In this step, the aim is to remove suspended solid such as bark particles, fiber, fiber debris, filler and coating materials and consequently organic materials. Primary clarification can also be achieved without sedimentation and flotation. However Thompson *et al.* (2001) mentioned that sedimentation is generally preferred application for the pulp and paper mills in UK and approximately 80% of suspended solid was removed successfully. Also

Rajvaid and Markandey (1998) reported 70-80% of removal in the sedimentation. Dissolved air flotation and filtration are the other option as primary treatment for pulp and paper mills.

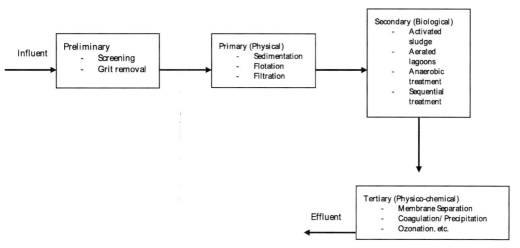

Fig. 3. Flow scheme of general wastewater treatment plant of pulp and paper industry

Secondary Treatment

Aerobic lagoons, activated sludge systems, anaerobic treatment and sequential biological treatment (aerobic-anaerobic or anaerobic-aerobic) are the most common biological treatment application for pulp and paper mills. In this section, the details of these processes are given and they are discussed. Performances of various biological treatment processes are summarized in Tables 4.

Activated Sludge Systems:

This conventional treatment system is used in treatment of several industrial wastewater types in order to remove COD, BOD, SS, and AOX. There are a lot of studies in the literature to show the treatability of pulp and paper mills by activated sludge system. Some of them focused on the BOD, COD, AOX and other specific compound removal under different operation conditions. Schnell et al. (1997) showed that 74% of filtered COD, nearly %100 BOD5, resin and fatty acid removal were achieved in the full-scale plant. Saunamaki (1997) reported that 82% and 60% COD removal efficiency at paper mills and pulp mills, respectively in full-scale activated sludge systems of Finland. Knudsen et al. (1994) claimed high COD and BOD removal efficiency by two stage activated sludge process. Also Hansen et al. (1999) and Chandra (2001) showed similar results.

The other part of these studies focused on the removal of AOX and other specific compounds such as chlorinated phenols, guaiacols, catechols, vanillins, 1,1-dichlorodimethyl sulfone (DSS), and chlorinated acetic acid (Mohamed et al., 1989; Demirbas et al., 1999; Bajpai, 2001; Chandra, 2001). The main operational problems of the pulp and paper mills are macro nutrient (N and P) limitation in the systems and growth of the filamentous microorganisms and bulking problems. The nutrient limitation problem is overcome by addition of nutrient. However, the dosage is important point on this step because the external addition causes adverse environmental effects such as eutrophication.

Cingolani *et al.* (1994) highlighted that the main causes of bulking in the pulp and paper mills treatment are poor oxygenation, low organic loading rates and also nutrient limitations. This problem can also be controlled by installation of a selector or addition of chemicals such as chlorine, ferrous salts, lime or talk powder. Selectors are mostly preferred application for bulking (Forster, 1996; Marten and Daigger, 1997; Prendle and Kroiss, 1998; Andreasen *et al.*, 1999).

Aerated Lagoons (Stabilization Basins):

Aerated lagoons are the simple and economical biological systems and they have been studies very well as lab-scale and full-scale at the pulp and paper mills. These systems have been used for removal of BOD, low-molecular weight AOX and fatty acids at full-scale applications (Bajpai, 2001). Stuthridge and Macfarlane (1994) showed that 70% of AOX could be removed efficiently in a short residence time. Welander *et al.* (1997) reported that COD removal was achieved as 30-40% in a full-scale lagoon and 60-70% in a pilot-scale plant. Lab-scale treatability studies were conducted by Chernysh *et al.* (1992) to monitor the AOX and TOC removal of bleached kraft effluent. Slade *et al.* (1999) also reported three aerated stabilization basins, which treated elemental chlorine free (ECF) integrated bleached Kraft mill effluents.

Anaerobic Treatment Processes:

Anaerobic treatment processes are more suitable for treatment of high strength wastewater such as pulp and paper mills. In the literature, there are a variety of studies on the anaerobic treatability and microbial community of this type of effluents (Poggi-Varaldo *et al.*, 1996; Bajpai, 2000; Ince *et al.*, 2007). Also, anaerobic microorganisms are more efficient than aerobics in order to degrade chlorinated organic compounds. However, the sulphur content in the wastewaters is the main disadvantages for application of anaerobic systems, because one of the end products is hydrogen sulphide in the anaerobic biodegradation in the presence of sulphate (Lettinga *et al.*, 1991). Although Hamm *et al.* (1991) reported that the toxic effect of H_2S is less than high concentration of Ca^{2+} and SO_4^{2-}. The other important issues for the application of anaerobic treatment in pulp and paper mills are toxicity of wastewater, anaerobic biodegradability characteristic of specific waste types such as lignin derivates, resin and fatty acids, loading capacity, response to loading fluctuation, and recovery of energy and chemicals (Sumathi and Hung, 2006). Several hundred tons of inorganic chemicals per day for delignification are used in a conventional pulp and paper mill. So, the recovery and reuse of these chemicals are one of the most economical and environmental concern. Addition of it, the black liquor is rich in lignin and a conventional pulp and paper mill produces 1.7-1.8 tons dry solid of black liquor per ton produced pulp and the potential energy of this liquor from anaerobic digestion is 250-500 MW (Stigsson, 1998; Larson *et al.*, 2000). Anaerobic contact reactor, up-flow anaerobic sludge blanket (UASB) reactor, anaerobic filter, and fluidized bed reactor are mostly employed reactor types in pulp and paper mills. The anaerobic treatment efficiency of different plants from pulp and paper industry is given in Table 5.

Fungal Treatment:

Fungal species have been used to remove colour and COD from pulp and paper mills (Eaton *et al.*, 1980; Livernoche *et al.*, 1983; Wang *et al.*, 1992; Gokcay and Dilek, 1994; Duran *et al.*,

1994; Sakurai *et al.*, 2001). Pencillium sp., P. chrysosporium and white rod fungi are the most widely used species. Choudhury *et al.* (1998) reported that Pleurotus ostreatus was removed 77% of lignin, 76.8% of BOD, 60% of COD, and 80% of colour.

Tertiary Treatment

Coagulation/Precipitation:

Addition of metal salts to generate larger flocs from small particles for removing the pollutants easily is the main principle of this method. There are some studies to find the most effective chemicals such as horseradish peroxide (chitosan), $Al_2(SO_4)_3$, hexamethylene diamine epichlorohydrin polycondensate (HE), polyethyleneimine (PEI) to remove AOX, total organic carbon and colour (Tong *et al.*, 1999; Ganjidoust *et al.*, 1997). The authors reported that chitosan is more effective to remove these pollutants from others. Dilek and Gokcay (1994) stated that alum salts as coagulant were removed 96% of COD from the paper machine, 50% of COD from pulping, and %20 COD from bleaching effluents. The other study showed that polyelectrolytes were more effective than the conventional coagulant on the removal of turbidity, COD, and colour (Rohella *et al.*, 2001).

Adsorption:

This method relies on the addition of an adsorbant such as activated coke, fuller's earth, coal ash, activated carbon, and activated charcoal to the wastewater to remove the pollutants. High removal of colour by activated charcoal, fuller's earth, and coal ash was reported (Murthy *et al.*, 1991). Also Shawwa et al (2001) showed that high removal of colour, COD, DOC, and AOX from bleaching wastewater by activated coke.

Chemical Oxidation:

Advanced oxidation methods such as photocatalysis, photo-oxidation, Fenton type reactions, wet oxidation, ozonation are used to achieve the destruction of chromophoric and nonchromophoric pollutants in pulp and paper mills. The achievement of photocatalytic reaction in the removal of COD is depended on the concentration of COD and chloride, which are below a certain level (Balcioglu and Ferhan, 1999). Fenton and photo-fenton reactions are highly effective for the treatment of bleaching kraft mill effluent (Perez *et al.*, 2002). Verenich *et al.* (2000) showed that wet-oxidation are increased the biodegradability of the pulp and paper mill effluent from 30% to 70%. Also ozonation is one of the most effective methods. Several author showed that the effectiveness of this method (Hostachy *et al.*, 1997; Zhou and Smith, 1997; Yamamoto, 2001; Freire *et al.*, 2000).

Membrane Filtration:

Membrane filtration is a potential method to remove colour, COD, AOX, salts, heavy metals, and total dissolved solids from pulp and paper mills (Zaidi *et al.*, 1992; Afonso and Pinho, 1991; Falth, 2000; Merrill *et al.*, 2001). The effluent of membrane filtration can be used again in production process or discharge directly to the receiving water bodies. Dube *et al.* (2000) showed that 88% and 89% removal of BOD and COD, respectively was achieved by reverse osmosis (RO).

The performance of physico-chemical process at the pulp and paper industry is summarized in Table 6.

Treatment Process		TSS		BOD		COD		AOX		Chlorinated Phenolics		Color		Methanol		References
		Influent (mg/L)	Removal Efficiency (%)	Influent (mg/L)	Removal Efficiency (%)	Influent (mg/L)	Removal Efficiency (%)	Influent (mg/L)	Removal Efficiency (%)	Influent (mg/L)	Removal Efficiency (%)	Influent (Pt-Co)	Removal Efficiency (%)	Influent (mg/L)	Removal Efficiency (%)	
Activated sludge	Paper mill	1435	90.6	512	94.2	1210	82.4	-	-	-	-	-	-	-	-	Saunamaki (1997)
	Pulp mill	738	76.4	336	93.8*	1192	57.1	11.7	55	-	-	-	-	-	-	Saunamaki (1997)
	Kraft mill I	-	-	270	>95*	660 (F)	60	22.5	36	0.255	74	-	-	-	-	Schnell et al. (2000a)
	Kraft mill II	-	-	270	>98	660 (F)	70	22.5	40	0.255	83	-	-	-	-	Schnell et al. (2000a)
	Pulp and paper mill	-	-	-	96.63	-	96.8	-	-	-	96.92	-	-	-	-	Chandra (2001)
	Paper mill	-	-	1000	99	1533a	85	-	-	-	-	-	-	-	-	Knudsen et al. (1994)
Aerobic stabilization basin	Kraft mill I	-	-	270	>95	660 (F)	62	22.5	53	0.255	85	-	-	-	-	Schnell et al. (2000a)
	Kraft mill II	-	-	270	>98	660 (F)	73	22.5	55	0.255	86	-	-	-	-	Schnell et al. (2000a)
	Kraft mill	-	-	-	-	-	20-65	-	17-70	-	-	-	-	-	-	Chernysh et al. (1992)
Other Biological Reactor Types	HRC (TMP Mill)	-	-	1150	98	3340	79	-	-	-	-	-	-	-	-	Magnus et al. (2000a)
	Total plant efficiency	-	-	1490	99	5000	86	-	-	-	-	-	-	-	-	Magnus et al. (2000a)
	MBBR (HRT 4.5 hrs)	-	-	-	65-75	-	85-95	-	-	-	-	-	-	-	-	Borch-Due et al. (1997)
	SBR	-	-	-	98	-	85-93	-	-	-	-	-	-	-	-	Franta and Wilderer (1997)
	Anaerobic (GAC)	-	-	1400	-	-	50	-	-	-	-	1300	50	-	-	Jackson-Moss et al. (1992)
	Kraft mill Windsor	-	-	1429	69	2036b	59	-	-	-	-	-	-	1095b	84	Dufresne et al. (2001)

Table 4. Typical wastewater quality of pulp and paper industry and biological treatment efficiencies of these wastewaters ([1] "f" means fraction of COD or soluble COD; [2] Period 1: operating conditions for activated sludge-HRT 2 days, SRT 25 days, Temp. 30 jC, VSS 1800 mg/l.; [3] Period 1: operating conditions for aerated stabilization basin-HRT 15 days, SRT 15 days, Temp. 30 jC, VSS 60 mg/ l.; [4] Period 2: operating conditions for activated sludge-HRT 1 day, SRT 25 days, Temp. 30 jC, VSS 2800 mg/ l.; [5] Period 2: operating conditions for aerated stabilization basin-HRT 15 days, SRT 15 days, Temp. 20 jC, VSS 70 mg/ l; [6] "a" means soluble COD, [7] "b"means unit in g/ d; and [8] "*" means BOD7).

Reactor Type	Mill location	Wastewater Source	Loading Rate (kg COD/m3/d)	BOD5 (mg/L)	BOD5 Removal %	COD (mg/L)	COD Removal %	TSS (mg/L)
Anaerobic contact reactor	Hylte Bruk, AB, Sweden	TMP, groundwood, deink	2.5	1300	71	3500	67	520
	SAICA, Zaragoza, Spain	Waste paper alkaline cooked straw	4.8	10,000	94	30,000	66	
	Hannover paper, Alfred, Germany	Sulfite effluent condensate	4.2	3000	97	6000	85	
	Niagara of Wisconsin, USA	CTMP	2.7	2500	96	4800	77	3300
	SCA Ostrand, Ostrand, Sweden	CTMP	6	3700	50	7900	40	
	Alaska Pulp Corporation, Sitka	Sulfite condensate, bleach caustic and pulp whitewater	3	3500	85	10,000	49	
Upflow anaerobic sludge blanket	Celtona, Holland	Tissue	3	600	75	1200	60	
	Southern paper converter, Australia	Wastepaper	10		80	10,000	> 80	
	Davidson, United Kingdom	Linerboard	9	1440	90	2880	75	
	Chimicadel, Friulli, Italy	Sulfite condensate	12.5	12,000	90	15,600	80	
	Quesnel River Pulp, Canada	TMP/CTMP	18	3000	60	7800	50	
	Lake Utopia Paper, Canada	NSSC	20	6000	80	16,000	55	
	EnsoGutzeit, Finland	Bleached, TMP/CTMP	13.5	1800	75	4000	60	
	McMillan Bloedel, Canada	NSSC/CTMP	15	7000	80	17,500	55	
Anaerobic filter	Lanaken, Belgium	CTMP	12.7	4000	85	7900	70	
Anaerobic fluidized bed:	France	Paperboard	35	1500	83.3	3000	72.2	

Table 5. Selected anaerobic process performance at different pulp and paper industries (Bajpai, 2000)

Treatment Process		TSS Influent (mg/L)	TSS Removal Efficiency (%)	COD Influent (mg/L)	COD Removal Efficiency (%)	TOC Influent (mg/L)	TOC Removal Efficiency (%)	AOX Influent (mg/L)	AOX Removal Efficiency (%)	Color Influent (Pt-Co)	Color Removal Efficiency (%)	Lignin/Resin or Fatty acid Influent (mg/L)	Lignin/Resin or Fatty acid Removal Efficiency (%)	References
Coagulation	Polyelectrolyte	3620	100	4112	55.65	–	–	–	–	4667.5	82.58	480	98.91	Rohella et al. (2001)
	Chitosan	–	–	–	–	–	70	–	–	–	90	–	–	Ganjidoust et al. (1997)
	PE/PEI	–	–	–	–	–	30	–	–	–	80	–	–	Ganjidoust et al. (1997)
	Alum	–	–	–	–	–	40	–	–	–	80	–	–	Ganjidoust et al. (1997)
Adsorption	Charcoal #1	–	–	–	–	–	–	–	–	3.9 mg/L	98.13	–	–	Murthy et al. (1991)
	Coal ash #2	–	–	–	–	–	–	–	–	3.9 mg/L	98.5	–	–	Murthy et al. (1991)
	Fuller earth #3	–	–	–	–	–	–	–	–	3.9 mg/L	99.21	–	–	Murthy et al. (1991)
	Activated coke #4	–	–	2126	>90	–	–	80.2	>90	2300	>90	–	–	Shawwa et al. (2001)
Oxidation	Wet oxidation	–	–	10,000–19,000	80	3500–4100	80	–	–	–	–	–	–	Verenich et al. (2000)
	Ozone + Fenton	–	–	–	–	–	–	–	–	–	~100	–	–	Hassan and Hawkyard (2002)
	Ozone+UV	–	–	~550	82	–	–	–	–	–	–	–	–	Oeller et al. (1997)
Ozonation	Photocat. ozone	–	–	515	85	306	88	27.7	92.5	250	100	–	–	Torrades et al. (2001)
	Photocat. ozone	–	–	3700	57.5	1380	38	69.8	50	7030	65	–	–	Torrades et al. (2001)
Membrane	Ultrafiltration	–	–	–	85–90	–	–	–	85–91		93–98	–	–	Zaidi et al. (1992)
	Nanofiltration	–	–	–	–	–	–	–	93–96		99.2–99.9	–	–	Zaidi et al. (1992)
	Dissolved air +UF	397	100	–	–	828	65	–	–	1747	90			De Pinho et al. (2000)
	Microfiltration +UF	397	100	–	–	828	54	–	–	1747	88			De Pinho et al. (2000)

Table 6. Typical wastewater quality of pulp and paper industry and physico-chemical treatment efficiencies of these wastewater (#1) Charcoal dose 0.4 g/L and pH 2.0; (#2) Coal ash dose 12 g/L and pH 2.0; (#3) Fuller earth dose 4 g/L and pH 2.0; (#4) activated coke dose 15,000 mg/L

3.2.2 Management and disposal of solid wastes

Integrated solid waste management of pulp and paper mills are through anaerobic digestion, composting, land applications, thermal processes such as incineration/combustion, pyrolysis, steam reforming, and wet oxidation.

Anaerobic Digestion: This process type is a cost effective way due to the high-energy recovery (Verstraete and Vandevivere, 1999; Mata-Alvarez et al., 2000). Industrial wastes, which have high organic content and digestable, are suitable for anaerobic digestion like paper sludge and wastewater treatment plant sludge (Kay, 2003; CANMET, 2005).

Composting: This method is suitable for the wastes and sludge, especially paper fibres and organic materials. The wastes are stabilized via microorganisms with minimal carbon loss. The end product of this process, humus-like material, can be used for houseplants, greenhouse and agriculture (Jokela et al., 1997; Hackett et al., 1999; Christmas, 2002; Gea et al., 2005).

Land Application: This method has been preferred disposal method, especially for the acidic soil due to $CaCO_3$ content of sludge. This application is widely used in the United Kingdom and Northern Europe. Before the application, dewatering and/or incineration treatment are done to the waste/sludge in order to reduce volume (Carr and Gay, 1997; Van Horn, 1997).

Incineration (Combustion): Combination of incineration with power and steam generation is one of the most applied methods in Europe, especially for wastewater treatment plant sludge. However, water and ash content of most sludges cause the energy deficiency. Fluidized bed boiler technology is becoming the one of the best solution for the final disposal of paper mill wastes in order to provide successful thermal oxidation of high ash, high moisture wastes (Busbin, 1995; Fitzpatrick and Seiler, 1995; Davis et al., 1995; Albertson, 1999; Porteous, 2005; Oral et al., 2005).

Pyrolysis: In this process, organic wastes are converted to gaseous and liquid phase under high temperature and in the absence of oxygen. This is an alternative technology to incineration and landfill. This method is suitable for organic content high wastes such as wood, petroleum, plastic waste. However this technology is not sufficient for pulp and paper mill waste. Some investigations have been continue to adapt this technology to pulp and paper mills (Fio Rito, 1995; Frederik et al., 1996; Kay, 2002; Fytili and Zabaniotou, 2008).

Steam Reforming: This technology is used for sludge treatment, however it is still considered as an emerging technology for paper sludges. Steam reforming is a novel combustion technology, which carries out in a steam reforming reaction system (Durai-Swamy et al., 1991; Aghamohammadi and Durai-Swamy, 1995; Demirbas, 2007).

Wet Oxidation: The principle of wet oxidation is that organic compound as solid or liquid form is firstly transferred to water where it contacts with an oxidant under high temperature and pressure. During wet oxidation, waste pulped with water is carbonized and its fuel value increases to the equivalent of medium-grade coal. The waste does not cause any air emission in order to combust without flame or smoke (Kay, 2002). This technology is also considered as an emerging technology like steam reforming.

3.2.3 Treatment of gas emissions

Air pollution control at pulp and paper mills has been important concern in the recent years. Especially VOCs produced form pulp and bleaching steps and steam are conventionally treated by physico-chemical methods such as adsorption to activated coal filters, absorption, thermal oxidation, catalytic oxidation, and condensation (Eweis et al., 1998). I spite of these pollutants are removed from gaseous phase, they transferred another phase and they are also different pollutants for environment. More innovative approach to solve this problem is biofilters and bioscrubbers that have three steps to remove pollutants from gaseous phase;

- The transfer of pollutants from air to liquid phase,
- The transfer of pollutants from liquid phase to biofilm phase where microorganisms are located, and
- Mineralization of pollutants by microorganisms.

4. Conclusion

The paper demand increases every day as a result of developed population and industrialisation. Water and energy utilization and in particularly waste generation are becoming more important concern ever worldwide. A major goal is to decrease damage to environment by waste minimization, reuse and recycle. To use best available techniques and innovative methods is becoming more an issue. However, end-of-pipe treatment is still the major approach to minimize the risk. To evaluate pollutants and to develop treatment technologies need a holistic approach.

The major pollution load constitutes wastewaters from pulp and paper mills. A variety of wastewater is generated from diverse processes. Different technologies and their combinations have been used for their treatment. The most common applied systems are biological treatment, sequential anaerobic and aerobic systems, followed after primary treatment. Solid waste management and disposal are also another concern. During the final disposal step, the aim should be chemical compound and energy recovery because of environmental and economical aspects. However, the waste minimization has still the first and important approach. Biofilters and bioscrubbers are mostly used for removal of air pollutants and other applications are limited.

The best available treatment technology for all three waste phases depends on the production processes, raw materials and the regulations, which the industries have to obey.

5. References

Afonso, M.D. &Pinho, M.N. (1991). Membrane separation processes in pulp and paper production. *Filtr. Sep.*, Vol.2, No.1, pp.42– 4.

Aghamohammadi, B. & Durai-Swamy, K. (1995). A disposal alternative for sludge waste from recycled paper and cardboard. Environmental Issues and Technology in the Pulp and Paper Industry. *A TAPPI Press Anthology of Published Papers*, 1991–1994, pp. 445–449.

Albertson, D.M. (1999). Paper sludge – waste disposal problem or energy opportunity. *Energy Products of Idaho.*

Andreasan, K.; Agertved, J.; Petersen, J.O. & Skaarup, H. (1999) Improvement of sludge settleability in activated sludge plants treating effluent from pulp and paper industries. *Water Sci. Technol.*, Vol. 40, No.11 –12, pp.215–21.

Bajpai, P. (2000). Treatment of pulp and paper mill effluents with anaerobic technology. *Randalls Road*, Leatherhead, UK: Pira International.

Bajpai, P. (2001). Microbial degradation of pollutants in pulp mill effluents. *Adv. Appl. Microbiol.*, Vol.48, pp. 79–134.

Balcioglu, A.I. & Ferhan, C. (1999). Treatability of kraft pulp bleaching wastewater by biochemical and photocatalytic oxidation. *Water Sci. Technol.*, Vol. 40, No.1, pp.281–8.

Billings, R.M. & DeHaas, G.G. (1971). Pollution control in the pulp and paper industry. In: *Industrial Pollution Control Handbook*, Lund, H.F. (Ed.), McGraw-Hill, New York, pp. 18-28.

Borch-Du, A.; Anderson, R. & Opheim, B. (1997). Treatment of integrated newsprint mill wastewater in moving bed biofilm reactors. *Water Sci. Technol.*, Vol.35, No.2–3, pp.173– 180.

Busbin, S.J. (1995). Fuel specifications – sludge. *Environmental Issues and Technology in the Pulp and Paper Industry. A TAPPI Press Anthology of Published Papers*, 1991–1994, pp. 349–353.

Cabral, F.; Vasconcelos, E.; Goss, M. & Cordovil, C. (1998). The value, use, and environmental impacts of pulp-mill sludge addition to forest and agricultural lands in Europe. *Environmental Reviews*, Vol.6, p. 55–64.

CANMET Energy Technology Centre. (2005). Pulp and paper sludge to energy – preliminary assessment of technologies. Canada

Carr, J.M. & Gay, C.L. (1997). Demonstrating the environmental benefit of land application of kraft mill biosolids. In: *Environmental Conference and Exhibit. TAPPI Proceedings, Book 2*, Minneapolis Convention Center, pp. 849–852.

Cecen, F.; Urban, W. & Haberl, R. (1992). Biological and advanced treatment of sulfate pulp bleaching *Water Sci. Technol.*, Vol.26, pp.435-444.

Chandra, R. (2001). Microbial decolourisation of pulp mill effluent in presence of nitrogen and phosphorous by activated sludge process. *J Environ Biol.*, Vol.22, No.1, pp.23–27.

Chernysh, A.; Liss, N.S. & Allen, G.D. (1992). A batch study of the aerobic and anaerobic removal of chlorinated organic compounds in an aerated lagoon. *Water Pollut. Res. J. Can.*, Vol.27, No.3, pp.621– 38.

Cheremisinoff, N.P. & Rosenfeld, P.E. (1998). The best practices in the wood and paper industries, ISBN 978-0-08-096446-1, Elsevier, Burlington, USA.

Choudhury, S.; Sahoo, N.; Manthan, M. & Rohela R.S. (1998). Fungal treatment of pulp and paper mill effluents for pollution control. J. Ind. Pollut. Control, Vol. 14, No.1, pp.1– 13.

Christmas, P. (2002). Building materials from deinking plant residues – a sustainable solution. In: *COST Workshop Managing Pulp and Paper Residues*, Barcelona, Spain.

Cingolani, L.; Ciccarelli, E.; Cossigani, M.; Tornari, Q. & Scarlata, V. (1994). Management of paper mill wastes: the role of filamentous microorganisms as indicators. *Water Sci. Technol.*, Vol. 29, pp. 185-188.

Daneault, C.; Leduce, C. & Valade, J.L. (1994). The use of xylanases in Kraft pulp bleaching: a review. *Tappi J.*, Vol. 77, pp. 125–131.

Davis, D.A.; Gounder, P.K. & Shelor, F.M. (1995). Combined cycle fluidized bed combustion sludges and other pulp and paper mill wastes to useful energy. *Environmental*

Issues and Technology in the Pulp and Paper Industry. A TAPPI Press Anthology of Published Papers, 1991–1994, pp. 379–381.

De Pinho, M.N.; Minhalma, M.; Rosa, M.J. & Taborda, F. (2000). Integration of flotation/ultrafiltration for treatment of bleached pulp effluent. *Pulp Pap Can.,* Vol. 104, No. 4, pp.50– 54.

Demirbas, A. (2007). Progress and recent trends in biofuels. *Prog. Energ. Combust. Sci.,* Vol. 33, No. 1, pp.1–18.

Demirbas, G.; Gokcay, C.F. & Dilek, F.B. (1999). Treatment of organic chlorine in pulping effluents by activated sludge. *Water Sci Technol.,* Vol. 40, No. 1, pp. 275 –9.

Dilek, F.B. & Gokcay, C.F. (1994). Treatment of effluents from hemp-based pulp and paper industry: waste characterization and physicochemical treatability. *Water Sci. Technol.* Vol. 29, No. 9, pp. 161– 3.

Dube, M.; McLean, R., MacLatchy, D. & Savage, P. (2000). Reverse osmosis treatment: effects on effluent quality. *Pulp Pap Can.,* Vol. 101, No. 8, pp. 42– 5.

Dufresne, R.; Liard, A. & Blum, S.M. (2001). Anaerobic treatment of condensates: at a kraft pulp and paper mill. *Water Environ Res.,* Vol. 73, No.1, pp.103–9.

Durai-Swamy, K.; Warren, D.W. & Mansour, M.N. (1991). Indirect steam gasification of paper mill sludge waste. *TAPPI J.,* 137–143.

Duran, N.; Esposito, E.; Innicentini-Mei, L.H. & Canhos, P.V. (1994). A new alternative process for kraft E1 effluent treatment. *Biodegradation,* Vol. 5, pp. 13– 9.

Eaton, D.; Chang, H.-M. & Kirk, T.K. (1980). Fungal decolorization of Kraft bleach effluents. *Tappi J.,* Vol. 63, pp. 103–106

EPA Office of Compliance Sector Notebook Project. Profile of the Pulp and Paper Industry. 2nd ed. Washington, November 2002.

Erisction, G. & Larsson, A. (2000). DNA A dots in perch (Perca fluviatillis) in coastal water pollution with bleachen in pulp mill effluents. *Ecotoxicol Environ Saf.,* Vol. 46, pp. 167–73.

Eweis, J.B.; Ergas, S.J.; Chang, D.P.Y. & Schroeder, E.D. (Eds.), (1998). *Bioremediation Principles,* ISBN 9780070577329, McGraw-Hill, Singapore

Falth, F. (2000). Ultrafiltration of E1 stage effluent for partial closure of the bleach plant. Proc. 86th PAPTAC annual meeting, Montreal, Quebec. Canada: Pulp and Paper Technical Association of Canada, p. B85.

FAOSTAT, – Forestry, Food and Agriculture Organization of the United Nations, February 2011. <http://faostat.fao.org/site/630/default.aspx>.

Fitzpatrick, J. & Seiler, G.S. (1995). Fluid bed incineration of paper mill sludge. Environmental Issues and Technology in the Pulp and Paper Industry. *A TAPPI Press Anthology of Published Papers, 1991–1994,* pp. 369–376.

Fio Rito, W.A. (1995). Destructive distillation. Paper mill sludge management alternative. Environmental Issues and Technology in the Pulp and Paper Industry. *A TAPPI Press Anthology of Published Papers, 1991–1994,* pp. 425–427.

Forster, C.F., 1996. Aspects of the Behaviour of Filamentous Microbes in Activated Sludge. *J. Inst. Water & Environ. Mange.,* Vol. 12, pp. 290-294.

Franta, J.R. & Wilderer, P.A. (1997). Biological treatment of papermill wastewater by sequencing batch reactor technology to reduce residual organics. *Water Sci. Technol.*, Vol. 35, No.1, pp. 129– 136.

Frederik, W.M.J.; Iisa, K.; Lundy, J.R.; O'Connor, W.K.; Reis, K.; Scott, A.T.; Sinquefield, S.A.; Sricharoenchaikul, V. & Van Vooren, C.A. (1996). Energy and materials recovery from recycled paper sludge. *TAPPI J.*, Vol. 79, No. 6, pp. 123–131.

Freire, R.S.; Kunz, A. & Duran, N. (2000). Some chemical and toxicological aspects about paper mill effluent treatment with ozone. *Environ Technol.*, Vol. 21, pp. 717– 721.

Fytili, D. & Zabaniotou, A. (2008). Utilization of sewage sludge in EU application of old and new methods – a review. *Renew. Sustain. Energy Rev.*, Vol. 12, No. 1, pp. 116–140.

Ganjidoust, H.; Tatsumi, K.; Yamagishi, T. & Gholian, R.N. (1997). Effect of synthetic and natural coagulant on lignin removal from pulp and paper wastewater. *Water Sci Technol.*, Vol. 35, No.2– 3, pp. 291– 296.

Gea, T.; Artola, A. & Sanchez, A. (2005). Composting of deinking sludge from the recycled paper manufacturing industry. *Bioresource Technol.*, Vol. 96, pp. 1161–1167.

Gokcay, F.C. & Dilek, F.B. (1994). Treatment of effluents from hemp-based pulp and paper industry biological treatability of pulping effluents. *Water Sci Technol.*, Vol. 29, No.9, pp.165– 168.

Gullichsen, J. (1991). Process internal measures to reduce pulp mill pollution load. *Water Sci. Technol.*, Vol. 24 , No. 3-4, pp. 45–53.

Hackett, G.A.R.; Easton, C.A. & Duff, S.J.B. (1999). Composting of pulp and paper mill fly ash with wastewater treatment sludge. *Bioresource Technol.*, Vol. 70, No. 3, pp. 217–224.

Hamm, U.; Bobek, B. & Goyysching, L. (1991). Anaerobic treatment of wastewater from wastepaper converting paper-mills. *Papier*, Vol. 45, pp. 55-63.

Hansen, E.; Zadura, L,; Frankowski, S. & Wachowicz, M. (1999). Upgrading of an activated sludge plant with floating biofilm carriers at Frantschach Swiecie S.A. to meet the new demands of year 2000. *Water Science and Technology*, Vol. 40, No. 11– 12, pp. 207– 214.

Hassan, M.M. & Hawkyard, C.J. (2002). Decolourisation of aqueous dyes by sequential oxidation treatment with ozone and Fenton's reagent. *Journal of Chemical Technology and Biotechnology*, Vol. 77, pp. 834–841.

Hickey, C.W. & Martin, M.L. (1995). Relative sensitivity of five benthic invertebrate species to reference toxicants and resin acid contaminated sediments. *Environ. Toxicol. Chem.*, Vol. 14, pp. 1401–1409.

Holland, R.M. (1997). A unique approach to solid waste reduction. In: *Environmental Conference and Exhibit. TAPPI Proceedings, Book 1*. Minneapolis Convention Center, pp. 489–490.

Holmberg, J. & Gustavsson, L. (2007). Chemical mechanical Biomass use in chemical and mechanical pulping with biomass-based energy supply. *Resources, Conservation and Recycling*, Vol. 52, pp. 331–350.

Hostachy, J.C.; Lenon, G.; Pisicchio, J.L.; Coste, C. & Legay, C. (1997). Reduction of pulp and paper mill pollution by ozone treatment. *Water Sci. Technol.*, Vol. 35, pp. 261-268.

Ince, O.; Kolukirik, M.; Cetecioglu, Z.; Eyice, O.; Tamerler, C. & Ince, B. (2007). Methanogenic and sulfate reducing bacterial population levels in a full-scale anaerobic reactor treating pulp and paper industry wastewater using fluorescence in situ hybridization. *Water Science and Technology*, Vol. 55, No. 10, pp. 183–191

Jackson-Moss, C.A.; Maree, J.P. & Wotton, S.C. (1992). Treatment of bleach plant effluent with the biological granular activated carbon process. *Water Sci. Technol.*, Vol. 26, No. 1-2, pp. 427–434.

Johnsen, K.; Tana, J.; Lehtinen, K.J.; Stuthridge, T.; Mattsson, K.; Hemming, J. & Carlberg, G.E. (1998). Experimental field exposure of brown trout to river receiving effluent from an integrated newsprint mill. *Ecotoxicology and Environmental Safety*, Vol. 40, pp. 184– 193.

Jokela, J.; Rintala, J.; Oikari, A.; Reinikainen, O.; Mutka, K. & NyroÅNnen, T. (1997). Aerobic composting and anaerobic digestion of pulp and paper mill sludges. *Water Sci. Technol.*, Vol. 36, No. 11, pp. 181–188.

Kay, M. (2002). Development of waste management options for paper sludge. In: *4th Annual Dutch International Paper and Board Technology Event*. Pira International.

Kay, M. (2003). What to do with sludge? It's best to determine local needs before choosing an option. *Pulp Pap. Int.*, Vol. 45, No. 8, pp. 19–21.

Kirk, T.K. & Jeffries, T.W. (1996). Roles for microbial enzymes in pulp and paper processing. In *Enzymes for Pulp and Paper Processing*; Jeffries, T.W., Viikari, L., Eds.; American Chemical Society Symposium, Series 655, 2–14.

Kirkpatrick, N.; Reid, I.D.; Ziomek, F. & Paice, M.G. (1990). Biological bleaching of hardwood Kraft pulp using Trametes (Coriolus) versicolor immobilized in polyurethane foam. *Appl. Microbiol. Biotechnol.*, Vol. 33, pp. 105–108.

Knudsen, L.; Pedersen, J.A. & Munck, J. (1994). Advanced treatment of paper mill effluents by a two-stage activated sludge process. *Water Sci Technol.*, Vol. 30, No. 3, pp. 173–181.

Kovacs, T.G. Martel, P.H. & Voss, R.H. (2002). Assessing the biological status of fish in a river receiving pulp and paper mill effluents. *Environ Pollut.*, Vol. 118, pp. 123–140.

Larson, E.; Consonni, S. & Kreutz, T. (2000). Preliminary economics of black liquor gasifier/gas turbine cogeneration at pulp and paper mills. *Journal of Engineering for Gas Turbines and Power*, Vol. 122, No. 3, pp. 255–261.

Leppanen, H. & Oikari, A. (1999). Occurrence of retene and resin acids in sediments and fish bile from lake receiving pulp and a paper mill effluents. *Environ. Toxicol. Chem.*, Vol. 18, No. 7, pp. 1498– 505.

Lettinga, G.; Field, J.A.; Alvarez, R.S.; Vanlier, J.B. & Rintala, J.B. (1991). Future perspectives for the anaerobic treatment of forest industry wastewaters. *Water Sci. Technol.* Vol. 24, pp. 91-102.

Lindstrom-Seppa, P.; Hunskonen, S.; Kotelevtsev, S.; Mikkelson, P.; Rannen, T. & Stepanova, L. (1998). Toxicity and mutagenity of wastewaters from Baikalsk pulp and paper mill: evaluation of pollutant contamination in lake Baikal. *Mar Environ Res.*, Vol. 46, No. 1– 5, pp. 273– 277.

Liss, S.N.; Bicho, P.A.; McFarlane, P.N. & Saddler, J.N. (1997). Microbiology and degradation of resin acids in pulp mill effluents: a mini review. *Can. J. Microbiol.*, Vol. 75, pp. 599–611.

Livernoche, D.; Jurasek L.; Desrochers, M.; Dorica J. & Veliky, I.A. (1983). Removal of color from Kraft mill wastewaters with the cultures of white-rot fungi and with immobilized mycelium of Coriolus versicolor. *Biotechnol. Bioeng.*, Vol. 25, pp. 2055–2065.

Magnus, E.; Carlberg, G.E. & Norske, H.H. (2001). TMP wastewater treatment including a biological high-efficiency compact reactor. *Nord. Pulp. Pap. Res. J.*, Vol. 15, No. 1, pp. 29– 36.

Marten, W.L. & Daigger, G.T. (1997). Full-scale evaluation of factors affecting the performance of anoxic selectors. *Water Environ. Res.*, Vol. 69, pp. 1272-1281.

Mata-Alvarez, J.; MaceÅL, S. & LlabreÅLs, P. (2000). Anaerobic digestion of organic solid wastes. An overview of research achievements and perspectives. *Bioresource Technol.*, Vol. 74, No. 1, pp. 3–16.

McDonough, T. (1992). Bleaching agents (pulp and paper). In: *Kirk-Othmer Encyclopedia of Chemical Technology*; Grayson, M., Ed., 4th ed.; John Wiley and Sons: New York, 301–311.

Mehta, V. & Gupta, J.K. (1992). Biobleaching eucalyptus Kraft pulp with Phanerochaete chrysosporium and its effect on paper properties. *Tappi J.*, Vol. 75, pp. 151–152.

Merrill, D.T.; Maltby, C.V.; Kahmark, K.; Gerhardt, M. & Melecer, H. (2001). Evaluating treatment process to reduce metals concentrations in pulp and paper mill wastewaters to extremely low values. *Tappi J.*, Vol. 84, No. 4, pp. 52.

Mohamed, M.; Matayun, M. & Lim, T.S. (1989). Chlorinated organics in tropical hardwood kraft pulp and paper mill effluents and their elimination in an activated sludge treatment system. *Pertanika*, Vol. 2, No. 3, pp. 387– 394.

Monte, M.C.; Fuente, E.; Blanco, A. & Negro, C. (2009). Waste management from pulp and paper production in the European Union. *Waste Manag.*, Vol. 29, pp. 293-308.

Murthy, B.S.A.; Sihorwala, T.A.; Tilwankar, H.V. & Killedar, D.J. (1991). Removal of colour from pulp and paper mill effluents by sorption technique—a case study. *Indian J Environ Prot.*, Vol. 11, No. 5, p.360.

Nurmesniemi, H.; Poykio, R. & Keiski, R.L. (2007). A case study of waste management at the Northern Finnish pulp and paper mill complex of Stora Enso Veitsiluoto Mills. *Waste Management*, Vol. 27, pp. 1939-1948, ISSN 0956-053X

Oeller, H.J.; Daniel, I. & Weinberger, G. (1997). Reduction in residual COD in biologically treated paper mill effluents by means of combined Ozone and Ozone/UV reactor stages. *Water Sci. Technol.*, Vol. 35, No. 2–3, pp. 269 –276.

Oral, J.; Sikula, J.; Puchyr, R.; Hajny, Z.; Stehlik, P. & Bebar, L. (2005). Processing of waste from pulp and paper plant. *J. Cleaner Production.*, Vol. 13, pp. 509–515.

Owens, J.W.; Swanson, S.M. & Birkholz, D.A. (1994). Environmental monitoring of bleached kraft pulp mill chlorophenolic compounds in a Northern Canadian River system. *Chemosphere*, Vol. 29, No. 1, pp. 89–109.

Perez, M.; Torrades, F.; Domenech, X. & Peral, J. (2002). Treatment of bleaching Kraft mill effluents and polychlorinated phenolic compounds with ozonation. *J Chem Technol Biotechnol.*, Vol. 77, pp.891–897.

Poggi-Varaldo, H.M.; Estrada-Vazquez, C.; Fernandez-Villagomez, G. & Esparza-Garcia, F. (1996). Pretreatment of black liquor spills effluent. *Proceedings of the Industrial Waste Conference*, West Lafayette, USA , Vol. 51, pp. 651–61.

Pokhrel, D & Viraraghavan, T. (2004). Treatment of pulp and paper mill wastewater – a review. *Sci. Tot. Env.*, Vol. 333, pp. 37-58.

Porteous, A. (2005). Why energy from waste incineration is an essential component of environmentally responsible waste management. *Waste Manag.*, Vol. 25, pp. 451–459.

Prendl, L. & Kroiss, H. (1998). Bulking sludge prevention by an aerobic selector. *Water Sci. Technol.*, Vol. 38, pp. 19-27.

Rajvaidya, N. & Markandey, D.K. (1998). *Advances in environmental science and technology: treatment of pulp and paper industrial effluent.* Ansari Road, New Delhi, India: A.P.H. Publishing.

Rohella, R.S.; Choudhury, S.; Manthan, M. & Murthy, J.S. (2001). Removal of colour and turbidity in pulp and paper mill effluents using polyelectrolytes. *Indian J Environ Health*, Vol. 43, No. 4, pp. 159–63.

Rouleau, G. & Sasseville, M. (1996). Waste reduction: a sound business decision. *Pulp Paper Canada*, Vol. 97, No. 12, pp. 114–116.

Sakurai ,A.; Yamomoto, T.; Makabe, A.; Kinoshita, S. & Sakakibara, M. (2001). Removal of lignin in a liquid system by an isolated fungus. *J Chem Technol Biotechnol.*, Vol. 77, pp. 9– 14.

Saunamaki, R. (1997). Activated sludge plants in Finland. *Water Sci. Technol.* Vol. 35, No. 2–3, pp. 235– 243.

Schnell, A.; Sabourin, M.J.; Skog, S. & Garvie, M. (1997). Chemical characterization and biotreability of effluents from an integrated alkalineperoxide mechanical pulping/machine finish coated paper mill. *Water Sci Technol.*, Vol. 35, No. 2–3, pp. 7– 14.

Schnell, A.; Steel, P.; Melcer, H.; Hodson, P.V. & Carey, J.H. (2000a). Enhanced biological treatment of bleached kraft mill effluents: I. Removal of chlorinated organic compounds and toxicity. *Water Res.*, Vol. 34, No. 2, pp. 493– 500.

Schnell, A.; Steel, P.; Melcer, H.; Hodson, P.V. & Carey, J.H. (2000b). Enhanced biological treatment of bleached kraft mill effluents: II. Reduction of mixed function oxygenase (MFO) induction in fish. *Water Res.*, Vol. 34, No. 2, pp. 501–9.

Shawwa, A.R.; Smith, D.W. & Sego, D.C. (2001). Color and chlorinated organics removal from pulp wastewater using activated petroleum coke. *Water Res.*, Vol. 35, No. 3, pp. 745 –749.

Slade, A.H.; Nicol, C.M. & Grigsby, J. (1999). Nutrients within integrated bleached Kraft mills: sources and behaviour in aerated stabilization basins. *Water Sci. Technol.*, Vol. 40, No. 11–12, pp.77–84.

Smook, G.A. (1992). Handbook for Pulp & Paper Technologists. Second edition. Vancouver: Angus Wilde Publications.

Stigsson, L. (1998). Chemrec Black Liquor Gasification. Proceedings, *International Chemical Recovery Conference*, Tampa, Florida, pp. 663–674

Stuthridge, T.R. & Mcfarlane, P.N. (1994). Adsorbable organic halide removal mechanisms in a pulp and paper mill aerated lagoon treatment system. *Water Sci Technol.*, Vol. 29, No. 5–6, pp. 195–208.

Sumathi, S. & Hung, Y.T. (2006). Treatment of pulp and paper mill wastes, In: *Waste treatment in the process industries*. Eds: Wang, L.K, Hung, Y.T., Lo, H.H., Yapijakis, C. pp. 453-497. Taylor&Francis. ISBN 0-8493-7233-X, USA.

Taseli, B. & Gokcay, C.F. (1999). Biological treatment of paper pulping effluents by using a fungal reactor. *Water Sci Technol.*, Vol. 40, No. 11– 12, pp. 93–09.

Thompson, G.; Swain, J.; Kay, M. & Forster, C. (2001). The treatment of pulp and paper mill effluent: a review. *Bioresource Technology*, Vol. 77, pp. 275–286.

Tong, Z.; Wada, S.; Takao, Y.; Yamagishi, T.; Hiroyasu, I. & Tamatsu, K. (1999). Treatment of bleaching wastewater from pulp-paper plants in China using enzymes and coagulants. *J. Environ. Sci.* Vol. 11, No. 4, pp. 480–484.

Torrades, F.; Peral, J.; Perez, M.; Domenech, X.; Hortal, J.A.G. & Riva, M.C. (2001). Removal of organic contaminants in bleached kraft effluents using heterogeneous photocatalysis and ozone. *Tappi J.* Vol. 84, No. 6, pp. 63.

US EPA. EPA office of compliance sector notebook project: profile of pulp and paper industry. Washington, DC 20460, USA: EPA/310-R-95-015; 1995.

Vass, K.K.; Mukopadhyay, M.K.; Mistra, K. & Joshi, H.C. (1996). Respiratory stresses in fishes exposed to paper and pulp wastewater. *Environ Ecol.*, Vol. 14, No. 4, pp. 895–897.

Verenich, S.; Laari, A. & Kallas, J. (2000). Wet oxidation of concentrated wastewater of paper mills for water cycle closing. *Waste Manage (N.Y.)*, Vol. 20, No. 4, pp. 287– 293.

Verstraete, W. & Vandevivere, P. (1999). New and broader applications of anaerobic digestion. *Crit. Rev. Environ. Sci. Technol.* Vol. 29, No. 2, pp. 151–173.

Van Horn, J.T. (1997). Land Application of Solid Waste Stone Container Corporation. Environmental Conference and Exhibit. *TAPPI Proceedings*. Minneapolis Convention Center, pp. 845–848.

Wang, S.H.; Ferguson, J.F. & McCarthy, J.L. (1992). The decolorization and dechlorination of Kraft bleach plant effluent solutes by use of three fungi: Ganderma lacidum, Coriolus versicolor and Hericium erinaceum. *Holzforschung*, Vol. 46, pp. 219–233

Welander, T.; Lofqvist, A. & Selmer, A. (1997). Upgrading aerated lagoons at pulp and paper mills. *Water Sci Technol.*, Vol. 35, No. 2–3, pp. 117– 122.

Yamamoto, S. (2001). Ozone treatment of bleached kraft pulp and waste paper. *Japan Tappi J.*, Vol. 55, No. 4, pp. 90–97.

Yen, N.T.; Oanh, N.T.K.; Reutergard, L.B.; Wise, D.L. & Lan, L.T.T. (1996). An integrated waste survey and environmental effects of COGIDO, a bleached pulp and paper mill in Vietnam on the receiving water body. *Global Environ Biotechnol.*, Vol. 66, pp. 349– 364.

Zaidi, A.; Buisson, H.; Sourirajan, S. & Wood, H. (1992). Ultra-and nano-filtration in advanced effluent treatment schemes for pollution control in the pulp and paper industry. *Water Sci Technol.*, Vol. 25, No. 10, pp. 263– 276.

Zhou, H. & Smith, D.W. (1997). Process parameter development for ozonation of kraft pulp mill effluents. *Water Sci. Technol.*, Vol. 35, No. 2–3, pp. 251– 259.

12

Retrofit Approach for the Reduction of Water and Energy Consumption in Pulp and Paper Production Processes

Jesús Martínez Patiño and Martín Picón Núñez
University of Guanajuato
México

1. Introduction

This chapter describes a comprehensive approach that allows a water and energy reduction in industrial processes. This technique is based on the retrofit concept. An analysis of retrofit has the feature to perform in a systematic way, a series of steps that guides practices and help to identify opportunities for saving water and energy.

Methodologies and techniques have been implemented independently in (pulp) industries in order to reduce water and energy consumption. At industry level and particularly in real pulp and pulp processes, methodologies and techniques to reduce independently water consumption as well as energy consumption have been implemented.

Pinch Technology began its application to this kind industry in 1990 (Calloway et at. 1990) to optimize energy using the traditional methodology introduced by Linnhoff et al. (1982). Subsequently, using the Pinch Analysis concept, Berglin et al. (1997) incorporated a mathematical programming work and an exergy analysis; they achieved the reduction of energy consumption in two pulp mills. Koufus et al. (2001), used sequentially Pinch Analysis and later on Water Pinch Analysis (WPA) methodology for these industries (Pulp and Paper), getting first of all an energy reduction and then a water reduction. In the paper of Rouzinuo et al. (2003) Pinch Technology proved to be a great tool for the integration of new equipment in processes for pulp and paper industry at an application in Albany (Oregon, USA) achieving the reduction of energy consumption significantly. Savulescu et al. (2005c), presented a processes integration technique based on Pinch Technology to reduce water (WPA) and energy (Pinch Analysis) in a Kraft process pulp mill; in the same way Towers (2007), applied Pinch Technology for water reduction.

The concept of energy reduction through the water reduction in the pulp and paper industry was applied by Wising et al. (2005). With the same concept, Nordam et al. (2006), presented a design for water and energy systems reducing energy consumption by reducing water use.

For water reduction (exclusively) in a pulp mill (Kraft process), Parthasarathy et al. (2001) used mass integration for effluent reuse and thereby reduce water consumption. Similarly Lovelady et. al (2007) reduced water consumption by optimizing the discharge effluent reuse water.

As it has been mentioned in the previous paragraphs, the application of technologies for the reduction of to reduce water and energy is performed independently, however, it has been established that water and energy are directly related. First these papers works analyze the opportunities for water minimization and later, an energy study is realized in order to conclude that reducing water, energy consumption also reduces.

The methodologies mentioned in previous paragraphs do not discuss the main characteristics concerning the operation of pulp and paper process; in fact, process conditions (stream flow rate, temperature, concentration, etc.) give the information to identify the objectives of the minimal use of water and energy.

Recently, Savulescu et al. (2008) published a work where heat is recovered through the mixing of streams and the dilutions that take place. However for this type of systems, they do not provide an integrated methodology where water and energy is reduced simultaneously.

The central premise of this work is that internal aspects of the process must be analyzed in order to look into opportunities that will change the operating conditions to achieve a more efficient use of water and energy. The internal aspects of the process that must be analyzed are: separation processes, reaction processes and equipment performance. The chemical operations involved are those used for the separation of (lignin), unwanted material that accompanies the final product (cellulose). Depending on the level of conversion in the reaction, the next step (washing) will require more or less amount of water. Therefore, by increasing the conversion, a decrease in the water consumption can be expected. By modifying the water streams, the energy requirements for the bleaching operation are also modified. Any change in the operating conditions, will have an effect on the equipment performance, and this should be evaluated.

This chapter presents a case study in a Kraft Pulp Mill (Fig. 1). The general process flowsheet is described in the following section.

2. Pulping process

Pulp is obtained from different types of cellulosic material sources, e.g. wood and other fibrous plants. The procedure for obtaining pulp from these materials is called pulping and its purpose is the purification and separation of cellulosic.

There are different categories of pulping processes: chemical and mechanical pulping. Chemical pulping methods rely on the effect of chemicals to separate fibers, whereas mechanical pulping methods rely completely on physical action. The two main chemical processes are: the Kraft process (alkaline) and the Sulfite process (acid). The mechanical process produces higher yields compared to the pulp process; Mechanical pulps are characterized by high yield, high bulk, high stiffness and low cost. They have low strength since the lignin interferes with hydrogen bonding between fibers when paper is made.

Wood is debarked and chipped, and the chips screened to eliminate fine material and over-sized chips. The "accepted" chips are fed to a pressure vessel, the digester. The chips are steamed with direct steam to eliminate as much of the air as possible. The cooking temperature is maintained until the desired degree of delignification is reached, after which the digester contents go to a blow tank. The pulp from the blow tank is then washed and screened. Residual lignin is removed from pulp by bleaching with chemical reagents. All bleaching treatments have certain common steps. The consistency of the pulp suspension is set in a washer or de-watering device to a target level; temperature and pH may be adjusted by controlling the wash water temperature and pH on the washer of a preceding stage. The suspension is pumped via one or several mixers to a co-current tubular reactor, which may be atmospheric or pressurised. The suspension is then transported to a washer for the removal of dissolved material. Finally, water is removed from the pulp through a drying process.

COOKING   WASHING AND SCREENING   BLEACHING   DRYING

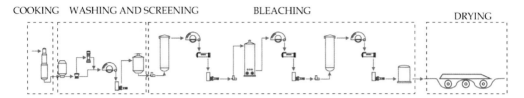

Fig. 1. Simplified diagram of a pulping process.

3. Overall retrofit strategy for the reduction of water and energy in pulp and paper processes

3.1 Hierarchical methodology

The guidelines set by Westerberg et al. (1979), the so-called strategy of the onion diagram (Linnhoff et al. 1982), (Shenoy, 1995) and the heuristic approach (Douglas, 1988), are examples of procedures for the design based on the decomposition of the process in stages. The philosophy behind each of these approaches is the basis for implementing the necessary strategies for the minimization of water and energy in real processes. In this work a hierarchical approach is developed for the retrofit of existing process aiming at the reduction of water and energy consumption.

Basic to this approach is a profound knowledge of the process; it continues then with the extraction of information and then the implementation of the heuristic rules and methodologies for analysis. A graphical diagram of the hierarchical approach is shown in Fig. 2 by means of an "onion diagram". The various steps are described below:

- Reaction:
  - Analysis of chemical reaction route
  - Reaction system (reactors)
- Water use system
- Water regeneration for reuse
- Heat recovery system

3.2 Reaction

The layer of reaction is **subdivided** into two levels: one is related to the analysis of the route of reaction and the other one is related to the system of reactors. In this stage, the type of chemical reaction, the kinetics and the reactor design are analyzed in detail.

3.2.1 Analysis of the chemical reaction route

The stage of bleaching is a section of the process for pulp production where chemical reactions take place. The purpose of the bleaching process is to withdraw the maximum amount of lignin contained within the pulp. In this stage, the type of reaction that is carried out in each of the different stages of the bleaching process is analyzed. The chemical compounds that are used in the bleaching stages are identified. In the case of an existing plant, the analysis of the route of reaction may trigger a series of actions allowing the implementation of technologies with greater reaction conversion while reducing the water consumption.

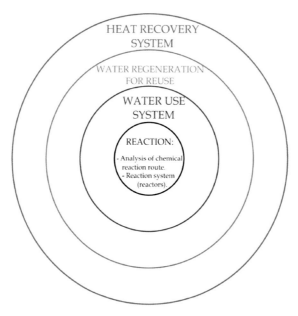

Fig. 2. Retrofit approach based on the concept of the "Onion Diagram ".

3.2.2 Reaction system (reactors)

Once the route of chemical transformation of the process is known, the reactor system design is then considered. This involves the examination of a three way trade-off between equipment, level of conversion and reduction in water consumption. In the case of the bleaching process, the lower the amount of solids product (pulp) at the outlet of the reactor; the lower is the amount of water that is needed to reach the required concentration in the filtering stage, as it is shown in the Fig. 3. Equation 1 (Walas, 1988) shows the relationship between mass flow rate, the volume of the reactor and concentrations.

$$\frac{V}{F} = \frac{x_e - x_F}{r_e} \tag{1}$$

F = Flow rate
V = Volume of the reactor
x_e = Final conversion
x_F = Initial conversion
r_e = Conversion rate

Knowledge of the characteristics of the bleaching reaction and reactor volume, the actual reaction rate can be determined. This information is then used to determine the additional reactor volume needed for more lignin to react. The flow diagram of Fig. 3 shows the way fresh water consumption is linked to the level of lignin conversion in the reactor. Since fresh water is used to dilute the reactor outlet stream for it to be filtered downstream, as amount of lignin that reacts increases, the lower the amount of solids at the reactor outlet. This condition results in less fresh water being needed for dilution and therefore water savings are obtained. In addition, warm water is added into the filter for furthering the removal of impurities from the cellulose.

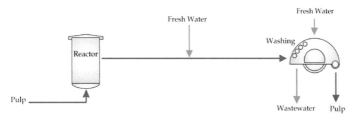

Fig. 3. Area of chemical reaction and filtering in the stage of bleaching.

3.3 Water use system

At this stage a water pinch analysis is carried out. Let us consider the washing section of the process that consists of a series of physical separations for the removal of impurities from the pulp coming out from the digester (Fig. 4). This pulp receives the name of raw flesh because it has not been bleached yet. At this stage, a large amount of water is used. It is therefore important the implementation of techniques that lead to the reduction of water. The large amounts of water used and the physical nature of the process are conducive for the implementation of the Water Pinch Analysis (WPA) technique which seeks to minimize the consumption of water. These conditions are also appropriate to pose an optimization problem by means of mathematical programming, seeking to reduce the total operation costs. Both techniques are effective for the analysis, synthesis and improvement of the water networks. Furthermore, they take into account the concepts of reuse and regeneration of water that have an impact on the generation of wastewater or effluents while minimizing the water consumption.

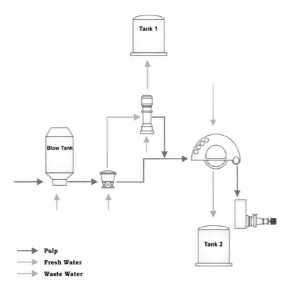

Fig. 4. Washing system.

3.4 Water regeneration for reuse

Once exploited and completed all the options for the reduction of water consumption through the measures implemented in the first two layers of the onion diagram, the next step consists in the application of water regeneration techniques. At this level, different techniques for feasible decentralized regeneration of the effluents for water reuse should be evaluated (Fig. 5). Among the typical regeneration technologies are those of physical, chemical and biological nature. The selection of the regeneration system should be based on a series of considerations such as: equipment cost, operating costs, ease of implementation, availability, etc.

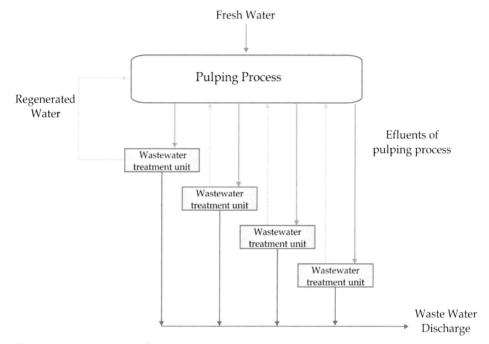

Fig. 5. Regeneration system for water reuse.

3.5 Heat recovery system

The last stage in the hierarchical strategy is to identify the options for reducing energy consumption through the maximization of the heat recovery and the quantification of direct savings generated by the simple reduction of the water consumption. In some cases, when the economic scenario is favorable, the savings of steam can be channeled to the production of electrical power in cases where the process plant is integrated with a cogeneration system.

4. Applications and case study

The case study in this section uses information from a real pulp plant. The methodology described in the previous section is implemented step by step with the aim of reducing energy and water consumption.

Knowledge of the various aspects of an existing plant allows us to identify particular situations that apart from theory lead us to incorporate certain considerations that make the application practical. For instance, the plant layout, the economic environment, the time required for the delivery of the projects which will require modifications and investment, the plant production rate and its fluctuations throughout the year, etc. The application is shown below.

4.1 Process description

The raw material used for the production of pulp is a short fiber wood from eucalyptus. The Kraft process is divided into four main stages, namely: cooking, screening and washing, bleaching and drying (see Fig. 1).

4.2 Application of the methodology
4.2.1 Analysis of the reaction stage in the bleaching process

As stated in the previous section, the first step consists in the analysis of the reaction route. In the case under consideration, chemical reactions take place during cooking and bleaching. The focus of the analysis will be around the former stage since it involves the consumption of fresh water.

The process proceeds by means of an Elemental Chlorine Free reaction (ECF) (Gullichsen et al., 1999) and takes place in three stages with three reactors arranged in series. The reactions are: D0 (oxygen delignification), EOP (Alkaline extraction reinforced with oxygen and hydrogen peroxide) and D1 (Chlorine dioxide). It is important to mention that the plant under consideration does not have an oxidizing stage previous to bleaching for the removal of lignin which implies that pulp reaches the process with a large Kappa number (the Kappa number that determines the weight percentaje of lignin in the pulp. This is: % lignin in pulp = 0.15 x Kappa number). It has been identified that as the lignin conversion increases in the reactor, the consumption of fresh water needed for effluent dilution for the filtering stage is reduced.

From equation 1 it is possible to calculate the rate of reaction (r_e) since the design parameters of the installed reactors are known. In the case of the D0 reactor, with a volume of 183.084 m³, the volumetric feed (water and pulp mixture) is 216 m³/hr. For the calculation of the reaction conversion as the kappa number moves from 28 to 8, the density of the mixture is needed. To this end, the pulp concentration of the feed is known to be 9.4% by weight; the density of the pulp is 1250 kg/m³, so the overall density is determined below:

$$\delta_{DO} = \left(1250 \times 0.094\right) + \left(1000 \times 0.906\right) \left(\frac{kg}{m^3}\right)$$
$$\delta_{DO} = 1023.5 \ \left(\frac{kg}{m^3}\right) \tag{2}$$

Knowing the kappa number at the inlet and outlet of the reactor, the amount of lignin is calculated to be:

$$Lignin_{initial} = 0.15 \times KappaNo._{initial} \ (\%)$$
$$Lignin_{initial} = 0.15 \times 28 \ = 4.2 \ \% \tag{3}$$

$$Lignin_{final} = 0.15 \times KappaNo._{final} \ (\%)$$
$$Lignin_{final} = 0.15 \times 8 \ = 1.2 \ \% \tag{4}$$

The inlet and outlet lignin concentration is found to be:

$$L_o = (\delta_{DO}) \times (Concentration_{flow}) \times \left(Lignin_{initial} / 100 \right)$$

$$L_o = \left(1023.5 \, kg / m^3 \right) \times (0.094) \times \left(4.2 / 100 \right) \tag{5}$$

$$L_o = 4.040778 \, kg / m^3$$

$$L_f = (\delta_{DO}) \times (Concentration_{flow}) \times \left(Lignin_{final} / 100 \right)$$

$$L_f = \left(1023.5 \, kg / m^3 \right) \times (0.094) \times \left(1.2 / 100 \right) \tag{6}$$

$$L_f = 1.154508 \, kg / m^3$$

Once the lignin concentrations are known it is possible to determine the reaction conversion (X_F) from:

$$X_F = \frac{(L_o - L_F)}{L_o}$$

$$X_F = \frac{(4.040778 - 1.154508)}{4.040778} \tag{7}$$

$$X_F = 0.7143$$

Then, the rate of reaction can be calculate from:

$$\frac{V}{F} = \frac{x_e - x_F}{r_e}$$

$$\frac{183.084}{216 / 3600} = \frac{0.7143}{r_e}$$

$$r_e = -0.000234089 s^{-1}$$

Knowing the rate of reaction it is possible to determine the reactor volumen needed to take the kappa number form 8 to 4 (Gullichsen et al. 1999). This is, achiving higher conversion at the expense of investing in additional reaction volumne. Under the information so far obtained, it is determined that a volume of 219.7 m³ is needed. Fig. 6 shows the process information and the water consumption that are required for the two scenarios, namely: a conversion corresponding to a kappa number of 8 (original) and a conversion correponding to a kappa number of 4 (new). From the results it can be concluded that the increase of the reactor volume by 36.61 m³ allows more lignin to be removed from the pulp and consequently a mass reduction in the effluent is achieved; therefore, less fresh water is required to achieve a concentration of 1.2% which is required for an effective operation ofthe filter. In addition, the filter will consume less water for washing.

If the rector volumen was increased by 40 m³, for a total volume of 223.084 m³, calculations show that the fresh water consumption would be reduced by 11.511 m³/hr. For an economical analysis, costs information is taken from Peters and Timmerhaus (1991). So, for the year 1990, the cost of a glass fiber linned reactor is approximately $190,000.00 USD. The cost is brought upto date by considering the the cost index according to:

$$f_\theta = \frac{Cost\ Index\ (August\ 2008)}{Cost\ Index\ (Reference\ year)}$$ (8)

Taking the cost indexes from Chemical: Engineering Plant Cost Index-USA (1990) and Economic Indicator, Chemical Engineering (August 2008), the following factor is obtained:

$$f_\theta = \frac{389}{660} = 1.6967$$

So, the approximate up-to-date cost is:

$$190000 \times 1.6967 = 322365\ US\$$$

To determine the fresh water consumption, the cost of extraction per m3 of water is 1.2 US$ [Robin Smith, 2005]; considering a total of 8000 working hours, the water cost is

$$Cost_{Water} = \left(1.2 \frac{US\$}{m^3}\right) \times \left(11.511 \frac{m^3}{hr}\right) \times (8000hrs)$$

$$Cost_{Water} = 110506\ US\$\ /\ year$$

From the information above, the payback period for the revamping of the bleaching reactor is approximately 3 years. For the second and third reaction stages, the lignin content is low enough to consider that the expected water saving would not justify the investment in reactor volume.

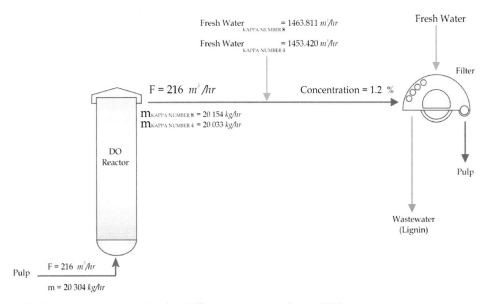

Fig. 6. Fash water consumption for different reactor volume (D0).

4.2.2 Water using system

Once the first hierarchical level has been covered, the second level is considered. This level corresponds to the pulp washing stage.

The purposes of the washing process are: a) the removal of un-reacted wood chips and non fibrous impurities from cellulose; b) the removal of soluble solids present in the fiber. The pulp washing step contains two filters that operate counter currently and a continuous rotary filter as shown in Fig. 4. Details of the operation of the equipment are shown in Fig. 7 and operating data are given in Table 1. The case is solved using a heuristic approach and the results are compared to those obtained a mathematical optimization.

No.	Flowrate (ton/hr)	Concentration (%)	Mass Load (Kg)	No.	Flowrate (ton/hr)	Concentration (%)	Mass Load (Kg)
1	72.250	12	8700	9	49.769	1.7	846
2	217.500	0	0	10	332.523	2.466	8223
3	290	3	8700	11	299.067	0	0
4	56.725	0	0	12	632.590	1.3	8223
5	62.971	2.1	1322.4	13	167.503	0	0
6	283.754	2.6	7377	14	732.134	0.009369	68.59
7	18.553	0	0	15	67.959	12	8155
8	31.755	1.5	476.3				

Table 1. Operating data of the washing step.

From Fig. 7 we see that the first filter removes the larger solids and its effluent is sent to filter 2 where smaller size solids are removed. The main stream from these two filters is sent to the rotary filter 3 where the pulp is finally washed for the bleaching step.

The total fresh water consumption in this process is of 759.348 ton/hr. As mentioned before, the effluent from the first filter (62.97 ton / hr) is processed again for further pulp recovery. Effluents reaching tanks 1 and 2 have different type of contaminant and different concentrations which imply that for water reuse, independent analysis must be conducted.

Total water usage is given by stream 2, 4, 7, 11 y 13 (759.348 kg / hr). Streams 2 and 11 give the pulp the required consistency whereas streams 4, 7 and 11 are used for washing. Table 1 shows the mass flow rates, concentrations and mass content of these streams.

In this part of the study, water pinch technology is applied (WPA). Some studies have been published on the application of this technology to total sites (Jacob et al., 2001; Koufus et al., 2001); however, in this work a local analysis is carried out. In a global study, one aspect that is ignored is the actual location of the water using operations; however, this aspect must be considered in a real plant application. Other aspects to be considered are: pulp recovery form water, the design of the piping network and the actual design and the operation of the equipment. For the case of filter 1, the operating data is:

$$f_1 = 56.712 \left(\frac{ton}{hr} \right)$$

$$C_{1,in} = 0 \ (ppm)$$

$$\Delta m_1 = 1324 \left(\frac{kg}{hr} \right)$$

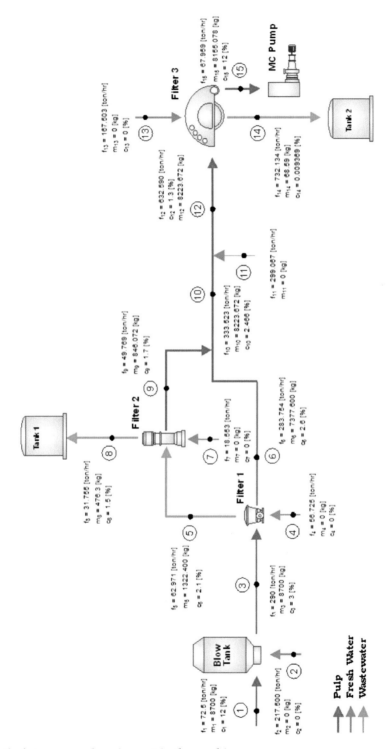

Fig. 7. Detail of streams and equipment in the washing process.

The outlet concentration limit, $C_{1,out,}$ is obtained from equation (9):

$$f_i^{\text{lim}} = \frac{\Delta m_{i,total}}{[C_{i,out}^{\text{lim}} - C_{i,in}^{\text{lim}}]} x 10^3 \qquad (9)$$

$$56.712(ton / hr) = \frac{1324(kg / hr)}{[C_{i,out}^{\text{lim}} - 0](ppm)} x 10^3$$

$$C_{1,out} = 23346 \; (ppm)$$

Table 2 shows the limit concentrations of the stream that will be used to remove the mass of contaminant (Δm) with the minimum amount of fresh water (56.712 ton/hr). The inlet and outlet concentrations of contaminant to the filters are given in Table 3.

The information from Table 3 is used to construct the concentration-composite curve where the pinch point is obtained (424 ppm). This point represents the concentration limit of contaminant that can be used; it also shows the minimum fresh water consumption considering water reuse.

Filter (no.)	f_i (ton/hr)	C_{in} (ppm)	C_{out} (ppm)	Δm (kg)
1	56.712	0	23346	1324
2	18.546	0	25666	476
3	167.520	0	424	71

Table 2. Fresh water data in filters.

The amount of contaminant removed from each process and the total removal (1871 kg/hr) are shown in Fig. 8. The analysis indicates that fresh water is fed to operation 3; part of its effluent is reused in operation 1 and 2 as shown in Fig. 9.

The data form Table 3 is used to design the water network structure by means of mathematical programming. The final design is shown in Fig. 10. Although using both approaches the same minimum water consumption is obtained; however, the network structure is different.

Filter (no.)	f_i (ton/hr)	C_{in} (ppm)	C_{out} (ppm)	Δm (kg)
1	290.000	18780	23346	1324
2	62.952	18105	25666	476
3	632.400	311	424	71

Table 3. Process data of stream feeding the filters

Both the structures of Fig. 9 and 10 represent grass-root designs and they can be used to identify ways to improve o the existing structures. Now, there are some operating aspects that the former designs do not consider. For instance, none of the designs considers the start up and stabilization of the plant; besides, they do not allow residual water to be used to take the filter inlet to the required concentration. The actual operation of the various pieces of equipment is difficult to incorporate in the design such as the case of the filters and its efficiency in connection to the concentration load and the required flow rate that will remove the contaminant. An important issue in this process consists in the removal undesirable material such as stones, plastic and other pulp residues. It is also true that the pulp still contains un-reacted wood chips that can be re-circulated back to the main reactor in order to increase the production of pulp. Taking all these elements into consideration, the series of practical implementations to the washing stage that allow for the reduction of water consumption are described below.

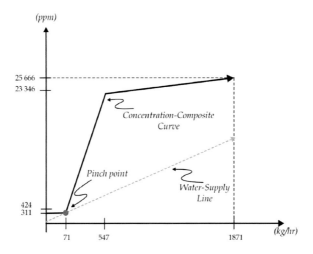

Fig. 8. Concentration composite curve for the washing process.

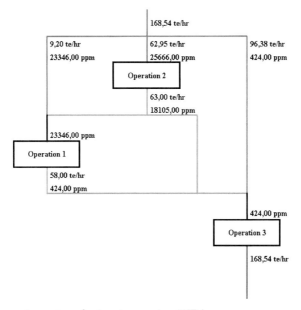

Fig. 9. Design of the water network structure using WPA.

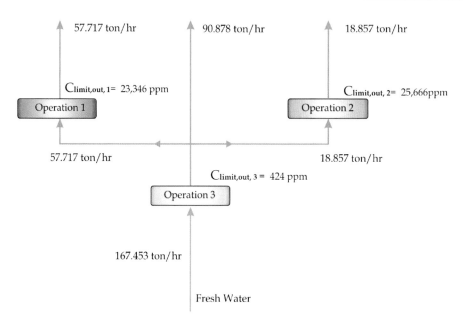

Fig. 10. Design of the water network structure using mathematical programming

Fig. 11, shows the washing process where two intermediate stages have been included. The first one removes non usable contaminants such as stones, plastic, etc., and those that can be reused in the process (i.e. pulp and wood chips). The effluent from this first stage passes through a second treatment where the pup is further cleaned prior to the bleaching stage.

In order to incorporate these aspects such as the plant start up and the way the operating conditions change as the steady state is reached. Table 4 shows the process information during the start up, on the other hand Fig. 11 and Table 5 present the operating data once the process has been stabilized.

No.	Flowrate (ton/hr)	Concentration (%)	Mass Load (Kg)	No.	Flowrate (ton/hr)	Concentration (%)	Mass Load (Kg)
1	72.500	12	8700	14	732.480	0.009369	68.6
2	217.440	0	0	15	67.920	12	8151
3	289.920	3	8700	16	591.678	0.009369	55.4
4	56.712	0	0	17	140.322	0.009369	13.2
5	62.940	2.1	1322	18	31.746	1.5	476
6	283.680	2.6	7376	19	5.589	2.316	129.5
7	18.546	0	0	20	26.157	1.326	346.9
8	31.746	1.5	476	21	26.157	1.326	346.9
9	49.758	1.7	846	22	26.157	1.326	346.9
10	334.020	2.466	8237	23	1.260	0.238	3
11	298.980	0	0	24	26.157	1.314	343.9
12	632.400	1.3	8222	25	1.260	0	0
13	167.520	0	0				

Table 4. Process information for the start up of the washing process.

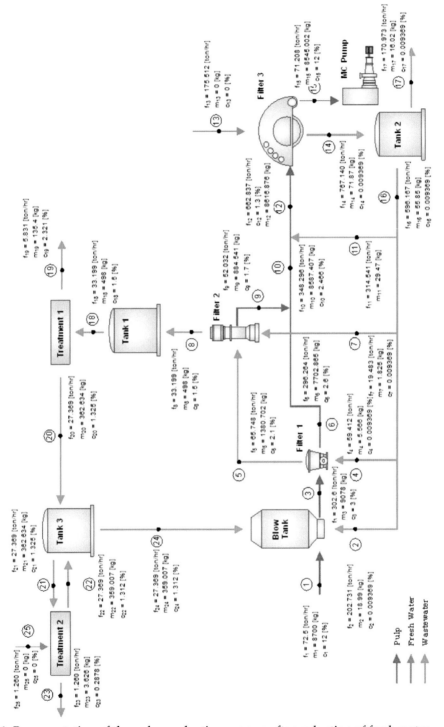

Fig. 11. Representation of the pulp production process after reduction of fresh water consumption.

No.	Flowrate (ton/hr)	Concentration (%)	Mass Load (Kg)	No.	Flowrate (ton/hr)	Concentration (%)	Mass Load (Kg)
1	72.500	12	8700	14	767.140	0.009369	71.87
2	202.731	0.009369	18.99	15	71.208	12	8545
3	302.600	3	9078	16	596.167	0.009369	55.85
4	54.412	0.009369	5.566	17	170.973	0.009369	16.02
5	65.748	2.1	1380.7	18	33.199	1.5	498
6	296.264	2.6	7702.9	19	5.831	2.321	135.4
7	19.483	0.009369	1.825	20	27.369	1.325	362.634
8	33.199	1.5	498	21	27.369	1.325	362.634
9	52.032	1.7	884.54	22	27.369	1.325	359.007
10	348.296	2.466	8547.4	23	1.260	0.2878	3.626
11	314.541	0.009369	29.47	24	27.369	1.312	359.007
12	662.837	1.3	8616.9	25	1.260	0	0
13	175.512	0	0				

Table 5. Process information for the stabilized process.

On the start up of the plant, 760.56 ton/hr of fresh water are needed. Of these, 168.78 ton/hr are sent to the washing stage while the rest, 591.678 ton/hr are used for dilution purposes before entering filter 3. Once the regeneration processes enter into operation and the reuse of effluent 3 is established, the fresh water consumption is reduced to 176.772 ton/hr. From the ongoing discussion it can be seen that regeneration and reuse considerable reduce the fresh water consumption by reducing the need of using fresh water to feed the filter at a concentration of 1.2%, thus achieving a saving of 582.626 ton/hr.

In the case under consideration there are various types of effluent stream with different contaminant concentrations, therefore it is important the adequate selection of the regeneration process for water reuse of recycling whatever the case. Regeneration processes are of the distributed type unlike the end of pipe treatment, which in the majority of cases is of centralized type. Fig. 12 shows the inlet and outlet process water flow rates.

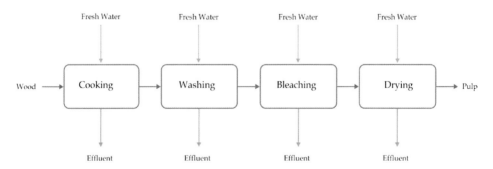

Fig. 12. Water effluent streams of the pulp production process.

4.2.3 Regeneration for water reuse

Fig. 13 shows the application of a specific treatment to each of the effluent streams in the pulp production process. Appropriate selection of each of these treatments is critical since given the different contaminant composition.

The characteristic of the effluents of the cooking processes as given by Sumathi and Hung (2006) are: high oxygen demand (BOD), color, it may have sulfur and resin reduced compounds. The effluent of the washing process, on the other hand, contains large amounts of suspended solids (SS), BOD and color. The effluent from the bleaching process contains organochloride compounds, BOD and resin. Now, the level of regeneration can be total or partial. The main types of regeneration processes can be divided in to physical-chemical and biological. Amidst the physical-chemical are: membrane separation techniques (inverse osmosis, ultrafiltration, nanofiltration, etc.), chemical flotation and precipitation and advanced oxidation processes. The biological processes are: activated sludge, anaerobic treatment, sequential anaerobic-aerobic system and fungi system for color and organo-halogenated derivatives.

It is important to emphasize that in the majority of cases 100% regeneration is not targeted; however, what is sought is the minimization of the fresh water consumption and the flow rate o the discharged effluent. In this part, no numerical results are presented since this is outside the scope of this work.

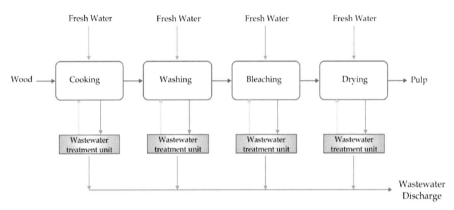

Fig. 13. Distributed treatment system for the effluents from each of the stages of the pulp production process.

4.2.4 Heat recovery system

The reduction of fresh water brings about important changes in the need of energy consumption since the pulp production process requires water streams at different temperatures. This stage of the analysis seeks to clearly identify the situations where energy is reduced as a result of a reduction in water consumption through the application of pinch analysis.

Fig. 14 shows the case where water consumption is reduced after increasing the conversion in one of the reactors if the bleaching stage. If fresh water is available at 40°C and it has to be heated up to 60 °C before been fed to the filter as shown in Fig. 15, the amount of energy saved is 52.1 kW . So, in order to take the temperature from 20 °C to 40 °C, the water and energy saving is 10.391 ton/hr and 242.45 kW, respectively.

Another type of sitations that arises is the one shown in Fig. 15, where stream 13 enters the process at 60 °C and stream 12 reaches the filter at a temperature equal or larger than 35 °C. After a water reuse scheme is applied, stream is reused 11 and since its temperature is above 35°C, an energy saving of 5,504 kW is achieved compared to the system where fresh water is used.

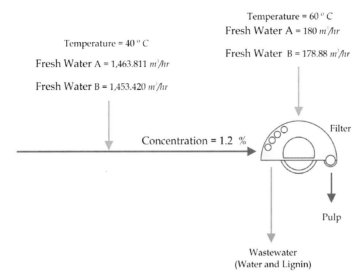

Fig. 14. Schematic of an energy saving application in the washing stage.

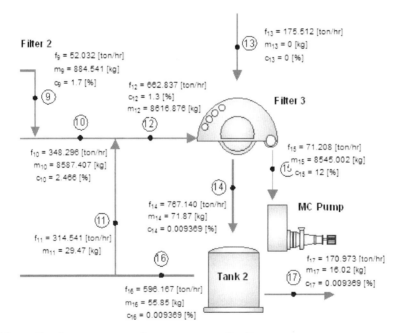

Fig. 15. Schematic of an energy saving process application.

In summary and putting together the results of the reviewed operations (washing and bleaching), the total amount of water saved is 582.626 ton/hr and an energy saving of 5504 kW is achieved. En el blanqueo se obtiene un ahorro de agua fresca de 11.511 ton/hr y un ahorro de energía de 294.55 kW. It is important to mention that water and energy savings have been achieved simultaneously by applying the methodology to particular unit operations.

5. Conclusions

This chapter has introduced a genera approach for the retrofit of existing processes for the reduction of water and energy consumption. The methodology introduced is based on a conceptual structured scheme with different hierarchical levels arranged in the following way:

Level 1. Analysis of the reaction system

Level 2. Analysis of the water using network

Level 3. Analysis and implementation of water regeneration schemes.

Level 4. Analysis of the heat recovery system.

This new approach direct us to determine the way changes to operating conditions affect the water and energy requirements in a process. In addition, these modifications can be viewed in the light of an economical analysis which shows the economical feasibility of the retrofit projects.

6. Acknowledgment

Thanks to Haydee Morales Razo. This work was supported by SEP-PROMEP (México) through grant PROMEP/103.5/11/0140.

7. References

Calloway, J., T. Retsina, et al. (1990). Pinch technology in practical kraft mill optimisation. Engineering Conference Proceedings.

Linnhoff B. Townsend, D.W., Boland, D., Hewitt, D.F., Thomas, B.E.A., Guy, A.R. and Marsland RH. (1982)User Guide on Process Integration for the Efficient Use of Energy, Institution of Chemical Engineers. IchemE, Rugby-UK.

Berglin, N., J. Strömberg, et al. (1997). Using process integration to approach the minimum impact pulp mill. Environmental Conference Proceedings.

Rouzinou, S., T. Retsina, et al. (2003). Pinch analysis: A powerful tool for the integration of new process equiment into existing pulp and paper. Fall Technical Conference.

Savulescu, L., B. Poulin, et al. (September 2005 c). "Water and energy savings at a kraft paperboard mill using process integration." Pulp & Paper Canada 106(9): 29 -31

Towers, M. (March 2005). "Energy reduction at a kraft mill: Examining the effects of process integration, benchmarking, and water reduction,." Tappi Journal 4 (3): 15 - 21.

Wising, U., T. Berntsson, et al. (2005). "The potencial for energy savings when reducing the water consumption in a Kraft Pulp Mill." Applied Thermal Engineering 25: 1057 - 1066.

Nordman, R. and T. Berntsson (2006). "Design of kraft pulp mill hot and warm water systems- A new method that maximizes excess heat." Applied Thermal Engineering 26: 363 - 373.

Parthasarathy, G. and G. Krishnagopalan (2001). "Sistematic reallocation of aqueous resources using mass integration in a typical pulp mill." Advances in Enviromental Research 5 61 - 79.

Lovelady, E. M., M. El-Halwagi, et al. (2007). "An integrated approach to the optimisation of water usage and discharge in pulp and paper plants." International Journal of Environment and Pollution 2007 29(No. 1/2/3): 274 - 307.

Savulescu L. E., A. Alva-Argáez, Direct heat transfer considerations for improving energy efficiency in pulp and paper Kraft mills, Energy, 33(10) (2008), 1562-1571.

European Commission (2001). "BREF in the Pulp and Paper Industry".

Westerberg A. W., H.P. Hutchinson, R.L. Motard y P. Winter (1979). "Process Flowsheeting", Cambridge Univ. Press, Cambridge, England.

Shenoy U. V. (1995)."Heat Exchanger network Synthesis", Gulf Publishing Co. 1995

Douglas J. (1988), "Conceptual Design of Chemical Processes". Mc Graw-Hill Co.

Walas S.M (1988) Chemical Process Equipment Selection and Design, Butterworths

Gullichsen J., C.J. Fogelholm, Papermaking Science and Technology – Chemical Pulping, Fapet OY, Helsinki, 1999.

Peters, M., Timmerhaus, K. 1991. Planta design and economics forchemical engineers. 4. ed. Mc.Graw Hill. Nueva York, NY. EEUU.

R. Smith, Chemical Process Design and Integration, John Wiley & Sons Ltd., Chichester, 2005.

Jacob, J., H. Kaipe, et al. (2002). "Water network analysis in pulp and paper processes by pinch and linear programming techniques." chemical Engineering Communications 189(2): 184 - 206.

Koufos, D. and T. Retsina (2001). "Practical energy and water management through pinch analysis for the pulp and paper industry." Water Science Technology 43 (2): 327 - 332.

Sumathi S., Yung-Tse Hung ,(2006). Treatment of Pulp and Paper Mill Wastes. Treatment in the Process Industries. (Editores: Wang, L.K., Hung Y., Lo H.H., Yapijakis, C.). Editado por Taylor and Francis. Pp 453-497.

13

An Application Model for Sustainability in the Construction Industry

Fernando Beiriz and Assed Haddad

Federal Fluminense University and Federal University of Rio de Janeiro

Brazil

1. Introduction

Over the years, mankind's development of a large industrial capacity and its ability to create new technologies that turn easier society's daily life has been a mark of innovation era. In many developing industries, technologies are incorporated into daily life by becoming indispensable to the modern lifestyle. Waste production has been increasingly alarming throughout the world, standing as a major problem to be solved.In order to achieve life quality and be able to provide favorable environmental conditions to future generations, it is indispensable to become conscious about environmental effects of all mankind's production activities.

It is vital to promote and encourage an environmental sustainability culture development: meeting society's demand of industrial and technological products with the indispensable proper disposal of their products at the end of life, that is, discard minimizing environmental impacts on the completion of its life cycle.

Some measures have been taken over recent years, with the intention of minimizing the generation of environmentally hazardous waste in the world, emphasizing the relevance of changes in production processes. In the specific case of construction, begins to be aroused interest from external factors. Among them, there is the availability of solutions to minimize negative environmental impacts identified and applicable management tools.

Methods for evaluating environmental performance of the construction industry and increased competition in the industry and customer requirements are also seen as elements boosters, which come to be added to increase environmental awareness at the part of builders.

Similarly, as many construction companies have implemented quality management systems that have brought them considerable benefits, it increases their interest in introducing environmental elements into existing systems. However, there are few builders that are committed to environmental issues. Still, environmental solutions have begun to be applied in enterprises, although this does not ensure continuous improvement and sustainable development of the sector.

Despite its recognized economic impacts to the country such as: high job creation, income and viability of housing, infrastructure, roads and others; in the construction sector one still lacks a firm policy for disposal of solid waste, mainly in urban centers.

The need to take the RCC not only results in a desire to economize. This is a fundamental attitude towards the preservation of our environment.

The important thing to be improved in this sector is the management process, with the decrease in solid waste generation and appropriate management of the same construction site, building awareness of the actors involved, creating the methodology.

It is noteworthy that is necessary a change of culture among all those involved in the process of IC, indicating the importance of preserving the environment we live.

Therefore, it is notorious the necessity of a mentality change in the aspect of environmental sustainability at the IC sector's stakeholders, in order to fortify and develop a responsible conduct, aware of the relevance of preserving and extracting as better as possible the environment's resources.

2. Construction industry sustainability

The term sustainable development can be seen as a key word this time. As there are numerous definitions for this term, the two most common definitions known, cited and accepted are the Brundtland Report (WCED, 1987) and the document known as Agenda 21. The best known definition of the Brundtland Report, presents the question of future generations and its possibilities. It contains two key concepts: the necessity and the idea of limitation. The first refers particularly to the needs of developing countries and, second, the idea imposed by the state of technology and social organization to meet the needs of present and future.

The question of emphasis on the social component of sustainable development is reflected in the debate taking place about the inclusion or not of social measures in the definition. This discussion appears in the variety of ideas about sustainability that contains components that are not usually measured, such as cultural and historical. Social indicators are considered particularly controversial, since they reflect political contexts and value judgments. The integration of mitigation measures is further complicated because of different and often conflicting dimensions. The definition of the Brundtland Report does not provide a static state, a more dynamic process that can continue to exist without self-defeating logic prevailing. The different forces acting on the system must be in balance for the system as a whole is maintained over time.

According to Pearce (1993), there are different environmental ideologies that make environmentalism a complex and dynamic phenomenon. Inside of environmentalism, the author identifies two ideological extremes: on one hand the technocentrism, and the other the "ecocentrism". Within this continuum one can identify four fields, with particular characteristic.

Pearce uses four classifications: sustainability very weak (very weak sustentability), weak sustainability (weak sustentability), strong sustainability (strong sustentability) and sustainability very strong (very strong sustentability).

You can also find a parallel Naess (1966) makes between Deep Ecology (deep ecology) and ecology superficial (shallow ecology). In ecology the central objective is superficial affluence and health, along with the fight against pollution and resource depletion. Focus on deep ecology focuses on biospheric egalitarianism and the principles of diversity, complexity and autonomy.

Authors linked the trend technocentric believe that sustainability refers to the maintenance of total capital available on the planet and that it can be achieved by substituting natural capital for capital created by human ingenuity. In extreme ecocentric the authors emphasize the importance of natural capital and the need to preserve it, I value not only for financial but mainly for its substantive value.

Ecological sustainability means to expand the capacity of the planet by using the potential found in diverse ecosystems, while the continuing deterioration in a minimum level.

It should reduce fossil fuel use and emission of pollutants, but also adopt policies for the conservation of energy and resources to replace.

The geographical sustainability can be achieved through a better distribution of human settlements and economic activities. It must seek a rural-urban setting most appropriate to protect biological diversity, while it improves the quality of life.

Finally, cultural sustainability, the most difficult to bring the second SACHS (1997), is related to the path of modernization without the disruption of cultural identity within specific spatial contexts. To SACHS (1997), the concept of sustainable development refers to a conception of the limits and the recognition of the weaknesses of the planet; focuses on both the socioeconomic problem and satisfying the basic needs of populations. Although the starting point of the various approaches is different, there is a recognition that there is a space of interconnection or overlap between these different dimensions.

Achieve progress toward sustainability is clearly a choice of society, organizations, communities and individuals. How covers different choices, change is only possible if there is greater involvement of society.

In short, sustainable development requires the society to think in terms of long-term and recognize its place within the biosphere. The concept provides a new perspective of observing the world, which has proven to be the current state of human activity inadequate to meet existing needs, and seriously threaten the prospect of future generations.

The goals of sustainable development challenge contemporary institutions. They have governed global changes reluctant to recognize that this process is actually occurring. The differences in the concept of sustainable development are so great that there is no consensus on how to measure sustainability. Unfortunately, for most authors cited earlier, does not have an operational definition of minimally acceptable.

All definitions and tools related to sustainability must consider the fact that no one knows fully how the system operates; one can only discover environmental impacts of activities and interaction as human welfare, the economy and the environment. In general, it is known that the system interacts between different dimensions, but do not know specifically the impact of these interactions. All aspects presented show the diversity and complexity of the term sustainable development.

3. Reverse logistics and waste management

The high competition among companies and constant increase in efficiency in the management processes of production, has characterized the current business environment.

Among the many processes present in a company, there is the logistics business, which is geared to ensure the delivery of the product produced correctly in the right place at the moment and want the lowest possible cost. In many industries, logistics has received more attention, mainly due to the globalization of markets and consumer pressure to reduce distribution costs.

The client, in turn, is embedded in consumer culture, which is driven by the cycle "buy-use-disposal", demonstrating that culture is unsustainable and inadequate to perishable perpetuation of current conditions for survival in contemporary society, because it stimulates the increasing manufacture of new products to the detriment of reuse and recycling of byproducts or waste.

Thus it is observed that actions to boost consumption are not planned with a systemic view, since their products are not useless options, structured reuse, leaving only the landfilling as a solution to dispose of them.

In this scenario, reverse logistics, or more precisely the deployment of reverse logistics gains importance in the supply chain. The structure of the reverse channel is a way to make new use of these products, through a new job or a transformation of industrial processing, in other useful products.

Thus, reverse logistics has a great interface with sustainable development, since the mobilization of the chains allows the reuse of reverse obsolete products, byproducts and waste, reducing the volume of discarded into the environment and the extraction of new resources. It also presents another favorable feature, since the emergence of new business also promotes the social, financial returns and allows companies involved in chains reverses.

Particularly in the construction industry, reverse logistics systems are designed to develop reverse chain for reuse of products and waste generated in production processes and establish the agents working in it, the census of responsibility throughout the product life cycle.

This attitude is shared not only by builders but, especially, by supplying materials for these are in an industrial environment, where there is less variability of the process. Thus, these companies can become drivers of implementation of this concept throughout the production chain construction.

In the construction sector, it is assumed that interest is still incipient and demonstrated by a few industries, as are the Brazilian initiatives for the reuse of industrial waste.

Applying the concept of reverse logistics in IC may occur in several ways. It can form themselves into organizational tool for the flow of aftermarket products, post-consumer waste from the production process of mobilization and demobilization of equipment used during construction of the project, and set yourself up as a new initiative or as an enhancement of existing reverse channel.

Specifically, with regard to flows, the amount and variability of waste composition of the construction industry generate flows of very different characteristics.

IC flows in post-consumption and production (waste) are hardly distinguished, because they occur simultaneously, except when the demolition of a building, a notoriously product stream after consumption.

Flows of products after sale are mainly for returns sent by mail-order and are usually intended for the secondary market, which, for example, donated to charity. Still others come from equipment and transportation as the return and withdrawal of lifts and cranes.

The biggest concern now rests on the post-consumer products or processes, generally named construction waste.

Applying the concept of reverse logistics in IC may also have coverage from a company in isolation, this and its supply chain, as well as sectored organization, or the entire production chain (the reverse supply chain). When the reverse logistics systems of IC are shared by all actors in the chain and these are strategic objectives aligned on the reuse of reverse flow, consolidates the management of reverse supply chain (reverse supply chain management).

The reverse logistics systems are formed by flows, distribution channels, reverse, or simply reverse channels. In this study of reverse logistics systems IC correspond to the flows of waste from construction and demolition-RCD and its reverse channels.

Flows of post-consumer products industry, construction and demolition have their roots in construction sites. In this environment has recently developed some RCD management initiatives.

The analysis of the requirements of laws versus the needs of the construction leads to the conclusion about the actions necessary for the establishment of a reverse logistics system for the RCD.

Quantifying the generation of RCD is complex because it involves the collection of field data, since there are no precise data , nor indicators released. The generation relies heavily on project design and technologies used, the organization of the plot, containers for packaging of the various "bumps" of waste, and vary according to the stage of the work.

Become evident throughout the academic, claims that the IC, as well as other industrial chains, must promote sustainable development, ie, it must develop in order to not compromise the ability of future generations to do it too. Among the many issues involved in policies for sustainable development of the productive chain of the IC in relation to environmental and social dimensions, are responsible for the use of natural resources and disposal of waste from industrial activities.

4. Brazilian environmental legislation general requirements for construction companies

There are several Brazilian environmental legislation aspects that affect the Construction Industry and construction companies operations in Brazil. The Waste Management Program for construction sites and Environmental Impact Assessment Program with respective Report and License are the most important items to be taken care. All construction sites demand waste management attention although this Environmental Impact Assessment Program and Report (*Estudo de Impacto Ambiental - EIA/RIMA*) are only mandatory in special cases.

4.1 The waste management program

This waste management program aims at the reduction of waste production and correct destination of what remains in activities involving in construction, retrofitting, remodeling, maintenance and demolition in all types of construction related activities and subsectors of the Construction Industry.

Table 1. shows Brazilian Construction Waste Classification according to the legislation and its respective destinations.

Reuse is the process of reapply some waste without transforming itself and Recycling is the process of reapply some waste after some transformation. These are possible final destination of A and B waste classes.

Class A wastes, before reuse and recycle, can be stored in Building Construction landfills. In these sites special disposal storage techniques are used having in mind preservation of these segregated materials for its future use or the use of the land itself throughout application of some engineering principles to confine them. The **Construction Industry Waste Management Integrated Plan** (*Plano Integrado de Gerenciamento de Resíduos da Construção Civil*) structured as shown above.

Construction Waste Classification			
Classification	Characteristics	Examples	Destination
Class A	Reusable waste or recyclable as aggregate	Brick blocks and tiles, dirt, concrete, mortar	Reused or recycled
Class B	Recyclable	Plastics, paper/cardboard, metal, glass, wood pieces	
Class C	Not existent technology for recycling	Gypsum	Stored, transported and disposed in conformity with specific standards.
Class D	Hazardous Waste	Coats, solvents, oil	

Table 1. Brazilian Construction Waste Classification

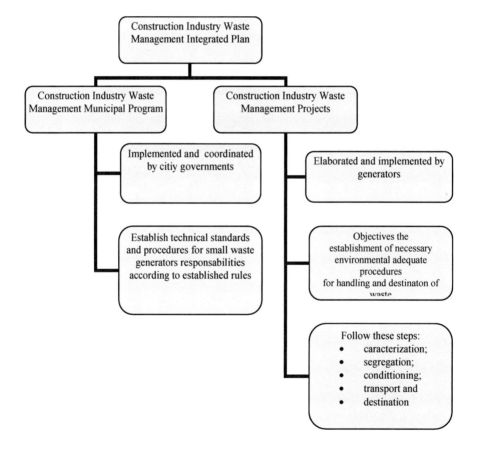

Fig. 1. Construction Industry Waste Management Integrated Plan Scheme.

This plan must have:

- Technical standards and procedures for the Construction Industry Waste Management Municipal Program and the Construction Industry Waste Management Projects, elaborated by large waste generators, aiming the creation of a sense of responsibility by all generators;
- Mapping of public or private areas, suitable for receiving, segregation a temporary storage of small waste volumes, according to urban municipal zoning. This allows further destination for waste management plants or recycling;
- Establishment of licensing procedures for areas of processing and final waste destination;
- Determination of prohibition of disposal in non licensed areas;
- Incentives towards reuse or recycling;
- Determination of parameters and criteria for registration of waste transportation companies;
- Environmental education actions towards waste management of construction waste.

4.2 Environmental impact assessment program and report

An Environmental Impact Assessment Program and Report is mandatory for CC seeking construction licenses for construction sites in which considerable environmental impacts will happen, such as:

- Roads with two or more lanes;
- Railroads;
- Ports and terminals for oil and gas, chemicals products and mining;
- Aeroports;
- All types of pipelines including sewage, oil, gas, mining and others;
- Power lines, beyond 230KV;
- Water resources facilities including Hydro Plants beyond 10MW, irrigation works, sewers, navigation channels, etc;
- Fossil fuels extraction;
- Mining extraction;
- Sanitary landfills, toxic or hazardous;
- Power Plants generating more than 10MW;
- Industrial and agricultural units and complexes;
- Industrial districts and strictly industrial zones;
- Wood exploration in large areas or in some subject to special environmental interest;
- Urban Projects in large areas or in some subject to special environmental interest;
- Any activity use coal from vegetal sources in excess to ten tons a day.
- Canals and Harbour structures

The Environmental Impact Assessment must: I - evaluate all technological and location alternatives for the project including the possibility of non development; II - identify and evaluate systematically all environmental impacts taken place during the implementation and operation phases of the project; III – determine the project directly and indirectly affected area geographic boundaries subject to environmental aspects and impacts of the project (denominated project influence area); IV - consider governmental proposed pans and programs for the project influence area and their compatibility.

4.3 Environmental licenses

The Environmental License is an administrative act by which the environmental agency, establish conditions, restrictions and environmental control actions to be followed by companies and enterprises seeking construction, installation, addition and operation of projects and activities that which to use natural resources, with the potential to harm or affect the environment. The following construction activities demand licensing in Brazil:

- Highways, railroads, subways and waterways;
- Barrages and levees;
- Drainage channels;
- Water courses rectification;
- Opening of channels, enlargement of rivers
- Transposition of river basins;
- Other special works.

ENVIRONMENTAL LICENSING		
License type	Characteristics	Validity
Previous License Licença Prévia (LP)	• Preliminary or in the planning phase of the project • Approves localization and concept • Ensures environmental availability • Basic requisites and conditions to fulfill in further phases towards project implementation	**Minimum:** according to what was scheduled in the activity or project approved plans, programs and designs **Maximum:** 5 years
Operation License *"Licença de Operação (LO)"*	• Authorizes installation according to specifications from approved plans, programs and designs • Includes environmental control actions and conditions	**Minimum:** according to what was scheduled in the activity or project **Maximum:** 6 year
Installation License *"Licença de Instalação (LI)"*	• Verifies effective accomplishment of previous licenses, conditions and environmental control plans for the operation • Authorizes the activity or project operation	Should consider the environmental control plans **Minimum:** 4 years **Maximum:** 10 years

Table. 2 Brazilian environmental Licenses.

The Brazilian Environmental Criminal Law (Brazilian Federal Law 9.605/98) was an important mark that determined higher attention in licensing activities. It determines that "Build, restore, addition, install or operate, in any part of the country, establishments, construction sites or services potentially hazardous without license or authorization from environmental agencies or against the rules and regulations ins unlawful and is subject to imprisonment from one to six months and fine".

5. A model for sustainability in the construction industry

The model presented here will apply for technical and economic issues, the major producing areas of waste. These regions represent large urban centers or may result from the formation of a conglomerate or consortium of adjacent municipalities, bringing together the legislation compatible.

Importantly, the current stage of the construction industry in Brazil, already in itself justify the existence of a rigid model of treatment and recovery of debris from the construction industry in all regions of the country This scenario will be aggravated and may even be become untenable, with the advent of achievement, in Brazil, Football World Cup in 2014 and the Olympics in 2016, when major works and demolitions have to be made, generating an abnormal amount of debris. Moreover, the practice of waste treatment of IC is very incipient in the country, and even negligible in the State of Rio de Janeiro, where he will focus the Olympic Games of 2016.

5.1 Principles of motion

Any model to be functional and efficient it has to rely on a set of interdependent and harmonious elements, rules and procedures. In the proposal in focus, we list the main points and actions that should be considered:

- Clear and comprehensive legislation - the recent National Policy on Solid Waste culminating in Brazil in August, 02 of 2010, is a great motivator to take seriously the treatment of waste from the construction industry. But, it is necessary that the state and local public authorities commensurate with their organic laws that policy, clearly and objectively, and promote a public-private partnership, to put into practice the recycling of construction debris in their areas of coverage ;
- Effective supervision - one of the major problems faced by municipalities is the illegal dump sites and on public roads, including transport companies themselves accredited. It is essential to pursuing a proactive surveillance for the balance of the process, using modern technology, such as control by GPS;
- Existence of incentives for products and services involved in the process - is important, for example, that recycled materials are treated with different taxes in relation to new products;
- Existence of penalties for violating a law by service providers and generators of rubble - the penalties should be meaningful in order to promote greater accountability of individuals and companies in the process of disposal of construction waste, in favor of environmental control and panorama of cities;
- Encouraging the use of modern techniques and methodologies for building large projects in order to reduce the debris - debris is often generated by deficiencies in the construction process, such as failures or omissions in the preparation of projects and their implementation, poor quality of materials employees, for losses in transport and storage, improper handling by the workforce, as well as replacement components for the reform or reconstruction. Improved management and control of works, use of modulation techniques and also joint work with companies and construction workers can help to alleviate this waste;
- The whole region should be provided with one or more treatment plants and waste processing, depending on the volume to be processed;
- Strategic location of collection points and disposal of debris (Ecopoints) for small and medium-sized generators of rubble;

- Area of Transshipment and Triage (ATT), which is the equivalent of an Eco Center for the receipt of large volumes of debris, from large generators;
- Location of areas of rubble landfill officials IC;
- Implementation of policies for environmental management and waste treatment in large generators, such as construction and demolition;
- Specialized transportation network;
- Educational campaign at all levels, including the population in general - is to clarify and encourage the integration of the self in the process.

5.2 Operational architecture model

The following Figure illustrates the components involved in the model for treatment of wastes from the construction industry, as well as the flow routing in each of the elements produced at each location.

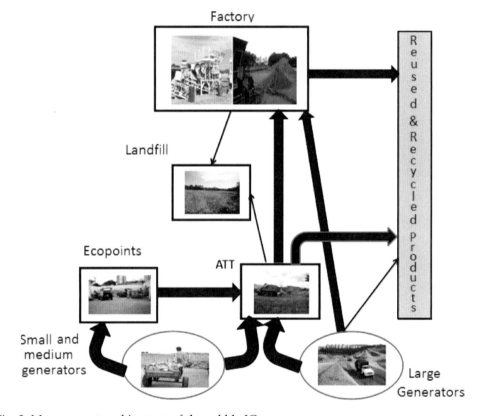

Fig. 2. Management architecture of the rubble IC

5.2.1 Small and medium generators of the debris of the IC and Ecopoints

According to the definition given in Resolution No. 307 of CONAMA, generators are individuals or entities responsible for activities or enterprises that produce construction waste. Constitute small and medium-sized generators, for example, construction projects and reforms implemented in commercial or residential units of small or medium size.

The existence and management of eco-points are essential for efficient control of collection of debris from construction, to avoid dropping these, irregular, illegal or inappropriate points.
Ecopoint sites are provided, usually by public authorities, waste disposal in a voluntary and free basis. They can be made simply by buckets, properly prepared by a land or a house, always located near point of generation potential, and easy access.
Figure 3 shows some examples of existing Ecopoints in the State of São Paulo.

Fig. 3. Ecopoint Bresser and Ecopoint Pinheiros

The process for using these services is simple: just take the waste from construction such as cement, bricks, tiles, plaster, wood and other debris from construction, Ecopoints. It is anticipated with the disposal of debris up to 1m ^{3} cubic volume per user per day, equivalent to roughly 25% of a bucket. If the construction or renovation generates a tremendous amount to be disposed of more than 200 liters, it will be needed to hire a company specialized in the collection services and transportation of debris.
As the debris in Ecopoints received, from small and medium generators are generally very impure, must be carefully separated, to be given the correct destination for each type of material found in them. Therefore, they should be compulsorily transferred to a triage area and Transshipment of Waste (TTA) for treatment.

5.2.2 Large generators of the debris of IC

Large debris generators generate over 1m ^{3} of waste from construction or demolition. Are those that require buckets to carry your trash. Usually they are responsible for construction and remodeling of large, for example contractors, builders and technicians responsible for works. The big generators are responsible for disposal of rubbish they generate. In such cases it is necessary to hire a transport company of construction waste.
In the case of buildings with more than 500m ^{2}, the generator must develop and deploy rubble in building site, a Waste Management Program of Construction and prove that the waste generated was disposed of in an environmentally correct.
The waste in construction site varies according to the execution phase of services. Much of the debris generated during the entire construction can be used as aggregate in various

stages of the building, considering, however, that the mineral fraction (cementitious material and ceramic) is the only one to be recycled and used on the construction, the other fractions as wood, metal, plaster, plastics and paper, should be directed to the appropriate local recycling or disposal of these materials, such as ATT's and Plants. Other components can even be sold or donated for reuse in the case of demolition, such as doors, windows, bathrooms and kitchens metals, etc.

Therefore, it is necessary to be aware of the entire site, followed by pre-established procedures for the use and destination of the waste. First you must establish debris generated separation: ceramic and cement, wood, contaminants, metals, plastics and paper, for example. Each fraction will have its place of deposit in the quarry. This separation plot is not complex, because the debris is generated by separate activities, such as the use of mortars have will only cementitious material and other activities on the debris will only generate carpentry wood. The non-recyclable rubbish is disposed off on site, while recyclable rubbish is processed subsequently disposed.

Fig. 4. Segregation of waste at the construction site

In large enterprises, it is sometimes advantageous and desirable that the machining is done on the construction work. In this case, for crushing are generally used small equipment, with an average production of about 2m³ per hour, with power and manual removal of the products. Equipment is simple and easy to use, where: mortar-mill, hammer mill, grinder or plaster jaw crusher.

Besides improvements on the environment, the management of recycling at construction site brings good economic advantages, such as:

- Reducing the volume of rubbish sent to ATT or plant, reducing the cost of removal;
- More organized and clean site;
- Reduced acquisition of aggregate material;

The large main emphasis is to recycle the rubble in the works is the financial aspect: do not waste material already paid and still be able to produce products with low costs are rather compelling reasons. As an example we have that the projected cost per cubic meter of mortar with recycled material is around U$ 36, while a cubic meter of conventional mortar is **US $ 62.00.**

5.2.3 Area overflow and waste segregation (ATT)

Transshipment Areas and Waste Sorting of Construction (ATT) are the premises for the receipt of bulky construction waste collected by private agents, which should be used for screening of incoming materials, processing and any subsequent removal for proper disposal. So are sites used for routing and segregation of waste for disposal.

ATT is typically a business that belongs to the autonomous initiative of collecting small businesses or cooperatives, and are deployed and operated by observing the law of municipal land use and occupation, as well as federal and state legislation to control environmental pollution when appropriate.

As these are areas, in the context of the proposed architecture, are administered by the private sector, generating jobs and revenues for receiving debris from the construction and sale of sorted waste, which could enable an effective overview for the efforts that are being developed in favor of a sustainable environment. This initiative is breaking old paradigms, showing that waste reduction can be combined with cost reduction, combining behavior change in various work to build partnerships with various vendors, abolishing the provision is irresponsible outlaws illegal boot through committed the allocation of each component of sorted waste, so that the responsibility to the environment that anchors the economic activity is exercised. The following picture illustrates an overview of the Transfer Area and Screening.

Fig. 5. ATT in the outskirts of Guarulhos in Sao Paulo

5.2.4 Landfills of waste places

In most cases, the debris is removed and disposed of the work clandestinely in places like vacant lots, riverbanks and streets of the suburbs. The social and environmental cost of this is beyond the control of the calculations, although its consequences are permanently noted. We can see the deterioration of quality of life in urban areas such as transport, flood, visual pollution, proliferation of disease vectors, among others. One way or another, the whole society suffers from the uneven deposition of debris.

The debris is residue from a large volume, occupying so much space in landfills, transportation, depending not only on volume but the weight, it becomes expensive. Recycling and reuse of rubble are therefore of fundamental importance for the control and mitigation of environmental problems caused by the generation of waste.

The existence of authorized local landfill dump in the context of this proposal is due to the fact that some debris from work, or certain residues after machining or segregation from the rubble at the ATT, is not be recovered. Have to be discarded, and this time it is important that they are received at licensed sites and specific for this purpose.

The landfill is now the most widely used solution for its ease of implementation and others. But still has a very high environmental cost, and some administrators end up not respecting the rules or find other alternatives. When implementing the standards are not met, the sanitary landfill is no longer and begins to set up the so-called dump.

A plausible alternative is the separation of waste into inert and non-polluting material (domestic waste, commercial, industrial and hospital) and material (waste derived from construction). This alternative, while reducing costs, since the landfill for inert material is cheaper than landfill, allows it to be used mainly in projects that address the reuse and recycling of such materials. This idea becomes valid once the aggregates are a major source of raw material at a relatively low cost.

Fig. 6. Landfill construction debris (Hall BH)

5.2.5 Treatment plants and processing waste IC

In the current global context is essential to improve the construction processes. However, recycling of rubbish comes as a solution to the materials that are inevitably lost. Recycling allows the reuse of raw materials, reducing the demand for more material, reducing energy consumption and protecting the environment more and more waste, which would take millions of years to be decomposed by nature. Recycling becomes disordered the mountains of building materials, piles of raw material, which serves both as building works for public works. There are two ways to turn losses into profits: one for the private sector and another for local governments.

The process of recycling the rubble for obtaining aggregates basically involves the selection of recyclable materials from rubbish and grinding in their proper equipment. The screening phase of an ATT must proceed independently or integrated into the processing plant.

The recycling of rubble can be done at facilities with different characteristics for equipment used which may be mobile or fixed.

Fig. 7. Plant equipment: a set vibrating feeder jaw crusher + + belt

5.2.6 Logistics of moving the rubble

The debris generated by small works must necessarily be disposed in Ecopoints. Therefore, their transport should be done by an independent group of carriers, using vehicles intended for freight, cars and even wheelbarrows. Optionally, the service of withdrawal of small volumes of debris generated in small works may be offered by the city. In this case, the municipality may dismiss them Ecopoint a neighbor, or even carry an ATT.

The transportation of debris from the ecopoint, should be done by the municipality or by an outside company for her. Should be discarded in an ATT, because it is a very heterogeneous rubble.

For works of medium sized businesses that generate significant amounts of debris, transport must be hired by the generator, companies accredited by the Government, working with the transport of rubble multi cranes using trucks and dumpsters. In this case, the debris must be disposed directly in ATT, because it is a dump, as a rule, heterogeneous, with a disposal cost based on volume, the carrier paid to ATT.

In large constructions and demolitions, debris intended for disposal should be conducted at a plant where have characteristics suitable for recycling at no cost by the receiving plant. When the debris is heterogeneous, an ATT should be discarded with the burden of the cost of disposal by the generator.

The transfer of rubble in an ATT and screened for the disposal shall be transported to a recycling plant to the landfill or dump, depending on their character, on behalf of the Government, that you can do so directly or through third party service .

The waste is not usable in a plant should be discarded in a landfill dump, under the responsibility of the plant.

6. Validation of the model

The economic infeasibility of a CDR of recycling is often a logistical problem results mainly from the high cost of collection and transportation arising from the existence of many points of consumption and few points of waste recovery.

The main objective of the recycling center regardless of whether a, private or public, is to diminish the distance between the product and its potential buyers. Consequently, this reduces the environmental and economic impacts arising from that transport.

Efforts can be properly rewarded by the possibilities of raw material savings - as demonstrated in the analysis of economic viability, partnership with large generators, acting responsibly towards the environment and differential image in the marketplace.

The simulations of economic viability analysis proved that, currently, there are conditions for the economic viability of waste recycling of ICC.

The most appropriate model is the one that would establish co-responsibility, including environmental liabilities, among the managers of plants and ATT, waste generators and transporters. The manufacturer must develop, together with research institutions, appropriate disposal options and the developer must ensure that the flow of waste will be properly addressed to the appropriate places.

7. Conclusions

Government agencies need to establish laws, which define:
- Responsibilities and joint responsibilities of each agent on the management of RCD;
- Forms of surveillance and punishment of its fulfillment;
- A ban on the disposal of certain wastes at landfills, especially those based on plaster;
- Tax on the disposal of certain wastes at landfills;
- Tax on the purchase of certain products that generate waste disposal difficult to manage and / or high negative environmental impact;
- Subsidies for the implementation and operation of recycling plants;
- Minimum and maximum indices of recycled content in certain products;
- The environmental certification of products.

Trade unions should organize their members assisting in the dissemination studies and awareness of environmental responsibility and sustainable construction. The academy needs to develop knowledge about, especially the technical restrictions and new applications of the RCD.

Consumers of recycled products shall also assist in establishing clear and objective specifications and minimum quality and performance required for their consumption.

Despite growing concern for companies of ICC in relation to environmental sustainability, few initiatives have been taken. This finding is confirmed in the case of manufacturers who have a low involvement with respect to the disposal of waste solutions from the works, without taking into account that the generators and transporters do not show any commitment to proper disposal.

It appears that manufacturers should encourage and support the research and take more active role in finding solutions and provision of recycling and take the RCD in a vertical process. This position might provide a differential in the relationship with customers, in particular the construction companies, with more active role in the searching of appropriate solutions for the allocation, since they are the manufacturers who have greater knowledge about the product.

Builders, distributors, installers and ATT should consolidate the processes of performing sorting and packaging accurately and hiring only suitable transport. They may also, through its purchasing power, pressuring suppliers to find solutions for allocation.

Transport, in turn, must meet the stock of transport and disposal under the laws, and even agents of change in the behavior of generators. Finally, everyone needs to establish information system and effective communication between them.

The establishment of reverse supply chain is subject to a strong cooperation between agents, which should be strategically aligned and have a shared vision and holistic environment in which they live, and census of all responsibilities on product life.

We noted also that the consolidation of reverse logistics is a progressive and interdependent relationship between the suppliers and contractors. Efforts of a single side (agent) or scattered efforts tend to produce mediocre results and consequently no spread of its principles.

8. References

Pinto, T. P. (1999). Metodologia para a Gestão Diferenciada de Resíduos Sólidos da Construção Urbana. São Paulo: EPUSP

Manoliadis, O. G. (2007). The Role of Adaptive Environmental Management in Sustainable Development Case Study Assessing the Economical Benefits of Sustainable Construction in Greece, *Environmental Technologies: New Developments*, E. B. Ö. Güngör (Ed.), pp. 85-96, InTech, ISBN 978-3-902613-10-3, Democritus University of Thrace, Greece

Chan, H. K., (2010). A Process Re-engineering Framework for Reverse Logistics based on a Case Study, University of East Anglia, Norwich, Norfolk, UK

Naess, A. (1996). *Ecology: The shallow and the deep*. In: CAHN, MA. ; O'BRIEN, R. *Thinking about the environment – readings on politics, property and the physical world*. London: M. E. Sharpe

Reinhardt, F. L. (1999). *Bring the environment Down to Earth Harvard Review*. Nov. – Dec..

RESOLUÇÃO CONAMA 307 DE 05 DE JULHO DE 2002. Dispõe sobre Gestão dos Resíduos da Construção Civil

Chattopadhyay, S. & Mo, John P.T. (2010). Modelling a Global EPCM (Engineering, Procurement and Construction Management) Enterprise, RMIT University, Australia

Couto A. & Couto, J. P. (2010). Guidelines to Improve Construction and Demolition Waste Management in Portugal, *Process Management*, pp. 285-208, Intech, ISBN 978-953-307-085-8, University of Minho, Portugal

Rutherford, I. (1997). Use of models to link indicators of sustainable development. In: *MOLDAN, B; BILHARDZ, S.; Sustainability indicators: report of the Project on indications of sustainable development*. Chichester: John Willey & Sons ltd

Sachs, I. (1997). Desenvolvimento sustentável, Bioindustrialização descentralizada e novas configurações rural-urbanas. Os casos da Índia e Brasil. In: VIEIRA, P. F.; WEBBER, *J. Gestão de recursos naturais renováveis e desenvolvimento*, Cortez (Ed.), São Paulo, Brasil

Secretaria do Meio Ambiente do Estado de São Paulo. Governo do Estado Instituiu Selo Verde para Produtos que respeitem a Natureza. http://. www.ambiente.sp.gov.br, acess May 2010.

Serviço de limpeza urbana da prefeitura municipal de Belo Horizonte – SLU/PMBH. Belo Horizonte, Feb. 2004

14

Assessing the SMEs' Competitive Strategies on the Impact of Environmental Factors: A Quantitative SWOT Analysis Application

Hui-Lin Hai

Department of Information Management, Shih Chien University, Kaohsiung Campus
Taiwan, R.O.C.

1. Introduction

In today's highly competitive environment, strategic management has been widely used by all enterprises to withstand fierce competition. Environmental management has quickly emerged as an essential strategic factor in many industries. Environmental considerations are clearly becoming increasingly important and will be considered as one of the key factors in most companies' success stories. For example, recently there are many firms in Asia that had already received ISO 14001 certification and adopted these Environmental Management Systems (EMS) standards as their state policy. No doubt that many firms have recognized the compatibility between environmental performance and profitability, as it witnessed by increasing interest in recycling programs and green marketing, in part due to realizing that the futility of running from such pressures.

Melnyk et al. (2003) apply a survey of North American managers to demonstrate that firms having gone through EMS certification experience a greater impact on performance than do firms that have not certified their EMS. Pan (2003) applies questionnaires to the organizations within Taiwan, Japan, Hong Kong and Korea on regards of ISO9000 and ISO14000 issues. He uses statistical analysis results of the survey data to gain eight common points for ISO9000 and ISO14000 certified firm within these four countries. Tan et al. (2003) develop an e-commerce structure for sorting, selecting and utilizing information for the effect of ISO9000 system. The related studies of environmental issues will be listed in Environment Management (Ahsen and Funck, 2001; Rao et al., 2006; Gernuks et al., 2007), Environmental Management Accounting (Jasch, 2003), ISO14001 Certification (Fryxell and Szteo, 2002; Mbohwa and Fukada, 2002; Rennings et al., 2006) and Life Cycle Assessment for EMS (Zobel, 2002).

In a country's endeavor to implement EMS in both manufacturing and service sectors, the significance of Small and Medium Enterprises (SMEs) deserves special attention. In Taiwan, a SME is set under either two conditions. First, it is defined by the number of employees that they often refer to those with less than 200 employees involved in manufacturing, building and mining industries. Second, it is defined by its capital volume that is less than 80 million Taiwan dollars. The SMEs are typically much smaller in operation compared to the global and multinational enterprises, whereas most of the SEMs in Taiwan are positioned in the ending-role of the supply chain. Most EMSs in Taiwanese SMEs are implemented in accordance to specification in ISO 14001 or QC080000 standards, in which contain requirements that have to be fulfilled before third-party certification and /or registration can be achieved.

Strength, Weakness, Opportunity and Threat (SWOT) analysis is an important support tool for decision-making, and is commonly used as a means to systematically analyze an organization's internal management capability and its external environment. The purpose of the analysis on internal strengths and weaknesses is to assess how an enterprise carries out its internal work, such as R&D, day to day business operation, etc. On the other hand, the purpose of the analysis on the external opportunities and threats is to assess whether or not an enterprise can seize opportunities and avoid threats, whilst facing an uncontrollable external environment, such as fluctuating prices, political destabilization, etc. SWOT analysis has been successfully applied in EMS fields, such as the environmental impact assessment in India (Paliwal, 2006), the development of an environmental management system (Lozano and Vallés, 2007) and regional energy planning for renewable development (Terrados et al., 2007).

For a quantitative SWOT, Kuttila et al. (2000) develop a hybrid method, the Analysis Hierarchy Process (AHP) in the SWOT analysis, to eliminate the weakness in the measurement and evaluation steps of the SWOT analysis. Examples in literature of studies that follow the method of Kuttila et al. include those by Kajanus et al. (2004), Leskinen et al. (2006) and Chang and Huang (2006). Yüksel and Dağdeviren (2007) demonstrate a process for quantitative SWOT analysis that can be performed even when there is dependence among strategic factors. They use the Analytic Network Process (ANP) that allows measurement of the dependency among the strategic factors as well as its AHP, which is based on independence between the factors. ANP is a more general form of its predecessor, the AHP, for ranking alternatives based on some set of criteria. Unlike AHP however, ANP is capable of handling feedbacks and interdependencies, which exist, in complex systems like a manufacturing system. ANP problem formulation starts by modeling the problem that depicts the dependence and influences of the factors involved to the goal or higher-level performance objectives. Dependence among the SWOT factors is observed to effect the strategic and sub-factor weights, as well as to change the strategy priorities. Dyson (2004) provides an SWOT and TOWS analysis to create strategy formation and its incorporation into the strategic development process at University of Warwick by scoring SWOT factors. A variation of SWOT analysis is the TOWS matrix. In the TOWS matrix the various factors are identified and these are then paired e.g. an opportunity with a strength, with the intention of stimulating a new strategic initiatives (Table 1).

A "top-down" way of thinking could be used to guide the formulation of decision hierarchy. In this paper, a new quantitative SWOT analysis is provided that allows measurement of the strategic factors as well as its vote-ranking method. The first task is to invite eighteen certificated ISO9000 and ISO14000 auditors (or lead auditors) to organize a "Task Force (TF)". The TF will discuss SWOT of Taiwanese SMEs within their EMS issues and assess the competitive strategies. The second task is to apply the internal competitive strengths to find external market opportunities. As a result, the strategy combination for max {strengths, opportunities} and min {weaknesses, threats} will be provided. The third task is to regard these SWOT indexes and their sub-criteria as the candidates voted by the task force. In conclusion, the different results of ranking will expose different weights among the votes of the candidates.

This paper discusses the environmental issues of the SMEs not only by drawing insights from research conducted in different countries, but also look into the use of environmental factors of SWOT through their development, their context and adaptability to enhance the environment performance of SMEs. As for the medium, the vote-ranking method will be used to rank the different competitive strategies and priorities. This specific method provides a new quantitative SWOT methodology that will be extended to decision-making issues. The rest of this paper is organized as follows: Section 2 illustrates the vote-ranking method and the conceptual approach. Section 3 discloses the use of vote-ranking method to provide a quantitative SWOT method for assessing the SMEs' competitive strategies in EMS by six-step procedure. Section 4 discusses the results of different strategies and suggestions. Section 5 highlights some conclusions and offers directions for further researches.

2. Vote-ranking methodology

Data Envelopment Analysis (DEA) is an analytical procedure developed by Charnes et al. (1978) for measuring the relative efficiency of decision-making units (DMUs) that perform the same types of functions and have identical goals and objectives. The weights used for each DMU are those which maximize the ratio between the weighted output and weighted input. DEA is a mathematical programming technique that calculates the relative efficiencies of multiple DMUs, based on multiple inputs and outputs. A well-known method for ranking candidates in a ranked voting system is to compare the weighted sum of their votes after determining suitable weights. Cook and Kress (1990, 1992) present an approach to the problem of ranking candidates in a preferential election. They consider an alternative method which does not specify the sequence of weights by applying DEA. One would imagine that any reasonable person, voter, candidate or poll manager would agree that the first place votes should weigh at least as much as second place votes, and so on. They provide the following DEA model to obtain the total score for each candidate:

$$Z_{rr}(\varepsilon) = \max \sum_{s=1}^{S} u_{rs} x_{rs}$$

$$s.t. \quad Z_{rq}(\varepsilon) = \sum_{s=1}^{S} u_{rs} x_{qs} \leq 1, \quad q = 1, 2, \ldots, R; \tag{1}$$

$$u_{rs} - u_{r(s+1)} \geq d(s, \varepsilon), \quad s = 1, 2, \ldots, S - 1;$$

$$u_{rS} \geq d(s, \varepsilon).$$

Where,
s: the number of places, $s = 1, \ldots, S$.
r: the number of candidates, $r = 1, \ldots, R$.
u_{rs}: the weights of the sth place with respect to the rth candidate.
x_{rs}: the total votes of the rth candidate for the sth place.
$d(s, \varepsilon)$: the given difference in weights between sth place with $(s+1)$th place; $d(., \varepsilon)$, called the discrimination intensity function, is nonnegative and non-decreasing in ε. Parameter ε is nonnegative.
The Cook and Kress's ranked voting model (1) is assumed that in a voting system, each voter selects R candidates and ranks them from the 1st to the Sth places, $S \leq R$. The $d(s, \varepsilon)$ is to ensure that first place votes are valued at least as highly as second place votes which are valued at least as highly as third place votes etc. The Z_{rq} is the cross-efficiency which can be thought of here as candidate r's evaluation of candidate q's desirability. The constraints Z_{rq}

are the usual DEA constraints i.e. that no candidate q should have a desirability greater than 1 under r's weights. The Z_{rr} has been used in the objective function to emphasize the candidate r's evaluation of his/her own desirability. The rth candidate wishes to be assigned the weight u_{rs} so as to maximize the weighted sum of votes to candidate r, that is when the score Z_{rr} becomes the largest. Notionally, each candidate was permitted to choose the most favorable weights to be applied to his/her standings in the normal DEA manner, with the additional 'assurance region' restriction, in which the weight for a sth place vote should be greater than the one for a $(s+1)$th place vote by some amount. Hashimoto and Ishikawa (1993) consider the candidates in ranked voting systems as the DMUs in DEA, and each is considered to have many outputs and only one input with unity. He also deems that it is fair to evaluate each candidate in terms of the weights optimal to himself/ herself.

Green et al. (1996) further develop this model by setting certain constraints to the weights. They point out that the form of d(s, ε) affects the ranking results and does not allow DMUs to choose their own weights unreservedly. Therefore, they present an alternative procedure that involved using each candidate's rating of him/herself along with each candidate's rating of all the other candidates. They utilize the cross-efficiency model to DEA to obtain the best candidate. On the other hand, Hashimoto (1997) proposes a method to determine a total ordering of candidates specifying nothing arbitrary, but only assuming the condition of decreasing and convex sequence of weights. They incorporate the condition of decreasing and convex sequence of weights into DEA as the assurance region. Green et al. and Hashimoto proposes these methods, whereabouts the existence of low preference candidates may change the ranks and DEA exclusion model, which seems to be unstable with respect to the inefficient candidates. Obata and Ishii (2003) consider that, the instability is caused by the fact mentioned above and that the inefficient candidates should not be used to discriminate efficient candidates. They also use this information only on efficient candidate while discriminating and realizing that the order of efficient candidates never changes even though the inefficient candidates are added or removed. Foroughi and Tamiz (2005) simplify the model of Obata and Ishii and extend it to rank the inefficient candidates as well as the efficient one.

Noguchi et al. (2002) revise the application of Green's method and show that different weights among objects gave rise to different ranking results. If one wants to set particular constraints to a weight can be employed, which is characterized by the following constraints: (a) $u_{r1} \geq 2 u_{r2} \geq 3 u_{r3} \ldots \geq S u_{rS}$, (b) $u_{rs} \geq 1/[(1+2+\ldots+S)*n] = 2/(n* S(S+1))$, where n is the number of voters. In this multiple criteria case, the vote-ranking model is defined as follows:

$$Z_{rr} = \max \sum_{s=1}^{S} u_{rs} x_{rs}$$

$$s.t. \quad Z_{rq} = \sum_{s=1}^{S} u_{rs} x_{qs} \leq 1 \quad q = 1, 2, \ldots, R;$$

$$s u_{rs} \geq (s+1) u_{r(s+1)}, \quad s = 1, \ldots, (S-1); \quad\quad\quad (2)$$

$$u_{rS} \geq \frac{1}{[(1+2+\ldots+S)n]} = \frac{2}{n * S(1+S)}.$$

Where, these variables are the identical as model (1).

As for ranking of alternatives, one of the most popular methods compares the weighted sum of votes after determining suitable weights for each alternative. The different weights among objects resulted in different ranking results and propose a new method of ordering in order to solve the problem of weights ranking. As a final point, the module solver imbedded in EXCEL of Microsoft Office [2003] will be applied to solve the above linear programming problems (Liu and Hai, 2005).

3. The competitive strategies of the Taiwanese SMEs for EMS

This study proposes six-step procedure for selecting the competitive strategies of the Taiwanese SMEs. They are obtained from TF which will fall into four subjective criteria that discuss and analyze SWOT of Taiwan's SMEs in the EMS. The first step is structuring the problem into a SWOT hierarchy. On the top level is the overall goal of selection competitive strategies. On the second level are the four SWOT criteria that contribute to the overall goal. The criteria (sub-criteria) for strengths (S1, S2, S3), opportunities (O1, O2, O3), weaknesses (W1, W2, W3) and threats (T1, T2, T3) are individually presented into Level 2 and 3. On the second level is that four criteria are decomposed into twelve sub-criteria under SWOT; additionally on the bottom (or fourth) level, there are five alternative competitive strategies that are to be evaluated in terms of the sub-criteria listed on the third level. These competitive strategies (OS-1, OS-2, OW-1, TS-1 and TW-1) are assessed in Level 4 and illustrated in Fig.1.

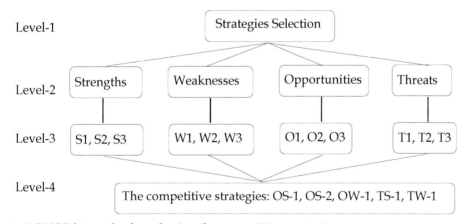

Fig. 1. A SWOT hierarchy for selecting the competitive strategies

3.1 Step 1: SWOT analysis

First of all, the author invites the eighteen certificated ISO9000 or ISO14000 auditors (or lead auditors), consists of 14 part-time and 4 full-time auditors, to organize a TF in this particular study. They are first briefed about the overall objective of the study, then specifically on the SWOT and vote-ranking methodologies. The questionnaires are used for interviewing purposes; however they mainly use a board or group decision method to determine the criteria and sub-criteria for selecting the competitive strategies. The study is to apply the internal competitive strengths to find external market opportunities. This is followed by the analysis on the organization's external competitive environment and internal operating environment. Consequently, the internal analysis is followed by the selection and implementation of strategies. Due to highly global nature of the "Green House", the requirements of EMS are also applicable for other countries in the European Union. For selecting the competitive strategies of SMEs for EMS, the TF has been mainly on the discussion of the SWOT method and problem defining after a series of revision. The strategy combination of EMS for max {strengths, opportunities} and min {weaknesses, threats}, OS-1, OS-2, OW-1, TS-1 and TW-1, is provided in Table 1.

	Strengths: +S1: Capability to execute and develop EMS certification +S2: Synergy with commerce, environmental protection and education units +S3: Possessing high level of environmental education	Weaknesses: -W1: SMEs respond slowly and difficultly for external customer requirements -W2: Some suppliers or manufacturers are unwilling to face higher environmental regulation required and seek other markets with lower quality consciousness -W3: The government's regulations of environmental protection are too loose
Opportunities: +O1: Change in customers' preferences (increase in market demand for EMS or QMS certification) +O2: Increase value-added of product +O3: Improvement in Green House and in environment	Maxi-maxi (O-S) Strategies OS-1: Extend EMS Certification effects to create high value-added markets OS-2: Involve in improving environment issues and promote company image and profits	Maxi-mini (O-W) Strategies OW-1:Change directly in manufacture preferences to create products of high environmental requirement standard
Threats: -T1: Diminishing specific market demand and profitability -T2: Government or industry restrictive practices -T3: Negative corporation image if EMS certification is abandoned	Mini-maxi (T-S) Strategies TS-1: Increase strictly government or industry environmental regular	Mini-mini (T-W) Strategies TW-1: Government impel environmental education and assistance for SMEs

Table 1. SWOT and TOWS matrixes for EMS

3.2 Step 2: priority votes of criteria and sub- criteria in SWOT

The second task is to regard these SWOT indexes as candidates that are voted by TF. The four criteria are the strength, weakness, opportunity and threat indexes and the twelve sub-criteria are S1-3, W1-3, O1-3 and T1-3 alternatively, within the SWOT. They are regarded as the selected items and expected to receive votes with respect to the related elements within the model, as shown in Table 1.

The TF illustrate the order for the four criteria and the votes for each which are shown in Table 2. Every members will vote from 1 to S, (S≤R), where R is the number of criteria or sub-criteria. They are regarded as candidates whom are to be voted by different places. Afterward, TF will list its priority votes of sub-criteria in fixed first criterion within Table 3. They were only asked to determine the order of the criteria or sub-criteria, however not the weight of each criterion or sub-criterion.

Criteria	1st	2nd	3rd	4th	Weights
Strengths	4	8	4	2	0.264
Opportunities	7	4	7	0	0.299
Weaknesses	2	0	7	9	0.174
Threats	5	6	0	7	0.263

The weights are normalized and totally equal to one.

Table 2. Priority votes of four criteria

3.3 Step 3: calculate the weights of criteria and sub- criteria in SWOT

The votes on Table 2 are used to calculate the weights of the four criteria by model (2), $R=4$, $S=4$, $n=18$ and the lowest weights of the fourth place are $\frac{1}{180}$ ($u_{r4} \geq 2/ [n*S(S+1)] =2/ [18*4(5)$ $=0.0056]$). The weights for strength, weakness, opportunity and threat at the second level are 0.884, 1.000, 0.581 and 0.882, respectively. After normalizing these data, the weights of outcome are 0.264, 0.299, 0.174 and 0.263, as it is illustrated in column 6 of Table 2, respectively. For "Strengths" in the Table 3, there are variables $R=3$, $S=3$, $n=18$ and the lowest weights of the third place are $1/108$ ($u_{r3} \geq 2/ [n*S(S+1)] =2/ [18*3(4) =0.0093]$). Similarly, the votes within Table 3 are using the same procedure in order to determine the weights of the sub-criteria. The results of the weight of sub-criteria are listed in columns 5 and 10 of Table 3.

Criteria	Votes 1st	2nd	3rd	Weights	Criteria	Votes 1st	2nd	3rd	Weights
Strengths					Opportunities				
S1	13	4	1	0.465	O1	15	2	1	0.495
S2	0	9	9	0.227	O2	0	15	3	0.258
S3	5	5	8	0.308	O3	3	1	14	0.247
Total	18	18	18		Total	18	18	18	
Weaknesses					Threats				
W1	11	7	0	0.439	T1	5	5	8	0.304
W2	3	3	12	0.258	T2	5	9	4	0.336
W3	4	8	6	0.303	T3	8	4	6	0.360
Total	18	18	18		Total	18	18	18	

The weights are normalized and totally equal to one.

Table 3. Priority votes and weights of twelve sub-criteria

3.4 Step 4: scores of competitive strategies in SWOT

The competitive strategies, OS-1, OS-2, OW-1, TS-1 and TW-1 are subjective indices that could be translated into numerical ratings using different methods, such as questionnaire, AHP or vote-ranking and so much more. TF may ask their colleagues to answer these questionnaires in order to rate the competitive strategies of sub-criteria of each SWOT. A major problem was thus, to ensure the consistency between managers and to avoid any bias creeping in. A set of standard guidelines was placed after discussions with the TF (voters). It is mainly agreed that all performance scores would be based on a nine points grade scale.

Each grade would have an adjective descriptor and an associated point score or range of point scores. The TF makes their judgment on the qualitative scale of adjectival descriptors.

Table 4 lists the example for rating the strength and opportunity indices, where the lower and upper scores are predetermined from 1-9. The strength and opportunity indices should be maximized, the least-favorable candidate is assigned the smallest value and the most-favorable candidate is assigned the largest value. On the other hand, the weakness and threat indices need to be minimized, where the least-favorable candidate is assigned the largest value and the most-favorable candidate is assigned the smallest value. The overcoming range of subjective indices is set between 1 and 9 illustrated in Table 5. Therefore, each of the competitive strategy can be awarded a 'score' from 1 to 9 on each sub-criterion.

Scores	Rules
9	Greatly conforming to market and sub-criteria of requirement, successful probability more than 90%
7	Better conforming to market and sub-criteria of requirement, successful probability about 70%
5	Conforming to market and sub-criteria of requirement, successful probability about 50%
3	Slightly conforming to market and sub-criteria of requirement, successful probability about 30%
1	Not conforming to market and sub-criteria of requirement, successful probability about 10%

Table 4. Grading different strategy scores in strength and opportunity indexes

Scores	Rules
9	Greatly overcoming sub-criteria requirement, successful probability more than 90%
7	Better overcoming sub-criteria requirement, successful probability about 70%
5	Exactly overcoming sub-criteria requirement, successful probability about 50%
3	Slightly overcoming sub-criteria requirement, successful probability about 30%
1	Not overcoming sub-criteria requirement, successful probability about 10%

Table 5. Grading different strategy scores in weakness and threat indexes

The five competitive strategies, OS-1, OS-2, OW-1, TS-1 and TW-1, by means of the highest rating were regarded as the best competitive strategies, with the rest being ranked accordingly. The competitive strategies will earn the average scores of questionnaires within Table 4 and Table 5 by TF. The average of collected scores is listed in the columns 5-9 of Table 6.

3.5 Step 5: total weighted scores of competitive strategies

This step requires the TF to assess the performance of all the competitive strategies within the twelve sub-criteria of SWOT identified as important for competitive strategies rating. Simple score sheets were provided to assist the manager to record the scores for each strategy on each of the twelve sub-criteria. An example of this strategy is shown in Table 6. In the first row of Table 6, the number 0.123 is equal to the product of the "Strength" criterion score 0.264 multiply with the S1 given value of "0.465". Moreover, the same method is applied to obtain

Assessing the SMEs' Competitive Strategies on the Impact
of Environmental Factors:A Quantitative SWOT Analysis Application

293

other results. Once the weights for sub-criteria have been determined, it is relatively easy to calculate the resulting competitive strategies rating scores.

Mathematically, the rating is equivalent to the sum of the product of each sub-criterion weight and the competitive strategy performance score. The rating value of competitive strategies is obtained by summing the products of the respective elements. The competitive strategies rating value for strategy OS-1 is obtained by summing up the products of the respective elements in columns 4 and 5 for each row; given in the final column 10, the over all total weighted scores of the row is "6.859". The rating method used in strategy OS-1, can be used to find the total scores of the other four strategies stated in columns 11-14 of Table 6. The rating value for each competitive strategy is obtained by summing the products of the respective elements in the matrix; given in the final score, the values of over all competitive strategies of OS-1, OS-2, OW-1, TS-1 and TW-1 respectively is, 6.859, 8.357, 7.532, 7.298 and 8.274 stated within the last row of Table 6. This gave a rating score for each competitive strategy, whereas the higher the rating, the better the overall performance for competitive strategy.

3.6 Step 6: assessment of competitive strategies

In the last row of Table 6, the rating value for each strategy is obtained; the final score and the ranking of competitive strategies for OS-2, TW-1, OW-1, TS-1 and OS-1 is first, second, third, fourth and fifth respectively. Even though the score of OS-2 is only higher by 0.083 than TW-1 and the score of OW-1 is higher by 0.234 than TS-1, however for both of the competitive strategies, the difference of scores will definitely change the overall final rank. These results will be regarded as sensitivity analysis for five competitive strategies.

Criteria (A)	Sub-criteria (B)		Weights (C= A×B)	Grade Strategies Scores					Weighted Strategies Scores				
				OS-1	OS-2	OW-1	TS-1	TW-1	OS-1	OS-2	OW-1	TS-1	TW-1
Strengths	S1	**0.465**	**0.123**	6.833	8.889	8.056	6.944	8.722	0.839	1.091	0.989	0.853	1.071
0.264	S2	0.227	0.060	6.944	8.944	7.611	7.278	8.500	0.416	0.536	0.456	0.436	0.509
	S3	0.308	0.081	7.056	8.833	7.556	8.611	8.611	0.574	0.718	0.614	0.700	0.700
Opportunities	O1	0.495	0.148	6.833	7.778	7.389	7.278	8.167	1.011	1.151	1.094	1.077	1.209
0.299	O2	0.258	0.077	6.944	8.000	7.611	7.389	8.000	0.536	0.617	0.587	0.570	0.617
	O3	0.247	0.074	6.778	8.111	7.778	7.500	7.944	0.501	0.599	0.574	0.554	0.587
Weaknesses	W1	0.439	0.076	6.611	7.778	7.222	6.944	7.833	0.505	0.594	0.552	0.530	0.598
0.174	W2	0.258	0.045	6.500	7.833	7.278	7.056	7.778	0.292	0.352	0.327	0.317	0.349
	W3	0.303	0.053	6.667	7.944	7.500	7.278	7.722	0.351	0.419	0.395	0.384	0.407
Threats	T1	0.304	0.080	7.056	8.611	7.278	7.000	8.444	0.564	0.688	0.582	0.560	0.675
0.263	T2	0.336	0.088	7.111	8.722	7.556	7.167	8.389	0.628	0.771	0.668	0.633	0.741
	T3	0.360	0.095	6.778	8.667	7.333	7.222	8.556	0.642	0.821	0.694	0.684	0.810
Total Weighted Scores									6.859	8.357	7.532	7.298	8.274

Table 6. The SWOT analysis of different strategies

4. Discussion

First of all, considering that the strategy OS-1 has the lowest score within the strategy analysis, most of the SMEs supposed that this strategy is quite acceptable even though there are still have some doubts present, especially on whether or not by obtaining the EMS related international standard authentication, such as ISO14000, it will certainly create a high value-added market. From a present market condition which is quite unfeasible to reflect the practical demand, frequently as a final result it is invested in fund or modification. Even though most of the customers are quite optimistic and agreed to this way of doing, however when everything is fully involved within EMS in the future, it will certainly has some affect on its capital or product selling price. Which means that at the present moment, the demand on this particular product is lacking, furthermore, it might resulted in the incapability to agree on these certain analysis by some SMEs.

Moreover, from the strategy analysis OW-1and TS-1 point of view, direct changes in manufacture preferences to create products of high environmental requirement standard has a bigger risk toward the SMEs in term of direct investment. Generally, average companies do not have certain investment planning until it has reached a deal, order placement or customer's promise in advance. Additionally, an increasingly strict government or industry environmental in carrying out this phase is facing difficulty, where presently the government mostly is using counseling method or fund assistance to encourage and urge the industry to increase its EMS ability in order to reach the low price product strategy and high level of product diversification.

Lastly, the strategy OS-2 imposes a similar way of thinking with strategy TW-1. Taiwanese SMEs apperceive the significance of EMS and also recognize the importance to survive within the diversified competing market environment, whereas they need to build up its environmental management that has to suit the EMS specification and attention. However, the investment within environmental protection for its resources and facilities requires a great amount of expenditures. Under this major investment, if the expected outcomes are unpredictable, therefore the willingness on investing within the environmental management will suffer an enormous drawback. These SMEs certainly would hope that government will work together with country resources, providing some assistance in procuring EMS needed facilities and equipments or even any related training within the environmental management scope, moreover guidance or counselling in obtaining different kinds of ISO authentic certificate will also be valuable resource.

Obviously, most people are familiar with the conflicts between environmental protection and economic development. Those who are convinced of the consequences of global warming will remain convinced, while those suspicious will remain suspicious. After all, economic development means bread, while the mankind cannot immediately appreciate the deep implications of its damage to the great nature. Therefore, politicians should be aware of the environmental implications of legal provisions and regulations. Likewise, the industry authorities, when developing new products, should consider the intangible social cost of pollution as a part of the overall cost and deal with the issue of pollution as a part of life cycle management, so that such considerations and practices will benefit our earth. In EMS, this will further our understanding of the potential poisonous substances to be produced in production, deployment and replacement stages, and will help us minimize pollution and thus contribute to environmental protection.

5. Conclusions

With the continuing development of human civilization and technology, the life cycle of any products, from production, consumption to final waste, it is involving more and more external adverse factors which bring about direct or indirect impact on the environment.

Economists said that we should stop aggravation of global warming now; and there is only one earth; therefore, be environmentally friendly.

Lastly, the competitive strategies OS-2 and TW-1 will be provided to Taiwanese SME department and industry union. The main contributions of this study are as follows:

1. The selection procedure of competitive strategies in SWOT can assist the audience to think in a very comprehensive and detailed manner, while allowing them to categorize various issues.
2. In this field, many researchers have sought to improve the different capabilities of quantitative SWOT, such as AHP, ANP or fully rank decision-making units. In this case, the vote-ranking methodology incorporated with SWOT is applied and as a result, it became the easiest and most convenient method compared to others.

The vote-ranking is presented as an approach to the problem of ranking candidates in a preferential election. The future researches had suggested that the cross-evaluation method is better off to be applied to assess candidates through peer-group, whereas one can attain a more balanced view of the weight-setting. The cross evaluation can be used to overcome the problem of maverick decision-makers. The proposed methodology can be utilized to issues of SWOT, such as AHP or ANP within this study.

6. References

Ahsen, A.V. ; Funck, D. (2001). Integrated management systems - opportunities and risks for corporate environmental protection. *Corporate Environmental Strategy* 8(2), pp. 165-176.

Chang, H.H. ; Huang, W.C. (2006). Application of a quantification SWOT analytical method. *Mathematical and Computer Modelling* 43, pp. 158-169.

Charnes, A. ; Cooper, W.W. & Rhodes, E. (1978). Measuring the efficiency of decision-making units. *European Journal of Operational Research* 2, pp. 429-444.

Cook, W.D. ; Kress, M. (1990). A data envelopment model for aggregating preference rankings. *Management Science* 36(11), pp. 1302-1310.

Cook, W.D. ; Kress, M. (1992). *Ordinal information and preference structure: decision models and applications*. Prentice Hall, New Jersey.

Dyson, R.G. (2004). Strategic development and SWOT analysis at University of Warwick. *European Journal of Operational Research* 152, pp. 631-640.

Foroughi, A.A. & Tamiz, T. (2005). An effective total ranking model for a ranked voting system. *OMEGA* 33, pp. 491-496.

Fryxell, G.E. & Szteo, A. (2002). The influence of motivations for seeking ISO 14001 certification an empirical study of ISO 14001 certified facilities in Hong Kong. *Journal of Environmental Management* 65, pp. 223-238.

Gernuks, M. ; Buchgeister, J. & Schebek, L. (2007). Assessment of environmental aspects and determination of environmental targets within environmental management systems (EMS) – development of a procedure for Volkswagen. *Journal of Cleaner Production* 15, pp. 1063-1075.

Green, R.H. ; Doyle, J.R. & Cook, W.D. (1996). Preference voting and project ranking using DEA and cross-evaluation. *European Journal of Operational Research* 90, pp. 461-472.

Hashimoto, A. (1997). A ranked voting system using a DEA/ AR exclusion model: a note. *Journal of the Operational Research* 97, 600-604.

Hashimoto, A. & Ishikawa,H. (1993). Using DEA to evaluate the state of society as measured by multiple social indicators. *Socio-Economic Planning Sciences* 27(4), pp. 257-268.

Jasch, C. (2003). The use of environment management accounting (EMA) for identifying environmental costs. *Journal of Cleaner Production* 11, pp. 667-676.

Kajanus, M. ; Kangas, M. & Kuttila, M., (2004). The use of value focused thinking and the A'WOT hybrid method in tourism management. *Tourism Management* 25, pp. 499-506.

Kuttila, M. ; Pesonen, M. ; Kangas, J. & Kajanus, M. (2000). Utilizing the analysis hierarchy process (AHP) in SWOT analysis – a hybrid method and its application to a forest-certification case. *Forest Policy and Economics* 1, pp. 41-45.

Leskinen, L.A. ; Leskinen, P. ; Kuttila, M. ; Kangas, M. & Kajanus, M. (2006). Adapting modern strategic decision support tools in the participatory strategy process- a case study of a forest research station. *Forest Policy and Economics* 8, pp. 206-216.

Liu, F.H.F. & Hai, H.L. (2005). The voting analytic hierarchy process method for selecting suppliers. The International *Journal of Production Economics* 97, pp. 308-317.

Lozano, M. & Vallés, J. (2007). An analysis of the implementation of an environmental management system in a local public administration. *Journal of Environmental Management* 82, 495-511.

Mbohwa, C. & Fukada, S. (2002). ISO 14001 certification in Zimbabwe experiences, problems and prospects. *Corporate Environmental Strategy* 9(4), pp. 427-436.

Melnyk, S.A. ; Sroufe, R.P. & Calantone, R. (2003). Assessing the impact of environmental management systems on corporate and environmental performance. *Journal of Operations Management* 21, pp. 329-351.

Noguchi, H. ; Ogawa, M. & Ishii, H. (2002). The appropriate total ranking method using DEA for multiple categorized purposes. *Journal of Computational and Applied Mathematics* 146, pp. 155-166.

Obata, T. & Ishii, H. (2003). A method for discriminating efficient candidates with ranked voting data. European Journal of *Operational Research* 151, pp. 233-237.

Paliwal, R. (2006). EIA practice in India and its evaluation using SWOT analysis. *Environmental Impact Assessment Review* 26, pp. 492-510.

Pan, J.N. (2003). A comparative study on motivation for and experience with ISO9000 and ISO14000 certification among Far Eastern countries. *Industrial Management & Data Systems* 103(8), 564-578.

Rao, P. ; Casttillo, O. ; Intal Tr, P.S. & Sajid, A. (2006). Environmental indicators for small and medium enterprises in the Philippines: An empirical research. *Journal of Cleaner Production* 14, pp. 505-515.

Rennings, K. ; Ziegler, A. ; Ankele, K. & Hoffmann, E. (2006). The influence of different characteristics of the EU environmental management and auditing scheme on technical environmental innovations and economic performance. *Ecological Economics* 57, pp. 45-59.

Tan, B. ; Lin, C. & Hung, H.C. (2003). An ISO 9001: 2000 quality information system in e-commerce environment. *Industrial Management & Data Systems* 103(9), pp. 666-676.

Terrados, J. ; Almonacid, G. & Hontoria, L. (2007). Regional energy planning through SWOT analysis and strategic planning tools: impact on renewable development. *Renewable & Sustainable Energy Reviews* 11, pp. 1275-1287.

Yüksel, İ. & Dağdeviren, M. (2007). Using the analytic network process (ANP) in a SWOT analysis – a case study for a textile firm. *Information Sciences* 177, pp. 3364-3382.

Zobel, T. ; Almroth, C. ; Bresky, J. & Burman, J-O. (2002). Identification and assessment of environmental aspects in an EMS context an approach to a new reproducible method based on LCA methodology. *Journal of Cleaner Production* 10, pp. 381-396.

15

Implementation of ISO 14000 in Luggage Manufacturing Industry: A Case Study

S. B. Jaju
G. H. Raisoni College of Engineering,
Department of Mechanical Engineering, Nagpur
India

1. Introduction

Definitions of EMS as provided by three separate documents on environmental management systems are as given below

ISO 14001: "the organizational structure, responsibilities, practices, procedures, processes and resources for implementing and maintaining environmental management"

BS 7750: "the organizational structure, responsibilities, procedures, processes and resources for implementing environmental management"

Eco-Management and Audit Scheme (EMAS): "that part of the overall management system which includes the organizational structure, responsibilities, practices, procedures, processes and resources for determining and implementing the environmental policy"

2. Development of the ISO 14000 series

The ISO 14000 family includes the ISO 14001 standard, which represents the set of standards used by various types of organizations for designing and implementing an effective environmental management system. The major objective of the ISO 14000 series of norms is "to promote more effective and efficient environmental management in organizations and to provide useful and usable tools - ones that are cost effective, system-based, and flexible and reflect the best organizations and the best organizational practices available for gathering, interpreting and communicating environmentally relevant information".

Unlike previous environmental regulations, which began with command and control approaches, later replaced with ones based on market mechanisms, ISO 14000 was based on a voluntary approach to environmental regulation. The series includes the ISO 14001 standard, which provides guidelines for the establishment or improvement of an EMS. The standard shares many common traits with its predecessor ISO 9000, the international standard of quality management, which served as a model for its internal structure and both can be implemented side by side. As with ISO 9000, ISO 14000 acts both as an internal management tool and as a way of demonstrating a company's environmental commitment to its customers and clients.

Prior to the development of the ISO 14000 series, organizations voluntarily constructed their own EMS systems, but this made comparisons of environmental effects between companies difficult and therefore the universal ISO 14000 series was developed. An EMS is defined by

ISO as: "part of the overall management system, that includes organisational structure, planning activities, responsibilities, practices, procedures, processes and resources for developing, implementing, achieving and maintaining the environmental policy'.

3. Driving forces

Environmental concerns

For a number of years preceding the introduction of a formal EMS, there was a genuine concern about its various environmental impacts. Some typical examples of impacts are:

- energy and resource usage (electricity, gas , water)
- raw material usage (paper, plates, inks, packaging, chemicals, film)
- general waste (domestic)
- recyclable waste (paper, timber, aluminum, silver, plastics)
- hazardous waste (chemical wastes, liquid effluent, air emissions)
- nuisances (noise, litter, dust, odors)
- contracted activities (transport, subcontracted printing work)
- product end use and disposal

Legal obligations

Over recent years, there have been considerable changes in environmental legislation. Every organisation wants to address its legal obligations, such as compliance with effluent discharge license parameters, or local authority planning requirements. Integrated Pollution Control licensing, for instance, will eventually oblige most industries to comply with stricter industry guidelines on pollution control, with the threat of heavy financial penalties resulting from non-compliance.

Customer pressure

Lot of pressure is from customer end that is the basic aim of any organisation. Ultimately customer should have faith in the industry that the said industry is having compliance for environmental parameters.

4. Basic principles and methodology

The fundamental principle and overall goal of the ISO 14001 standard, is the concept of continual improvement. ISO 14001 is based on the Plan-Do-Check-Act methodology, grouped into five phases that relate to Plan-Do-Check-Act; Environmental Policy, Planning, Implementation & Operation, Checking & Corrective Action and lastly Management Review.

Plan – establish objectives and processes required

Prior to implementing ISO 14001, an initial review or gap analysis of the organisation's processes and products is recommended, to assist in identifying all elements of the current operation and if possible future operations, that may interact with the environment, termed environmental aspects. Environmental aspects can include both direct, such as those used during manufacturing and indirect, such as raw materials (Martin 1998). This review assists the organisation in establishing their environmental objectives, goals and targets, which should ideally be measurable; helps with the development of control and management procedures and processes and serves to highlight any relevant legal requirements, which can then be built into the policy.

Do – implement the processes

During this stage the organisation identifies the resources required and works out those members of the organisation responsible for the EMS' implementation and control. This includes documentation of all procedures and processes; including operational and documentation control, the establishment of emergency procedures and responses, and the education of employees, to ensure they can competently implement the necessary processes and record results. Communication and participation across all levels of the organisation, especially top management is a vital part of the implementation phase, with the effectiveness of the EMS being dependant on active involvement from all employees.

Check – measure and monitor the processes and report results

During the check stage, performance is monitored and periodically measured to ensure that the organisation's environmental targets and objectives are being met (Martin 1998). In addition, internal audits are regularly conducted to ascertain whether the EMS itself is being implemented properly and whether the processes and procedures are being adequately maintained and monitored.

Act – take action to improve performance of EMS based on results

After the checking stage, a regular planned management review is conducted to ensure that the objectives of the EMS are being met, the extent to which they are being met, that communications are being appropriately managed and to evaluate changing circumstances, such as legal requirements, in order to make recommendations for further improvement of the system. These recommendations are then fed back into the planning stage to be implemented into the EMS moving forward.

5. Role of EMS

1. An assessment of the existing practices and situation of an organization.
2. A register of all environmental effects associated with the company's activities, established through an initial environmental review.
3. A list of all legislation relevant and applicable to the environmental aspects of the activities, products and services of the organization.
4. Development of a corporate environmental policy and environmental management plan
5. The setting of environmental performance objectives and targets for both current and future activities.
6. Development of environmental performance evaluation procedures.
7. Establishment of an effective environmental training program for all employees within the organization, which will raise awareness, enhance skills for dealing with environmental issues and stress compliance with relevant legislation.
8. Implementation of a system, which reliably manages the performance of the organization, for both current and future activities.
9. Documentation of the system communicated to all employees and distributed to all interested parties, especially to the public.
10. Establishment of non-conformance and corrective and preventive action procedures.

11. Regular checking, reviewing and auditing of company practices and management commitment to reflect changing conditions with a focus on continual improvement.

6. Benefits of EMS implementation

6.1 Natural
1. Clean Air, Water, Soil.
2. Prevention and/or significant reduction of pollution and waste Generation.
3. Improved health and safety of interested parties.
4. Reduction in the use of non-renewable resources.
5. Improved conservation and efficient use of natural resources.

6.2 Corporate
1. Reduced financial costs through reduction in consumption of resources and through waste minimization.
2. Reduction and/or avoidance of potential emergency situations.
3. Avoidance of incidence of non-compliance with legislation and reduction in fines and cleanup costs.
4. Reduction in the cost of gaining capital, financial backing, insurance and valuation by becoming an "environmentally friendly" organization.
5. Improved marketing advantage as a "green" operation.
6. Increased staff morale and occupational safety and health standards.
7. Improved customer, client and community relations.
8. Increased documentation, communication and feedback of environmental policies and initiatives.

7. Major requirements of ISO 14000

Following are some of the requirements of ISO 14000:
1. Environmental protection as one of the highest corporate priorities with clear assignment of responsibilities and accountabilities to all employees.
2. Compliance with all environmental laws and regulations applicable to the company's activities, products and services.
3. Ongoing communications on environmental commitment and performance with all shareholders.
4. Strategic planning that sets forth environmental performance objectives and targets, implemented through a disciplined management process.
5. Periodic performance measurement (as well as systems audits and management reviews) to achieve continual improvement wherever possible.
6. Full integration with health and safety, quality, finance, business planning and other essential management processes.
7. Focus on EMS and looks for attributes that would sustain sound environmental decision making and performance.
8. Top management commitment.
9. Third-party registration, through ISO 14001, or self-declaration for companies that meet the ISO 14000 standards. ISO 14001 includes discrete elements of environmental aspects, legal requirements, objectives and targets, environmental management program, communications, and emergency preparedness and response.

8. Stage by stage implementation of ISO 14001

First stage: commitment and policy

i.   Environmental policy

Second stage: Planning

i.   Environmental aspects
ii. Legal and other requirements
iii. Objectives and targets
iv. Environmental management program

Third stage: Implementation

i.   Structure and responsibility
ii. Training, awareness and competence
iii. Communication
iv. Environmental documentation
v.   Document control

Fourth stage: Operational control measurement and evaluation

i.   Monitoring and measurement
ii. Non-conformance and corrective and preventive action
iii. Records
iv. Environmental management system audit

Fifth stage: Review and improvement

i.   Management review

9. Benefits of developing ISO 14000 series

1. Having a single, global set of environmental management system guidance standards.
2. The development of a common, global approach to voluntary and self-directed environmental management.
3. Enhancement of the ability to measure levels of sustainability and environmental performance through auditing methods.
4. Harmonization of non-uniform standards for a range of environmental impact issues.

10. Implelementation OF ISO 14000 in luggage manufacturing industry:

The study is done for Canteen and Tools and Mould repairing.
CANTEEN: Firstly the various input to canteen are identified viz. Vegetables, spices, oil, food grains, water, LPG gas, Electricity. Output of the canteen is Food products.
The various effects of the canteen on the environment as a whole are identified

1. Used water discharged to drainage.
2. Fire in L. P. G. (Emergency).
3. Solid waste non biodegradable (Carboys, drums, containers, empty milk bags).
4. Solid waste biodegradable (spent food and vegetables).
5. Fume generation.
6. Heat loss to atmosphere.

7. Noise generation.

The complete canteen as process showing input and output as well its effects on environment are tabulated in aspect register as shown in Table I.

Each aspect is studied carefully for the following category of aspects:

1. Normal aspects: Effects of aspects are negligible.
2. Abnormal Aspects: Severe effect on environment.
3. Emergency Aspects: Nature of Aspect is emergency. Emergency prepared plan has to be there. Proper training to be given to the people for handling the emergency situations. They should be equipped with safety devices to tackle the emergency. For example: Suppose if there is a fire hazard. Whether the fire fighting equipment is there or not. If it is there then whether the people are trained to operate it and so on.

Emergency preparedness plan for every department, which will consist of the following few points:

1. Fire equipments are available or not that too in proper place.
2. Are the people trained to handle the situations?
3. Security people should be trained.
4. First aid training is to be given to all.
5. Fire equipments layout, number of fire equipments, is to be planned.
6. Emergency siren should start immediately after the fire.
7. All people should assemble at one place.

Factor rating is applied to each aspect depending on various factors. The various ratings used are

A: Occurrence

Continuous (8hours & above)/day	5
Less than 8 hours/day	4
Less than 8 hours/week	3
Less than 8 hours/month	2
Less than 8 hours/year	1

C: Significance of Impact

Causing death to human being on site/ offsite, damage to flora fauna, air, water, land (offsite).	5
Damage to flora fauna, air, water, land or hospitilisation to human being on site.	4
Damage to flora fauna, air, water, land or first aid to human being on shop	3
Damage to flora fauna, air, water, land and or first aid to human being on shop	2
Negligible impact	1

D: Controls

Controls absent	5
Controls present	4
Controls present but needs human intervention	3
Controls present no human intervention	2
Closed loop control	1

E: Frequency of Detection

Once in a year & above	5
Once in six months	4
Once in one to three months	3
Once in a week	2
Once in a day	1

F: Category of waste

Hazardous waste	5
Non-hazardous waste (High)	4
Non-hazardous waste (Low)	3
100% recycled in house or recycled from outside party for inside use	2
Negligible waste generation	1

The factor rating of impacts for each aspect is shown in Table II.

After categorisation of aspects, their impact has to be ascertained. Then whether they can be measured or not. If measured, what is the present status? Then the frequency of occurrence is to be known. Further what is the treatment given to nullify the bad effects of aspects on environment? All these analysis is depicted in Table III.

After rating and critical analysis of each aspect one should have the action plan for the aspect, which is affecting severely on environment. Meetings should be conducted to take reviews on the improvement after the implementation of action plan. The improved status to be maintained and periodic review are done to ascertain.

In the similar way study is carried out for process of **TOOL AND MOULD REPAIR** and the reports are shown in Table IV, V and VI.

11. Conclusion

With the implementation of EMS, communications concerning environmental practices were streamlined. It was possible to identify areas where utility savings existed. EMS defined roles and responsibilities towards each aspect of the process and their impacts on the environment. A systematic approach is understood to handle environmental issues in place and the overall plant cost savings coming from tracking resources and accounting for them. The EMS also provides the more intangible benefit of employee taking pride of working in the plant that is a good environmental neighbour.

Table No. I

LUGGAGE INDUSTRIES LTD.	ASPECT REGISTER DOC No. : ASP – 27	SHEET No. : 1 of 3
Dept. : Pers & Admn		ISSUE DATE : 1-08-2003
		REV No. : 00
Process :- Canteen		REV. DATE : 00

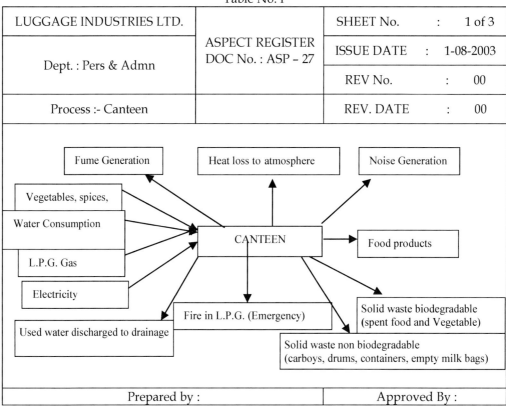

Prepared by :	Approved By :

Table No. II

LUGGAGE INDUSTRIES LTD.	ASPECT REGISTER DOC No. : ASP – 27		SHEET No. : 3 of 3			
Dept. : Pers & Admn			ISSUE DATE : 1-08-2003			
			REV No. : 00			
Process :- Canteen			REV. DATE : 00			

Sr. No.	ASPECT	FACTOR RATING						TOTAL RATING	IS IT SIGNIFICANT
		A	B	C	D	E	F		
NORMAL ASPECTS									
01	Fume Generation	5	1	1	2	5	1	15	No
02	Heat loss	5	1	1	2	5	1	15	No
03	Noise generation	-- -- -- -- -- S T A T U T O R Y -- -- -- -- --							YES
04	Discharge of used water	5	3	1	3	3	3	18	YES
05	Solid waste biodegradable spent food vegetable	5	3	1	3	3	3	18	YES
06	Solid waste non biodegradable corboys drums containers etc.	2	1	1	3	3	3	13	No
ABNORMAL ASPECTS									
07	Nil	Nil	Nil	Nil	Nil	Nil	Nil	Nil	No
EMERGENCY ASPECTS									
08	Fire in L.P.G. Storage area								YES
Prepared by :				Approved By :					

Table No. III

LUGGAGE INDUSTRIES LTD.			ASPECT REGISTER			SHEET No.	:	2 of 3		
Dept. : Pers & Admn			DOC No. : ASP – 27			ISSUE DATE	:	1-08-2003		
						REV No.	:	00		
Process :- Canteen						REV. DATE	:	00		
Sr. No.	Aspect	Impact	Measur. Indicator	Present status	Frequency of		Present treatment	Type of control	Remarks reference	
					Occur	Meas				
NORMAL ASPECTS										
01	Fume generation	Air Pollution	Not measured	Not measured	Cont.	Not Measured	Nil	Nil	Nil	
02	Heat loss	Ambient warming	Deg. Celsius	Not measurable	Cont.	Not measurable	Nil	Nil	Nil	
03	Noise generation	Noise pollution	dB	72 dB	Cont.	Negligible	Nil	Statutory	Noise level report	
04	Solid waste biodegradable spent food and vegetable	Land Contamination	Kgs/Day	45 –50 kgs	Cont.	Once in a day	Disposed to animal feeder	Self	EMP-P&A01	
05	Discharge of used water to drainage	Water pollution	K Ltrs.	Not measured	Daily	Not measured	Disposed to sewage	Self	EMP-P&A02	
06	Solid waste non-biodegradable carboys, drums, containers	Land contamination	Nos./month	18 Tins 20 Gunny bags 900 milk bags	Cont.	Once in a month	Disposed to recyclers	Self	Nil	
ABNORMAL ASPECTS										
07	Nil	Nil	Nil	Nil	Nil	Nil	Nil	Nil	Nil	
EMERGENCY ASPECTS										
08	Fire in L.P.G. storage area	Damage to flora fauna, air, land, human being & assets	-	No incident so far	-	-	-	-	Emergency preparedness & response plan	
Prepared by :						Approved By :				

Table No. IV

LUGGAGE INDUSTRIES LTD	ASPECT REGISTER DOC No. : ASP – 13	SHEET No. : 1 of 3
Dept. : Tool Room		ISSUE DATE : 1-08-2003
		REV No. : 01
Process :- Tool / Mould Repairing		REV. DATE : 18/01/2004

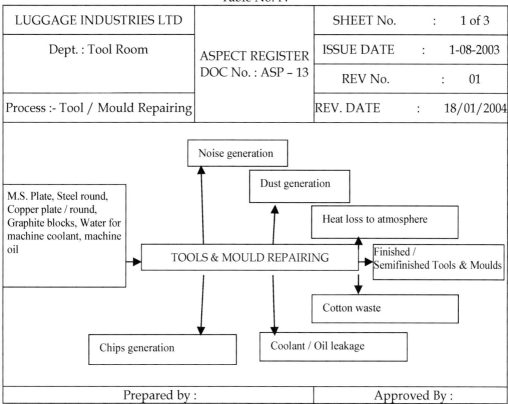

Prepared by :	Approved By :

Table No. V

LUGGAGE INDUSTRIES LTD	ASPECT REGISTER DOC No. : ASP – 13	SHEET No. : 3 of 3
Dept. : Tool Room		ISSUE DATE : 1-08-2003
		REV No. : 01
Process :- Tool/ Mould Repairing		REV. DATE : 18/01/2004

Sr. No.	ASPECT	FACTOR RATING						TOTAL RATING	IS IT SIGNIFICANT
		A	B	C	D	E	F		
NORMAL ASPECTS									
01	Noise generation	-- -- -- -- -- S T A T U T O R Y -- -- -- -- --							YES
02	Heat loss to atmosphere	5	1	1	3	5	1	16	NO
03	Dust generation	3	1	1	5	5	1	16	NO
04	Cotton waste generation	5	1	1	3	3	3	16	NO
05	Metal scrap	5	1	1	3	3	1	14	NO
06	Spent coolant	-- -- -- -- -- S T A T U T O R Y -- -- -- -- --							YES
ABNORMAL ASPECTS									
07	Oil leakage	-- -- -- -- -- S T A T U T O R Y -- -- -- -- --							YES
EMERGENCY ASPECTS									
08	Nil	Nil	Nil	Nil	Nil	Nil	Nil	Nil	nil
Prepared by :							Approved By :	

Table No. VI

LUGGAGE INDUSTRIES LTD.		ASPECT REGISTER DOC No. : ASP – 13	SHEET No.	:	2 of 3

LUGGAGE INDUSTRIES LTD.	ASPECT REGISTER DOC No. : ASP – 13	SHEET No. : 2 of 3
Dept. : Tool Room		ISSUE DATE : 1-08-2003
Dept. : Tool Room		REV No. : 01
Process :- Tool / Mould Repairing		REV. DATE : 18/01/2004

Sr. No.	Aspect	Impact	Measur. Indicator	Present status	Frequency of		Present treatment	Type of control	Remarks reference
					Occur	Meas			
				NORMAL ASPECTS					
01	Noise generation	Noise pollution	dB	80	Cont.	Once in 6 months	Nil	Statutory	Measurement of noise level report
02	Dust generation (By Grinding)	Air Pollution	Mg./Nm³	Negligible	Cont.	Not measured	Nil	Nil	Nil
03	Heat loss to atmosphere	Ambient warming	° Cent.	Max. 5°C above ambient te perature	Cont.	Not Measured	Nil	Nil	Nil
04	Cotton waste generation	Land Contamination	Kgs	Approx. 60 Kgs/Month	Cont.	Monthly	Disposed to recyclers	Nil	Monthly issue from store
05	Metal scrap	Land Contamination	Kgs.	Appr x. 30 Kgs/Month	Cont.	Monthly	Disposed to recyclers	Nil	Scrap ticket
06	Spent coolant	Water pollution	Ltrs.	Approx. 30 Ltr./Month	Cont.	Monthly	Effluent treatment plant	Statutory	Register for spent coolant to powder coating
				ABNORMAL ASPECTS					
07	Oil leakage	Land Contamination	Ltrs.	Negligible	Rare	Not Measured	Secondary containment	Statutory	Nil
				EMERGENCY ASPECTS					
08	Nil	Nil	Nil	Nil	Nil	Nil	Nil	Nil	nil

Prepared by :	Approved By :

12. References

[1] Ambika Zutshi and Amrik S. Sohal, (2000), *Environmental management systems auditing: auditors' experiences in Australia,* Int. J. Environment and Sustainable Development, Vol. 1, No. 1, pp 73-87.

[2] Subhash Babu, A., Madhu, K. and Sahani, N. (1998), *Positioning ISO 14000 standards an investigative study covering selected Indian Industries,* Proc. ISME Conference, Dec 1998, IIT Delhi, pp 286-291.

[3] Fabio Orecchini, (2000), *The ISO 14001 certification of a machine process,* Journal of Cleaner Production, Vol. 8, Issue 1, February 2000, pp 61-68.

[4] Martin, R 1998, ISO 14001 Guidance Manual, National Centre for environmental decision-making research: Technical report, viewed 23 August 2010

[5] Company manual.

Part 3

Technical Aspects of
Environmental Management

16

The Statistical Distributions of Industrial Wastes: an Analysis of the Japanese Establishment Linked Input-output Data

Hitoshi Hayami[1] and Masao Nakamura[2]
[1]*Faculty of Business and Commerce, Keio University*
[2]*Sauder School of Business, University of British Columbia*
[1]*Japan*
[2]*Canada*

1. Introduction

Both waste management policies and the economic theories underlying them model the behaviour of a representative company or establishment using. For example, toxic wastes such as dioxin are regulated by the mean emission volume standard measured per Nm^3, where the mean is estimated using data. As we will show, most establishments (particularly combustion plants) satisfy the required emission standard, while only a few exceed the regulation limit and must be checked by the authorities until regulation standards are met. But regulators must monitor all establishments incurring unnecessary costs.

Fullerton and Kinnaman 1995, among other theoretical contributions, show that taxing downstream establishments can achieve the second best policy. (See also Walls & Palmer 1998, who discuss more general market conditions.) Recent research shows that regulating downstream establishments promotes research and development by firms in upstream stages of a supply chain under certain market conditions (Calcott & Walls, 2000; Greaker & Rosendahl, 2006). These theoretical implications are important for policy making about how to design a tax system, but these theories also assume a typical producer and the regulation standard with respect to their mean emissions of waste materials. In practice, however, even though the coefficients of variation for the distributions of heavy metals in fly ash found in municipal solid waste are known to reach 50% (Nakamura et al., 1997), little statistical evidence in the published literature exists on the variation in industrial establishments' waste generation and reuse-recycling per unit production, which is basic information required for economic and ecological design and general policy decisions.

In this paper we fill this gap in the literature and show the distributions of generation rates for various types of wastes and by-products in the production processes of establishments in Japanese manufacturing industries. We use the METI survey data (Survey on the Industrial Waste and By-Products, Japanese Ministry of Economy, Trade and Industry, 2005 and 2006). This survey gives the amounts of 37 types of industrial wastes generated for four different levels of the production processes (generation, intermediate reduction, reuse-recycle, and disposal to landfill) at 5048 establishments.[1]

---

[1] See the Clean Japan Center (2005 and 2006) for details of this survey data.

We have linked the METI survey data with the Japanese Input-Output (I-O) table. Using this linked data and the data on energy/CO_2 requirements in industrial waste treatment, we are able to calculate the induced amounts of industrial wastes.[2] For example, waste oil and waste plastic are generated in large quantities at 3080 and 3694 establishments, respectively. Estimated amounts of waste oil and waste plastic generated range, respectively, between 0 and 2.50 and between 0 and 2.11 (metric) tonnes per million yen of output. On the other hand, waste ferroalloy slag is produced at only 11 establishments, and its quantity ranges from 5.8 to 64.6 tonnes per million yen of output. We estimate that production of every car with a 2000cc engine or its equivalent induces, for example, 0.051 tonnes of all types of wastes combined in hot rolling processes and 0.677 tonnes of all types of wastes combined in iron steel making in upstream production activities. We estimate that a 2000cc equivalent automobile production generates 1.49 tonnes of all types of wastes combined. We believe that these averages and the distributions for waste generation rates along a production supply chain provide (currently unused) useful information for policy makers for further reductions in the generation of waste materials.

2. Using the input-output analysis for evaluating waste management policies

2.1 Economic input-output-LCA: the theoretical background

The input-output analysis is a powerful tool to evaluate environmental impacts within an interdependent economic system (Leontief 1970, Baumol and Wolff 1994). When production of a final product requires intermediate goods (e.g. parts), inter-industry effects along a supply chain generate various wastes in stages of the life cycle of the final product.

The input-output (I-O) table is like a recipe of all economic activities for a national economy. Each column describes all the inputs used for an immediate economic activity, such as producing an automobile, supplying services such as education. It covers all economic activities and I-O relations are described in monetary terms. Recently publicly available I-O tables have been applied to the Economic Input-Output Life Cycle Assessment (EIO-LCA) (Hendrickson et al., 2006; Suh, 2010). Eiolca.net summarizes limitations of EIO-LCA compared to Process-Based LCA.

One such limitation that EIO-LCA is difficult to apply to an open economy is overcome by using the methods given by us (Hayami & Nakamura, 2007). The most apparent disadvantage of EIO-LCA is that product assessments contain aggregate data containing uncertainty as Eiolca.net describes. Assume there are n commodities (including services) in an economy, each of which is an input for production of other commodities. A typical producer k produces output $x_j^{(k)}$ of j-th commodity, which requires as inputs $X_{ij}^{(k)}$, where $i=1,2,...,n$. Governments provide the official I-O table with aggregate figures for all producers of j-th commodity $x_j=\sum_{k=1}^{mj}x_i^{(k)}$, where m_j is the number of producers of the j-th commodity. The same aggregation procedure is applied to inputs as follows: $X_{ij}=\sum_{k=1}^{mj} X_{ij}^{(k)}$. EIO-LCA assumes that matrix of input coefficients A_{ij} defined below is stable and represents a typical producer's activity.

$$A_{ij} = X_{ij}/x_j = \sum_{k=1}^{mj} X_{ij}^{(k)} \Big/ \sum_{k=1}^{mj} x_j^{(k)} \qquad i,j = 1,2,...,n \qquad (1)$$

---

[2] Induced amounts of output mean the amounts of output generated by upper (supplier) stages of a production supply chain in response to the production activities undertaken at downstream establishments.

But these input coefficients A_{ij} are different from producer k's input coefficients A_{ij}

$$A_{ij}^{(k)} = X_{ij}^{(k)} / x_j^{(k)} \qquad i,j = 1,2,\ldots,n \text{ and } \quad k = 1,2,\ldots,m_j \qquad (2)$$

Similarly, by applying EIO-LCA to waste management with the same assumptions made above, we get the amount of waste i generated in producing output x_j (we consider 37 waste materials as defined below):

$$W_{ij} = Waste_{ij} / x_j = \sum_{k=1}^{mj} W_{ij}^{(k)} / \sum_{k=1}^{mj} x_j^{(k)} \qquad i = 1,2,\ldots,37 \quad j = 1,2,\ldots,n \qquad (3)$$

Similarly, producer (k) generates i-th waste producing the j-th product:

$$W_{ij}^{(k)} = Waste_{ij}^{(k)} / x_j^{(k)} \qquad i = 1,2,\ldots,37 \; , \; j = 1,2,\ldots,n \text{ and } \quad k = 1,2,\ldots,m_j \qquad (4)$$

Japan Ministry of Economy, Trade and Industry (METI) conducts an annual survey that reports the amounts of 37 types of wastes observed in 4 stages: amounts generated by final production, $W_{ij}^{(k)}$; amounts of reduction in intermediate steps of production, $V_{ij}^{(k)}$; amounts recycled, $U_{ij}^{(k)}$; and amounts sent for landfill, $T_{ij}^{(k)}$.[3] The most important assumption in our I-O analysis is that input coefficients and waste coefficient per output remain constant over time. If we can show empirically that these coefficients have narrow bell shape distributions, then the relative stability of these coefficients follows. In this paper, we will show using our data how the coefficients of waste generation $W_{ij}^{(k)}$ distribute.

Using input coefficients, A_{ij}, we can calculate the demand for goods made in stages of upstream sectors of a supply chain. Unit production of j-th sector output induces production of i-th sector whose output is given by A_{ij}. Similarly production of A_{ij} induces production of $A_{ki} A_{ij}$ in k-th sector. Repeating this, we can obtain output induced for any stage in upstream portions of a supply chain. Formally, multiplication of the I-O coefficients matrix A from left gives us induced output for all relevant goods and services in the immediate upstream stage of a supply chain.

$$f, \; Af, \; A^2 f, \; \cdots \qquad (5)$$

where f is a vector of demands for final goods and services

By multiplying production output for final production (downstream) stage and subsequent upstream stages $(f, Af, \ldots)$ by waste generation matrix W, we obtain the amounts of waste generated in the corresponding stages of a supply chain: $Wf, WAf, WA^2f, \ldots$.

2.2 Construction of a linked data set

We briefly describe the procedure we used to link the Wastes and By-products Survey (WBS) data to the I-O table. We first note that the definition of a sector is different between the two data sets. WBS is based on the Japan Standard Industry Classification (JSIC) system,

---

[3] $V_{ij}^{(k)}$ is defined as: $V_{ij}^{(k)} = Intermediate \; Reduction/Waste \; Generated \; (Waste_{ij}^{(k)})$; and $U_{ij}^{(k)}$ and $T_{ij}^{(k)}$ are similarly defined. The denominator is the amount of waste generated, rather than production output. The waste generated is measured at the gate of an industrial process. Generated wastes are reduced (sludge dewatering), recycled/reused, and finally disposed of (mainly by landfill). Waste reduction is often undertaken in production processes, for example, for reducing the failure rate (or increasing yields) for the processes.

but the I-O table uses its own more detailed classification system so that the stability of I-O coefficients over time is preserved. JSIC codes are divided into one or more of 401 I-O sectors, using the allocation matrix given in the appendix tables of the I-O table. This allocation method depends on the sales figures reported for different products of each establishment in WBS. One difficulty we encountered was for the steel industry sector. The steel industry in the I-O table is divided into 13 sectors and two related sectors (coal products and self power generation). Many of these I-O sectors belong to a single establishment in WBS because of their continuous casting production, and there are no sales figures reported on WBS for transactions for these I-O sector goods since these transactions occur within the same establishment. To properly allocate output of steel industry establishments in WBS among relevant I-O sectors, we have collected needed information by interviewing the Japan Iron and Steel Federation and the Nippon Slag Association. We then modified the allocation table to reflect our information.

Secondly, in order to obtain the total amounts of industrial wastes in Japan, we multiplied the amounts derived from WBS by the proportionality constant since WBS is a survey and does not cover all Japanese establishments. The proportionality constant for each sector was obtained by comparing sales figures for the sector from the Census of Manufacturers data and WBS. Sectors of these two data sets are comparable since both use the JSIC system to define their sectors.

Table 1 lists 37 types of industrial wastes discussed in this paper. Industrial wastes in Japan are classified into (1)37 types given in Table 1 and (2)especially regulated industrial wastes. Special industrial wastes in the latter category (2) are highly hazardous and include material contaminated with PCB, asbestos, strong acid with pH less than 2, strong alkali with pH higher than 12.5, highly inflammable waste oil and infectious wastes. WBS excludes wastes in category (2) that need to be treated separately. Industrial wastes other than those in category (2) include certain toxic substances (e.g. heavy metals, Pb, Cd) that must be treated properly.

For each establishment and each type of waste, the following material balance equation must hold:

$$Waste_{ij}^{(k)} = W_{ij}^{(k)} x_{j}^{(k)} \text{ and } 1 = V_{ij}^{(k)} + U_{ij}^{(k)} + T_{ij}^{(k)} \quad i=1,...,37 \,; j=1,...,401, \text{ and } k=1,...,5048 \quad (6)$$

All wastes are measured by weight in metric tonnes, and output $x_j^{(k)}$ is measured in monetary unit (in 1 million yen).

3. The estimated results

3.1 Distributions of unit waste generation rates

The first objective of this paper is to estimate the statistical distributions of waste generation rates among establishments.

Table 2 presents descriptive statistics for these waste generation rates, $W_{ij}^{(k)}/x_j^{(k)}$, for waste of type i for establishment k in sector j. The number of observations (Nobs) denotes the number of establishment with non-zero production, $x_j^{(k)}>0$. Waste plastics other than synthetic rubber have the largest number of observations, which means waste plastics are the most common industrial waste. For all industrial wastes except waste animal-solidified, the sample mean is larger than the median, and the maximum value is far larger than the sample mean. This means that the distributions of unit waste generation rates W/x are asymmetric to left, with a few smaller values occur with very high frequencies and a long tail for large values.

JSIC: 0110	Cinders other than coal	0111	Coal cinders
0210	Inorganic sludge other than polishing sand	0211	Inorganic sludge of polishing sand
022	Organic sludge	0230	Organic-inorganic mixed sludge other than polishing sand
0231	Organic-inorganic mixed sludge of polishing sand	031	Waste oil other than chlorinated solvent waste
032	Waste oil chlorinated solvent waste	040	Used acidic liquid
050	Waste alkali	061	Waste plastics other than synthetic rubber
062	Waste plastics synthetic rubber	070	Wastepaper
080	Chips and sawdust	090	Waste textile
100	Animal and vegetable remnants	101	Waste animal-solidified
110	Rubber waste	121	Scrap iron
122	Non-ferrous metal scrap	131	Scrap glass
132	Clay, porcelain, ceramic scrap	133	Scrap slab concrete
141	Waste moulding sands	1420	Slag other than steel, ferroalloy, and copper
1421	Iron-steel slag	1422	Ferroalloy slag
1423	Copper slag	1430	Slag other than aluminum dross
1431	Aluminum dross	150	Demolition debris
160	Animal manure	170	Animal carcasses
1800	Soot and dust other than coal ash	1810	Soot and dust flay ash
190	Processed material for disposal		

Table 1. 37 waste materials reported in the Wastes and By-Products Survey (WBS)

Waste	Nobs	Mean	Median	Max	SD
cinders other than coal	306	0.137	0.002	20.524	1.204
coal cinders	50	0.038	0.003	0.957	0.141
inorganic sludge excl. polishing sand	1815	0.091	0.006	25.744	0.905
inorganic sludge polishing sand	52	0.157	0.003	6.453	0.893
organic sludge	986	0.268	0.007	47.229	2.082
organic and inorganic mixed sludge	776	0.049	0.005	1.583	0.165
mixed sludge polishing sand	18	0.171	0.003	2.829	0.664
waste oil excl. chlorinated solvent waste	3080	0.019	0.002	2.495	0.090
waste oil chlorinated solvent waste	303	0.018	0.001	1.425	0.099
used acidic liquid	1242	0.153	0.002	50.131	1.738
waste alkali	1184	0.045	0.002	2.937	0.192
waste plastics excl. synthetic rubber	3694	0.027	0.005	2.114	0.080
waste plastics synthetic rubber	282	0.038	0.005	0.610	0.071
wastepaper	2612	0.069	0.005	2.631	0.244
chips and sawdust	2089	0.035	0.002	5.796	0.295

waste textile	261	0.033	0.001	5.898	0.366
animal and vegetable remnants	443	0.103	0.002	3.109	0.309
waste animal-solidified	2	1.174	1.174	2.230	1.494
lubber waste	61	0.017	0.000	0.280	0.051
scrap iron	3037	0.066	0.008	5.991	0.233
non-ferrous metal scrap	1464	0.017	0.002	0.561	0.050
scrap glass	1492	0.012	0.000	3.612	0.140
clay, porcelain, ceramic scrap	620	0.030	0.001	3.319	0.195
scrap slab concrete	8	0.687	0.008	4.733	1.653
waste moulding sands	214	0.493	0.195	4.326	0.708
slag excl. steel, ferroalloy, and copper	74	0.316	0.052	7.561	0.966
iron-steel slag	111	1.859	1.291	22.222	2.678
ferroalloy slag	11	11.191	3.956	64.592	19.683
copper slag	17	3.479	0.050	23.219	7.228
slag other than aluminum dross	192	0.193	0.038	4.485	0.527
aluminum dross	50	0.144	0.058	1.825	0.277
demolition debris	303	0.077	0.001	19.809	1.139
animal manure	6	0.001	0.000	0.003	0.001
animal carcasses	12	0.003	0.000	0.017	0.006
soot and dust excl. coal ash	434	0.160	0.008	3.462	0.354
soot and dust fly ash	46	0.067	0.032	0.534	0.109
processed material for disposal of industrial waste	119	0.007	0.001	0.170	0.020

Table 2. Descriptive Statistics for the unit waste generation rate W/x in 2006

Several typical shapes of statistical distributions are shown in Figures 1a and 1b. Figure 1a shows the distributions for waste moulding sands and iron and steel slag. Iron and steel slag does not have a large distance between the mean and the median, but it has a large maximum, 22.22 tonnes per 1 million yen, which is 12 times as large as the mean, 1.859 tonnes per 1 million yen. Standard deviation (SD) is larger than the mean, and the coefficient of variation is 1.44. Figure 1b shows two of common types of distributions for W/x for wastepaper and waste plastics, which concentrate around 0. Both have the median of 0.005 tonnes per 1 million yen of production. But the mean is 0.069 tonnes for wastepaper and 0.027 for waste plastics, with a maximum, 2.631 for wastepaper, and 2.114 for waste plastics. Extremely large maximum values may reflect irregular production and inventory practices at some establishments.

Figure 2 shows that the distributions for recycling rates for inorganic sludge and polishing sand. Both figures have concentrations around 0 and 1. This means that establishments face an all or nothing choice. Once a waste material is recycled, the establishment should choose recycling all wastes. This result follows because of the high initial cost of recycling equipment and the availability of outsourcing. But outsourcing is not available if the establishment location is far from the center of the recycling industry. As a result, the final disposal method (landfill here) is also highly concentrated around 0 and 1, as in Figure 3.

We have tried statistical fitting of these empirical distributions derived here with only a partial success. First, we tried to use the Gamma distribution to fit observed distributions for unit generation rate, *W/x*. But only 7 out of 37 distributions for industrial waste have been found not to be significantly different from the Gamma distribution. An appropriate theoretical distribution to fit the empirical distributions for recycling ratio, *U/W*, is the Beta distribution since recycling rations range between 0 and1. But our test of the goodness of fit rejected the Beta distribution for all cases.

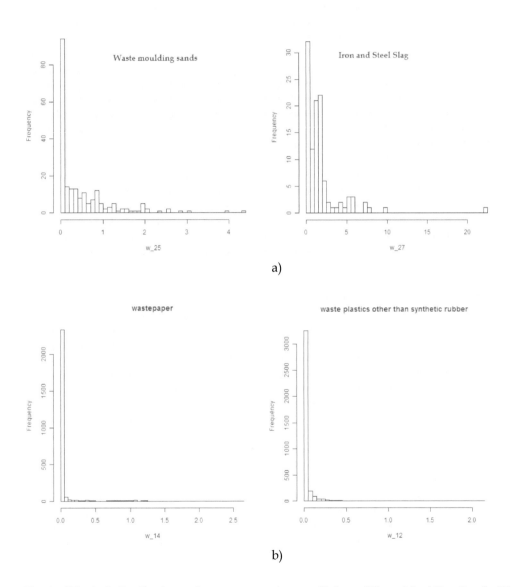

Fig. 1. a)Typical distributions of waste generation coefficients: Waste Moulding Sands (214 establishments and Iron and Steel Slag (111 establishments), b) Typical distributions of waste generation coefficients: Wastepaper (2612 establishments), and Waste plastics other than synthetic rubber (3614 establishments)

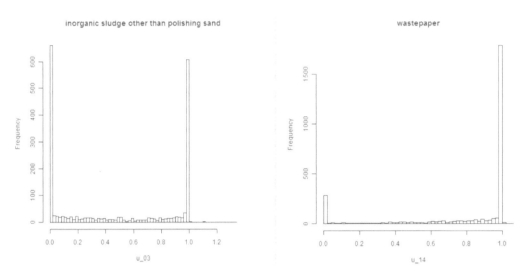

Fig. 2. Typical distributions of recycling rates: Inorganic sludge other than polishing sand (1815 establishments), and Wastepaper (2612 establishments)

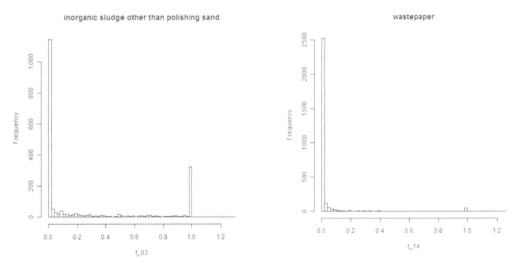

Fig. 3. Typical distributions of landfill rates: Inorganic sludge other than polishing sand of 1815 establishments (left), and wastepaper of 2612 establishments (right)

Bootstrap resampling can calculate confidence intervals for the unit waste generation rate, W/x, from estimated empirical distributions. Table 3 shows simulated confidence intervals and the mean. The empirical distribution of $W_{ij}^{(k)}/x_j^{(k)}$ used is based on observations from WBS 2005 and 2006. We used as re-sampling size 5000 for non-parametric estimation. The simulated mean uses weighs of output and our results correspond to unit waste generating rate W/x.[4] We find that six out of seven wastes show the same statistical characteristics: (1)the median is smaller than the mean; and (2)the distributions have a long tail. But iron-steel slag (193 observations) has a nearly symmetric distribution as shown in Figure 4a. According to the central limit theorem, the distribution of a sample mean with a finite variance converges to the normal distribution. But our statistical test of the goodness of fit does not support gamma or normal distributions. The convergence in distribution to the normal distribution is not seen for distributions of other wastes either as shown in Figure 4b. The distribution for a positive random variable becomes exponential at the maximum entropy; in the present case a statistical test rejects the exponential distribution also.

	2.50%	5%	Median	95%	97.50%	Mean
Inorganic sludge	0.0073	0.0089	0.0343	0.2271	0.5347	0.0887
Sludge of polishing sand	0.0055	0.0071	0.0396	1.0490	1.1367	0.1888
Waste plastics	0.0062	0.0074	0.0227	0.0822	0.1100	0.0322
Waste paper	0.0024	0.0029	0.0156	0.4156	0.5044	0.0714
Scrap iron	0.0097	0.0119	0.0431	0.1666	0.2272	0.0623
Scrap glass	0.0001	0.0001	0.0007	0.0292	0.0822	0.0110
Iron-steel slag	1.4132	1.4787	1.9442	2.6046	2.7613	1.9810

Table 3. Simulated confidence intervals and the mean for unit waste generation rate W/x

Results for the distributions of the recycling rate using the same procedure as before are given in Table 4 and Figures 5a and 5b. Compared to distributions for the waste generation rates, distributions for the recycling rates are nearly symmetric. And the figures are clearly different from those given in Figure 2 for population the distributions (histograms) of the waste generation rate. This difference arises because, in case of distributions for recycling rates, there is the effect of aggregation of recycling rates. The sample mean is almost the same value as the sample median in Table 4. We can conclude that, for the distributions for recycling rates, U/W, for all sectors, observed values are close to both the mean and median of the simulated value and their confidence intervals are symmetric.

These results on the distributions of unit waste generation rate W/x and recycling rate U/W imply that the potential problems in policy making from assuming the representative (average) waste management activity come mostly from the distributions for unit waste generation rates W/x. The mean assumed in theory does not always reflect the typical intensity of waste generation. It also means that regulations based on the mean of a representative establishment does not always give effective regulations to the majority of establishments. Most of the establishments can clear the regulation standard, because the standard is based on the mean of the distribution. But as we have shown, the mean does not capture the essential property of the distributions underlying the waste generation rate.

---

[4] This is because $W_{ij} = \dfrac{\sum_k Waste_{ij}^{(k)}}{\sum_k x_j^{(k)}} = \sum_k \left(\dfrac{x_j^{(k)}}{x_j} \right) \left(\dfrac{Waste_{ij}^{(k)}}{x_j^{(k)}} \right) = \sum_k \left(\dfrac{x_j^{(k)}}{x_j} \right) W_{ij}^{(k)}$, generating Wij(k) from the

empirical distribution of Wij(k) and taking the weighted average gives Wij, which the Input-Output calculation uses.

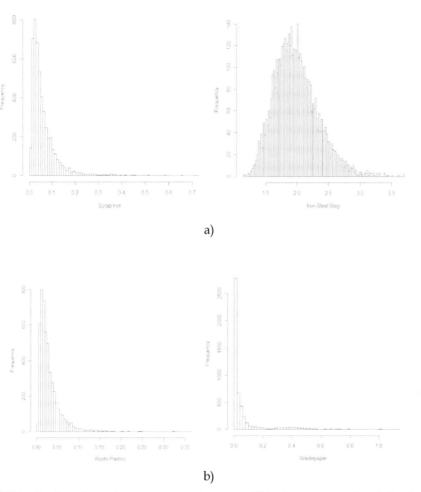

Fig. 4. a) Distributions for unit waste generation rates, W/x, (bootstrapped weighted mean): Scrap Iron (left) and Iron-Steel Slag (right) b) Distributions for unit waste generation rates, W/x, (bootstrapped weighted mean): Waste plastics (left) and Wastepaper (right)

	2.50%	5%	Median	95%	97.50%	Mean
Inorganic sludge	0.398	0.414	0.513	0.609	0.626	0.513
Sludge of polishing sand	0.158	0.212	0.513	0.825	0.861	0.513
Waste plastics	0.546	0.552	0.584	0.616	0.622	0.584
Waste paper	0.730	0.741	0.791	0.831	0.837	0.789
Scrap iron	0.894	0.905	0.953	0.974	0.977	0.949
Scrap glass	0.436	0.480	0.677	0.858	0.886	0.679
Iron-steel slag	0.798	0.822	0.920	0.979	0.984	0.913

Table 4. Simulated confidence interval and mean of the recycling rate U/W

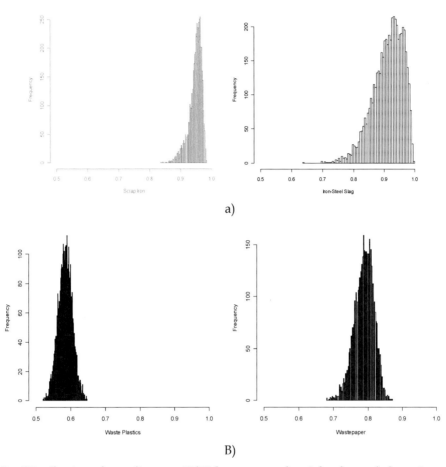

Fig. 5 a. Distribution of recycling rate U/W (bootstrapped weighted mean): Scrap Iron (left), and Iron-Steel Slag (right)b. Distribution of recycling rate U/W (bootstrapped weighted mean): Waste plastics (left), and Wastepaper (right)

3.2 Upstream waste generation: Calculation from the input-output analysis

The second objective of this paper is to estimate the amounts of waste generated in various stages of production along a supply chain, starting from downstream production the final product to upstream production of supplies. We us the I-O table linked to the WBS data set explained in Section 2.1 above. Tables 5a and 5b, respectively, describe the total amounts of wastes generated average production supply chains for cellular phones and passenger car production in Japan in 2000. In both cases, pig iron is the most significant contributor of industrial waste. This is because production of pig iron generates heavy wastes such as iron-steel slag. The second most significant contributor is electricity for cell phones and passenger car final assembly for passenger cars. The total amounts of wastes generated are about 410 thousand tonnes for cellular phones and over 9 million tonnes for passenger car production. The cellular phone assembly sector generates relatively small amounts of wastes but the passenger car assembly sector generates large amounts of wastes.

One of the most important wastes generated in producing pig iron is iron-steel slag, whose unit generation rate distributes in a rather narrow range, has a symmetric distribution as shown in Figure 4a and its variance is smaller compared to other wastes generated in any other sectors. Unit waste generation rate for iron and steel slag lies between 1.4132 and 2.7613 at a 95% level (Table 3).

Cellular phone production supply chain in Japan, 2000: final assembly and associated indirect (induced) stages of production by upstream suppliers	Total amounts of wastes and by-products generated in stages of a supply chain (in tonnes)
Pig iron	44,620
Electricity	42,440
Other electronic components	35,617
Copper	26,882
Plastic products	22,913
Crude steel (converters)	18,306
Paper	17,331
Cellular phone final assembly (direct stage)	*13,434*
Printing, plate making and book binding	13,367
Cyclic intermediates	12,002
Thermoplastics resins	9,258
Reuse and recycling	8,043
Aliphatic intermediates	7,925
Crude steel (electric furnaces)	7,782
Paperboard	6,832
Hot rolled steel	6,731
Cold-finished steel	6,151
Corrugated card board boxes	5,437
Petrochemical basic products	5,092
Lead and zinc (inc. regenerated lead)	4,490
Pulp	3,768
Other non-ferrous metals	3,696
Ferro alloys	3,621
Liquid crystal element	3,344
Integrated circuits	3,297
Other industrial inorganic chemicals	2,922
Iron and steel shearing and slitting	2,891
Electric wires and cables	2,802
Corrugated cardboard	2,791
Other metal products	2,601
Direct (final assembly of cell phones)	*13,433*
Total (all stages of production supply chain combined)	*410,713*

Table 5a. Generated wastes and by-products induced by cellular phone production

Passenger car production supply chain in Japan, 2000: final assembly and associated indirect (induced) stages of production by upstream suppliers	Total amounts of wastes and by-products generated in stages of a supply chain (in tonnes)
Pig iron	1,822,777
Passenger car final assembly (direct stage)	*1,486,409*
Crude steel (converters)	835,245
Motor vehicle parts and accessories	766,708
Electricity	422,843
Crude steel (electric furnaces)	365,982
Hot rolled steel	307,681
Internal combustion engines for motor vehicles and parts	276,001
Motor vehicle bodies	235,853
Cold-finished steel	200,976
Cast and forged materials (iron)	198,766
Ferro alloys	173,293
Coated steel	147,778
Reuse and recycling	132,619
Plastic products	120,871
Sheet glass and safety glass	108,440
Paper	89,860
Copper	84,560
Cyclic intermediates	81,456
Printing, plate making and book binding	70,531
Aliphatic intermediates	57,100
Thermoplastics resins	55,511
Synthetic rubber	46,305
Non-ferrous metal castings and forgings	44,044
Paperboard	39,111
Petrochemical basic products	37,843
Iron and steel shearing and slitting	37,178
Other metal products	37,135
Electrical equipment for internal combustion engines	36,679
Steel pipes and tubes	33,723
Direct (final assembly of passenger cars)	*1,486,409*
Total (all stages of production supply chain combined)	*9,090,400*

Table 5b. Generated wastes and by-products by Passenger Car production

Electricity sector also generates a significant amount of waste material, fly ash. The distribution for its unit waste generation rate is shown in Figure 6, with its 95% confidence interval (0.040, 0.110). Another waste, ferroalloy slag is generated by production supply chain stages for both cell phones and passenger cars. Its unit waste generation rate has a rather irregular distribution as shown in Figure 6, with its 95% confidence interval being very wide and given by (2.47, 34.96). This suggests that waste management policies based on point estimates for the unit waste generation rate for ferroalloy waste may lead to quite erroneous implications in practice.

We have shown that unit waste generation rates for various wastes generated by production supply chains distribute in different manners, sometimes with large variances and asymmetric ways. This means serious limitations about the accuracy of policy decision making relying on point estimates for the waste generation by production supply chains as we do in EIO-LCA and other types of life cycle analyses.

Given this limitation in mind, we may still be able to use information on waste generation in upstream production stages. Table 6 shows the total amounts of all wastes combined and amounts of CO_2 emissions in the final (direct) assembly stage, a few upstream stages and all stages combined of the average production supply chain for passenger cars with 2000cc engines. Table 6 gives information about the stages which generate more waste than others. Generally waste materials tend to be generated evenly along stages of a supply chain while CO_2 emissions tend to be generated more unevenly and fluctuate widely along stages of a supply chain. From policy perspectives, we conclude that application of production process LCA is more difficult for CO_2 emissions than for generation of the 37 waste materials.

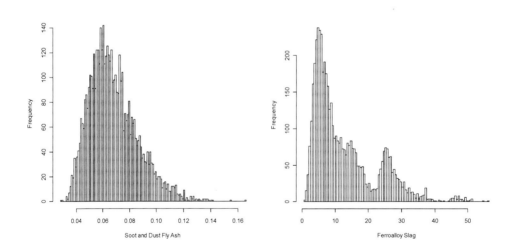

Fig. 6. Distribution of the unit waste generation rate W/x (bootstrapped weighted mean): Fly ash (left) and ferroalloy slag (right)

All wastes combined (summed in weight)	Each Stage (in tonnes)	Cumulative (in tonnes)	Ratio
direct stage (final assembly)	0.244	0.244	0.164
1st indirect stage	0.263	0.507	0.340
2nd indirect	0.226	0.733	0.491
3rd indirect	0.255	0.988	0.662
4th indirect	0.232	1.219	0.817
……	……	……	…..
Total (all stages combined)		1.493	1

CO_2 emissions	Each Stage (in tonnes)	Cumulative (in tonnes)	Ratio
Direct	0.108	0.108	0.020
1st Indirect	0.707	0.814	0.155
2nd Indirect	1.206	2.020	0.384
3rd Indirect	1.152	3.172	0.602
4th Indirect	0.897	4.069	0.773
……	…..	…..	…..
Total		5.266	1

Table 6. Total wastes combines and CO_2 generated by stages of the average production supply chain in Japan: passenger cars with 2000cc engines

4. Conclusion

Using the datasets that recently became available, we have obtained empirical distributions for generation, recycling and landfill rates for the 37 types of waste materials that are generated in the production processes of Japanese manufacturing establishments. Some of the statistics reported are for the total amounts of all the wastes combined to save space. Many empirical distributions obtained are not symmetric and have a long tail with the mean much larger than the median, making it inappropriate for policy decision making based on the mean generation rates. For example, if the regulation level is set at the industry mean, it is likely that most establishments satisfy the regulation level without efforts while a few large violators exceed the level by a big margin. In such a case it is more cost effective to set the regulation standard at a level much higher than the mean, thus saving the monitoring costs at most establishments while spending efforts to identify the few violators.

In the second part of the paper we have shown how to estimate the amounts of wastes generated along stages of the average production supply chain and then given estimates for production processes of cellular phones and passenger cars. We have repeated this for emissions of carbon dioxide. In this supply chain analysis, we have shown that, given the large amounts of wastes generated in stages of upstream production supply chains, it is misleading to formulate waste management policies based only on the wastes generated in the final demand stages of supply chains. Our estimation results suggest that, in setting waste management policies, policy makers need to consider (1)not only the wastes generated from the final assembly stage but also the wastes generated from upstream stages of production supply chains and (2)such policies need to have different regulation standards for upstream stages depending on the final sector product and also the waste being considered to be regulated. For example, we have found that the amounts of CO_2 emissions vary significantly from one stage to another of the Japanese production supply chain for passenger cars.

5. Acknowledgments

This research was in part supported by the Keio University Fukuzawa Fund and the Social Sciences and Humanities Research Council of Canada.

6. Endnotes

An earlier version of this paper was presented at the 18th International Input-Output Association Conference held at the University of Sydney in Australia, June 20-25, 2010. Preparation of the datasets used was done using Programming Language Pyhon 2.7 and statistical analyses were done using R 2.12.1. Further details are available by e-mailing: hayami@sanken.keio.ac.jp.

7. References

Baumol, W.J. & Wolff, E.N. (1994) A Key Role for Input-Output Analysis in Policy Design, Vol.24, 93-113.

Calcott, P. & Walls, M. (2000) Can Downstream Waste Disposal Policies Encourage Upstream „Design for Environment"? American Economic Review, Vol.90, 233-237.

The Clean Japan Center (2005 and 2006) CJC-0708 and CJC-0809. Available from http://www.cjc.or.jp/.

Eiocla.net www.eiocla.nt, Carnegie Mellon.

Fullerton, D. & Kinnaman, T.C. (1995) Garbage, Recycling, and Illicit Burning or Dumping, *Journal of Environmental Economics and Management*, Vol.29, 78-91.

Greaker, M. & Rosendahl, K.E. (2008) Environmental Policy with Upstream Pollution Abatement Technology Firms, *Journal of Environmental Economics and Management*, Vol.56,246-259.

Hayami, H. & Nakamura, M. (2007) Greenhouse gas emissions in Canada and Japan: Sector-specific estimates and managerial and economic implications. *Journal of Environmental Management*, Vol. 85, 371-392.

Hendrickson, C. T.; Lave, L. B. & Matthews, H. S. (2006). *Environmental Life Cycle Assessment of Goods and Services: An Input-Output Approach*, Resources for the Future Press, ISBN-13 978-1933115245, Washington DC, USA.

Japan Ministry of Economy, Trade and Industry (METI) (2005 and 2006) the Waste and By-Products Surveys on Establishments („Haikibutsu-Fukusanbutsu Hasseijoukyo-tou no Chosa").

Japan Ministry of Internal Affairs and Communications (2000 and 2005) *The Input Output Tables.* Available from http://www.go.jp/

Leontief, W. (1970) Environmental Repercussions and the Economic Structure: An Input-Output Approach, *Review of Economics and Statistics*, Vol.52, No.3, 262-271.

Nakamura, K.; Kinoshita, S. & Takatsuki, H. (1996) The Origin and Behavior of Lead, Cadmiun, and Antimony in MSW Incinerator, *Waste Management*, Vol.16 No.5/6, 509-517.

Suh, S., editor (2010) *Handbook of Input-Output Economics in Industrial Ecology*, Springer, ISBN-13 978-1402061547, New York, USA.

Walls, M. & Palmer, K. (2001) Upstream Pollution, Downstream Waste Disposal, and the Design of Comprehensive Environmental Policies, *Journal of Environmental Economics and Management*, Vol. 41, 94-108.

17

The Effects of Paper Recycling and its Environmental Impact

Iveta Čabalová, František Kačík, Anton Geffert and Danica Kačíková
Technical University in Zvolen, Faculty of Wood Sciences and Technology
Slovakia

1. Introduction

It is well known the paper production (likewise the other brands of industry) has enormous effects on the environment. The using and processing of raw materials has a variety of negative effects on the environment.

At the other hand there are technologies which can moderate the negative impacts on the environment and they also have a positive economical effect. One of these processes is the recycling, which is not only the next use of the wastes. The main benefit of the recycling is a double decrease of the environment loading, known as an environmental impact reducing. From the first view point, the natural resources conserves at side of the manufacturing process inputs, from the second view point, the harmful compounds amount leaking to the environment decreases at side of the manufacturing process outputs.

The paper production from the recycled fibers consumes less energy; conserves the natural resources viz. wood and decreases the environmental pollution. The conflict between economic optimization and environmental protection has received wide attention in recent research programs for waste management system planning. This has also resulted in a set of new waste management goals in reverse logistics system planning. Pati et al. (2008) have proposed a mixed integer goal programming (MIGP) model to capture the inter-relationships among the paper recycling network system. Use of this model can bring indirectly benefit to the environment as well as improve the quality of waste paper reaching the recycling unit.

In 2005, the total production of paper in Europe was 99.3 million tonnes which generated 11 million tonnes of waste, representing about 11% in relation to the total paper production. The production of recycled paper, during the same period, was 47.3 million tonnes generating 7.7 million tonnes of solid waste (about 70% of total generated waste in papermaking) which represents 16% of the total production from this raw material (CEPI 2006).

The consumption of recovered paper has been in continuous growth during the past decades. According to the Confederation of European Paper Industries (CEPI), the use of recovered paper was almost even with the use of virgin fiber in 2005. This development has been boosted by technological progress and the good price competitiveness of recycled fiber, but also by environmental awareness – at both the producer and consumer ends – and regulation that has influenced the demand for recovered paper. The European paper industry suffered a very difficult year in 2009 during which the industry encountered more down-time and capacity closures as a result of the weakened global economy. Recovered paper utilisation in Europe decreased in 2009, but exports of recovered paper to countries outside CEPI continued to rise, especially to Asian markets (96.3%). However, recycling rate expressed as "volume of paper recycling/volume of paper consumption" resulted in a record high 72.2% recycling rate after having reached 66.7% the year before (Fig. 1) (Hujala et al. 2010; CEPI 2006; European Declaration on Paper Recycling 2010; Huhtala & Samakovlis 2002; CEPI Annual Statistic 2010).

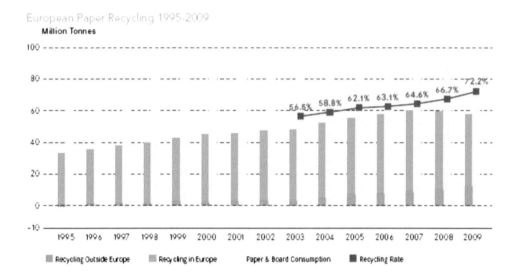

Fig. 1. European paper recycling 1995-2009 in million tonnes (European Declaration on Paper Recycling 2006 – 2010, Monitoring Report 2009 (2010) (www.erpa.info)

Recycling is not a new technology. It has become a commercial proposition since Matthias Koops established the Neckinger mill, in 1826, which produced white paper from printed waste paper. However, there were very few investigations into the effect of recycling on sheet properties until late 1960's. From then until the late 1970's, a considerable amount of work was carried out to identify the effects of recycling on pulp properties and the cause of these effects (Nazhad 2005; Nazhad & Paszner 1994). In the late 1980's and early 1990's, recycling issues have emerged stronger than before due to the higher cost of landfills in developed countries and an evolution in human awareness. The findings of the early 70's on recycling effects have since been confirmed, although attempts to trace the cause of these effects are still not resolved (Howard & Bichard 1992).

Recycling has been thought to reduce the fibre swelling capability, and thus the flexibility of fibres. The restricted swelling of recycled fibres has been ascribed to hornification, which has been introduced as a main cause of poor quality of recycled paper (Scallan & Tydeman 1992). Since 1950's, fibre flexibility among the papermakers has been recognized as a main source of paper strength. Therefore, it is not surprising to see that, for over half a century, papermakers have supported and rationalized hornification as a main source of tensile loss due to drying, even though it has never been fully understood (Sutjipto et al. 2008).

Recycled paper has been increasingly produced in various grades in the paper industry. However, there are still technical problems including reduction in mechanical strength for recycled paper. Especially, chemical pulp-origin paper, that is, fine paper requires a certain level of strength. Howard & Bichard (1992) reported that beaten bleached kraft pulp produced handsheets which were bulky and weak in tensile and burst strengths by handsheet recycling. This behaviour could be explained by the reduction in re-swelling capability or the reduction in flexibility of rewetted pulp fibers due to fiber hornification and, possibly, by fines loss during recycling processes, which decrease both total bonding area and the strength of paper (Howard 1995; Nazhad & Paszner 1994; Nazhad et al. 1995; Khantayanuwong et al. 2002; Kim et al. 2000).

Paper recycling is increasingly important for the sustainable development of the paper industry as an environmentally friendly sound. The research related to paper recycling is therefore increasingly crucial for the need of the industry. Even though there are a number of researches ascertained the effect of recycling treatment on properties of softwood pulp fibres (Cao et al. 1999; Horn 1975; Howard & Bichard 1992; Jang et al. 1995), however, it is likely that hardwood pulp fibres have rarely been used in the research operated with recycling treatment. Changes in some morphological properties of hardwood pulp fibres, such as curl, kink, and length of fibre, due to recycling effects also have not been determined considerably. This is possibly because most of the researches were conducted in the countries where softwood pulp fibres are commercial extensively (Khantayanuwong 2003). Therefore, it is the purpose of the present research to crucially determine the effect of recycling treatment on some important properties of softwood pulp fibres.

2. Alterations of pulp fibres properties at recycling

The goal of a recycled paper or board manufacturer is to make a product that meets customers' specification and requirements. At the present utilization rate, using recycled fibres in commodity grades such as newsprint and packaging paper and board has not caused noticeable deterioration in product quality and performance (Čabalová et al. 2009). The expected increase in recovery rates of used paper products will require a considerable consumption increase of recycled fibres in higher quality grades such as office paper and magazine paper. To promote expanded use of recovered paper, understanding the fundamental nature of recycled fibres and the differences from virgin fibres is necessary.

Essentially, recycled fibres are contaminated, used fibres. Recycled pulp quality is, therefore, directly affected by the history of the fibres, i.e. by the origins, processes and treatments which these fibres have experienced.

McKinney (1995) classified the history into five periods:
1. fibre furnish and pulp history
2. paper making process history
3. printing and converting history
4. consumer and collection history
5. recycling process history.

To identity changes in fibre properties, many recycling studies have occurred at laboratory. Realistically repeating all the stages of the recycling chain is difficult especially when including printing and deinking. Some insight into changes in fibre structure, cell wall properties, and bonding ability is possible from investigations using various recycling procedures, testing methods, and furnishes.

Mechanical pulp is chemically and physically different from chemical pulp then recycling effect on those furnishes is also different. When chemical fibres undergo repeated drying and rewetting, they are hornified and can significantly lose their originally high bonding potential (Somwand et al. 2002; Song & Law 2010; Kato & Cameron 1999; Bouchard & Douek 1994; Khantayanuwong et al. 2002; Zanuttini et al. 2007; da Silva et al. 2007). The degree of hornification can be measured by water retention value (WRW) (Kim et al. 2000). In contrast to the chemical pulps, originally weaker mechanical pulps do not deteriorate but somewhat even improve bonding potential during a corresponding treatment. Several studies (Maloney et al. 1998; Weise 1998; Ackerman et al. 2000) have shown good recyclability of mechanical fibres.

Adámková a Milichovský (2002) present the dependence of beating degree (°SR – Schopper-Riegler degree) and WRV from the relative length of hardwood and softwood pulps. From their results we can see the WRV increase in dependence on the pulp length alteration is more rapid at hardwood pulp, but finally this value is higher at softwood pulps. Kim et al. (2000) determined the WRV decrease at softwood pulps with the higher number of recycling (at zero recycling about cca 1.5 g/g at fifth recycling about cca 1.1 g/g). Utilisation of the secondary fibres to furnish at paper production decrease of the initial need of woody raw (less of cutting tress) but the paper quality is not significantly worse.

2.1 Paper recycling

The primary raw material for the paper production is pulps fibres obtaining by a complicated chemical process from natural materials, mainly from wood. This fibres production is very energy demanding and at the manufacturing process there are used many of the chemical matters which are very problematic from view point of the environment protection. The suitable alternative is obtaining of the pulp fibres from already made paper. This process is far less demanding on energy and chemicals utilisation. The paper recycling, simplified, means the repeated defibring, grinding and drying, when there are altered the mechanical properties of the secondary stock, the chemical properties of fibres, the polymerisation degree of pulp polysaccharidic components, mainly of cellulose, their supramolecular structure, the morphological structure of fibres, range and level of interfibres bonds e.g.. The cause of above mentioned alterations is the fibres ageing at the paper recycling and manufacturing, mainly the drying process.

At the repeat use of the secondary fibres, it need deliberate the paper properties alter due to the fiber deterioration during the recycling, when many alteration are irreversible. The alteration depth depends on the cycle's number and way to the fibres use. The main problem is the decrease of the secondary pulp mechanical properties with the continuing recycling, mainly the paper strength (Khantayanuwong et al. 2002; Jahan 2003; Hubbe & Zhang 2005; Garg & Singh 2006; Geffertová et al. 2008; Sutjipto et al. 2008). This decrease is an effect of many alterations, which can but need not arise in the secondary pulp during the recycling process. The recycling causes the hornification of the cell walls that result in the decline of some pulp properties. It is due to the irreversible alterations in the cells structure during the drying (Oksanen et al. 1997; Kim et al. 2000; Diniz et al. 2004).

The worse properties of the recycled fibres in comparison with the primary fibres can be caused by hornification but also by the decrease of the hydrophilic properties of the fibres surface during the drying due to the redistribution or migration of resin and fat acids to the surface (Nazhad & Paszner 1994; Nazhad 2005). Okayama (2002) observed the enormous increase of the contact angle with water which is related to the fiber inactivation at the recycling. This process is known as „irreversible hornification".

Paper recycling saves the natural wood raw stock, decreases the operation and capital costs to paper unit, decrease water consumption and last but not least this paper processing gives rise to the environment preservation (e.g. 1 t of waste paper can replace cca 2.5 m^3 of wood). A key issue in paper recycling is the impact of energy use in manufacturing. Processing waste paper for paper and board manufacture requires energy that is usually derived from fossil fuels, such as oil and coal. In contrast to the production of virgin fibre-based chemical pulp, waste paper processing does not yield a thermal surplus and thus thermal energy must be supplied to dry the paper web. If, however, the waste paper was recovered for energy purposes the need for fossil fuel would be reduced and this reduction would have a favourable impact on the carbon dioxide balance and the greenhouse effect. Moreover, pulp production based on virgin fibres requires consumption of round wood and causes emissions of air-polluting compounds as does the collection of waste paper. For better paper utilization, an interactive model, the Optimal Fibre Flow Model, considers both a quality (age) and an environmental measure of waste paper recycling was developed (Byström & Lönnstedt 1997).

2.1.1 Influence of beating on pulp fibres

Beating of chemical pulp is an essential step in improving the bonding ability of fibres. The knowledge complete about beating improves the present opinion of the fibres alteration at the beating. The main and extraneous influences of the beating device on pulps were defined. The main influences are these, each of them can be improve by the suitable beating mode, but only one alteration cannot be attained. Known are varieties of simultaneous changes in fibres, such as internal fibrilation, external fibrilation, fiber shortening or cutting, and fines formation (Page 1989; Kang & Paulapuro 2006a; Kang & Paulapuro 2006c).

- Freeing and disintegration of a cell wall affiliated with strong swelling expressed as an internal fibrilation and delamination. The delamination is a coaxial cleavage in the middle layer of the secondary wall. It causes the increased water penetration to the cell wall and the fibre plasticizing.
- External fibrillation and fibrils peeling from surface, which particularly or fully attacks primary wall and outside layers of secondary walls. Simultaneously from the outside layers there are cleavage fibrils, microfibrils, nanofibrils to the macromolecule of cellulose and hemicelluloses.
- Fibres shortening in any place in any angle-wise across fibre in accordance with loading, most commonly in weak places.
- Concurrently the main effects at the beating also the extraneous effects take place, e.g. fines making, compression along the fibres axis, fibres waving due to the compression. It has low bonding ability and it influences the paper porosity, stocks freeness (Sinke & Westenbroek 2004).

The beating causes the fibres shortening, the external and internal fibrillation affiliated with delamination and the fibres plasticizing. The outside primary wall of the pulp fibre leaks water little, it has usually an intact primary layer and a tendency to prevent from the swelling of the secondary layer of the cell wall. At the beating beginning there are disintegrated the fibre outside layers (P and S1), the fibrilar structure of the fibre secondary layer is uncovering, the water approach is improving, the swelling is taking place and the fibrillation process is beginning. The fibrillation process is finished by the weaking and cleavaging of the bonds between the particular fibrils and microfibrils of cell walls during the mechanical effect and the penetration into the interfibrilar spaces, it means to the amorphous region, there is the main portion of hemicelluloses.

Češek & Milichovský (2005) showed that with the increase of pulp beating degree the standard rheosettling velocity of pulp decreases more at the fibres fibrillation than at the fibres shortening.

Refining causes a variety of simultaneous changes in the fiber structure, such as internal fibrillation, external fibrillation and fines formation. Among these effects, swelling is commonly recognized as an important factor affecting the strength of recycled paper (Kang & Paulapuro 2006d).

Scallan & Tigerstrom (1991) observed the elasticity modulus of the long fibres from kraft pulp during the recycling. Flexibility decrease was evident at the beating degree decrease (°SR), and also with the increase of draining velocity of low-yield pulp.

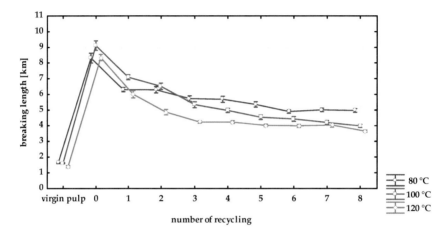

Fig. 2. Alteration of the breaking length of the paper sheet drying at the temperature of 80, 100 a 120 °C during eightfold recycling

properties of paper sheets by drying temperature 80 °C	number of recycling									
	virgin pulp	0	1	2	3	4	5	6	7	8
Breaking length [km]	1.6	8.3	6.3	6.3	5.7	5.7	5.4	4.9	5.0	5.0
Tear index [mN.m²/g]	1.6	2.1	2.5	2.7	2.8	2.8	2.5	3.1	2.7	2.7
Brightnees [%MgO]	83.8	80.0	82.2	82.8	82.5	82.4	82.0	82.4	82.5	82.6
Opacity [%]	71.4	63.9	68.8	67.8	69.5	69.1	70.0	70.1	69.1	70.3
DP by viscometry	699	666	661	663	653	642	642	608	607	611
DP by SEC	1138	1128	1126	1136	1115	1106	1094	1069	1053	1076

properties of paper sheets by drying temperature 100 °C	number of recycling									
	virgin pulp	0	1	2	3	4	5	6	7	8
Breaking length [km]	1.5	9.1	7.1	6.5	5.4	5.0	4.3	4.4	4.2	4.0
Tear index [mN.m²/g]	1.5	2.2	2.3	2.6	2.7	2.9	2.7	3.0	2.8	2.7
Brightnees [%MgO]	83.4	81.0	81.8	81.8	82.9	82.4	82.8	82.5	82.3	82.4
Opacity [%]	72.0	64.4	67.7	68.5	69.3	70.1	70.8	71.0	71.1	71.2
DP by viscometry	699	689	688	680	650	672	660	646	636	624
DP by SEC	1138	1012	1010	938	923	918	901	946	942	941

properties of paper sheets by drying temperature 120 °C	number of recycling									
	virgin pulp	0	1	2	3	4	5	6	7	8
Breaking length [km]	1.4	8.4	6.0	4.9	4.2	4.2	4.0	4.0	4.0	3.7
Tear index [mN.m²/g]	1.4	2.1	2.5	2.7	2.8	2.9	2.7	3.1	2.7	2.7
Brightnees [%MgO]	83.2	79.8	80.6	80.5	81.3	81.2	81.3	81.1	81.1	80.7
Opacity [%]	72.9	65.4	69.0	70.7	71.6	71.7	72.4	72.6	72.4	72.8
DP by viscometry	699	677	665	658	675	677	672	658	673	662
DP by SEC	1138	1030	1015	1059	1042	950	947	945	944	933

Table 1,2,3. The selected properties of the pulp fibres and the paper sheets during the process of eightfold recycling at three drying temperatures of 80 °C, 100 °C a 120 °C.

From the result on Fig. 2 we can see the increase of the pulp fibres active surface takes place during the beating process, which results in the improve of the bonding and the paper strength after the first beating. It causes also the breaking length increase of the laboratory sheets. The secondary fibres wear by repeated beating, what causes the decrease of strength values (Tab. 1,2,3).

The biggest alterations of tear index (Fig. 3) were observed after fifth recycling at the bleached softwood pulp fibres. The first beating causes the fibrillation of the outside layer of the cell wall, it results in the formation of the mechanical (felting) and the chemical bonds between the fibres. The repeated beating and drying dues, except the continuing fibrillation of the layer, the successive fibrils peeling until the peeling of the primary and outside secondary layer of the cell wall. It discovers the next non-fibriled layer S2 (second, the biggest layer of the secondary wall) what can do the tear index decrease. The next beating causes also this layer fibrillation, which leads to the increase of the strength value (Fig. 3, Tab. 1,2,3). Paper strength properties such as tensile strength and Scott bond strength were strongly influenced by internal fibrillation; these could also be increased further by promoting mostly external fibrillation (Kang & Paulapuro 2006b).

The course of the breaking length decrease and the tearing strength increase of the paper sheet is in accordance with the results of Sutjipto et al. (2008) at the threefold recycling of the bleached (88 % ISO) softwood pulps prepared at the laboratory conditions, beated on PFI mill to 25 °SR.

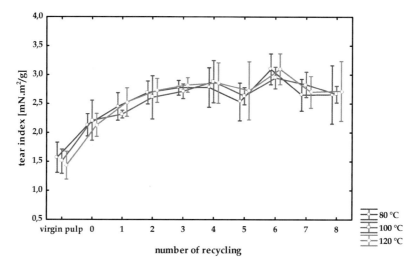

Fig. 3. Tear index alteration of the paper sheets drying at the temperature of 80, 100 a 120 °C, during eightfold recycling

Song & Law (2010) observed kraft pulp oxidation and its influence on recycling characteristics of fibres, the found up the fibre oxidation influences negatively the tear index of paper sheets. Oxidation of virgin fibre prior to recycling minimized the loss of WRV and sheet density.

The beating causes the fibres shortening and fines formation which is washed away in the large extent and it endeds in the paper sludges. This waste can be further processed and effective declined.

Within the European Union several already issued and other foreseen directives have great influence on the waste management strategy of paper producing companies. Due to the large quantities of waste generated, the high moisture content of the waste and the changing composition, some recovery methods, for example, conversion to fuel components, are simply too expensive and their environmental impact uncertain. The thermal processes, gasification and pyrolysis, seem to be interesting emerging options, although it is still necessary to improve the technologies for sludge application. Other applications, such as the hydrolysis to obtain ethanol, have several advantages (use of wet sludge and applicable technology to sludges) but these are not well developed for pulp and paper sludges.

Therefore, at this moment, the minimization of waste generation still has the highest priority (Monte et al. 2009).

2.1.2 Drying influence on the recycled fibres

Characteristic differences between recycled fibres and virgin fibres can by expected. Many of these can by attributed to drying. Drying is a process that is accompanied by partially irreversible closure of small pores in the fibre wall, as well as increased resistance to swelling during rewetting. Further differences between virgin and recycled fibres can be attributed to the effects of a wide range of contaminating substances (Hubbe et al. 2007). Drying, which has an anisotropic character, has a big influence on the properties of paper produced from the secondary fibres. During the drying the shear stress are formatted in the interfibrilar bonding area. The stresses formatted in the fibres and between them effect the mechanical properties in the drying paper. The additional effect dues the tensioning of the wet pulp stock on the paper machine.

During the drying and recycling the fibres are destructed. It is important to understand the loss of the bonding strength of the drying chemical fibres. Dang (2007) characterized the destruction like a percentage reduction of ability of the water retention value (WRV) in pulp at dewatering.

$$\text{Hornification} = [(WRV_0 - WRV_1)/WRV_0]. \ 100 \qquad\qquad [\%],$$

$$WRV_0 - \text{ is value of virgin pup}$$

$$WRV_1 - \text{ the value of recycled pulp after drying and reslushing.}$$

According to the prevailing concept, hornification occurs in the cell wall matrix of chemical fibres. During drying, delaminated parts of the fiber wall, i.e., cellulose microfibrils become attached as Fig. 4 shows (Ackerman et al. 2000).

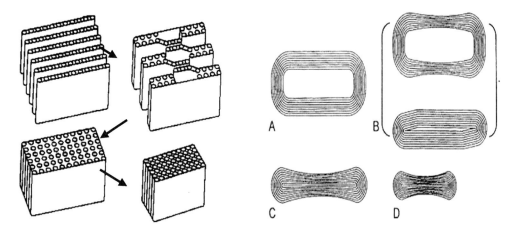

Fig. 4. Changes in fiber wall structure (Weise & Paulapuro 1996)

Fig. 5. Shrinkage of a fiber cross section (Ackerman et al. 2000)

Hydrogen bonds between those lamellae also form. Reorientation and better alignment of microfibrils also occur. All this causes an intensely bonded structure. In a subsequent reslushing in water, the fiber cell wall microstructure remains more resistant to delaminating forces because some hydrogen bonds do not reopen. The entire fiber is stiffer and more brittle (Howard 1991). According to some studies (Bouchard & Douek 1994; Maloney et al. 1998), hornification does not increase the crystallinity of cellulose or the degree of order in the hemicelluloses of the fiber wall.

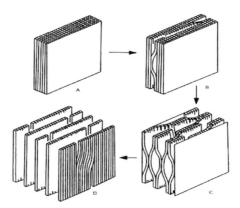

Fig. 6. The drying model of Scallan (Laivins & Scallan 1993) suggests that hornification prevents the dry structure in A from fully expanding to the wet structure in D. Instead, only partial expansion to B may be possible after initial drying creates hydrogen bonds between the microfibrils (Kato & Cameron 1999)

Weise & Paulapuro (1996) did very revealing work about the events during fiber drying. They studied fiber cross section of kraft fibers in various solids by Confocal Laser Scanning Microscope (CLSM) and simultaneously measured hornification with WRV tests. Irreversible hornification of fibers began on the degree of beating. It does not directly follow shrinkage since the greatest shrinkage of fibers occurs above 80 % solids content. In Figs. 4 and 5, stage A represented wet kraft fiber before drying. In stage B, the drainage has started to cause morphological changes in the fiber wall matrix at about 30 % solids content. The fiber wall lamellae start to approach each other because of capillary forces. During this stage, the lumen can collapse. With additional drying, spaces between lamellae continue shrinking to phase C where most free voids in the lamellar structure of the cell wall have already closed. Toward the end of drying in stage D, the water removal occurs in the fine structure of the fiber wall. Kraft fiber shrink strongly and uniformly during this final phase of drying, i.e., at solid contents above 75-80 %. The shrinkage of stage D is irreversible.

At a repeated use of the dried fibres in paper making industry, the cell walls receive the water again. Then the opposite processes take place than in the Fig. 4 and 5. It show Scallan´s model of the drying in Fig. 6.

The drying dues also macroscopic stress applied on paper and distributed in fibres system according a local structure.

2.1.3 Properties of fibres from recycled paper

The basic properties of origin wet fibres change in the drying process of pulp and they are not fully regenerated in the process of slushing and beating.

The same parameters are suitable for the description of the paper properties of secondary fibres and fibres at ageing as well as for description of primary fibres properties. The experiences obtained at the utilisation of waste paper showed the secondary fibres have very different properties from the origin fibres. Next recycling of fibres causes the formation of extreme nonhomogeneous mixture of various old fibres. At the optimum utilisation of the secondary fibres it need take into account their altered properties at the repeated use. With the increase number of use cycles the fibres change irreversible, perish and alter their properties. Slushing and beating causes water absorption, fibres swelling and a partial regeneration of properties of origin fibres. However the repeated beating and drying at the multiple production cycles dues the gradual decrease of swelling ability, what influences a bonding ability of fibres. With the increase of cycles number the fibres are shortened. These alterations express in paper properties. The decrease of bonding ability and mechanical properties bring the improving of some utility properties. Between them there is higher velocity of dewatering and drying, air permeability and blotting properties improve of light scattering, opacity and paper dimensional stability.

The highest alterations of fibres properties are at the first and following three cycles. The size of strength properties depends on fibres type (Geffertová et al. 2008).

Drying influences fibres length, width, shape factor, kinks which are the important factors to the strength of paper made from recycled fibres. The dimensional characteristics are measured by many methods, known is FQA (Fiber Quality Analyser), which is a prototype IFA (Imaging Fiber Analyser) and also Kajaani FS-200 fibre-length analyser. They measure fibres length, different kinks and their angles. Robertson et al. (1999) show correlation between methods FQA and Kajaani FS-200. A relatively new method of fibres width measurement is also SEM (Scanning Electron Microscope) (Bennis et al. 2010). Among devices for analyse of fibres different properties and characteristics, e.g. fibres length and width, fines, various deformations of fibres and percentage composition of pulp mixture is L&W Fiber Tester (Lorentzen & Wettre, Sweden). At every measurement the minimum of 20 000 fibres in a sample is evaluated. On Fig. 7 there is expressed the alteration of fibres average length of softwood pulps during the eightfold recycling at the different drying temperature of pulp fibres.

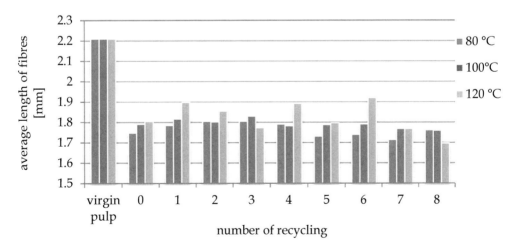

Fig. 7. Influence of recycling number and drying temperature on length of softwood pulps

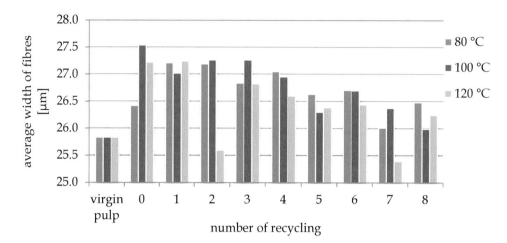

Fig. 8. Influence of recycling number and drying temperature on width of softwood pulps

The biggest alteration were observed after first beating (zero recycling), when the fibres average length decrease at the sheet drying temperature of 80 °C about 17%, at the temperature of 100 °C about 15.6% and at the temperature of 120 °C about 14.6%.

After the first beating the fibres average width was markedly increased at the all temperatures dues to the fibrillation influence. The fibres fibrillation causes the fibre surface increase. Following markedly alteration is observed after fifth recycling, when the fibres average width was decreased. We assume the separation of fibrils and microfibrils from the cell walls dues the separation of the cell walls outside layer, the inside nonfibriled wall S2 was discovered and the fibres average width decreased. After the fifth recycling the strength properties became worse, mainly tear index (Fig. 3).

The softwood fibres are longer than hardwood fibres, they are not so straight. The high value of shape factor means fibres straightness. The biggest alterations of shape factor can be observed mainly at the high drying temperatures. The water molecules occurring on fibres surface quick evaporate at the high temperatures and fibre more shrinks. It can result in the formation of weaker bonds between fibres those surfaces are not enough near. At the beginning of wet paper sheet drying the hydrogen bond creates through water layer on the fibres surface, after the drying through monomolecular layer of water, finally the hydrogen bond results after the water removal and the surfaces approach. It results in destruction of paper and fibre at the drying.

Chemical pulp fines are an important component in papermaking furnish. They can significantly affect the mechanical and optical properties of paper and the drainage properties of pulp (Retulainen et al. 1993). Characterizing the fines will therefore allow a better understanding of the role of fines and better control the papermaking process and the properties of paper. Chemical pulp fines retard dewatering of the pulp suspension due to the high water holding capacity of fines. In the conventional method for characterizing the role of fines in dewatering, a proportion of fines is added to the fiber furnish, and then only the drainage time. Fines suspension is composed of heterogeneous fines particles in water. The suspension exhibits different rheological characteristics depending on the degree of interaction between the fines particles and on their hydration (Kang & Paulapuro 2006b).

From Fig. 9 we can see the highest formation of fines were after seventh and eight recycling, when the fibres were markedly weakened by the multiple using at the processes of paper making. They are easier and faster beating (the number of revolution decreased by the higher number of the recycling).

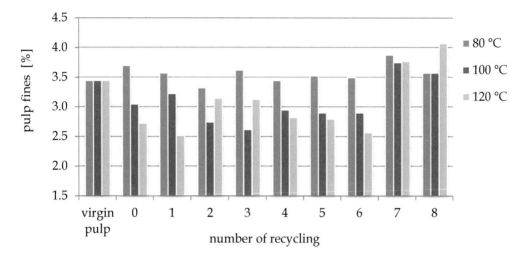

Fig. 9. Influence of recycling process and drying temperature on pulp fines changes

The macroscopic level (density, volume, porosity, paper thickness) consists from the physical properties very important for the use of paper and paperboard. They indirectly characterize the three dimensional structure of paper (Niskanen 1998). A paper is a complex structure consisting mainly of a fibre network, filler pigment particles and air. Light is reflected at fibre and pigment surfaces in the surface layer and inside the paper structure. The light also penetrates into the cellulose fibres and pigments, and changes directions. Some light is absorbed, but the remainder passes into the air and is reflected and refracted again by new fibres and pigments. After a number of reflections and refractions, a certain proportion of the light reaches the paper surface again and is then reflected at all possible angles from the surface. We do not perceive all the reflections and refractions (the multiple reflections or refractions) which take place inside the paper structure, but we perceive that the paper has a matt white surface i.e. we perceive a diffuse surface reflection. Some of the incident light exists at the back of the paper as transmitted light, and the remainder has been absorbed by the cellulose and the pigments. Besides reflection, refraction and absorption, there is a fourth effect called diffraction. In other contexts, diffraction is usually the same thing as light scattering, but within the field of paper technology, diffraction is only one aspect of the light scattering phenomenon. Diffraction occurs when the light meets particles or pores which are as large as or smaller then the wavelength of the light, i.e. particles which are smaller than one micrometer (μm). These small elements oscillate with the light oscillation and thus function as sites for new light sources. When the particles or pores are smaller than half of the light wavelength the diffraction decreases. It can be said that the light passes around the particle without being affected (Pauler 2002).

The opacity, brightness, colouring and brilliance are important optical properties of papers and paperboards. For example the high value of opacity is need at the printing papers, but opacity of translucent paper must be lower. The paper producer must understand the physical principles of the paper structure and to determine their characteristics composition. It is possible to characterize nondirect the paper structure. The opacity characterizes the paper ability to hide a text or a figure on the opposite side of the paper sheet. The paper brightness is a paper reflection at a blue light use. The blue light is used because the made fibers have yellowish colour and a human eye senses a blue tone like a white colour. The typical brightness of the printing papers is 70 – 95% and opacity is higher than 90% (Niskanen 1998).

3. Paper ageing

The recycled paper is increasingly used not only for the products of short term consumption (newspaper, sanitary paper, packaging materials e.g.), but also on the production of the higher quality papers, which can serve as a culture heritage medium. The study of the recycled papers alterations in the ageing process is therefore important, but the information in literature are missing.

The recycling is also another form of the paper ageing. It causes the paper alterations, which results in the degradation of their physical and mechanical properties. The recycling causes a chemical, thermal, biological and mechanical destruction, or their combination (Milichovský 1994; Geffertová et al. 2008). The effect of the paper ageing is the degradation of cellulose, hemicelluloses and lignin macromolecules, the decrease of low molecular fractions, the degree of polymerisation (DP) decrease, but also the decline of the mechanical and optical properties (El Ashmawy et al. 1974; Valtasaari & Saarela 1975; Lauriol et al. 1987a,b,c; Bansa 2002; Havermans 2003; Dupont & Mortha 2004; Kučerová & Halajová, 2009; Čabalová et al. 2011). Cellulose as the most abundant natural polymer on the Earth is very important as a renewable organic material. The degradation of cellulose based paper is important especially in archives and museums where ageing in various conditions reduces the mechanical properties and deteriorates optical quality of stored papers, books and other artefacts. The low rate of paper degradation results in the necessity of using accelerating ageing tests. The ageing tests consist in increasing the observed changes of paper properties, usually by using different temperature, humidity, oxygen content and acidity, respectively. Ageing tests are used in studies of degradation rate and mechanism. During the first ageing stages—natural or accelerated—there are no significant variations in mechanical properties: degradation evidence is only provided by measuring chemical processes. Oxidation induced by environmental conditions, in fact, causes carbonyl and carboxyl groups formation, with great impact on paper permanence and durability, even if mechanical characteristics are not affected in the short term (Piantanida et al. 2005). During the degradation two main reactions prevail – hydrolysis of glycosidic bonds and oxidation of glucopyranose rings. As a result of some oxidation processes keto- and aldehyde groups are formed. These groups are highly reactive; they are prone to crosslinking, which is the third chemical process of cellulose decay (Bansa 2002, Calvini & Gorassini 2006).

At the accelerated paper ageing the decrease of DP is very rapid in the first stages of the ageing, later decelerates. During the longer time of the ageing there was determined the cellulose crosslinking by the method of size exclusion chromatography (SEC) (Kačík et al. 2009). The similar dependences were obtained at the photo-induced cellulose degradation (Malesic et al. 2005).

An attention is pay to the kinetic of the cellulose degradation in several decades, this process was studied by Kuhn in 1930 and the first model of the kinetic of the cellulose chains cleavage was elaborated by Ekenstam in 1936. This model is based on the kinetic equation of first-order and it is used to this day in modifications for the watching of the cellulose degradation in different conditions. Hill et al. (1995) deduced a similar model with the

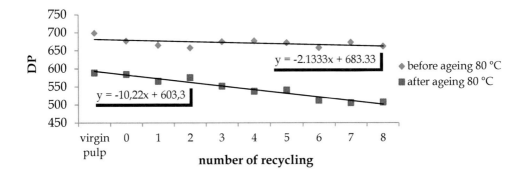

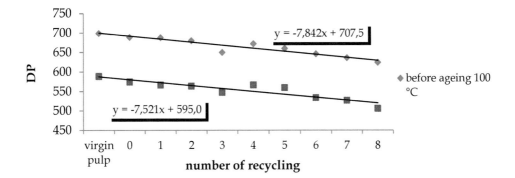

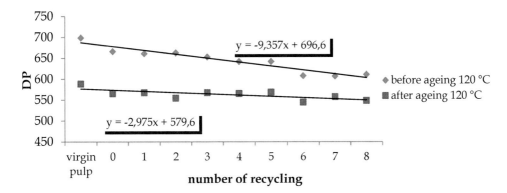

Fig. 10. Alterations of DP (degree of polymerisation) of cellulose fibres due to recycling and ageing at the pulp fibres drying temperature of   80 °C, 100 °C a 120 °C.

contribution of the zero order kinetic. Experimental results are often controversial and new kinetic model for explanation of cellulose degradation at various conditions was proposed (Calvini et al. 2008). The first-order kinetic model developed by these authors suggests that the kinetics of cellulose degradation depends upon the mode of ageing. An autoretardant path is followed during either acid hydrolysis in aqueous suspensions or oven ageing, while the production of volatile acid compounds trapped during the degradation in sealed environments primes an autocatalytic mechanism. Both these mechanisms are depleted by the consumption of the glycosidic bonds in the amorphous regions of cellulose until the levelling-off DP (LODP) is reached.

At the accelerated ageing of newspaper (Kačík et al. 2008), the cellulose degradation causes the decrease of the average degree of polymerisation (DP). The DP decrease is caused by two factors in accordance with equation

$$DP = LODP + DP01.e^{-k1.t} + DP02.e^{-k2.t},$$

where LODP is levelling-off degree of polymerisation. There is a first factor higher and quick decreasing during eight days and a second factor is lower and slow decreasing and dominant after eight days of the accelerating ageing in the equation. The number of cleavaged bonds can be well described by equation

$$DP_0/DP_t - 1 = n_0.(1-e^{-k.t}),$$

where n_0 is an initial number of bonds available for degradation. The equation of the regression function is in accordance with Calvini et al. (2007) proposal, the calculated value (4.4976) is in a good accordance with the experimentally obtained average values of DP_0 a DP_{60} (4.5057). The DP decreased to cca 38% of the initial value and the polydispersity degree to 66% of the initial value. The decrease of the rate constant with the time of ageing was obtained also by next authors (Emsley et al. 1997; Zervos & Moropoulou 2005; Ding & Wang 2007). Čabalová et al. (2011) observed the influence of the accelerated ageing on the recycled pulp fibres, they determined the lowest decrease of DP at the fibres dried at the temperature of 120 °C (Fig. 10).

The simultaneous influence of the recycling and ageing has the similar impact at the drying temperatures of 80 °C (decrease about 27,5 %) and 100 °C (decrease about 27.6%) in regard of virgin pulp, lower alterations were at the temperature of 120 °C (decrease about 21.5%). The ageing of the recycled paper causes the decrease of the pulp fiber DP, but the paper remains good properties.

4. Conclusion

The recycling is a necessity of this civilisation. The paper manufacturing is from its beginning affiliated with the recycling, because the paper was primarily manufactured from the 100 % furnish of rag. It is increasingly assented the trend of the recycled fibers use from the European and world criterion. The present European papermaking industry is based on the recycling.

The presence of the secondary fibres from the waste paper, their quality and amount is various in the time intervals, the seasons and the regional conditions. It depends on the manufacturing conditions in the paper making industry of the country.

At present the recycling is understood in larger sense than the material recycling, which has a big importance from view point of the paper recycling. Repeatedly used fibres do not fully regenerate their properties, so they cannot be recycled ad anfinitum. It allows to use the alternative possibilities of the paper utilisation in the building industry, at the soil reclamation, it the agriculture, in the power industry.

The most important aim is, however, the recycled paper utilisation for the paper manufacturing.

5. Acknowledgment

This work was financed by the Slovak Grant Agency VEGA (project number 1/0490/09).

6. References

Ackerman, Ch., Göttsching, L. & Pakarinen, H. (2000). *Papermaking potential of recycled fiber*, In: Göttsching, L. & Pakarinen, H. (eds.). *Recycled Fiber and Deiking*. Papermaking Science and Technology. Finland. Chapter 10, pp. 358-438, ISBN 952 – 5216 – 07 – 1 (book 7)

Adámková, G. & Milichovský, M. (2002). Beating of Mixtures Hardwood and Softwood Pulps. *Papír a celulóza*, 57(8), 2002, pp. 250 – 254, ISSN 0031 - 1421

Bansa, H. (2002). Accelerated Ageing of Paper: Some Ideas on its Practical Benefit. *Restaurator* 23(2), 2002, pp. 106-117, ISSN 0034-5806

Bennis, H., Benslimane, R., Vicini, S., Mairani, A. & Princi, E. (2010). Fibre width measurement and quantification of filler size distribution in paper-based materials by SEM and image analysis. *Journal of Electron Microscopy* 59(2), 2010, pp. 91-102, ISSN 0022-0744

Bouchard, J. & Douek, M. (1994). The effects of recycling on the chemical properties of pulps. *Journal of pulp and paper science* 20(5), 1994, pp. 131-136, ISSN 0826-6220

Byström, S. & Lönnstedt, L. (1997). Paper recycling: environmental and economic impact. *Resources, Conservation and Recycling* 21, 1997, pp. 109-127, ISSN 0921-3449

Calvini, P. & Gorassini A. (2006). On the rate of paper degradation: lessons from the past. *Restaurator* 27, 2006, pp. 275–290, ISSN 0034-5806

Calvini, P., Gorassini, A. & Metlami, A. L. (2007). Autocatalytic Degradation of Celulose Paper in DealerVessels. *Restaurator* 28, 2007, pp. 47-54 ISSN 0034-5806

Calvini, P., Gorassini, A. & Metlami, A. L. (2008). On the kinetics of cellulose degradation: looking beyond the pseudo zero order rate equation. *Cellulose* 15, 2008, pp. 193–203, ISSN 0969-0239

Cao, B., Tschirner, J. & Ramasway, S. (1999). Study of changes in wet- fiber flexibility and surface condition of recycled fibers. *Paperi ja Puu /Paper and Timber* 81(2), 1999, pp. 117-122, ISSN 0031-1243

CEPI (Confederation of European Paper Industries). (2006). Special Recycling 2005 Statistics - European Paper Industry Hits New Record in Recycling. 27.02.2011, Available from: http://www.erpa.info/images/Special_Recycling_2005_statistics.pdf

CEPI (Confederation of European Paper Industrie). (2010). Annual Statistic 2009. 27.02.2011, Available from:
http://www.erpa.info/download/CEPI_annual_statistics%202009.pdf

Čabalová, I., Kačík, F. & Sivák, J. (2009). Changes of molecular weight distribution of cellulose during pulp recycling. *Acta Facultatis Xylologiae Zvolen* 51(1), 2009, pp. 11-17, ISSN 1336-3824

Čabalová, I., Kačík, F. & Sivák, J. (2011). The changes of polymerization degree of softwood fibers by recycling and ageing process. *Acta Facultatis Xylologiae Zvolen* 53(1), 2011, pp. 61-64, ISSN 1336-3824

Češek, B. & Milichovský, M. (2005). Rheosedimentation – a Tool for Evaluation of Pulp Fibre Behaviour in Wet State. *Papír a celulóza* 59 (7–8), 2005, pp. 224–229, ISSN 0031–1421

El Ashmawy, A. E., Danhelka, J. & Kössler, I. (1974). Determination of molecular weight distribution of cellulosic pulps by conversion into tricarbanilate, elution fractionation and GPC. *Svensk Papperstidning* 16, 1974, pp. 603-608, ISSN 0283-6831

Emsley, A. M., Heywood, R. J., Ali, M. & Eley, C. (1997). On the kinetics of degradation of cellulose. *Cellulose* 4, 1997, pp. 1-5, ISSN 0969-0239

European Declaration on Paper Recycling 2006 – 2010, Monitoring Report 2009 (2010), 27.02. 2011, Available from: http://www.erpa.info/images/monitoring_report_2009.pdf

da Silva, T. A., Mocchiutti, P., Zanuttini, M. A. & Ramos, L. P. (2007). Chemical characterization of pulp components in unbleached softwood kraft fibers recycled with the assistance of a laccase/HTB system. *BioResources* 2(4), pp. 616-629, ISSN 1930-2126

Dang, Z., Zhang, J. & Ragauskas, A.J. (2007). Characterizing TEMPO-mediated oxidation of ECF bleached softwood kraft pulps. *Carbohydrate polymers*, Vol. 70, pp. 310 – 317, ISSN 0144-8617

Diniz, J.M.B.F., Gil, M.H. & Castro, J.A.A.M. (2004). Hornification- its origin and interpretation in wood pulps. *Wood Science Technology* 37, 2004, pp. 489-494, ISSN 0043-7719

Ding, H. Z. & Wang, Z. D. (2007). On the degradation evolution equations of celulose. *Cellulose*, 2007, DOI 10.1007/s10570-007-9166-4, 09.04. 2008, Available from: http://springerlink.metapress.com/content/6h55q04l34700348/

Dupont, A. L. & Mortha G. (2004). Comparative evaluation of size-exclusion chromatography and viscometry for the characterisation of cellulose. *J. Chromatogr. A.* 1026(1-2), 2004, pp. 129-141, ISSN 0021-9673

Garg, M. & Singh, S.P. (2006). Reason of strength loss in recycled pulp. *Appita Journal* 59(4), pp. 274-279, ISSN 1038-6807

Geffertová, J., Geffert, A. & Čabalová, I. (2008). Hardwood sulphate pulp in the recycling process. *Acta Facultatis Xylologiae Zvolen*, L (1), pp. 73 – 81, ISSN 1336 – 3824

Havermans, J. (2003). The impact of European research on paper ageing and preventive conservation strategies. *Protection and treatment of paper, leather and parchment. EC 5th Conference, Krakow, Poland*, pp. 87-91, 27. 20. 2011. Available from: http://www.cyf-kr.edu.pl/~ncbratas/pdf/full_havermans.pdf

Hill, D. J. T., Le, T.T., Darveniza, M. & Saha, T. A. (1995). A study of degradation of cellulosic insulation materials in a power transformer. Part 1. Molecular weight study of cellulose insulation paper. *Polymer Degradation and Stability* 48, 1995, pp. 79-87, ISSN 0141-3910

Horn, R.A. (1975). What are the effects of recycling on fiber and paper properties? *Paper Trade J.* 159(7/8), pp. 78-82, ISSN 0031-1197

Howard, R. C. (1991). The effect of recycling on paper technology. *Paper technology* 32(4), pp. 20-25, ISSN 0031-1189

Howard, R. C. (1995). The effects of recycling on paper quality. *Technology of Paper Recycling*; Mc Kinney, R. W. (ed.); Chapman & Hall: London, 1995, pp. 180-203

Howard, R.C. & Bichard, W.J. (1992). The basic effect of recycling on pulp properties, *Journal of pulp and paper science* 18 (4), 1992, pp. 151-159, ISSN 0826-6220

Hubbe, M.A. & Zhang, M. (2005). Recovered kraft fibers and wet-end dry-strength polymers. *Proc. TAPPI 2005 Practical Papermakers Conf., TAPPI Press,* Atlanta

Hubbe, M.A., Venditti, R.A. & Rojas, O.J. (2007). What happens to cellulosis fibers during papermaking and recycling? A review. *BioResources 2(4),* pp. 739-788, ISSN 1930-2126

Huhtala, A., & Samakovlis, E. (2002). Does International Harmonization of Environmental Policy Instruments Make Economic Sense? *Environmental and Resource Economics,* 21(3), pp. 261-286, ISSN 0924-6460

Hujala, M., Puumalainen, K., Tuppura, A. & Toppinen, A. (2010). Trends in the Use of Recovered Fiber – Role of Institutional and Market Factors. *Progress in Paper Recycling,* Vol. 19, No. 2, 2010, pp. 3-11, ISSN 1061-1452

Jahan, M.S. (2003). Changes of paper properties of nonwood pulp on recycling. *Tappi Journal* 2(7), pp. 9-12, ISSN 0734-1415

Jang, H.F., Howard, R.C. & Seth, R.S. (1995). Fiber characterization using confocal microscopy. Effects of recycling. *Tappi Journal* 78(12), pp. 131-137, ISSN 0734-1415

Kačík, F., Geffertová, J. & Kačíková, D. (2009). Characterisation of cellulose and pulps by the methods of gel permeation chromatography and viscometry. *Acta Facultatis Xylologiae Zvolen,* 51(2), 2009, pp. 93-103, ISSN 1336-3824

Kačík, F., Kačíková, D. & Vacek, V. (2008). Kinetics of cellulose degradation at accelerated paper ageing. *Acta Facultatis Xylologiae Zvolen,* 50(1), 2008, pp. 83 - 90. ISSN 1336 – 3824

Kačík, F., Kačíková, D., Jablonský, M. & Katuščák, S. (2009). Cellulose degradation in newsprint paper ageing. *Polymer Degradation and Stability* 94. 2009, pp. 1509–1514, ISSN 0141-3910

Kang, T. & Paulapuro, H. (2006a). Effect of External Fibrillation on Paper Strength. *Pulp & Paper Canada* 107(7/8), pp. 51-54, ISSN 0316-4004

Kang, T. & Paulapuro, H. (2006b) Characterization of Chemical Pulp Fines. *Tappi Journal* 5, 2006, 2, pp. 25-28, ISSN 0734-1415

Kang, T. & Paulapuro, H. (2006c). New Mechanical Treatment for Chemical Pulp. *Proceedings of the Institution of Mechanical Engineers, Part E: Journal of Process Mechanical Engineering* 220 ,2006, 3, pp.161-166, ISSN: 0954-4089

Kang, T. & Paulapuro, H. (2006d). Recycle Potential of Externally Fibrillated Chemical Pulp. *Progress in Paper Recycling* 15, 2006, 2, pp. 11-17, ISSN 1061-1452

Kato, K.L. & Cameron, R.E. (1999). A review of the relationship between thermally-accelerated ageing of paper and hornification. *Cellulose* 6, pp. 23-40, ISSN 0969-0239

Khantayanuwong, S. (2003). Determination of the Effect of Recycling Treatment on Pulp Fiber Properties by Principal Component Analysis. *Kasetsart J. (Nat. Sci.) 37,* pp. 219 – 223, ISSN 0075-5192

Khantayanuwong, S., Toshiharu, E. & Fumihiko, O. (2002). Effect of Fiber Hornification in Recycling on Bonding Potential at Interfiber Crossings: Confocal Laser-scanning Microscopy (CLSM). *Japan Tappi Journal* 56(2), 2002, pp. 239-245, ISSN 0022-815X

Kim, H.J., Oh, J.S. & Jo, B.M. (2000). Hornification Behaviour of Cellulosic fibres by Recycling. *Applied Chemistry* 4(1), May 2000, pp. 363-366, Available from: http://210.101.116.28/W_kiss61/10906405_pv.pdf

Kučerová, V. & Halajová, L. (2009). Evaluation of changes of the recycled pulps by method the gel permeation chromatography. *Acta Facultatis Xylologiae Zvolen*, 51(2), 2009, pp. 87-92, ISSN 1336-3824

Laivins, G. V. & Scallan, A. M. (1993). The Mechanism of Hornification of Wood Pulps. *Products of Papermaking, Tenth Fundamental Research Symposium, (C. F. Baker, ed.)* Vol. 2, Oxford, September 1993, Pira International, pp. 1235-1260

Lauriol, J. M., Froment, P., Pla, F. & Robert, A. (1987a). Molecular weight distribution of cellulose by on-line size exclusion chromatography - low angle laser light scattering. Part I: Basic experiments and treatment of data. *Holzforschung* 41, No. 2, pp. 109 – 113, ISSN 0018-3830

Lauriol, J. M., Comtat, J., Froment, P., Pla, F. & Robert, A. (1987b). Molecular weight distribution of cellulose by on-line size exclusion chromatography - low angle laser light scattering. Part II : Acid and Enzymatic Hydrolysis. *Holzforschung* 41, No. 3, pp. 165 – 169, ISSN 0018-3830

Lauriol, J. M., Froment, P., Pla, F. & Robert, A. (1987c). Molecular weight distribution of cellulose by on-line size exclusion chromatography - low angle laser light scattering. Part III: Oxygen-alkali oxidation. *Holzforschung* 41, No. 4, pp. 215 – 224, ISSN 0018-3830

Malesic, J., Kolar, J., Strlic, M., Kocar, D., Fromageot, D., Lemaire, J. & Haillant, O. (2005). Photo-induced degradation of cellulose. *Polymer Degradation and Stability* 89(1), pp. 64-69, ISSN 0141-3910

Maloney, T. C., Todorovic, A. & Paulapuro, H. (1998). The effect of fiber swelling in press dewatering. *Nordic Pulp Paper Res. J. 13(4)*, pp. 285-291, ISSN 0283-2631

McKinney, R.W.J. (1995). *Technology of paper recycling*. BLACKIE A&P, pp: 401, ISBN 0-7514-0017-3, 12.03.2011, Available from: (http://cgi.ebay.com/Technology-Paper-Recycling-NEW-R-W-J-McKinney-/130395108560)

Milichovský, M. (1994). Recirkulace a recyklace – výzva současnosti. *Papír a celulóza* 49 (2), pp. 29 – 34, ISSN 0031-1421

Monte, M. C., Fuente, E., Blanco, A. & Negro, C. (2009). Waste management from pulp and paper production in the European Union. *Waste Management* 29, 2009, pp. 293–308, ISSN 0956-053X

Nazhad, M. M. & Paszner, L. (1994). Fundamentals of Strength Loss in Recycled Paper, *Tappi*, 77(9), pp. 171-179, ISSN 0039-8241

Nazhad, M. M., Ramos, L. P., Paszner, L. & Saddler, J. N. (1995). Structural constraints affecting the initial enzymatic hydrolysis of recycled paper. *Enzyme and Microbial Technology* 17, 1995, pp. 66–74, ISSN 0141-0229

Nazhad, M. M. (2005). Recycled fibre quality – A review', Journal of industrial and engineering chemistry, *In: Korean Journal,* 11(3), pp. 314, 17.02. 2011, Available from http://www.cheric.org/research/tech/periodicals/view.php?seq=497896&jourid=13&mode=ref

Niskanen, K. (1998). *Paper Physics*. Papermaking Science and Technology. In: Retulianen, E. Niskanen, K. & Nilsen, N. (eds.). *Fibers and bonds*. Finland. Chapter 2, pp. 324, ISBN 952 – 5216 – 16 – 0 (book 16)

Okayama, T. (2002). The effeect of recycling on pulp and paper properties. *Japan Tappi Journal* 56(7), pp. 62-68, ISSN 0022-815X

Oksanen, T., Buchert, J. & Viikari, L. (1997). The role of hemicelluloses in the hornification of bleached kraft pulps. *Holzforschung*, Vol. 51, pp. 355 – 360, ISSN 0018-3830

Page, D.H. (1989). The beating of chemical pulps - The action and the effects. *Papermaking Raw Materials. Symp.*, Vol. 1., pp. 1-37

Pati, R.K., Vrat, P. & Kumar, P. (2008). A goal programming model for paper recycling system. *Omega* 36, 2008, pp. 405 – 417, ISSN 0305-0483

Pauler, N. (2002). *Paper optics*. Elanders Tofters, Östervála, Sweden. ISBN 91-971 765-6-7

Piantanida, G., Bicchieri, M. & Coluzza, C. (2005). Atomic force microscopy characterization of the ageing of pure cellulose paper. *Polymer* 46, 12313–12321, ISSN 0032-3861

Retulainen, E., Moss, P. & Nieminen, K. (1993). Transactions of the 10th Fundamental Research Symposium, Pira International, Leatherhead, UK, pp. 727.

Robertson, G., Olson, J., Allen, P., Chan, B. & Seth, R. (1999). Measurement of fiber length, coarseness, and shape with the fiber quality analyser. *Tappi Journal* 82(10), pp. 93-98, ISSN 0734-1415

Scallan, A. & Tigerstrom, A. C. (1991). Elasticity of fiber wall, effects of pulping and recycling. *CPPA, 1st Research Forum on Recyclin*, Montreal, pp. 149-154

Scallan, A.M. & Tydeman, A.C. (1992). Swelling and elasticity of the cell walls of pulp fibres, *J. Pulp Paper Sci.* 18(5), pp. 188-193, ISSN 0826-6220

Sinke, R.J. & Westenbroek, A.P.H. (2004). How to deal with the effects of recycling? *Paper and Board*. *8th Pira Paper Recycling Technology Conference*, Prague, Czech Republic, 17-18 February 2004, 17.02. 2011. Available from:
http://www.papierenkarton.nl/publications.htm#2004

Somwand, K., Enomae, T. & Onabe, F. (2002). Effect of Fiber Hornification in Recycling on Bonding Potential at Interfiber Crossings, Confocal Laser Scanning Microscopy. *Japan TAPPI Journal*, Vol.56, No.2, pp. 239 -245, ISSN 0022-815X

Song, X. & Law, K.N. (2010). Kraft pulp oxidation and its inluence of recycling characteristics of fibres. *Cellulose Chemistry and Technology* 44(7-8), pp. 265-270, ISSN 0576-9787

Sutjipto, E.R., Li, K., Pongpattanasuegsa, S. & Nazhad, M.M. (2008). Effect of recycling on paper properties, *TAPPSA (Technical articles)*, 07.02.2011. Available from:
http://www.tappsa.co.za/archive3/index.html

Valtasaari, L. & Saarela, K. (1975). Determination of chain lenght distribution of cellulose by gel permeation chromatography using the tricarbanilate derivate. *Paper och Tra – Paperi ja Puu* 1, pp. 5-10, ISSN 0031-1243

Zanuttini, M. A., McDonough, T. J., Courchene, C. E. & Mocchiutti, P. (2007). Upgrading OCC and recycled liner pulps by medium-consistency ozone treatment. *Tappi Journal* 6(2), pp. 3-8, ISSN 0734-1415

Zervos, S. & Moropoulov, A. (2005). Cotton cellulose ageing in sealed vessels. Kinetic model of autocatalytic depolymerization. *Cellulose* 12, 2005, pp. 485-496, ISSN 0969-0239

Weise, U. & H. Paulapuro. (1996). Relation between fiber shrinkage and hornification. *Das Papier* 50(6), pp. 328-333, ISSN 0031-1340

18

Overview Management Chemical Residues of Laboratories in Academic Institutions in Brazil

Patrícia Carla Giloni-Lima, Vanderlei Aparecido de Lima
and Adriana Massaê Kataoka
Universidade Estadual do Centro Oeste (UNICENTRO)
Brazil

1. Introduction

In the last decades the discussion regarding the environmental theme has acquired concerning proportions for planetary order. Taking into account the civilization crisis in which we are immersed, the environment has been associated to a problem.

During the process of civilization, we perceive an accelerated growth of human population and the various wastes generated as byproducts of their activities surpass the resilience capacity of the environment, generating imbalances in their original cycles. Large discharges of artificial elements in high concentrations (many of them toxic and harmful to life) are constantly deposited in regions where its subsystem revolves around nature's own dynamics. This flow of residues deposition returns to human beings life cycle as pollution, radiation, contamination, acid rain, among others (Jardim, 1993).

In this sense, generation and fate of wastes have been one of the themes treated by environmental education means and the media. This outcome is a consequence of a capitalist society in which consumerism is required for its own maintenance. It is no surprise that the issue of waste generation and its fate are present in scientific discussions, as well as in common sense. It could not be different since each of us has its own direct contribution to this framework.

The technical solution for the problem is fundamental and represents a challenge and an important research field for professionals in the area. But that technical knowledge alone is not adequate to solve the problem. Most waste management initiatives in universities emphasize the importance of environmental education, but merely quote them without exploring their full potential in addressing these issues. These works point out that one of the obstacles for the success of such management programs are the people, and more precisely, their understanding.

Working with people in regards to environmental issues is exactly the field of action of environmental education in which, in general, universities employ professionals set in departments of biology, education, among others. It is worthwhile to ask ourselves: why do not these professionals working at universities communicate with each other? Another important inquiry: why cannot a university composed of professionals that comprise different fields of knowledge work in an interdisciplinary fashion on a problem generated by the university itself? Such discussion has been intensively investigated by universities and disseminated to society.

Next we will try to answer these questions from reflections addressed by environmental education firstly contextualizing this matter in a broader perspective for we do not agree that a punctual approach could satisfactorily explain the complexity of this subject, incurring the risk of simplification, which would be insufficient to the quest for a more effective solution.

1.2 Overview of universities and institutions of higher education and research developed in Brazil

The 2009 census on Higher Education in Brazil, carried out by INEP (Instituto Nacional de Estudos e Pesquisas Educacionais Anísio Teixeira; "National Institute of Educational Studies and Research Anísio Teixeira", http://www.inep.gov.br/) showed that the number of Brazilian Higher Education Institutions (HEI) grows every year (Figure 1).

In 2009, 2 314 HEI were registered, being 89.4 % (p <0.001) private and only 10.6% public institutions. Colleges still account for most HEI's, representing 85 % of them. Nevertheless, the majority of courses are conglomerate on universities, with 49.8% of undergraduate courses.

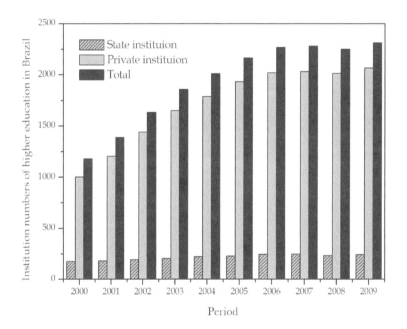

Fig. 1. Evolution the number of Institutions of Higher Education (HEI) - Brazil - 2000/2009. Source: INEP, http://www.inep.gov.br/.

In Brazilian HEI's, the top ten courses in number of enrolled students are: administration, law, pedagogy, engineering, nursing, accountancy, communication, languages and literature, physical education and biology. These courses comprise 66.4% of students enrolled in Brazilian higher education institutions.

Modern Chemistry has revolutionized mankind for many years and is undoubtedly one of the basic sciences more present in people's lives through closely related segments (e.g., textile, chemical, food and pharmaceutical industry). Chemistry has also contributed to develop human life's quality for the last 40 years (Coelho, 2001). Institutes and departments of Chemistry at universities, as well as all segments that make use of chemicals in their daily work, have been confronting the issues linked to treatment and disposal of wastes brought forth in their teaching and research laboratories for many years (Gerbase et al., 2005). This is the reason why Chemistry courses are the target of discussions in this text, as it presents certain intrinsic features concerning the organization system of laboratory classes.

In Brazil, only larger universities have programs for waste management and treatment. Among them are: IQ/USP - Instituto de Química da Universidade de São Paulo ("Chemistry Institute of São Paulo University"); IQSC/USP - Instituto de Química da Universidade de São Paulo do Campus São Carlos ("Chemistry Institute of São Paulo University at São Carlos"); CENA/USP - Centro de Energia Nuclear na Agricultura da Universidade de São Paulo ("Center of Nuclear Energia in Agriculture of São Paulo University"); UNICAMP - Universidade de Campinas ("Campinas State University"); IQ/UERJ - Instituto de Química da Universidade do Estado do Rio de Janeiro ("Chemistry Institute of Rio de Janeiro State University"); DQ/UFPR – Departamento de Química da Universidade Federal do Paraná ("Chemistry Department of Paraná Federal University"); IQ/UFRGS - Instituto de Química da Universidade Federal do Rio Grande do Sul ("Chemistry Institute of Rio Grande do Sul Federal University"); UCB - Universidade Católica de Brasília ("Brasília Catholic University"); UFSCar - Universidade Federal de São Carlos ("São Carlos Federal University"); FURB – Universidade Regional de Blumenau ("Blumenau Regional University"); URI – Universidade Regional Integrada do Alto Uruguai e das Missões ("Alto Uruguai e das Missões Regional Integrate University"); UFRJ – Universidade Federal do Rio de Janeiro ("Rio de Janeiro Federal University") (Afonso et al, 2004); UNIVATES – Centro Universitário Univates ("Univates University Center").

Usually in Brazilian universities, Chemistry departments, in addition to their practice classes in laboratories for their own students, they also attend to other undergraduate courses.

A survey taken into account reagents used in basic experimental subjects within five major areas of Chemistry at Brazilian universities is presented. It includes about 180 substances among the ones applied and developed in laboratory activities. The curricular program for Chemistry undergraduates comprises five areas of experimental Chemistry: Experimental General Chemistry, Analytical Chemistry, Physical Chemistry, Organic Chemistry and Inorganic Chemistry.

Experimental General Chemistry covers the initial concepts of Chemistry, when students start their learning process in experimental classes in laboratories. The subject program involves the following topics: laboratory safety, nomenclature and characteristics of glassware, measures of mass, volume, density and temperature, physical and chemical processing, standardization of substances, acid/base titrations and determination of levels of substances in our daily lives. Although this course is an introductory practice, in which students carry out their first experiments in Chemistry, a certain number of substances are required for the development of such laboratory experiments.

The second area of experimental subjects is Qualitative and Quantitative Analytical Chemistry. Chemical reactions experienced in these subjects aim to identify and isolate cations and anions by reactions of neutralization, precipitation, complexation, oxidation-reduction, release of gases, as well as volumetric and gravimetric determinations.

Students are divided into groups of three or four for laboratory practices. A laboratory technician prepares and organizes the class so that students, under the professor's supervision, carry out experiments. In these practice classes, the volume of substances generated is relatively small when compared to industries; however, there is a wide range of chemical wastes generated. The list of chemicals produced in practice classes is considerable, so we listed some of the most important shown in Table 1.

The third area of experimental subject in Chemistry is called Physical Chemistry (Table 1) and deals with concepts of energy associated with molecules and chemical reactions, electrochemistry, the laws of ideal gases, chemical kinetics and chemical and physical adsorption.

The fourth area is Organic Chemistry, which studies carbon compounds and their reactions. There are two experimental subjects, organic Chemistry I and II. In those subjects, most compounds that are required and generated in these classes are organic and are also presented in Table 1.

Chemistry area	Chemistry products
1. Experimental general Chemistry	sodium hydroxide, oxalic acid, hydrochloric acid, benzoic acid, gasoline, solid iodine, phenolphthalein, methyl orange, thymol blue, magnesium, ammonium dichromate, phenol red sodium salt, alizarin yellow R sodium salt, methyl red sodium salt, bromo phenol, bromocresol green sultone, sodium bromide, sodium iodide, strontium chloride, copper(II) sulfate, chromium(III) chloride, potassium chloride, nickel(II) chloride, potassium iodate, potassium iodide, ethylene glycol, aniline, sodium sulfate, manganese(II) sulfate, iron(II) sulphate, aluminum sulfate, potassium nitrate, barium chloride, ferric chloride, butanol, ammonium carbonate, calcium hydroxide, cobalt(II) nitrate, lead II nitrate, sodium phosphate monobasic, ascorbic acid, lithium chloride, potassium permanganate, calcium cyanide, cobalt(II) sulphate.
2. Analytical Chemistry	sodium hydroxide, nitric acid, sulfuric acid, Hydrochloric acid, potassium thiocyanate, nickel salts, potassium ferrocyanide, and heavy metals in the form of their salts, as salts of silver, chromate and potassium dichromate, lead salts like lead II chloride, mercuric chloride, copper II salts and cadmium salts.
3. Physical Chemistry	chromate and potassium dichromate, ammonium thiocyanate, ethyl acetate, acetone, acetic acid, ethanol, naphthalene, diphenylamine, sodium dodecyl sulfate, copper sulfate, potassium chlorate, manganese(IV) oxide, phenol, zinc sulfate, nickel sulphate and silver chloride.
4. Organic Chemistry	glycerin, benzoic acid, dinitrobenzene, glucose, copper(II) oxide, barium hydroxide, sodium ferrocyanide, aminobenzene, benzoic acid, ethoxy ethane, hydrochloric acid, ethanol, cyclohexanol, sulfuric acid, cyclohexene, potassium permanganate, nitrobenzene, acetanilide, 2-propanol, acetone, n-butyl ether, phenylamine, sodium nitrite, copper sulfate, adipic acid, carbon tetrachloride, liquid bromine, eugenol, urea,

	formaldehyde, salicylic acid, methyl salicylate, acetic anhydride, acetylsalicylic acid, 4-aminoazobenzene, caffeine, ethyl acetate, methanol, dichloromethane, benzanilide, 4-nitroacetanilide, methyl benzoate, hydroquinone diacetate, benzocaine, 1,3-dibenzoylacetone, butyraldehyde, benzaldehyde, dimethyl phthalate, phthalic anhydride, 2,4,6-tribromoaniline, methyl salicylate, isopropyl bromide, among others.
5. Inorganic Chemistry	potassium permanganate, sulfuric acid, hydrogen peroxide solution, sodium thiosulfate, sulfur, potassium iodate, sodium metabisulfite, potassium hydroxide, sodium hypochlorite, ferrous sulfate, nickel(II) nitrate, cobalt(II) chloride, calcium carbonate, magnesium carbonate, magnesium chloride, ammonium chloride, ammonium hydroxide solution, strontium chloride, ammonium sulfate, barium chloride, acetic acid, sodium tetraborate, aluminum sulfate, sodium carbonate, nickel(II) nitrate, lead(II) nitrate, barium sulfate, calcium sulfate, magnesium sulfate, strontium chloride, sodium acetate, ferric chloride, ammonium thiocyanate, sodium chloride, potassium chloride, sodium bromide, potassium iodide, ammonium chloride, calcium hydroxide, ammonium iron(II) sulfate hexahydrate, potassium fluoride, potassium thiocyanate, copper(II) sulfate pentahydrate, lithium chloride, methanol, potassium oxalate, ethanol, cobalt(II) sulfate heptahydrate, sodium silicate, potassium chromium(III) oxalate trihydrate, tris(ethylenediamine) nickel(II) chloride hydrate, cobalt (II) nitrate, tris (ethylenediamine) cobalt(III) nitrate, tris (ethylenediamine) nickel(II) chloride hydrate, nickel(II) acetate tetrahydrate, ammonium nitrate, tetra amin cobalt (III) carbonate, pentaamminechlorocobalt(III) chloride, tris (oxalate) chromate (III), potassium copper chloride (II), tartaric acid, formaldehyde solution.

Table 1. A survey of reagents used in basic experimental subjects in five major areas of Chemistry in Brazilian universities.

The last but not the least important area listed herein is Inorganic Chemistry. It is the branch of Chemistry that studies chemical elements and nature substances that do not display carbon in their structures, investigates structures, properties and explains the mechanism of their reactions and transformations. In Experimental Inorganic Chemistry, various chemicals are necessary for reactions (Table 1), as well as other several chemicals are formed after reactions.

The great variety of substances used or generated during practice classes usually makes waste management in educational and research institutions or similar service providers more intricate than in industry. Unlike industries, these institutions generate small amounts of waste, most of which in laboratories. These wastes consist of a wide variety of substances, toxic or non-toxic, including new compounds of unknown toxicity. Besides, their compositions change on every new research project or experiment (Gerbase et al., 2005; Tavares & Bendassolli, 2005; Jardim, 1998; Ashbrook & Reinhardt, 1985).

Implantation of a Program Management of Chemical Residues (PMCR) should whenever possible accomplish the priority scales or hierarchy (Jardim, 1998):

- Prevent waste generation (hazardous or not);
- Minimize the amount of hazardous wastes that are inevitably generated;
- Segregate and concentrate waste currents in order to make possible and economically viable a managing activity;
- Reuse internal or external wastes;
- Recycle material or energetic components of the waste;
- Keep all waste at its most treatable conformation;
- Safely treat and dispose wastes.

In this context, can we achieve this premise if we promote changes in daily activities of professionals: professors, researchers and laboratory technicians directly involved in the generation of chemical wastes (Nolasco et al., 2006; Tavares & Bendassolli, 2005; Singh, 2000):

- a modification of a certain process (or analytical method), substitution of raw materials or inputs;
- minimization using microscale techniques;
- segregation of waste into different classes of compatibility;
- reapplication of waste inevitably produced by recycling or reuse;
- treatment through acid/base neutralization and chemical precipitation of metals.

In addition, practices of advanced oxidation processes (AOPs) (Pera-Titus et al., 2004; Perez et al., 2006), treatment and heavy metals recovery (Kurniawan et al., 2006), are already commonly used in several treatments of substances generated in laboratory. We can recommend other easily handling practices to reduce generated chemical wastes.

One example is the preparation of the dye 1 - (p-nitrophenylazo)-2-naphthol from p-nitroacetanilide. Initially in experiments performed in Organic Chemistry I, where the p-nitroacetanilide is prepared, serving as a substrate for the next reaction, the production of 1 - (p-nitrophenylazo)-2-naphthol. This last reaction is performed in experimental classes of Organic Chemistry II. Therefore, the product generated in a practice class is applied in another, minimizing then generation of chemical wastes in class.

We may also employ an alternative related to separation and identification of cations and anions in the subject Experimental Analytic Chemistry. Cations and anions not harmful to environment could be normally determined, but the identification of heavy metals, such as copper, silver, cadmium, lead, mercury and chromium, could be applied a single time. In experiments to be performed with these metals, procedures could be filmed and photographed step-by-step. Later, this material would be used to set a database with films and pictures containing all steps developed in the identification and determination of these elements. Then, the same experiments with these metals would not be conducted later, in the way that students of the following years would attend to audio-video classes, decreasing generation and supply of toxic residuals in laboratories.

The final disposal of wastes may be achieved in industrial disposal sites or other adequate locations, avoiding the misinformation that incineration and co-processing are ways of disposal. In such processes residual material is burnt, gases that should be treated are produced and ashes are subsequently sent to landfills (Nolasco et al., 2006).

The number of scientific publications coming from Brazil has grown steadily over the past 26 years, culminating in 26 482 in 2008 (Figure 2). In parallel, Brazil´s international contribution with articles has climbed from 0.8 % in 1992 to 2.7 % in 2008. There is a correlation between this increase and the growing number of PhDs awarded annually (UNESCO, 2010).

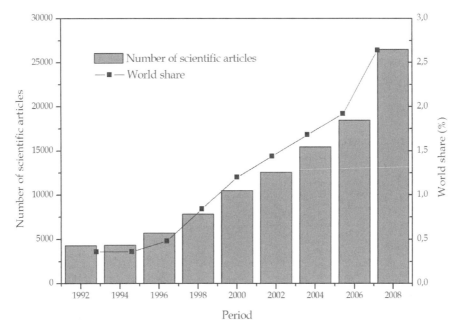

Fig. 2. Evolution of number of scientific publications from Brazil in period 1992 to 2008. Source: UNESCO, 2010.

We must be aware that benefits from our professional and scientific activities (publications, patents, scientific recognition, development of new products and technologies) may generate, on the other hand, chemical residues from varying degrees of dangerousness. They may require appropriate chemical treatment before being sent to final disposal (Afonso et al., 2003).

Universities represent places where scientific knowledge is produced, from where usually their new products and technologies arise, building up its part in society and directly interfering in it. We know that training goes well beyond the execution of a specific undergraduate program, experiences through contact with professors, laboratory technicians and staff, apprenticeships, basic scientific research activities, tutoring and degree dissertations, among others. They surpass content or technical aspects of each area. Thus, we are concerned about the example being given to students when professionals apparently turn their backs to such problem. That is, students experience a total lack of accountability before an issue present in their own immediate environment. There is no denying that such experience will be part of this future professional education with possible repercussions in their professional future.

Universities, as opinion builders, should take advantage of all opportunities to create conditions for self-evaluation, seeking the formation of future professionals with environmental awareness, ethics and co-responsibility. In this sense is relevant to emphasize the fact that there is no sustainability in the social-environmental structure of universities, either in the relationship among people, or the relationship among nature, people and their residuals.

Another aspect to be taken into account is that, in the structure of the university, still prevail the issues created by knowledge fragmentation. This criticism is made by some parties in the university itself through scientific papers, books and lectures, though it does not resonate inside its own walls.

We should not forget that universities are embedded in a social liberal context that seeks to adapt the principles of economic liberalism to the conditions of modern capitalism. Then, the entire academic community is suffocated by a "market" that requires high productivity and consequently hinders an integrated vision and a careful look to itself.

In this context, environmental education plays a crucial role which can manage hazardous wastes in universities. In order to start wondering how could be this performance of environmental education, it is important to comprehend the significance of environmental education and what are its principles.

1.3 Brazilian legislation relevant to the theme

There is a tendency in our society to consider harmful to the environment only those activities that generate large amounts of wastes. Consequently, these are great generators always under the supervision of state environmental protection agencies and subject to punishment. Small waste generators, such as educational and research institutions, biochemical and physicochemical laboratories, are usually considered not harmful to environment by inspection agencies and, therefore, rarely investigated as for discarding their chemicals wastes (Jardim, 1993).

Solid, industrial, radioactive and health services wastes are under control of a specific legislation with standard rules and procedures for storing, transportation and final disposal. In these cases the national and state legislations indicate specific controlling agencies, and a valid principle is that polluter pays for its violations. This principle is part of the environmental law that forces the polluter to compensate all damages caused to the environment.

In Brazil, Law 6.938/81 concerning the Environment National Policy establishes a "Objective Liability" which does not require proof of guilt in case of possible environment damage. That is, for a potential polluter to be punished it is solely necessary to demonstrate the link cause-effect between an activity developed by an organization and the given environmental damage. In summary, it means that a pollutant, even though being produced in acceptable concentrations established by current law, may cause environmental damage, subjecting responsible to compensation. Moreover, even if any indirect damage is detected, and since its connection to an organization is testified, the latter will be held responsible (Machado, 2002).

Applying the "Objective Liability" Law is hindered by the difficulty in inspection procedures in several industry areas, research institutions and universities, inducing environmental risks and contributing to its degradation. This problem is almost always avoided until more serious threats, iniquities and environmental conflicts may reach people directly engaged to these contexts, such as inhabitants surrounding a degraded area where residuals present potential and effectively high levels of pollution and contamination (Penatti , 2008).

ABETRE (Associação Brasileira de Empresas de Tratamento de Resíduos; "Brazilian Association of Waste Management Companies") estimate that only 22% of approximately

2.9 million tons of industrial hazardous wastes annually produced in the country receive adequate treatment (ABETRE, 2002). It is also plausible to assume that waste production is not exclusive of industries, once laboratories in universities, colleges and research facilities also generate chemical residuals in high diversity and low volume, yet it may represent 1% of all hazardous wastes generated in a developed country (Ashbrook & Reinhardt, 1985).

Such verification leads us to the fact that the matter of chemical residuals management, originated from research and teaching activities, should be taken as discussions and research themes that deserve more space in the Brazilian academic cycle. This should also be motivated by the important role that research and educational institutions play towards formation of human resources accustomed to environmental management practices (Afonso et al., 2003; Alberguini et al., 2003; Jardim, 1998).

A survey regarding several management programs at institutions of higher education shows that management of their own wastes is an actual concern for most of them, and they are aware of the issues related to environmental degradation. However, between a spoken or written commitment and effective actions, there is a great distance.

In this sense, we cannot just criticize universities for not complying with legislation, because, in most cases, the lack of infrastructure and resources, as well as public policies focused on the matter, limits the adequate disposal of wastes.

As many industries do, colleges and universities encounter thorny problems dealing with hazardous wastes. Industry and academia alike are saddled with the rising cost of waste management and face sensitive liability for costs of waste cleanup (Ashbrook & Reinhardt, 1985). One institution experiencing problems with the dramatically rising costs of hazardous waste management is the University of Illinois. In 1977, the University spent $2,000 to dispose of 100 drums of chemical wastes. By 1982, the cost of disposing of 265 drums had risen to $46,000, an 87 % annual increase in the cost of storing, transportation and disposing of wastes in a landfill (Ashbrook & Reinhardt, 1985).

Gerbase et al. (2005) suggest some actions meant to funding, research and teaching regulation agencies in Brazil, in order to defeat financial difficulties inherent to the installation of programs for managing hazardous waste, such as:

- resource allocation and specific convocations to Environmental and Hazardous Waste Management (chemical, biological and radioactive) in research and educational institutions;
- establishment of working groups of experts in order to propose standard rules for Safety in Chemistry for research and educational institutions;
- a quality criterion to be included as an item for evaluation by Ministério da Educação e Cultura ("Ministry for Education and Culture"; MEC) and Coordenadoria de Aperfeiçoamento de Profissional de Ensino Superior (" Coordination for Improvement of Higher Education Professional"; CAPES), the existence, or project implementation, of a program for hazardous waste management in graduate and undergraduate institutions for education and research.

Orloff and Falk (2003), discussing international perspectives on hazardous waste practices, suggest that an effective hazardous waste management program is a collaborative effort and must include input from all relevant parties: federal, state, and local government officials, citizens, academia, and representatives of industry and non-governmental organizations. Citizens are important stakeholders and their input about waste management is crucial to ensure acceptance of society.

2. Environmental education (EE) as a tool in the process of toxic waste management

Several authors have addressed the lack of environmental awareness within academic communities as an obstacle to greening (Riera, 1996; Meyerson & Massey, 1995; Creighton, 1999). The consensus is that people must be educated before a change can take place. As for the sampled institutions, a double set of morals seems to exist. On the one hand, they all considered the lack of awareness to prevent a greening process within energy and waste management from taking place. However, practically nothing had been done to raise environmental awareness.

The lack of environmental awareness was considered significant because people do not know how to act sustainable. In other words, investing in waste and energy reducing devices has no meaning unless people know how and why it should be carried out. Decision makers must be familiar with the benefits of greening to establish environmental policies and to invest in green devices, and academics must realize the necessity of being "green" role models to their students (Dahle & Neumayer, 2001). The importance of raising environmental awareness at high education institutions is now being recognized from various bodies; the UK Sustainable Development Education Panel (1999) notes that:

"All further and higher educational institutions should have staff fully trained and competent in sustainable development, and should be providing all students with relevant sustainable development learning opportunities."

In Brazil, EE is guided by the Treaty on Environmental Education for Sustainable Societies, Environmental Education Policy and PRONEA (National Environmental Education Program) and has sought to build an interdisciplinary perspective to understand the issues that affect relationships between human groups and their environment and to intervene on them, activating several areas of knowledge (Carvalho, 1998).

For the education to integrate in the process of Environmental Management, it is required that "conditions necessary for production and acquisition of knowledge and skills are provided and attitudes are developed attempting to individual and corporate participation in dealing with environmental resources and in conceiving and applying decisions that affect quality of physical-natural and sociocultural means" (Quintas, 2000).

Thus, it is clear that we cannot expect a ready recipe for how environmental education deals with the management process. We may however start out a discussion on the principles of environmental education, having in mind that one of the aspects to be considered is the quest for the solution of a problem through a dialogue amongst actors involved in the problem. Therefore, the construction of a management process will be conducted considering the several contributions by the actors involved, as well as its adequacy to local reality.

The environmental educator must look for the meanings of human action that are in the roots of socio-environmental processes that seem to synthesize the core of interpretative making of environmental education. By demonstrating cultural and political meanings taking place in the interactive processes society-nature, the educator would be a translator of perceptions – which are also, on their turn, social and historical interpretations – that mobilize several interests and human interferences in the environment. In the opposite direction of an objective vision, in which interpreting the environment would mean conceive it in its factual reality, describe its laws, mechanisms and operation, one should demonstrate the horizons of historical-cultural sense that configure relationships with the environment for a certain human community and in a given time (Carvalho, 1998).

Our consideration on the contribution of environmental education is twofold. The first would be a broader approach, whose fundamental idea would be the accomplishment of an Environmental Education Policy for Sustainability at the University. The implementation of such policy, involving the entire academic community prioritizing the search for solutions for experienced environmental issues and often generated by the university itself, which would be extremely desirable, then, includes the toxic residues problem on a broader context, due to the complexity of the environmental problems nature. In this sense, the hazardous wastes problem would be treated like the solid wastes, sewage contamination, the rationalization of water and energy consumption, the quality of environment and interpersonal relationships at work, the institutional master plan, among others. Such an environmental policy would contribute in the sense of giving direction to where the toxic wastes matter resides in broader context. The acceptance of a systemic approach would be suggested, with the possibility to become clearer, as some problems may bear a common cause or a common solution. Hence, the possibility to combine financial resources would be eased, as well as the so much recommended interdisciplinary integration.

The other approach would be associated to more technical aspects directly linked to management of self-generated wastes. In this sense, the interview methodologies, environment social representations, among others, would be applied at all times according to necessity, mainly during the development of work immediately with involved actors.

3. Overview of PMCR implanted and proposition integrated management of chemical residues (IMCR) based on a environmental education policy for sustainability in universities (EEPSU)

The system of environmental management is characterized by promoting sustainable development through a local procedure, aiming to develop a sense of global environmental responsibility. This system establishes in its execution general and specific processes for each section of activity in order to engage and involve all organization members. That is the reason why the institutional support is essential and the commitment of the highest hierarchies is an essential and ideal condition. Nevertheless, even when unconditional and unrestricted institutional support is lacking, is no reason for the process not to occur.

A critical analysis on several programs of laboratory chemical wastes management at universities carried out by Nolasco et al. (2006) reveals a significant homogeneity regards adopted principles and emphasizes the opinion of professionals directly related to the execution of such programs. These professionals select as main difficulties the investment need in infrastructure and institutional support.

Coelho (2001) states that within universities there is no lack of technical capability, yet political willingness of institutions in giving proper relevance to the matter, as well as the execution of internal policies, widely discussed and disseminated, involving the entire academic community and also support for scientific research by the responsible organs.

Izzo (2000) acknowledges other aspects that complicates the implementation of PMCR in universities, HEI and research institutes and hinders the program coordination: (1) decentralization of these institutions in which different administration sections and departments work independently; (2) rotation of undergraduate and graduate students; (3) variation on research projects conducted in these institutions; (4) most of them do not present a centralized purchase and storing section.

Variations in research projects and regular changes in lines of work reflect peculiarities in wastes generated in the universities when compared to industries. They present reduced volume, though also a great diversity of compounds, which makes any establishment of a chemical treatment and or a standardized final disposal difficult (Gerbase et al., 2005; Jardim, 1998; Ashbrook & Reinhardt, 1985).

The proposal to establish a Policy on Environmental Education for Sustainability in Universities (EEPSU) aims to unify planning, control and supervision of natural resources appliance that we use during our activities with awareness and always in search for sustainability. It also has to do with us becoming responsible for the consequences of using these resources, trying to minimize our consumerism, avoiding waste of natural resources and promoting reduction of wastes generation of all kinds. All this tends to minimize any type of environmental impact.

The policy established a pathway to best practice by requiring the establishment of an environmental management plan that would set out how the university would manage issues of environmental concern and interest "bearing in mind the commitment to principles of ecology-sustainable development". The universities surveyed (Australian and New Zealand) have an environmental policy. The importance of developing an environmental plan is to establish concrete guidelines. Where a policy states that a university is committed to sustainable development, a plan will outline how sustainability will be included in university operations. Other aspects are that, by outlining future environmental development, plans facilitate accountability and leave the university open to criticism. Plans can foster participation and representation; committees and working groups may be established as representatives of the university community (Carpenter & Meehan, 2002).

Dahle and Neumayer (2001) believed that the most important measure for reducing or overcoming established barriers to green university is to raise environmental awareness within campus communities, i.e. sustainable behavior cannot be expected to take place unless people understand the benefits and importance of doing so. Creighton (1999) suggests that, to achieve a "green" university that uses resources efficiently, creates little or no waste, and takes full responsibility for any waste that it does generate, a fundamental change in the thinking behind routine decisions of university administration, staff, faculty and students is needed.

These alternatives can be achieved through the implementation of EEPSU increasing ethical conscience and co-responsible for the academic community (teachers, laboratory technicians and administrative and academic), which lead to formation of professionals aware of their citizenship and their professional role.

Policies are necessary, it must be remembered that they are abstract statements of principles that, while creating a positive "environment", do little to improve environmental performance; it is only when policies become operationalised through the establishment of a plan and subsequent programs that environmental performance can be improved (Carpenter & Meehan, 2002).

The Integrated Management for Chemical Residues in High Education Institutions (IMCRHEI) proposed by Giloni-Lima and Lima (2008) drew the scientific community's interest, notwithstanding, as it was published in a Brazilian journal and written in Portuguese, its circulation was restrained. In this sense, we take the opportunity to spread it after revision and expansion, aiming to offer an integrated proposal, as its name implies, and in accordance with PEESU and other aspects of this chapter. It is worth mentioning that the MCRP is one of the problems experienced by HEI's and will be addressed by EEPSU, and the former may happen even if the latter does not. On the other hand, if the policy is active, waste management would be part of a wider process.

The participation of academics at all stages of the process would be of great value, because they would have the opportunity to demonstrate their interest in various working groups and act as multipliers, acting in the research for information and generating data applied for management of chemical residues.

The general structure of the flow chart proposed (Scheme 1) consists of four stages which

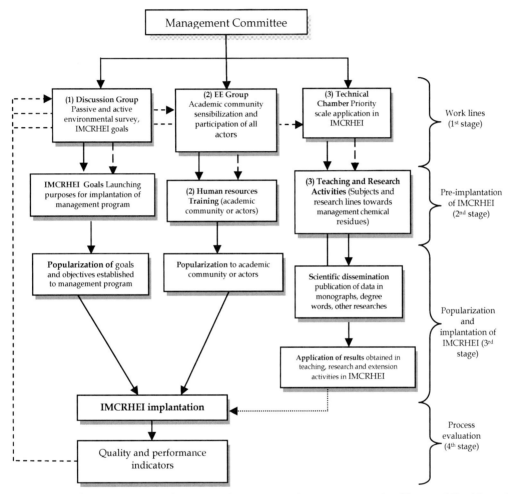

Fig. 3. Basic flow chart to implantation the Integrated Management for Chemical Residues in High Education Institutions (IMCRHEI). Solid lines: direction to basic lines of work; dashed lines: feedback; dotted lines: direct application to results in the implantation of IMCRHEI.

start from the constitution of a Manager Committee, which will coordinate the development process for deploying IMCRHEI, employing the formation of three Basic Work lines - 1st stage, with the formation of (1) Discussion Group, (2) Environmental Education Group and (3) of the Technical Chamber. The results of work developed in the first stage will define the main points to be worked out in stage 2, Pre-implantation of the Management Program. Once initiated this step, after gathering all basic requirements needed, i.e., setting goals and objectives of the management program, as well as a minimum training required for compliance, from where stage 3 - Divulgation and Implantation IMCRHEI can be initiated, one should look for unambitious and real goals, as failure in a first attempt tends to discourage further attempts (Jardim, 1998).

It is worth noting that there is a consensus that environmental education is an important tool in the execution of waste management programs, though they are usually based on activities of passive and active environmental surveys (task proposed to discussion group) and application of hierarchy scales proposed by technical chamber, where EE is only mentioned in almost all programs.

Activities of teaching and research for its peculiarities have a proper time to be concluded and execute the application of its results (dotted line in Scheme 1). The 4th stage, Process Evaluation, is the time to review achievements or failures from the Quality and Performance Indicators established by the basic lines of work, which can forward their findings to promote the necessary adjustments to the process as a whole.

The learning process generate information to permit self-regulatory and self-correcting activities to occur, while involving monitoring, applying systems thinking, and performing self-assessment. Without the use of environmental indicators for monitoring, environmental audits and self-assessments, learning might not take place. These tools enhance learning process (Herremans & Allwright, 2000).

Creation of the Manager Committee is based on a discussion process for the formation of groups of professionals from various fields of training and identified with the EEPSU. The form of constitution of the Manager Committee and groups which are willing to develop the lines of work can follow the own institution dynamics, or still can start from the creation of a discussion forum which may represent an open space for discussions about the theme, circulation of information about the institutional reality regarding the current management of self-generated waste, to exchange experiences, and especially will enable professionals to evaluate the profile that would be more suitable, aware and willing to engage in coordination of the process.

We suggest the formation of a multidisciplinary group, involving faculty members from areas of administration, chemistry and biology, education, and student body of the institution to coordinate the three basic lines of work (Stage 1) of IMCRHEI implementation, aiming to integrate the academic and scientific community in the process, being as follows:

1. Discussion Groups: These groups might work in survey information with two types of waste: the passive (which includes reaction from debris, passing through solid waste and bottles without labels) and active (continuously generated, the result of routines in the generating unit). The characterization of passives shall be equated as well and using simple tests (Jardim, 1998; Armour, 1996).

2. Group of Environmental Education aims to involve professionals in the field of Environmental Education (EE) and to promote a line of work to undertake a process to make the academic community aware of the relevance of the thematic, even before the establishment of plan goals. These professionals may also work in developing an Environmental Education Program based on information provided by discussion groups (1), in order to assist processes of dissemination and training of the academic community.

3. Technical Chamber: this group may act to evaluate the practical activities carried out in laboratories (in conjunction with the teachers responsible for them), the implantation of the priority scale (Jardim, 1998) seeking the best alternatives within its institutional reality. This group can also act as a generator of theme for future research directed to

monographs, works of completion and until the creation of lines of research in order to structure the management of hazardous chemicals or not, the proposition of safety standards chemistry, etc.

The environmental education group, due to its interdisciplinary, contextualized, critical and emancipatory nature must somehow be involved with groups 1 and 3. This situation is justified by the need for this group to understand all relationships involved in the management process. Its performance may occur at all times that involve human relations.

It is worth emphasizing that the participation of all stakeholders is crucial. In order to increase likelihood of successful management, actors must be heard and have opportunity of opinion for it generates commitment. A commonly used method for environmental education to achieve this practice is the research participant. The technique of social representations also brings great contributions. A social representation is the common sense that one has about a given topic (Reigota, 2010), through this technique, one can find out scientific concepts of how they were learned and perceived by people. It can also be understood as a set of principles built interactively and shared by different groups that understand and transform reality through it (Moscovici, 2003).

It is important to note that the information given here should be taken only as suggestions, because, as previously mentioned, the search for the paths to be followed will be built up by the group. Thus, the EE could help at times as in the situations listed below:

- assessment process through investigation of social representations of those involved: professors, students and laboratory technicians;
- in planning, involving results previously surveyed;
- on the destination, by minimizing waste generation or disposal, and proper destination, developing in all groups involved an environmental and ethical conscience;
- disseminating and instruction other laboratories that generate waste and chemicals which are not under the responsibility of professionals in the field;
- internal and external divulgation of the management program implantation.

The training program for the academic community may act in the formation of specialized human resources in the management and disposal of chemical waste, both undergraduates and graduates, which extends beyond technical skills, may further strengthen ethical and co-responsible conscience in regards of chemical safety in workplace and environmental liability.

Training courses could also involve practical actions that try to minimize environmental impact and risk to those involved with direct or indirect engagement with hazardous wastes, including chemical, biological and radioactive ones produced during teaching and research procedures (Gerbase at al., 2005). The acquiring funds could occur through projects submitted to funding agencies that support research through specific calls, or partnerships with public and private organizations that can be later profited with costless courses and supporting programs for social inclusion of people without qualifications. Such actions allow sharing with society the fundamental concepts of environmental wastes management through courses to the community (Bendassolli et al., 2003).

The problems raised by the Technical Chamber in implementing a priority scale (Jardim, 1998), within the activities developed in the generator unit, may guide teaching, research and extension activities to be developed. The creation of specific subjects or others related to the theme and the availabiliby of trainings (Alberguini et al., 2003; Tavares & Bendassolli,

2005; Bendassolli et al., 2003) are able to promote an interdisciplinary approach, stimulating the formation of academic student within a more holistic perspective, working on his technical training and environmental responsibility, and to promote ethical attitudes improving the profile of the future professional. In regards to research procedures, there are innumerable possibilities to include researchers, technicians and undergraduate and graduate students in generating data and information that reach the basic precepts and its major aspects in order to achieve the requirements of current environmental legislation.

Internal and external divulgation (Stage 3) of the Integrated Plan for Waste Management is essential for awareness and dissemination of ideas and attitudes that corroborate the process. Nolasco et al. (2006) posits that utilization of intercommunication ways in the unit eases maintenance and continuity of the program. The World Wide Web (Internet) has been extensively used for this purpose, facilitating communication and access to information relevant to the MCRP.

The fourth stage of the process is extremely important because it will promote an assessment process as a whole, through the use of Indicators of Quality and Performance, which could provide an evaluation of the process efficiency depending on the products you want to achieve allowing the use of feedback mechanisms and recurrence of achievements and failures, redirecting them in order to reach the intended goals and objectives.

Some elements that can assist in structuring indicators of quality and performance are: identifying the goals to be achieved, defining forms of measurement that may be used and for each raised indicator, how these are calculated, how often the assessment will occur and how to interpret results. These can provide information to raise the specific points in which objectives and goals are not yet reached and allowing to evaluate in which line (1, 2 or 3) adjustments are necessary and feedback subsequent actions (dashed lines in Scheme 1).

3. Conclusion

Chemistry is a basic science that has brought great benefits to humanity and is present in everyday life, in textile, food, pharmaceutical, agrochemical, petrochemical industries, etc., revolutionizing our lives in bringing comfort and technologies that translate into improved life quality and expectancy. This science, due to its own features, is linked to progress and development, representative characters of contemporary society, which, in search for life quality, generates concerning environmental impacts. We need to handle environmental impacts as political matters and to conceive the environment as a common public property, as well as its care as a political right, expanding its comprehension and citizenship practice.

The proposal for a Policy on Environmental Education for Sustainability at the University is conceived in order to assess possible environmental impacts related to activities undertaken by universities and by means of technical and scientific competence, the pursuit of interdisciplinary solutions, and more sustainable alternatives for managing, treatment, storage and disposal of chemical wastes generated in their teaching and research activities. The establishment of a sustainability policy can also facilitate access to financial resources, scarce on this issue, but unexpendable.

We regard that environmental legislation in Brazil and in the world is evolving and trying to adjust to technological, economical and social developments. Despite the lack of legislation specifically defined for peculiarities of waste generated in Institutions of Higher Education, a great deal of universities in Brazil and the world have expressed their concern on the issue, taking on their responsibility for the development of science and technology towards management of chemical waste.

Management of hazardous chemicals in universities is a problem that must be seriously considered and with responsibility, and face the consequences regarding the relevance of professional formation to academics with ability to fairly practice its profession committed to citizenship. The integrated management program for chemical residues in HEI's, pervades legal, educational, scientific and environmental management aspects. It involves the entire academic community where the priority would be the establishment of an environmental policy in the institution. The process begins with the composition of a manager committee that coordinates and directs the formation of the three basic lines of work: discussion groups, environmental education and the technical chamber (1st stage). The second stage is the IMCRHEI pre-implantation that establishes goals and objectives and where the sensibilization process on academic community begins, both encompassing the participation of all actors involved. It is important to emphasize that every line of work has different times for its consolidation, in particular the activities to be undertaken by the technical chamber. The proposal anticipates the circulation of goals and objectives planned cooperatively and, after implantation (stage 3), performance and quality indicators would be used in the evaluation process (stage 4), a feedback mechanism supports good results and indicates alternatives in case of failures.

Environmental education plays an extremely essential role in this process, since through the joint participation of the entire academic community (professors, administrative and laboratory technicians, students), shows where is the lack of sustainability in our activities (wastage, misuse of natural resources, in generating and disposing of solid and chemicals wastes) and, associated with institutional expertise, explains how to more sustainably execute them. Concerning more specific issues, such as the management of chemical wastes, EE presents an integrated proposal, where it is present since the conception of the politic-philosophical proposal, in sensibilization and training of actors involved.

EE may also act to minimize problems caused by knowledge fragmentation, helping to sensibilize skillful professionals to work in an ethical, conscious, responsible, critical and contextualized manner. Professionals able to execute their tasks in a "green" form, knowing the basic procedures of safety and environmental protection, both within and outside the university.

4. References

Associação Brasileira de Empresas de Tratamento de Resíduos, ABETRE. (July 2002). Brasil trata apenas 22% dos resíduos industriais perigosos, In: ABETRE, 25.04.2011, Available from http://www.abetre.org.br/noticia_completa.asp?NOT_COD=373

Alberguini, L. B. A.; Silva, L. C. & Rezende, M. O. O. (2003). Laboratório de Resíduos Químicos do Campus USP-São Carlos – Resultados da experiência pioneira em gestão e gerenciamento de resíduos em um campo universitário, *Química Nova*, Vol. 26, No.2, (Fevereiro/2003), pp. 291-295, ISSN 0100-4042

Afonso, J. C.; Noronha, N. A.; Felipe, R. P. & Freidinger, N. (2003). Gerenciamento de Resíduos Laboratoriais: Recuperação de elementos e preparo para descarte final, *Química Nova*, Vol. 26, No.4, (Outubro/2002), pp. 602-611, ISSN 0100-4042

Armour, M. A. (1996). *Hazardous Laboratory Chemicals Disposal Guide*, Press Inc. Boca Raton, ISBN 1–56670–108–2, Florida

Ashbrook, P. C. & Reinhardt, P. A. (1985). Hazardous Wastes in Academia, *Environmental Science & Technology*, Vol. 19, No.2, (Febuary/1985), pp. 1150-1155, ISSN 0013-936X

Bendassolli, J. A. ; Tavares, G. A. ; Ignoto, R. F. & Rosseti, A. L. R. M. (2003). Gerenciamento de Resíduos Químicos e Águas Servidas no Laboratório de Isótopos Estáveis do CENA/USP, *Química Nova*, Vol.26, No.4, (Abril/2003), pp. 612-617, ISSN 0100-4042 INEP (Instituto Nacional de Estudos e Pesquisas Anísio Teixeira), Ministério da Educação e Cultura (MEC). (2010). *Resumo Técnico – Censo da Educação Superior de 2009*, 23/March/2011, Available from: http://www.inep.gov.br/>, Brazil

Carpenter, D. & Meehan, B. (2002). Mainstreaming environmental management: Case studies from Australasian universities. *International Journal of Sustainability in Higher Education*, Vol.3, No.1, pp.19-37, MCB University Press 1467-6370

Carvalho, I. C. M. (1998). *Educação Ambiental : A formação do sujeito ecológico* (1 ed.), Cortez, ISBN 85-249-1068-2, São Paulo.

Coelho, F. A. S. (2001). Segurança Química nas Instituições de Ensino Superior, *Ciência Hoje*, Vol.29, no.169, (Março/2001), pp. 63-65 ISSN 0101-8515

Creighton, S.H. (1999). *Greening the Ivory Tower, Improving the Environmental Track Record of Universities, Colleges, and Other Institutions*, MIT Press, Cambridge, MA ISBN 0-262-53151-8

Dahle, M. & Neumayer, E. (2001). Overcoming barriers to campus greening: A survey among higher educational institutions in London, UK, International *Journal of Sustainability in Higher Education*, Vol.2, No.2, pp.139-160, MCB University Press 1467-6370

Gerbase, A. E.; Coelho, F. S.; Machado, P. F. L. & Ferreira, V. F. (2005). Gerenciamento de Resíduos Químicos em Instituições de Ensino e Pesquisa, *Química Nova*, Vol.28, No.1, (Fevereiro/2005), pp. 3-3, ISSN 0100-4042

Giloni-Lima, P. C. & Lima, V. A. (2008). Gestão Integrada de Resíduos Químicos em Insituições de Ensino Superior, *Química Nova*, Vol.31, No.6, (Agosto/Setembro/2008), pp. 1595-1598, ISSN 0100-4042

Herremans, I. & Allwright, D. E. (2000). Environmental Management systems at North American universities: what drives good performance? *International Journal of Sustainability in Higher Education*, Vol.1, No.2, pp.168-181, MCB University Press 1467-6370

Izzo, R. M. Waste minimization and pollution prevention in university laboratories. *Chemical Health & Safety*, Vol.7, No.3, (May/June/2000), pp. 29-33, ISSN 1871-5532

Jardim, W. F. (1993). As indústrias químicas e a preservação ambiental. *Revista de Química Industrial*, Vol.692, pp. 16-18, ISSN 0370-694X

Jardim, W. F. (1998). Gerenciamento de Resíduos Químicos em Laboratórios de Ensino e Pesquisa, *Química Nova*, Vol.21, No.5, (Maio/1998), pp. 671-673, ISSN 0100-4042

Kurniawan, T. A.; Chan, G. Y. S.; Lo, W.-H. & Babel, S. (2006). Physico-chemical treatment techniques for wastewater laden with heavy metals, *Chemical Engineering Journal*, Vol.118, No.1-2, (Mes/ano), pp.83-98, ISSN 1385-8947

Machado, P. A. L. (2002). *Direito Ambiental brasileiro* (10 ed.), Malheiros, ISBN 85-392-00589, São Paulo

Meyerson, J.W. & Massey, W.F. (1995). *Revitalising Higher Education*, Peterson's, Princeton, NJ. ISBN 978-1560796428

Moscovici, S. (2003). *Representações Sociais: Investigação em psicologia social* (1 ed.), Vozes, ISBN 85-326-28966, Rio de Janeiro

Nolasco, F. R.; Tavares, G. A. & Bendassolli, J. A. (2006). Implantação de Programas de Gerenciamento de Resíduos Químicos Laboratoriais em Universidades: Análise crítica e recomendações, *Engenharia Sanitária e Ambiental*, Vol.11, No.2, (Abril/Junho/2006), pp. 118-124, ISSN 1413-4152

Orloff, K. & Falk, H. (2003). An international perspective on hazardous waste practices, *International Journal of Hygiene and Environmental Health*, Vol. 206, pp. 291–302, ISSN 1438-4639

Penatti, F. E. (2008). Gerenciamento de resíduos químicos em laboratórios de análises e pesquisa: o desenvolvimento do sistema em laboratórios da área química. In: *II Workshop Internacional em Indicadores de Sustentabilidade (WIPIS)*, ISBN 978-85-85205-81-2, São Carlos, Agosto/2008

Pera-Titus, M.; García-Molina, V.; Baños, M. A.; Giménez, J. & Espulgas, S. (2004). Degradation of chlorophenols by means of advanced oxidation processes: a general review, *Applied Catalysis B: Environmental*, Vol.47, (September/2003), pp. 219-256, ISSN 0926-3373

Pérez, M. H.; Peñuela, G.; Maldonado, M. I.; Malato, O. Fernández-Ilbáñez, P.; Oller, I. Gernjak, W. & Malato, S. (2006). Degradation of pesticide in water using solar advanced oxidation processes. *Applied Catalysis B: Environmental*, Vol.64, No.3-4, (May/2006), pp. 272-281, ISSN 0926-3373

Quintas, J. S. (2000). *Pensando e praticando a Educação Ambiental na Gestão do Meio Ambiente* (1 ed.), IBAMA, Brasília, ISBN 0104-7892

Reigota, M. (2010). *Meio Ambiente e Representação Social* (8 ed.), Cortez, ISBN 85-249-15994, Rio de Janeiro

Riera, P. (1996). Environmental policy at the Universitat Autonomia de Barcelona, In: *Implementing Sustainable Development at University Level – A Manual of Good Pratice*, W. Leal Filho; F. MacDermot & J. Padgam (Eds), A Manual of Good Practice, CRE-COPERNICUS, Bradford.

Singh, M. M. (2000). A Comparative Study of Microscale and Standard Burets. *Journal of Chemical Education*, Vol.77, No.5, (May/2000), pp. 625-626, ISBN 0021-9584

Tavares, G. A. & Bendassolli, J. A. (2005). Implantação de um programa de gerenciamento de resíduos e águas servidas nos laboratórios de ensino e pesquisa no CENA/USP, *Química Nova*, Vol.28, No.4, (Julho/Agosto/2005), pp. 732-738, ISSN 0100-4042

UK Sustainable Development Education Panel. (1999). *First Annual Report 1998*, Department of the Environment, Transport and the Regions, London.

United Nations Educational, Scientific and Cultural Organization (UNESCO). (2010). *UNESCO Science Report 2010 – The current status of science around the world*, France, ISBN 978-92-3-104132-7

19

Lengthening Biolubricants´ Lifetime by Using Porous Materials

Estibaliz Aranzabe, Arrate Marcaide,
Marta Hernaiz and Nerea Uranga
Fundacion TEKNIKER
Spain

1. Introduction

The most of the lubricants such as automotive lubricants, gear oils, automatic transmissions fluids, engine lubricants, compressors oils... have being disposed on the environment for years, without any special care. Waste disposal is becoming a major source of concern and the tolerance of unnecessary pollution by society decreases[1].

As it has been described in the European General Instructions, 75/439/CEE, 78/319/CEE and 87/101/CEE, used lubricants as toxic disposals are attached to several rules and standards. One of the main problems of lubricants is the proportion of them lost into the environment in the course of routine usage[2]. The spillage of lubricants to the environment is one of the main problems during their routine usage. About 600000 Tonnes of lubricating oils per year are lost without control which implies a hard damage to the environment because just 1 litre of lubricant over the water is needed to form a film of oil of 4000 m^2.

In Europe the 50% of the lubricants are consumed for automotive purposes, and 35% for general industries (compressors, turbines, hydraulics, bearing, metal-working). More than 95% of the market is dominated by the mineral oil based lubricants which are polluting the environment but have in this moment a lower price and high availability. The market of biolubricants is still in a development stage and there is a priority to formulate high performance biodegradable lubricants.

The growing importance of environmental awareness and regulations has leaded to new demands of lubricants based on biodegradable materials. Several national eco-labels/schemes and one international standard have been developed in the recent years setting requirements for the ecological and technical characteristics of lubricants: The main difference relating to the ecological criteria for lubricants is the use of renewable raw materials, a newly included concept that aids to meet the three pillars of sustainability. An example of requirements concerning renewable raw material are the Swedish Standard for greases (SS 155470 Greases) and the Nordic Swan for lubricating oils.

---

[1] "Product Reviews: Liquid waste disposal and Recovery - Lubricant Recycling", *Ind. Lub. Trib.*, 1994, 46, (4), 18-26.
[2] "The Need For Biodegradable Lubricants", *Ind. Lubr. and Trib.*, 1992, 44, (4), 6-7.

The final criteria of European Eco-label[3] for lubricants was published in the Official Journal of 5 May 2005 and it will be valid until June 2011. It comprises hydraulic oils, greases, chainsaw oils, two stroke oils, concrete release agents and other total loss lubricants, for use by consumers and professional users. The ecological criteria for the product group "lubricants" shall be valid for 4 years from the date of notification of the Decision. On the occasion of the next revision particular attention will be paid to following issues: the possibility of including an additional test for toxicity to flora, the use of standardised performance tests, evaluating the criterion on biodegradability and bio-accumulative potential, the percentage&sourcing of the renewable raw materials, static or dynamic link to the OSPAR list and the Community list of priority substances in the field of the water policy, possible extension of the scope of the group, evaluating whether criteria need to be more ambitious, evaluating the consumer information.

The criteria are designed to reflect the philosophy of the new EU regulatory framework for chemicals (REACH - Registration, Evaluation and Authorization of Chemicals)[4] and are in line with the Dangerous Substances Directive and Dangerous Preparations Directive. Besides that, substances appearing in the Community list of priority substances in the field of water policy and the OSPAR List of Chemicals for Priority Action, shall not be intentionally added as an ingredient in a product eligible for the European eco-label.

According to the background document for the European Eco-label to lubricants, Several European countries regulations and policies exist in favour of biolubricants. In Germany, Austria and Switzerland is forbidden the use of mineral oil based lubricants around inland waterways and in forest areas. In Italy there is a tax for mineral oils. In Portugal there is a regulation that mandates the use of biolubricant two-stroke engine oils in outboard boat engines. In Belgium is required to use a biolubricant in all operations taking place near non-navigable waters. In the Netherlands there is an action programme in favour of biolubricants since 1996.

The use of non-toxic lubricant will improve health and safety of all individuals that are in contact with products and materials during their whole lifecycle. At the end of the life of the lubricants, recycling or disposal will release lubricants to the environment and again to individuals, either directly or via intermediate steps such as animal food or drinking water. Such a release of solid and/or liquid wastes can affect for many years the quality of life. For instance, the very harmful PCB´s have been already been banned 20 years ago. Notwithstanding that, they are still being released by dismantling of old electrical transformers containing these products as coolants.

The use of biodegradable lubricants will reduce problems on disposal. In most of the countries in the European Union each consumer is responsible of its own lubricant. It means that disposal of lubricants must be done by each consumer following the rules of each country. The non fulfillment of these rules can be fined or even imprisoned. Then, mineral oil based lubricants can be critical when arrive to the environment (earth and water). They contain substance which are not compatible with the biosphere and can cause damage to soil organisms, plants, aquatic organism. The use of biodegradable lubricant means that in 28 days, the 98% of the lubricant will be biodegradable and no film of oil will remain on the

---

[3] "Ecological Criteria for the award of the Community ecolabel to lubricants"- Regulatory Committee of the European Parliament and of the Council- 2005.
[4] Regulation of the European Parliament and of the council concerning the Registration, Evaluation, Authorisation and Restrictions of Chemicals.

water. The soft impact produced to the environment by biodegradable lubricants spill incidents due to their non toxic formulation makes it less worrying and preserves the environment from an irreversible deterioration. Try to restore the nature as well as difficult (sometimes impossible) is very expensive. Clearly, disposing of non-toxic and biodegradable lubricant will protect consumers.

Today, to deserve the name of "environmental friendly", a lubricant must possess several characteristics in different aspects as biodegradability, toxicity, emissions and efficiency. Vegetable oils, carefully selected esters and polyglycolethers form the bulk of base fluids in this type of product, generally given the generic name of biodegradable lubricants[5,6,7].

Esters in general are known as good lubricants[8], with low volatility, low pour points (-65 °C compared with -15 °C for mineral oils), good solubility for additives and high viscosity indexes. There are several types of biodegradable esters: dibasic esters or diesters, polyol esters (hindered esters), and phosphate esters. They find applications in engines, gears and compressors where cleanliness is important and the latter type as a fire-resistant fluid. Moderate corrosion behaviour is the major drawback. It is recommended to use saturated natural esters (low iodine value) to formulate biodegradable oils, because they have better thermal and oxidation stability.

Lubricants based on vegetable oils still comprise a narrow segment; however, they are finding their way into such applications as chainsaw bar lubricants, drilling muds and oils, straight metalworking fluids, food industry lubricants, open gear oils, biodegradable grease, hydraulic fluids, marine oils and outboard engine lubricants, oils for water and underground pumps, rail flange lubricants, shock absorber lubricants, tractor oils, agricultural equipment lubricants, elevator oils, mould release oils, two stroke engine lubricants and other. Volatility or viscosity index being cited the most often, vegetable oils clearly outperform mineral oils. Many of the other properties are similar between the fluids or may be manipulated with additives. However, low resistance to oxidative degradation and poor low temperature properties are major issues for vegetable oils.

The lubricant industry's inability to overcome these limitations ignited a rapid rise in demand of highly biodegradable synthetic basestocks as low molecular weight poly a-olefins (PAO 2 or PAO 4, essentially 20:1 and 10:1 mixtures of hydrogenated dimers:trimers of alpha-decene), di alkyl adipates (iso decyl, iso tridecyl) or polyol esters (mostly neopentyl glycol or trimethylol propane with fatty acids). The synthetic basestocks also have some imperfections, such as higher volatility of PAOs, seal swelling of adipates, questionable biodegradability of some polyols, and, frequently the major issue, costs of nearly three times higher than that of vegetable oils[9].

Polyalphaolefin fluids are enjoying a growing market share as synthetic base stocks. They are manufactured by the oligomerization of 1-decene, followed by hydrogenation and distillation into different viscosity grades. Applications range from hydraulic fluids to car

[5] Carnes K. "University Tests Biodegradable Soy-Based Railroad Lubricant", Hart's Lubricantes world 1998, Vol. September, pp 45-47.

[6] Glancey J.L., Knowlton S., Benson E.R. "Development of a High-Oleic Soybean Oil-based Hydraulic Fluid", Lubricants World 1999, Vol. January, pp 49-51.

[7] Rajewski T.E., Fokens J.S., Watson M.C., "The development and Application of Syntetic Food Grade Lubricants", Tribology, 2000, Vol 1, pp 83-89.

[8] W. J. Bartz: "Comparison of Synthetic Fluids", Lub. Eng., 1992, 48, (10), 765-774.

[9] S.Z.Erhan: "Lubricant basestocks from vegetable oils", Industrial Crops and Products 11 (2000) 277–282

motor oils[10,11,12].They have excellent thermal, oxidative and hydrolytic stabilities. Recently, it has been reported that 2cSt and 4cSt PAO fluids are easily biodegradable, so they can be used in environmentally sensitive applications[13].

From the Polyglycol side only *Polyethyleneglycols* (PEG) with mol-weights lower than 2000 are relatively good biodegradable, but water-soluble, means they migrate into the soil after an oil accident or via leakages. Polypropylenes (PPG) are not water-soluble but not easily biodegradable substance. Furthermore PAG´s are only partly or even not miscible with esters, mineral oils, etc. But the compatibility of all the fluids is an absolutely neccesary item in case of re-filling or replacement of mineral oil by biodegradable fluids.The polyglycol used in this study (of about 320cSt of viscosity at 40ºC) is not biodegradable.

There is still a priority to formulate high performance biodegradable lubricants. The main limitation to introduce bio-degradable lubricants is the lack of knowledge of the performance of the biolubricants. A review of the state of the art has been developed to check the status of condition monitoring in mineral and biodegradable oils and greases[14,15,16]. Results indicated that there is hardly any documentation (application note, technical papers, standards) concerning how to tackle bio-lubricants. Also, documentation concerning how to perform a condition monitoring of greases is hardly non-existant. The procedures and test methods to detect contaminants has been developed for mineral based lubricants, but new procedures has to be developed for environmentally friendly lubricants.

In order to assess this performance, it is important to understand how degradation processes occurs at biodegradable fluids[17,18,19] and identify adequate control parameters, limits and sampling frequency (or re-greasing frequency). Apart from hydraulic fluids[20], there is no information about how to efficiently handle the monitoring of biodegradable lubricants.

Table 1.1shows the status in the definition of parameters, limits and sample frequencies at different lubricant types (lubricating oils and greases and biodegradable lubricating oils and greases). The OK sign (√) indicates that the field (parameters, limits and sample frequencies)

---

[10] C-X. Xiong: "The structure and Activity of Polyalphaolefins as Pour-Point Depressants", *Lub. Eng.*, 1993, <u>49</u>, (3), 196-200.

[11] G Kumar: "New Polyalphaolefin Fluids for specialty applications", *Lub. Eng.*, **1993**, <u>49</u>, (x), 723-725.

[12] R. L. Shubkin: "Polyalphaolefins: Meeting the Challenge for High-Performance Lubrication", *Lub. Eng.*, 1994, <u>50</u>, (x), 196-201.

[13] J. F. Carpenter: "Biodegradability of Polyalphaolefin (PAO) Basestocks", *Lub. Eng.*, 1994, 50, (5), 359-362.

[14] M.K. Williamson "The emerging Role of Oil analysis in Enterprise-Wide decision making". Practicig Oil analysis 2000. pp. 187-200.

[15] "Lubricants and lubrication". T. Mang, W. Dresel (Eds). Wiley-VCH. 2001

[16] "Lubricating grease guide". Fourth Edition. National Lubricating Grease Institute (NLGI)

[17] A. Adhvaryu, "Oxidation kinetics studies of oils derived from unmodified and genetically modified vegetables using pressurized differential scanning calorimetry and nuclear magnetic resonance spectroscopy". Thermochimica Acta, 364, 87-97. 2000

[18] N.J. Fox, A.K. Simpson, G.W. Stachowiak, "Sealed Capsule Differential Scanning Calorimetry-An Effective Method for Screening the oxidation Stability of vegetable oil formulations". Lubrication Engineering, 57, 14-20. 2001

[19] A. Adhvaryu, "Tribological studies of thermally and Chemically modified vegetable oils use as environmentally friendly lubricants". Wear, 257, 359-367, 2004

[20] F.Novotny-Farkas, P. Kotal, W. Bohme. "Condition monitoring of biodegradable lubricants". World Tribology Congress. Vienna. 2001

has already been properly defined and all aspects of these fields have been put into practice. The OK sign and plus mark ($\sqrt{}$/+) indicates that some studies have been carried out, however a improvement of the definition is necessary. The plus sign (+) indicates the field that we are trying to improve by means of this study. A high advance has been obtained in the work of obtaining a proper definition of each of fields. The question mark (?) indicates that there is not any adequate definition of the field and it is not going to obtain by means of this study.

	Lubricating Oil	Biodegradable Lubricating Oil	Lubricating Grease	Biodegradable Lubricating Grease
Parameters	$\sqrt{}$	$\sqrt{}$	$\sqrt{}$/+	+
Limits	$\sqrt{}$	+	$\sqrt{}$/+	+
Sample frequencies	$\sqrt{}$	+	?	?

Table 1. Knowledge of parameters that have to be measured, limits and sample frequencies at lubricating oils, biodegradable lubricating oils, lubricating greases and biodegradable lubricating greases.

The development of the technology on different areas such as manufacturing, electronic and nanotechnology has allow us to develop new devices for improving the lubricants control and has opened an wide range of research areas. The main objectives of these developments are the following: to avoid the lubricant degradation by means of the use of filters or additives and to control "on-line" the condition of the lubricant by means of sensors[21,22].

This chapter includes a first proposal for the condition monitoring strategy developments of biolubricants (BIOMON Project contract N°COOP-CT-2004-508208) and some results concerning the potential of porous materials for trapping oxidation molecules of the biolubricants during use for lengthening their lifetime instead of traditional antioxidant additives (SOILCYProject contract N515848).

2. Degradation mechanism of biolubricants and analytical techniques used for biolubricants monitoring

A commercial hydraulic fluid (ISO VG 68/MP=Multi-purpose) which is currently in use for roller bearing purposes has been used in this study as fully formulated mineral oil. EP additives but no antioxidants have been included in its formulation. Secondly, a biodegradable nearly fully saturated ester has been developed in order to study its oxidation process. EP & antioxidant additives have been included in the formulation of the biodegradable oil.

---

[21] Arnaiz, A., Aranzabe, A., Terradillos, J., Merino, S., Aramburu, I.: New micro-sensor systems to monitor on-line oil degradation, Comadem 2004. pp. 466-475

[22] Kristiansen, P., Leeker, R.: U.S.Navy's in-line oil analysis program, , lubr. Fluid powerj. 3, 3–12, aug 2001.

2.1. Degradation mechanism

One of the important modes of lubricant degradation is oxidation. Oxidation products are the primary cause of metal corrosion, viscosity increase and sludge and varnish formation in lubrication systems. It is well-known that a lubricant when exposed to air at high temperatures undergoes a series of chain reactions that form peroxides, which upon further reaction produce low molecular weight products (products of the same or lower molecular weight than the original oil). The LMW products are a mixture of ketones, aldehydes, alcohols and acids. These primary oxidation products can polymerize to form higher molecular weight (HMW) viscous liquids, sludge and varnish.

Some studies of the oxidation mechanism of the vegetable oils reveal that the oxidation mechanism may be presented as a free radical chain reaction. It consists of four distinct reaction steps: initiation, propagation, branching and ending. These steps have been analyzed.

The *initiation step* consists of forming free radical derived from R substance that undertake the peroxidation and it takes place due the high transformation energy, UV light of the mechanical shear stresses applied to a molecule. The appearance of the free radicals is due to one or more external factors (high temperature, moisture, pressure, oxygen presence) or internal factors (easily oxidable impurities, for instance: aromatic diphenol compounds). Under certain conditions the external factors produce the O_2 activation and the development of some reactive elements and radicals. Although the radicals of the oxygen may accidentally appear, the reactions that release them are enough to initiate the formation of some free radicals from the initial organic substances.

The *propagation step* consists in the continuation of forming free radicals especially of the derived peroxides from the substance that bear the oxidation progress. The first propagation step involves an alkyl radical reacting with oxygen to form an alkyl peroxy radical (ROO·). The second propagation step is the hydrogen abstraction from a hydrocarbon molecule by an alkyl peroxy-radical to form a hydroperoxide and another alkyl radical.Generally the alkyl peroxy radicals are in a greater concentration than the alkyl radicals. This is due to the combination between high oxygen concentration with alkyl radical rather than the slow reaction rate of alkyl peroxy radical with hydrocarbon.

The *chain branching* steps begin with the decomposition of hydroperoxide (ROOH) in alkoxy radicals and hydroxy radical. This reaction has a great activation energy and the alkoxy and hydroxy radicals can react on with hydrocarbons to form more alkyl radicals, alcohols and water. Secondary and tertiary alkoxy radicals, will form aldehydes and ketones respectively. These condense via acid catalysed aldol reactions can lead to polymeric degradated products.

The *ending* step may take place by the combination of the alkyl radicals. Two alkyl radicals can combine to form a hydrocarbon molecule. Alternatively, an alkyl radical may combine with an alkyl peroxy radical (ROO.) to form a peroxide or two alkyl peroxy radicals (2ROO·) (ROOR·).

2.2 Oxidation tests

Oxidation tests can be differentiated into two groups: one kind of tests describe the condition of the lubricant after a defined test period by measuring several aging indicating parameters like acid number, viscosity change and sludge formation. The 1000-h TOST according to DIN 51587 and IP 280 oxidation test are examples for that kind of tests. Another group of oxidation tests measure the so-called induction time (time from the beginning of the oxidation to the autocatalytic phase of the autoxidation) by recording constantly or after defined periods of time the aging indicating parameters. Typical examples of this group are the lifetime TOST test according to ASTM-D 943 or the rotary bomb test (ASTM-D 2272) where the drop of oxygen pressure indicates the aging of the lubricant. More recently the high pressure differential scanning Calorimetry (HPDSC) as well as the sealed capsule differential scanning calorimetry (SCDSC) has been applied more and more to measure the stability of different antioxidants and formulations.

These tests for lubricants are a function of temperature or other parameters. These aging tests are carried out on base oils as well as fully formulated products to test the efficiency of additives. There is a big variety of standardized test methods where we have duration of test between hours and months. The majority of these tests is based on exposing the test fluids to oxygen or air at relatively high temperatures in presence of catalyst metals to increase oxidation rates and to reduce the testing period. Oxidation stability is assessed by quantitative determination of oxidation products, oxygen absorption, viscosity changes, change in acidity or formation of sludge.

The TOST (turbine oxidation stability test) is used to evaluate the oxidation stability of inhibited steam turbine oils in presence of oxygen, water, copper and iron catalyst at 95°C. The test is continued until the total acid number (TAN) measured reaches at least 2.0 mg/g KOH. The number of test hours required for the oil to reach 2.0 mg/g KOH is the "oxidation lifetime" of an oil.

The oxidation stability by rotary bomb test (ASTM D 2272) oxidizes the oil at 150°C in presence of water, metallic copper catalyst and oxygen at 620 kPa pressure. The time is registered to reach a specific pressure drop and this is an indication of the oxidation stability.

The aging test according to Baader (DIN 51554) is an oxidation test of atmospheric air and intermittent immersion of a copper spiral at a test temperature of 95°C. After a given time, the saponification number in mg/g KOH is measured.

For the oxidation stability of lubricating greases by oxygen bomb method grease is oxidized in a bomb heated to 99°C and filled with oxygen at 110 psig. After a defined time, the drop of pressure is recorded. The degree of oxidation after a given period of time is determined by the corresponding decrease of oxygen pressure.

In the table below equivalent standards are grouped together which are identical or technically equivalent respectively[23].

New biodegradable polyol ester base stocks formulated with the appropriate ashless additive technology outperform vegetable oils both hydrolytically and oxidatively and modified versions of the ASTM D 943 and D2274 tests, in which no water is employed have shown that they are very suitable for the evaluation of the long-term oxidative stability of biodegradable polyol esters[24].

Tekniker proposes the development of a new oxidation procedure for biodegradable lubricants because this kind of oils needs higher temperatures for degradation. Based on Tekniker experience, it is proposed a new oxidation test running in a bath reactor (figure 1) at 120°C with stirring, air flux and without presence of water and catalyst.

---

[23]Mang, T. y Dresel, W. (eds.), Lubricants and Lubrication, 2ª edición, Wiley-VCH, Weinheim (2007).
[24] C.Duncan (2002), Lubrication Engineering, "Ashless Additives and New Polyol Ester Base Oils Formulated for Use in Biodegradable Hydraulic Fluid Applications"

AFNOR	ASTM	DIN	IP	ISO	Test method
		51352t1	48		Determination of oxidation characteristics of lubricating oil
		51554			Determination of oxidation characteristics of lubricating oil acc.to Baader
			280		Determination of oxidation stability of inhibited mineral turbine oils
T60-150	D943	51587		4263	Determination of oxidation stability of inhibited mineral oils
	D2893	51586			Determination of oxidation characteristics of extreme-pressure lubricating oils
	D4742				Oxidation stability of gasoline engine oils by thin film oxygen uptake (TFOUT)
	D2274		229		Determination of the relative oxidation stability by rotating bomb of mineral turbine oil
	D942	51808	142		Determination of oxidation stability of lubricating grease- oxygen bomb method

Table 2. Equivalent oxidation standards

Fig. 1. Oxidation reactor

The table 3 shows the advantages of the oxidation procedure proposed for biolubricants compared with the oxidation standard procedure for mineral lubricants.

Heterogeneous samples are taken due to the absence of stirring	Homogeneous samples are taken due to the presence of stirring
Long degradation time due to the temperature of the test.	Shorter degradation time due to the temperature of the test
Heterogeneous samples are taken due to the absence of stirring	Homogeneous samples are taken due to the presence of stirring

Table 3. Oxidation standards

2.3 Analytical techniques used for biolubricants monitoring

Oxidation is a major source for viscosity increase, acid number increase or corrosion, additive depletions, dispersant failures, base oil deterioration, varnish and sludge formation, filter plugging, oil darkening, as well as many of the wear root causes. For this reason, there have been many analytical techniques to evaluate the oxidation state of the lubricant.

The table 4 shows the chemical, tribological and environmental analysis selected for monitoring biolubricants.

The chemical analysis includes the following parameters: Acid Number (ASTM D 974-04), Viscosity at 40ºC (ASTM D 445), Density (PE-5053-AI), Emulsification Capacity (ASTM D 1401), DSC (PE-5035-AI), Fourier Transform Infrared Spectroscopy (FTIR) (PE-5008-AI), Remaining Useful Life Number (RULER) (PE-TA.090) and %Solids. Sliding tests has been selected in the tribological field. Finally, in accordance with the European Ecolabel for lubricants, the following environmental analyses have been selected: Ready Biodegradability according to OECD 301F Test, Inherent Biodegradability according to OECD 302B Test and Toxicity according to OECD 202 Test.

Analytical parameter	Test
Acid Number	ASTM D 974-04
Viscosity at 40ºC	ASTM D 445
Density	PE-5053-AI
Emulsification capacity	ASTM D 1401
Differential Scanning Calorimetry	PE-5035-AI
Fourier Transform Infrared Spectroscopy	PE-5008-AI
Remaining Useful Life	PE-TA.090
Sliding tests	DIN 51834-2
Ready and Inherent Biodegradability	OECD 301F , 302B
Toxicity (algae, daphnia)	OECD 201, 202

Table 4. Analytical techniques for biolubricants monitoring

2.3.1 Chemical analysis

2.3.1.1 Acid number (ASTM D974-04)

Both in new lubricants and in-service lubricants, acidic constituents will appear, either in the form of additives or as a result of the oxidation of lubricant. The Acid Number test method is a measurement of the quantity of those acidic constituents. Measurement has been by titration which estimates the amount of KOH which is necessary to neutralize the acid compounds of the oil).

2.3.1.2 Viscosity at 40°C (ASTM D445)

The viscosity remains the most important property of the oil as part of the oil condition monitoring. Viscosity measurements have been done following **ASTM D 445** standard.
In general, the variation of oil viscosity can be caused by:
- The increase of viscosity results from the oxidation and/or polymerization of the oil, evaporation of the most light fractions even water presence or insoluble oxides formation.
- The decrease of viscosity may be due to thermal cracking of the molecules of the lubricant, or shear stress from the viscosity modifiers....

2.3.1.3 Density (PE-5053-AI)

Density is the mass of a unit volume of a substance. Its numerical value varies with the units used. A high level of oxidation and/or polymerization of the oil, causes an increase in density values.

2.3.1.4 Emulsification capacity (ASTM D1401)

This test method measures the ability of petroleum oils or synthetic fluids to separate from water. This test provides a guide for determining the water separation characteristics of oils subject to water contamination and turbulence. It is used for specification of new oils and monitoring of in-service oils.

2.3.1.5 Differential scanning calorimetry (PE-5035-AI)

Samples are tested at extreme conditions of temperature, pressure and in an oxidative environment. Remaining useful life can be determined concerning the oxidative stability. At constant temperature, the lubricant degradation takes place at a time called "onset time", with its corresponding heat exchange. This value can give an idea of the oil stability.

2.3.1.6 Fourier transform infrared spectroscopy (PE-5008-AI)

The IR Spectroscopy is a well known technique for analysing the chemical properties of the oil such as oxidation products or additives.

2.3.1.7 Remaining useful life. RULER. (PE-TA.90)

The RULER (Remaining Useful Life) is a useful parameter to control the antioxidants consumption in biodegradable oils.
The voltammetric test results are based on current, voltage and time relationships at the 3-electrode sensing system with a small, easily polarized microelectrode, and a large non-polarizable reference electrode. In performing a voltammetric analysis, the potential across the electrodes varies linearly with time (from 0 to 1.7 V at a rate of 0.1 V/second), and the resulting current is recorded as a function of the potential. With increased voltage to the sample in the cell, the various dissolved antioxidants oxidize electrochemically resulting in an oxidation reaction that can be used to predict the remaining useful life of the oil.

2.3.2 Tribological analysis

2.3.2.1 Sliding tests (DIN 51834-2)

With the SRV tribometer reciprocating sliding tests in standard conditions using AISI 52100 steel standard balls and discs can be useful for finding any difference in the behavior of new and aged oils based on the results of friction (COF) and wear obtained during the tribological tests.

2.3.3 Environmental analysis

2.3.3.1 Ready biodegradability (OECD 301F)

If a chemical gives positive in this test will undergo rapid an ultimate biodegradation (CO_2+H_2O) in the environment and no further work on the biodegradability on the chemical, or on the possible environmental effects of biodegradation products, normally is required. Ultimate biodegradation within 28 days higher than 60% according to OECD 301 F.

2.3.3.2 Toxicity algae, daphnia (OECD 201, OECD 202).

The level al which 50% of the test organisms show an adverse (lethal) effect.
Exponentially-growing cultures of selected green algae or certain percentage of daphnia are exposed to various concentrations of the test substance under defined conditions. The inhibition of growth in relation to a control culture or the inhibition of the capability of swimming of daphnia is determined over a fixed period.
The 50% effect level (EC50) is chosen, the level at which 50% of the test organisms show an adverse (lethal) effect.

2.4 Identification of main condition monitoring patterns

Regarding traditional lubricating oils, all condition monitoring parameters, limits and sample frequencies have been already established at different studies. However, there is not a clear rule of thumb, as small variations occurs in limits and sampling frequencies. Given this, the knowledge has been obtained through extensive usage occurred at WearCheck Ibérica Laboratories, which has helped to obtain enough expertise to study all condition monitoring fields.

Regarding biodegradable lubricating oil parameters that have to be measured, an extensive tribological and physico-chemical comparison has been performed between normal and bio-degradable lubricants, in order to assess their conditions. The tests have demonstrated a superior working life-time for bio-degradable lubricants with respect to traditional ones that is mostly reflected in a much higher AN limit allowed for operation.

As a result, similar parameters have been defined as of primary control. However, there are two important additions. The Ruler is a parameter for on site measurement of remaining useful lifetime of the oil. The analysis performed show that rules offer a quite reliable information on usage of the oil and can complement the information indicated by AN.

Also, the % of Solids parameter is a very useful parameter. However, it is very hard and expensive to measure and in the near future work the % of Solids parameter have to be eliminated to the monitoring routine and must be found a new parameter cheaper and easier to use it in the monitoring routine.

Of course, these are main parameters and limits. Depending on the type of lubricant and its application and the test cost, other parameters could be useful for mineral oils monitoring, and biodegradable oils. For engine oils for example, it could be necessary to analyse Base Number (BN) parameter. The work should be completed with a complete identification of sample frequencies.

			Monitor	Warning
Degradation		AN (mgKOH/g)	+ 0.5	+ 1.0
		Vis40°C (cSt)	± 15%	± 20%
Contamination		Water	0.1%	0.2%
		Si (ppm)	30	65
Wear Debris		Fe (ppm)	100	150
		Cu (ppm)	50	80

SAMPLE FRECUENCIES	1000 hours

ANALYTICAL EQUIPMENT

AN Titrometer	Viscometer
Karl-Fischer	ICP

Fig. 2. Parameters, monitor and warning limits, sample frequencies and analytical equipment for mineral oils.

			Monitor	Warning
Degradation		AN (mgKOH/g)	+ 2	+ 6
		RULER (WP4)	15%	10%
		% Solids (WP4)	> 1%	> 1.2%
		Vis40°C (cSt)	- 7%	+ 7%
Contamination		Water	0.1%	0.2%
		Si (ppm)	30	65
Wear Debris		Fe (ppm)	100	150
		Cu (ppm)	50	80

Fig. 3. Limits and parameters for biodegradable oils.

3. New materials for enlarge biolubricants´lifetime

One of the main concerns of lubricants is their performance which is improved using additives. The use of additives allows increasing the performance and physical properties of oil but they also increase the cost of lubricants and may even be harmful to health or environment.

Adsorption in a porous material of oxidation products from a biodegradable lubricant is a promising approach to improve the performance of biolubricants in an environmentally friendly way. Antioxidant additives are commonly used to improve performance of biolubricants but they are expensive and even may be harmful. The development of a sieve able to trap oxidation products may be a way to reduce or avoid the use of additives.

In our investigation, different oxidized samples of biolubricants obtained from the degradation process of TMP-trioleate have been characterized and the oxidation molecules to be trapped have been identified. The most suitable nanoporous material to trap the identified oxidation molecules has been selected. To do this the adsorption of biolubricant oxidation molecules in a nanoporous material has been examined by means of Monte Carlo (MC) and Molecular Dynamics (MD) computational methods and by means of Differential Scanning Calorimetry .

Among the different framework types BEA, MFI, LTL and FAU zeolitic structures were selected due to their suitable pore size of molecular dimensions. All of them present an extensive channel network with elliptical or circular shape and cross section ranging from 0.5 and 0.8 nm. Besides, structural criteria, different compositions have been selected in order to analyze the effect of the physico-chemical properties of the solid surfaces (functional groups, acidity, hydrophilicity,...).

It deserves to note that from the point of view of the composition, extremely hydrophobic materials with high silica content such as Silicalite-1, or highly hydrophilic materials with relatively low silica content such as zeolite x, have been considered.

Prior to their use all the materials were dried and activated trough a thermal treatment using an exposure times of 2 h and temperatures of 150 or 300 °C. Since crystal structure and grain size and morfology influences on total porosity of the material surface area of all the samples were measured after activation with a NOVA 1200e surface area and pore size analyzer from Quantachrome Instruments. Total surface area was computed according to BET Method.

3.1 Oxidation conditions

In order to analyze the capacity of the selective adsorption of oxidation by-products with nanoporous materials and predict the lubricating oil oxidation state, the *Differential Scanning Calorimetry (DSC)* analytical technique has been used. The experimental procedure consists on an analyzed sample heating it with a programmed temperature-time sequence: 3°C/min heating from 100°C at 600°C at 20 bar of pressure.

The oxidation method was described previously. The oxidation conditions were the following: 1.5 l of TMP-trioleate in a bath reactor at 95°C with stirring, air flux and without presence of water and catalyst.

The analytical parameters monitorized were the following: Acid Number (ASTM D 974-04), DSC (PE-5035-AI), Fourier Transform Infrared Spectroscopy (FTIR) (PE-5008-AI) and Density (PE-5053-AI). Besides that, the oxidation molecules identification at different hours of oxidation has been made by GCMS and HPLC.

After testing the capacity of different nanoporous materials, the most suitable has been tested with the TMP-trioleate at 95°C with stirring, air flux and without presence of water and catalyst.

3.2 MD simulations

Molecular Dynamics (MD) has been used to study the interaction between the identified oxidation molecules and the selected nanoporous material. Results of the ability of the proposed material as absorbing media in terms of molecules per unit computational cell and preferred absorption sites are obtained.

The simulations were performed at established conditions of pressure a temperature using the grand canonical and the NPT ensemble. Results of the ability of the proposed material as absorbing media in terms of molecules per unit computational cell and preferred adsorption sites are obtained.

3.3 Porous materials validation

The hydrophilic and hydrophobic solids have showed the best performance trapping the oxidation molecules of TMP-trioleate. After testing the capacity of different nanoporous materials, the most suitable has been tested with the TMP-trioleate at 95°C with stirring, air flux and without presence of water and catalyst. The chemical parameter which shows the effectiveness of the tested solid is Acid Number (AN). The following figure shows the trend of this parameter during the oxidation process. As it shows, both solids hydrophilic and hydrophobic one, delay the oxidation process of the oil due, these solids trap in their pores the acid compounds generated during the oxidation.

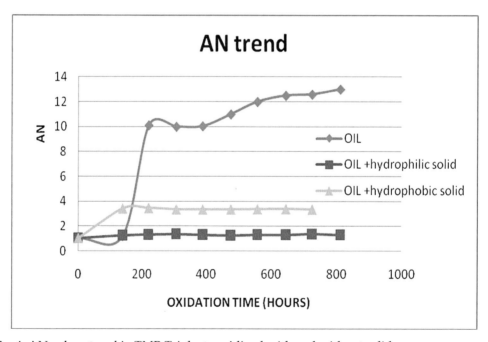

Fig. 4. AN values trend in TMP-Trioleate oxidized with and without solid.

4. Conclusions

In this chapter it has been exposed two main research works; the first one is a proposal for the condition monitoring strategy for biolubricants. In this sense two oils, mineral and biodegrable; have been oxidized under a new oxidation procedure, based on Tekniker experience, which provide more advantage than traditional tests. Thanks to the chemical, tribological and environmental analyses monitor and warning limits can be proposed for bio-oil.

As it can be sawn these limits are different as traditional limits for mineral oils, what is mean that biodegradable oils shows different oxidations trends and traditional limits used for mineral oils are nor accurate for these kind of biolubricants:

- Kinetic degradation reaction of biodegradable lubricants is differently than mineral oils and a specific maintenance approach is needed.
- DSC is a useful tool for studying the kinetic parameters of the new formulations.
- Important research must be carried out to establish warning limits for biolubricants in order to develop condition monitoring strategies, assessment in mechanical components lubricated with biodegradable fluids.
- In the standard tribological wear tests there is a direct relationship between aging hours and friction peaks. This test can be useful in the condition monitoring strategy.

The second research work exposed is the use of nanoporous materials as tramp for oxidation compounds instead to use antioxidant additives in the bio oil formulation Antioxidant additives are commonly used to improve performance of biolubricants but they are expensive and even may be harmful. The development of a sieve able to trap oxidation products may be a way to reduce or avoid the use of additives. Adsorption in a porous material of oxidation products from a biodegradable lubricant is a promising approach to improve the performance of biolubricants in an environmentally friendly way.

- The use of biodegradable lubricants will reduce problems on disposal. The biodegradability in use must be tested in these types of friendly formulations.
- The uses of hydrophilic solids delay oil oxidation, due the trap oxidation molecules.
- Acid Number (AN) seems to be a useful analytical technique for evaluate solid efficiency

5. References

"Product Reviews: Liquid waste disposal and Recovery - Lubricant Recycling », Ind. Lub. Trib., 1994, 46, (4), 18-26.

"The Need For Biodegradable Lubricants", Ind. Lubr. and Trib., 1992, 44, (4), 6-7.

"Ecological Criteria for the award of the Community ecolabel to lubricants"- Regulatory committee of the European Parliament and of the Council- 2005

Regulation of the European Parliament and of the council concerning the Registration, Evaluation, Authorisation and Restrictions of Chemicals.

Carnes K. "University Tests Biodegradable Soy-Based Railroad Lubricant", Hart's Lubricantes world 1998, Vol. September, pp 45-47.

Glancey J.L., Knowlton S., Benson E.R. "Development of a High-Oleic Soybean Oil-based Hydraulic Fluid", Lubricants World 1999, Vol. January, pp 49-51.

Rajewski T.E., Fokens J.S., Watson M.C., "The development and Application of Syntetic Food Grade Lubricants", Tribology, 2000, Vol 1, pp 83-89.

W. J. Bartz: "Comparison of Synthetic Fluids", Lub. Eng., 1992, 48, (10), 765-774.

S.Z.Erhan: "Lubricant basestocks from vegetable oils", Industrial Crops and Products 11 (2000) 277–282

C-X. Xiong: "The structure and Activity of Polyalphaolefins as Pour-Point Depressants", Lub. Eng., 1993, 49, (3), 196-200.

G Kumar: "New Polyalphaolefin Fluids for specialty applications", Lub. Eng., 1993, 49, (x), 723-725.

R. L. Shubkin: "Polyalphaolefins: Meeting the Challenge for High-Performance Lubrication", Lub. Eng., 1994, 50, (x), 196-201.

J. F. Carpenter: "Biodegradability of Polyalphaolefin (PAO) Basestocks", Lub. Eng., 1994, 50, (5), 359-362.

M.K. Williamson "The emerging Role of Oil analysis in Enterprise-Wide decision making". Practicig Oil analysis 2000. pp. 187-200.

Lubricants and lubrication". T. Mang, W. Dresel (Eds). Wiley-VCH. 2001

"Lubricating grease guide". Fourth Edition. National Lubricating Grease Institute (NLGI

A. Adhvaryu, "Oxidation kinetics studies of oils derived from unmodified and genetically modified vegetables using pressurized differential scanning calorimetry and nuclear magnetic resonance spectroscopy". Thermochimica Acta, 364, 87-97. 2000

N.J. Fox, A.K. Simpson, G.W. Stachowiak, "Sealed Capsule Differential Scanning Calorimetry-An Effective Method for Screening the oxidation Stability of vegetable oil formulations". Lubrication Engineering, 57, 14-20. 2001

A. Adhvaryu, "Tribological studies of thermally and Chemically modified vegetable oils use as environmentally friendly lubricants". Wear, 257, 359-367, 2004

F.Novotny-Farkas, P. Kotal, W. Bohme. "Condition monitoring of biodegradable lubricants". World Tribology Congress. Vienna. 2001

Arnaiz, A., Aranzabe, A., Terradillos, J., Merino, S., Aramburu, I.: New micro-sensor systems to monitor on-line oil degradation, Comadem 2004. pp. 466-475

Kristiansen, P., Leeker, R.: U.S.Navy's in-line oil analysis program, , lubr. Fluid powerj. 3, 3–12, aug 2001

C.Duncan (2002), Lubrication Engineering, "Ashless Additives and New Polyol Ester Base Oils Formulated for Use in Biodegradable Hydraulic Fluid Applications"

20

A Fuzzy Water Quality Index for Watershed Quality Analysis and Management

André Lermontov[1,2], Lidia Yokoyama[1],
Mihail Lermontov[3] and Maria Augusta Soares Machado[4]
[1]*Universidade Federal do Rio de Janeiro*
[2]*Grupo Águas do Brasil S/A*
[3]*Universidade Federal Fluminense*
[4]*IBMEC-RJ*
Brazil

1. Introduction

Climate change and hydric stress are limiting the availability of clean water. Overexploitation of natural resources has led to environmental unbalance. Present decisions relative to the management of hydric resources will deeply affect the economy and our future environment. The use of indicators is a good alternative for the evaluation of environmental behavior as well as a management instrument, as long as the conceptual and structural parameters of the indicators are respected.

The use of fuzzy logic to study the influence and the consequences of environmental problems has increased significantly in recent years. According to Silvert (1997), most activities, either natural of anthropic, have multiple effects and any environmental index should offer a consistent meaning as well as a coherent quantitative and qualitative appraisal of all these effects.

Among the several reasons for applying fuzzy logic to complex situations, the most important is probably the need to combine different indicators. Maybe the most significant advantage of the use of fuzzy logic for the development of environmental indicators is that it combines different aspects with much more flexibility than other methods, such as, for example, binary indices of the kind "acceptable vs. unacceptable."

Methods to integrate several variables related to water quality in a specific index are increasingly needed in national and international scenarios. Several authors have integrated water quality variables into indices, technically called Water Quality Indices (WQIs) (Bolton et al., 1978; Bhargava, 1983; House, 1989; Mitchell, 1996; Pesce and Wunderlin, 1999; Cude, 2001; Liou et al., 2004; Said et al., 2004; Silva and Jardim, 2006; Nasiri et al., 2007). Most are based in a concept developed by the U. S. National Sanitation Foundation (NSF, 2007).

There is an obvious need for more advanced techniques to assess the importance of water quality variables and to integrate the distinct parameters involved. In this context, new, alternative integration methods are being developed. Artificial Intelligence has thus become a tool for modeling water quality (Chau, 2006). Traditional methodologies cannot classify and quantify environmental effects of a subjective nature or even provide formalism for dealing with missing data. Fuzzy Logic can combine these different approaches. In this context new methodologies for the management of environmental variables are being developed (Silvert, 1997, 2000).

The main purpose of this research is to propose a new water quality index, called Fuzzy Water Quality Index (INQA – Índice Nebuloso de Qualidade da Água, originally in Portuguese), to be computed using Fuzzy Logic and Fuzzy Inference tools. A second goal is to compare statistically the INQA with other indices suggested in the literature using data from hydrographic surveys of four different watersheds, in São Paulo State, Brazil, from 2004 to 2006 (CETESB, 2004, 2005, 2006).

2. Background

2.1 Water quality indices

The purpose of an index is not to describe separately a pollutant's concentration or the changes in a certain parameter. To synthesize a complex reality in a single number is the biggest challenge in the development of a water quality index (IQA – Índice de Qualidade de Água, originally in Portuguese), since it is directly affected by a large number of environmental variables. Therefore, a clear definition of the goals to be attained by the use of such an index is needed. The formulation of a IQA may be simplified if one considers only the variables which are deemed critical for a certain water body. Among their advantages, indices facilitate communication with lay people. They are considered more trustful than isolated variables. They also integrate several variables in a single number, combining different units of measurement.

In a groundbreaking work, Horton (1965) developed general water quality indices, selecting and weighting several parameters. This methodology was then improved by the U.S. National Sanitation Foundation (NSF, 2007). The conventional way to obtain a IQA is to compute the weighted average of some predefined parameters, normalized in a scale from 0 to 100 and multiplied by their respective weights.

Conesa (1995) modified the traditional method and created another index, called Subjective Water Quality Index (IQA$_{sub}$), that includes a subjective constant, k. This constant assumes values between 0.25 and 1.00 at intervals of 0.25, with 0.25 representing polluted water and 1.00 a not polluted one. The parameters used to calculate this index (eq. 1) must be previously normalized using curves given by Conesa (1995). The Objective Water Quality Index (IQA$_{obj}$) results from the elimination of the subjective constant k.

$$IQA_{sub} = k \frac{\sum_i C_i \times P_i}{\sum_i P_i} \qquad (1)$$

where:

k is the subjective constant (0,25, 0,50, 0,75 and 1,00);

C_i the value of the ith normalized parameter (Conesa, 1995);

P_i the relative weight of the ith parameter (Conesa, 1995).

The Brazilian IQA is an adaptation from the NSF index. Nine variables, being the most relevant for water quality evaluation, are computed as the weighted product (eq. 2) of the normalized values of these variables, n_i: Temperature (TEMP), pH, Dissolved Oxygen (DO), Biochemical Oxygen Demand (BOD$_5$), Thermotolerant Coliforms (TC), Dissolved Inorganic Nitrogen (DIN), Total Phosphorus (TP), Total Solids (TS) and Turbidity (T). Each parameter is weighted by a value w_i between 0 and 1 and the sum of all weights is 1. The result is expressed by a number between 0 and 100, divided in 5 quality ranges: (100 - 79) - Excellent Quality; (79 - 51) - Good Quality; (51 - 36) - Fair Quality; (36 - 19) - Poor Quality; [19 - 0] - Bad Quality, normalization curves for each variable, as well as the respective weights, are available in the São Paulo's State Water Quality Reports (CETESB, 2004, 2005 and 2006).

$$IQA_{CETESB} = IQA = \prod_{i=1}^{n} q_i^{w_i} \qquad (2)$$

Silva and Jardim (2006) used the concept of minimum operator to develop their index, called Water Quality Index for protection of aquatic life (IQA_{PAL}). The IQA_{PAL} (eq. 3) is based on only two parameters, Total Ammonia (TA) and Dissolved Oxygen (DO):

$$IQA_{PAL} = min\ (TA_n, DO_n) \qquad (3)$$

A fourth index, called IQA_{min}, proposed by Pesce and Wunderlin (2000), is the arithmetic mean (eq. 4) of three environmental parameters, Dissolved Oxygen (DO), Turbidity (T) and Total Phosphorus (TP), normalized using Conesa's curves (Conesa, 1995).

$$IQA_{min} = \frac{DO+T+TP}{3} \qquad (4)$$

Other indices are found in the literature and will not be considered in this study (Bordalo et al., 2001; SDD, 1976; Stambuk Giljanovic, 1999).

2.2 Fuzzy inference

One of the research fields involving Artificial Intelligence - AI is fuzzy logic, originally conceived as a way to represent intrinsically vague or linguistic knowledge. It is based on the mathematics of fuzzy sets (Zadeh, 1965). Fuzzy inference is the result of the combination of fuzzy logic with expert systems (Yager, 1994). The commonest models used to represent the process of classification of water bodies are called deterministic conceptual models. They are deterministic because they ignore the stochastic properties of the process and conceptual because they try to give a physical interpretation to the several subprocesses involved. These models often use a large number of parameters, making modeling a complex and time demanding task (Barreto, 2001).

Models based on fuzzy rules are seen as adequate tools to represent uncertainties and inaccuracies in knowledge and data. These models can represent qualitative aspects of knowledge and human inference processes without a precise quantitative analysis. They are, therefore, less accurate than conventional numerical models. However, the gains in simplicity, computational speed and flexibility that result from the use of these models may compensate an eventual loss in precision (Bárdossy, 1995).

There are at least six reasons why models based on fuzzy rules may be justified: first, they can be used to describe a large variety of nonlinear relations; second, they tend to be simple, since they are based on a set of local simple models; third, they can be interpreted verbally and this makes them analogous to AI models; fourth, they use information that other methods cannot include, such as individual knowledge and experience; fifth, the fuzzy approach has a big advantage over other indices, once they have the ability expand and combine quantitative and qualitative data that expresses the ecological status of a river, allowing to avoid artificial precision and producing results that are more similar to the ecological complexity and real world problems in a more realistic panorama; and sixth, fuzzy logic can deal with and process missing data without compromising the final result.

The way systems based on fuzzy rules have been successfully used to model dynamic systems in other fields of science and engineering suggests that this approach may become an effective and efficient way to build a meaningful IQA.

Fuzzy inference is the process that maps an input set into an output set using fuzzy logic. This mapping may be used for decision making or for pattern recognition. The fuzzy inference process involves four main steps: 1) fuzzy sets and membership functions; 2) fuzzy set operations; 3) fuzzy logic; and 4) inference rules. These concepts are discussed in depth in Bárdossy (1995), Yen e Langari (1999), Ross (2004), Cruz (2004) and Caldeira et al. (2007).

The concept of fuzzy sets for modeling water quality was considered by Dahiya (2007), Nasiri et al. (2007) Chau (2006), Ocampo-Duque et al. (2006), Icaga (2007), and Chang et al. (2001), Lermontov et al. (2009), Ramesh et al. (2010), Taner et al. (2011).

2.3 Development of the fuzzy water quality index (INQA)

The fuzzy sets were defined in terms of a membership function that maps a domain of interest to the interval [0,1]. Curves are used to map the membership function of each set. They show to which degree a specific value belongs to the corresponding set (eq. 5):

$$\mu A : X \rightarrow [0,1] \qquad (5)$$

Trapezoidal and triangular membership functions (Figure 1) are used in this study, for the same nine parameters used by CETESB to calculate its IQA, so that this methodology can be statistically compared and validated. The data shown in Tables 1 and 2 are used according to Figure 1 to create the fuzzy sets:

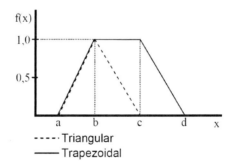

Fig. 1. Trapezoidal and triangular membership function.

In a rule based fuzzy system, a linguistic description is attributed to each set. The sets are then named according to a perceived degree of quality, that ranges from very excellent to very bad (Tables 1 and 2). For the parameters temperature and pH, two sets for each linguistic variable are used. Temperature and pH sets have the same linguistic terms above and under the Very Excellent point while distancing from it. The sets under are marked with a (▼) symbol. The trapezoidal function is only used for the Very Excellent linguistic variable and the triangular for all others. This study uses the linguistic model of fuzzy inference, where the input data set, the water quality variables, called antecedents, are processed using linguistic if/then rules to yield an output data set, the so-called consequents.

Parameter	Gr01 Temperature				pH				Gr02 Disolved Oxigen				Biochemical Oxigen Demand				Gr03 Thermotolerant Coliforms			
Symbol	Temp				pH				DO				BOD				Coli			
Unit	°C								mg/l				mg/l				Colonies/100ml			
Interval	-6 - 45				1 - 14				0 - 9				0 - 30				0 - 18000			
Linguistic Variable	a	b	c	d	a	b	c	d	a	b	c	d	a	b	c	d	a	b	c	d
Very Excellent - VE	15	16	21	22	6.80	6.90	7.10	7.75	7.0	7.5	9.0	9.0	0	0	0.5	2	0	0	1	1
Excellent - E	14	15	16		7.10	7.75	8.25		6.5	7	7.5		0.5	2	3		1	2	3	
Excellent - E▼	21	22	24		6.60	6.80	6.90													
Very Good - VG	13	14	15		7.75	8.25	8.50		6	6.5	7		2	3	4		2	3	8	
Very Good - VG▼	22	24	26		6.30	6.60	6.80													
Good - G	10	13	14		8.25	8.50	8.75		5	6	6.5		3	4	5		3	8	16	
Good - G▼	24	26	28		6.10	6.30	6.60													
Fair/Good - FG	5	10	13		8.50	8.75	9.00		4	5	6		4	5	6		8	16	40	
Fair/Good - FG▼	26	28	30		5.85	6.10	6.30													
Fair - F	0	5	10		8.75	9.00	9.20		3.5	4	5		5	6	8		16	40	100	
Fair - F▼	28	30	32		5.60	5.85	6.10													
Fair/Bad - FB	-2	0	5		9.00	9.20	9.60		3	3.5	4		6	8	12		40	100	300	
Fair/Bad - FB▼	30	32	36		5.20	5.60	5.85													
Bad - B	-4	-2	0		9.20	9.60	10.00		2	3	3.5		8	12	15		100	300	1000	
Bad - B▼	32	36	40		4.75	5.20	5.60													
Very Bad - VB	-6	-4	-2		9.60	10.00	10.50		1	2	3		12	15	22		300	1000	6000	
Very Bad - VB▼	36	40	45		4.00	4.75	5.20													
Poor - P	-6	-6	-4		10.00	10.50	12.00		0	1	2		15	22	30		1000	6000	18000	
Poor - P▼	40	45	45		2.00	4.00	4.75													
Very Poor - P	-6	-6	-6		10.50	14.00	14.00		0	0	1		22	30	30		6000	18000	18000	
Very Poor - P▼	45	45	45		1.00	1.00	4.00													

Table 1. Fuzzy sets and linguistic terms for input parameters of Group 01, 02 and 03

Parameter	Gr04 Dissolved Inorg. Nitrogen				Total Phosphorus				Gr05 Total Solids				Turbidity				Group Output Output			
Symbol	DIN				TP				TS				Turb							
Unit	mg/l				mg/l				mg/l				mg/l							
Interval	0 - 100				0 - 10				0 - 750				0 - 150				0 - 100			
Linguistic Variable	a	b	c	d	a	b	c	d	a	b	c	d	a	b	c	d	a	b	c	d
Very Excellent - VE	0	0	0.5	2	0	0	0.1	0.2	0	0	5	50	0	0	0.5	2.5	0	0	1	10
Excellent - E	0	2	4		0.1	0.2	0.3		0	50	150		0.5	2.5	7.5		0	10	20	
Very Good - VG	2	4	6		0.2	0.3	0.4		50	150	250		2.5	7.5	12.5		10	20	30	
Good - G	4	6	8		0.3	0.4	0.6		150	250	320		7.5	12.5	22.5		20	30	40	
Fair/Good - FG	6	8	10		0.4	0.6	0.8		250	320	400		12.5	22.5	35		30	40	50	
Fair - F	8	10	15		0.6	0.8	1		320	400	450		22.5	35	50		40	50	60	
Fair/Bad - FB	10	15	25		0.8	1	1.5		400	450	550		35	50	70		50	60	70	
Bad - B	15	25	35		1	1.5	3		450	550	600		50	70	95		60	70	80	
Very Bad - VB	25	35	50		1.5	3	6		550	600	650		70	95	120		70	80	90	
Poor - P	35	50	100		3	6	10		600	650	750		95	120	150		80	90	100	
Very Poor - P	50	100	100		6	10	10		650	750	750		120	150	150		90	100	100	

Table 2. Fuzzy sets and linguistic terms for input parameters of Group 04 and 05 and output parameters of all groups

Figure 2 shows the flow graph of the process, where the individual quality variables are processed by inference systems, yielding several groups normalized between 0 and 100. The groups are then processed for a second time, using a new inference, and the end result is the Fuzzy Water Quality Index – INQA/FWQI.

In the traditional methods used to obtain a IQA, parameters are normalized with the help of tables or curves and weight factors (Conesa, 1995; Mitchel, 1996; Pesce and Wunderlin, 1999; CETESB, 2004, 2005 and 2006; NSF, 2007) and then calculated by conventional mathematical methods, while in this work, parameters are normalized and grouped through a fuzzy inference system.

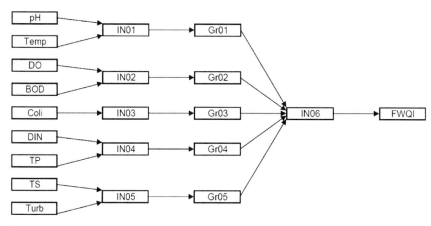

Fig. 2. Flow Graph

The NFS formulated the IQA as being a quantitative aggregation of various chosen and weighted water quality parameters to represent the best professional judgment of 142 expert respondants into one index (Mitchell, 1996). Working quantitatively with a mathematical equation, one uses a weight factor to differentiate the importance (weight - inferred and defined by experts) of each parameter for the outcoming result.

NFS, Brazilian CETESB, Ocampo-Duque et al. (2006), Conessa (1997) and other authors who proposed IQA's, used different weighting factors depending on the methodology and presence or absence of a specific monitoring parameter. Silva and Jardim (2006) and Pesce and Wunderlin (2000) did even not use weighting factors while developing respectively their IQA_{PAL} and IQA_{min}.

In a fuzzy inference system a quantitative numerical value is fuzzyfied into a qualitative state and processed by an inference engine, through rules, sets and operators in a qualitative sphere, allowing the use of information that other methods cannot include, such as individual knowledge and experience (Balas et al., 2004), permitting qualitative environmental parameters and factors to be integrated and processed (Silvert, 2000) producing similar to the real world results.

A rule in the inference system is a mathematical formalism that translates expert judgment expressed in linguistic terms (as in NFS's IQA formulation) and therefore is a subjective and qualitative weight factor in the inference engine. I.e.: Rule 1: *if Thermotolerant Coliform is very high and pH is lower than average than index is very poor*; Rule 2: *if Thermotolerant Coliform is very high and pH is excellent than index is poor*. One can notice that these rules have been designed as an expert system and a subjective and qualitative weight factor based on an expert judgment has been introduced in the process scoop. In spite of the strong pH variation, the final score is not strongly affected.

The physical parameters pH and Temp are normalized and aggregated into the first group (Gr01). DO and BOD comprise Gr02. Thermotolerant coliforms (Coli) were independently normalized as Gr03. The nutrients DIN and TP make up Gr04; TS and Turb are grouped in Gr05. The water analyses results used in this research were taken from the CETESB reports for the years of 2004, 2005 and 2006 (CETESB, 2004, 2005 and 2006). Curves to help in the creation and normalization of the fuzzy sets were taken these reports for the parameters pH, BOD, Coli, DIN, TP, TS and Turb and from Conesa (1995) for Temp and DO.

The rules for normalization and aggregation followed the logic described below and the consequent always obeyed the prescription of the minimum operator:

If FP is VE and SP is VE then GR output is VE
If FP is VE and SP is E then GR output is E
If FP is E and SP is VE then GR output if E

If FP is VE and SP is VP then GR output is VP
If FP is VP and SP is VE then GR output is VP

where: FP - First Parameter / SP - Second Parameter / GR - Group

The INQA was developed from a fuzzy inference that had Groups 01 to 05 as input sets and a series or rules. The antecedent sets (Groups) and the consequent set (INQA) were created by trapezoid (Excellent and Poor sets) and triangular pertinence (all others) functions (Table 3, Figure 3); the INQA classes were the same as for the CETESB's IQA quality standards (Table 3). For example, it was assumed that the boundary between Good and Excellent had a pertinence of 50% in the Excellent and Good fuzzy sets and so on, showing absence of a rigid boundary between classes.

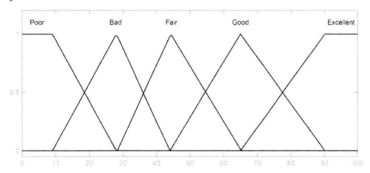

Fig. 3. Output Membership Function

Gr 01, 02, 03, 04, 05 and INQAI 0 - 100				IQA CETESB Classes
	a	b	c	d	
Excellent	65	90	100	100	79 < IQA ≤ 100
Good	44	65	90		51 < IQA ≤ 79
Fair	28	44	65		36 < IQA ≤ 51
Bad	0	28	44		19 < IQA ≤ 36
Poor	0	0	9	28	0 ≤ IQA ≤ 19

Table 3. Input and output fuzzy sets for inference IN06 and IQA$_{CETESB}$ classes

The fuzzy inference system used to compute the INQA has 3125 rules. Being impossible to write them all in this paper, some examples are given below:

Rule 01:

If Gr01 is Excellent and Gr02 is Excellent and Gr03 is Excellent and Gr04 is Excellent and Gr05 is Excellent then INQA is Excellent.

Rule 830:

If Gr01 is Excellent and Gr02 is Good and Gr03 is Bad and Gr04 is Excellent and Gr05 is Poor then INQA is Good.

Rule 1214:

If Gr01 is Good and Gr02 is Poor and Gr03 is Bad and Gr04 is Fair and Gr05 is Bad then INQA is Bad.

Rule 2445:

If Gr01 is Bad and Gr02 is Poor and Gr03 is Fair and Gr04 is Poor and Gr05 is Poor then INQA is Poor.

All the computations were processed using the *"fuzzy logic toolbox"* for MATLAB® (2006).

2.4 Study area
2.4.1 Ribeira do Iguape river – environmental conservation area
The watershed of Ribeira River and the Lagoone-Estuary Complex of Iguape, Cananéia and Paranaguá, called Ribeira Valley, comprises 32 counties and covers and area of 28,306 km2, with 9 cities and 12,238 km^2 in Paraná State and 23 cities and 16,068 km^2 in São Paulo State, Brasil. The economy of Ribeira Vally is based in livestock raising (200,421 hectares), fruticulture (49,942 hectares), silviculture (46,368 hectares), temporary cultures (15,965 hectares) and horticulture (2,773 hectares). Sand and turf extraction from low-lying areas are also significant. About 1% of the state population (396,684 people) live in this river basin, 68% of them in cities. About 56% of the effluents are collected and 49% are treated. It is estimated that approximately 8.8 tons of BOD_5 (remaining pollutant charge) are launched in rivers for disposal within this watershed (CETESB, 2006). The sampling points are given in Table 4 and an illustrative map for this area is shown in Figure 4.

Sampling Point	CETESB Sampling Code	Latitude W	Longitude S	Sampling Site Description	County
SP 01	JAPI 02100	24 41 49	48 00 58	under a bridge on the Jacupiranga-Eldorado highway	Jacupiranga
SP 02	JUQI 00800	23 56 29	47 05 33	under a bridge on highway BR-116	Juquitiba
SP 03	JUQI 02900	24 19 20	47 38 17	down from the confluence with São Lourenço River	Juquia
SP 04	RIBE 02500	24 39 15	48 49 37	at the barge platform, 3 km from downtown	Itaoca
SP 05	RIIG 02500	24 29 21	47 50 05	under a bridge on the highway BR-116	Registro
SP 06	RIIG 02900	24 41 43	47 34 11	is located in Valo Grande	Iguape

Table 4. Sampling point locations in the Ribeira do Iguape river

2.4.2 Paranapanema river – farming area
Paranapanema River has a total extension of 929 km, with eight dams and barrages along its length. The area under study is about 29,114 km^2. Soil use is predominantly rural and thus the region is considered a farming area, occupied mainly by pastures (1,781,625 ha) , followed by temporary cultures, such as sugar cane, soy and corn (764,476 ha) and silviculture (76,595 ha). Fruticulture occupies 40,917 ha and horticulture, 2,477 ha. The watershed comprises 63 counties, with a total population of 1,155,060, of which 88% is urban (CETESB, 2006). Approximately 95.5% of the effluents produced in this watershed are collected and about 79%of these are treated. It is estimated that approximately 20 tons of

BOD$_5$ are dumped in reception bodies of this watershed for disposal (CETESB, 2006). The sampling points are given in Table 5 and an illustrative map for this area is shown in Figure 5.

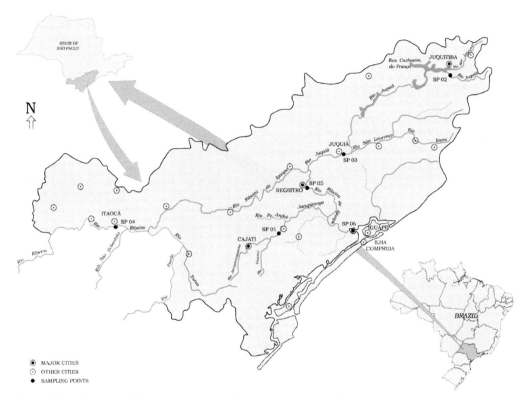

Fig. 4. Map showing Ribeira do Iguape River in a conservation area.

Fig. 5. Map showing Paranapanema River in a farming area.

Sampling Point	CETESB Sampling Code	Latitude W	Longitude S	Sampling Site Description	County
SP 01	PARP 02500	22 59 54	49 54 27	under a bridge on the highway BR-153, in Ourinhos county	Ourinhos
SP 02	PADO 02600	22 57 14	49 52 02	water intake dam in Ourinhos	Ourinhos
SP 03	PARP 02750	22 39 40	51 23 18	800m after the water intake dam in Capivara	Taciba
SP 04	PARP 02900	22 35 50	52 52 28	right after a dam in Usina de Rosana conty, on the SP-613 highway	Teodoro Sampaio
SP 05	PARN 02900	22 28 36	52 57 26	at the water dam in Porto Primavera county	Rosana

Table 5. Sampling point locations in Paranapanema River

2.4.3 Pardo river – industrializing area

Pardo River is born in a small spring in Minas Gerais state, crosses the northwest part of São Paulo state and, after running for 240 km with a watershed of 8,993 km², empties in the estuary of Mogi-Guaçu river. The main uses of the soil in this watershed are urban-industrial and farming, with predominance of sugar cane (329,924 ha), followed by pastures (261,999 ha), fruticulture (83,611 ha) and silviculture (46,640 ha). About 3% of the state population live in this UGRHI (1,056,658 people) with 97% of the population in urban areas, scattered over 23 cities. More than 99% of the effluents are collected and 51% are treated. It is estimated that approximately 31 tons of BOD_5 are dumped in reception bodies of this watershed for disposal (CETESB, 2006). The sampling points are given in Table 6 and an illustrative map for this area is shown in Figure 6.

Sampling Point	CETESB Sampling Code	Latitude W	Longitude S	Sampling Site Description	County
SP 01	PARD 02010	21 34 20	46 50 09	under a bridge on the SP-350 highway, between São Jose and Guaxupé	São Jose do Rio Pardo
SP 02	PARD 02100	21 37 24	47 02 36	under a bridge on the SP-340 highway, between Casa Branca a Mococa	Mococa
SP 03	PARD 02500	21 06 00	47 45 44	left margin, at Clube Ribeirão Preto's Regatas Club	Ribeirão Preto
SP 04	PARD 02600	20 57 58	48 01 40	right margin, 50 m from bridge under highway betwwen Pontal a Cândia	Pontal

Table 6. Sampling point locations in Pardo River

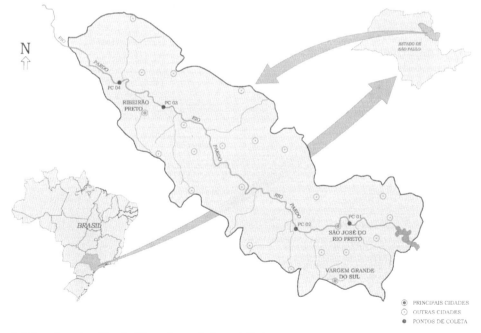

Fig. 6. Map showing Pardo River in an industrializing area.

2.4.4 Paraíba do Sul river – industrial aea

Paraíba do Sul River has an approximate length of 1,150 km (Jornal da ASEAC, 2001). Its watershed is located in the southwest region of Brazil and covers approximately 55,400 km², including the states of São Paulo (13,500 km²), Rio de Janeiro (21,000 km²) and Minas Gerais (20,900 km²). The watershed comprises 180 counties, with a total population of 5,588,237, 88.8% in urban areas. The river is used predominantly for irrigation (49.73 m³/s), without taking into account the transposition of the Paraíba do Sul (160 m³/s) and Piraí (20 m³/s) rivers to the metropolitan region of Rio de Janeiro. The urban supply amounts to about 16.5 m³/s, while the industrial sector uses 13.6 m³/s, surpassing only the cattle-raising sector, with less than 4 m³/s. The main uses of the soil are urban-industrial and rural, the second with pastures (545,156 ha), temporary cultures (57,709 ha), fruticulture (2,996 ha), horticulture (438) and silviculture (83,667 ha). About 5% of the state population (1,944,638) live in this watershed, with 91% in urban areas, scattered throughout 34 counties. Of the total effluents produced in this watershed, 89% are collected and 33% of these are treated. It is estimated that about 72 tons of BOD are dumped in this river for disposal (CETESB, 2006). The sampling points are given in Table 7 and an illustrative map for this area is shown in Figure 7.

Sampling Point	CETESB Sampling Code	Latitude W	Longitude S	Sampling Site Description	County
SP 01	PARB 02050	23 22 32	45 53 12	at the water intake point in Santa Branca county, in the Angola de Cima suburb	Santa Branca
SP 02	PARB 02100	23 22 05	45 53 59	under a bridge on the highway SP-77, between Jacareí and Santa Branca	Santa Branca
SP 03	PARB 02200	23 18 48	45 58 20	at the Jacareí water intake point	Jacareí
SP 04	PARB 02300	23 11 42	45 55 48	under the bridge that acesses Urbanova suburb, in São José dos Campos county	São Jose dos Campos
SP 05	PARB 02310	23 11 16	45 55 04	at the São José dos Campos water intake point	São Jose dos Campos
SP 06	PARB 02400	23 04 54	45 42 40	under the Porto street bridge, between Caçapava county and Menino Jesus	Caçapava
SP 07	PARB 02490	22 57 40	45 33 10	at the SABESP water intake point for Tremembé in Taubaté county	Tremembé
SP 08	PARB 02530	22 54 42	45 28 13	at the SABESP water intake point for Pindamonhangaba	Pindamonhangaba
SP 09	PARB 02600	22 50 40	45 14 04	at the water intake point for Aparecida	Aparecida
SP 10	PARB 02700	22 42 12	45 07 10	under a bridge on the highway BR-459, between Lorena and Piquete	Lorena
SP 11	PARB 02900	22 32 32	44 46 26	under the brigde in Queluz county	Queluz

Table 7. Sampling point locations in Paraíba do Sul River

Fig. 7. Map showing Paraíba do Sul River in an industrial area.

3. Index results and discussion

The IQA$_{\text{CETESB}}$ was taken from the *Relatórios de Qualidade das Águas Interiores do Estado de São Paulo* (CETESB, 2004, 2005, 2006). The IQA$_{\text{sub}}$ was calculated with a weight factor $k = 0.75$ for good quality water. The IQA$_{\text{min}}$ was calculated as described by Pesce and Wunderlin (2000) and the IQA$_{\text{PAL}}$ according to Silva e Jardim (2006), using the recommended technologies. The INQA was computed using the method previously outlined. In this work individual results will not be presented. The results will be graphically presented in the consolidated form of weighted averages. A statistical analysis of the results will then be performed. Factors or influences that lead to an increase or decrease of individual parameters will not be discussed, since this would take us too far afield. A discussion of the subject can be found in Lermontov (2009).

3.1 Ribeira do Iguape river indices – environmental conservation area

The annual averages of the indices for 2004, 2005 and 2006 are shown in Figure 8 for all sampling points. The IQA$_{\text{CETESB}}$, IQA$_{\text{sub}}$ and INQA indices are strongly correlated. In most cases, the IQA$_{\text{sub}}$ index is the stricter and IQA$_{\text{min}}$ is the less strict, attributing a better quality to the same water sample.

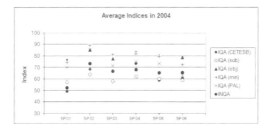

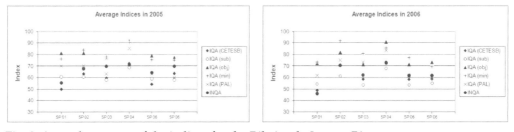

Fig. 8. Annual averages of the indices for the Ribeira do Iguape River.

3.2 Paranapanema river indices – farming area

The results for the Parapanema River are shown in Figure 9. The IQA$_{\text{min}}$ for 2004 is less strict than the other indices, while the IQA$_{\text{min}}$ is the stricter. The other the indices are very close for sampling points SP 03, 04 and 05, but diverge somewhat for sampling points SP 01 and 02.

In the case of 2005 data, the INQA stays close to the IQA$_{\text{CETESB}}$ for all sampling points but the two indices are weakly correlated, specially at sampling point SP 02. The IQA$_{\text{sub}}$ is again the stricter index and the IQA$_{\text{min}}$ the less strict. Data for 2006 confirm that the IQA$_{\text{sub}}$ is not the best indicator for the water quality of this river, since it diverges significantly from the other indices. The INQA is again very close to the IQA$_{\text{CETESB}}$, although slightly less strict.

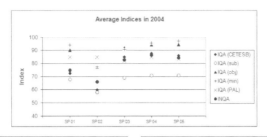

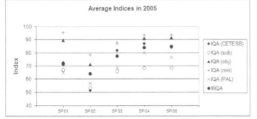

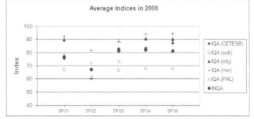

Fig. 9. Annual averages of the indices for the Paranapanema River.

3.3 Pardo river indices – industrializing area

The results for the Pardo River are shown in Figure 10. For 2004, que IQA_{CETESB}, IQA_{sub} e INQA índices are very close. A $k = 0.75$ value for the IQA_{sub} index shows a less strict evaluation, while a $k = 1.00$ for the IQA_{obj} shows a stricter evaluation. The INQA is in general close to the IQA_{CETESB}, albeit somewhat less strict for SP 04. The 2005 results show the INQA close to the IQA_{CETESB} for sampling points SP 01 e SP 02 but the indices diverge for SP 03 and SP 04. The IQA_{sub} is again the stricter index. The results for 2006 are similar.

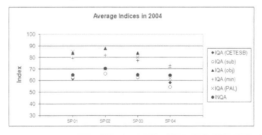

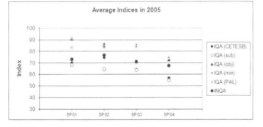

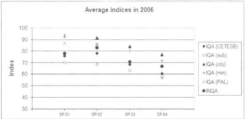

Fig. 10. Annual averages of the indices for the Pardo River.

3.4 Paraíba do Sul indices – industrial area

The results for the Paraíba do Sul River are shown in Figure 11. In the case, the IQA_{PAL} is the stricter index, while the IQA_{obj} and the IQA_{min} alternate as the less strict index, depending on the sampling point. The IQA_{CETESB}, IQA_{sub} and INQA are closely related.

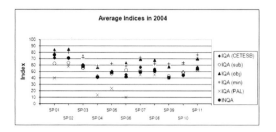

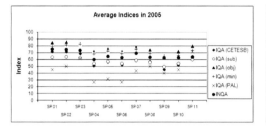
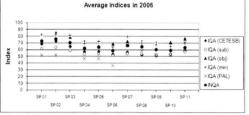

Fig. 11. Annual averages of the indices for the Paraíba do Sul River.

4. Statistical results, discussion and conclusions

4.1 Statistical results

The purpose of statistical analysis of the results for each watershed was to validate the use of fuzzy methodology to develop a fuzzy water quality index (INQA). In this process, the results for 2004, 2005 and 2006 were not separately studied, but were grouped in a single data set for each index. The results are shown in Table 8.

Catchment area	Indices	N	Arithmetic mean	Geometric mean	Harmonic mean	Median	Mode	Min	Max	Variance	Standard Deviation	Confidence -95%	Confidence 95%	Coefficients of variation
Ribeira do Iguape river 'Conservation area'	IQA (CETESB)	108	61.1	60.3	59.5	59.5	56.0	36	83	99.2	9.959	8.7845	11.498	16.299
	IQA (sub)	108	59.5	59.2	58.9	60.2	60.4	46	74	35.9	5.995	5.2880	6.921	10.073
	IQA (obj)	108	79.3	78.9	78.5	80.2	80.5	61	98	63.9	7.993	7.0506	9.229	10.073
	IQA (min)	108	79.8	78.9	77.9	80.0	80.0	43	100	132.6	11.513	10.1559	13.293	14.431
	IQA (PAL)	108	70.3	69.0	67.6	70.0	60.0	30	90	165.3	12.859	11.3424	14.846	18.297
	INQA	108	64.7	63.8	62.8	66.0	66.0	29	86	95.1	9.754	8.6039	11.262	15.083
Paranapanema river 'Farming area'	IQA (CETESB)	88	77.2	76.0	74.7	82.0	90.0	46	92	163.5	12.785	11.1351	15.014	16.558
	IQA (sub)	90	66.0	65.8	65.5	67.5	71.8	50	74	34.6	5.885	5.1331	6.897	8.911
	IQA (obj)	90	88.1	87.7	87.3	90.0	95.7	66	98	61.6	7.847	6.8441	9.197	8.911
	IQA (min)	90	90.2	89.6	89.0	93.3	96.7	60	100	89.0	9.433	8.2275	11.055	10.459
	IQA (PAL)	90	76.9	75.2	73.1	80.0	90.0	30	100	210.4	14.506	12.6527	17.002	18.867
	INQA	90	77.6	77.1	76.5	76.7	87.1	52	87	79.9	8.939	7.7963	10.476	11.516
Pardo river 'Industrializing area'	IQA (CETESB)	70	66.8	66.2	65.5	66.0	Multiple	41	87	87.2	9.341	8.0087	11.208	13.977
	IQA (sub)	72	63.1	62.7	62.3	63.8	63.2	46	74	42.6	6.529	5.6097	7.813	10.354
	IQA (obj)	72	84.1	83.6	83.1	85.0	84.3	61	98	75.8	8.706	7.4796	10.417	10.354
	IQA (min)	72	81.1	80.2	79.3	83.3	Multiple	53	100	134.9	11.615	9.9786	13.897	14.319
	IQA (PAL)	72	73.8	72.1	70.1	70.0	70.0	30	90	198.4	14.086	12.1019	16.854	19.100
	INQA	72	70.8	70.3	69.8	68.0	66.0	51	88	66.8	8.173	7.0216	9.779	11.547
Paraíba do Sul river 'Industrial Area'	IQA (CETESB)	184	57.1	55.9	54.8	56.0	54.0	35	87	138.2	11.758	10.6667	13.100	20.590
	IQA (sub)	190	54.9	54.4	53.8	55.7	Multiple	36	76	60.0	7.747	7.0386	8.615	14.105
	IQA (obj)	190	73.0	72.3	71.5	74.3	Multiple	48	93	103.8	10.188	9.2561	11.330	13.955
	IQA (min)	190	71.3	70.2	69.0	73.3	76.7	40	93	145.5	12.063	10.9602	13.416	16.915
	IQA (PAL)	190	46.8	-	-	50.0	50.0	0	80	419.8	20.489	18.6152	22.785	43.790
	INQA	190	61.4	59.8	58.0	64.5	Multiple	29	87	169.4	13.016	11.8261	14.475	21.210

Table 8. Statistical Data

The statistical data were computed using the StatSoft Statistica application and will be discussed in section 4.2. Figure 12 show the coefficient of variation of the indices.

Table 9 shows the relative differences between the means of the indices and the official index (IQA$_{CETESB}$) and the proposed new index (INQA), calculated using Equation 6:

$$\% \text{ variation} = (I1 - I2) / I1 \times 100 \tag{6}$$

Where:

I1 – First index

I2 – Second index

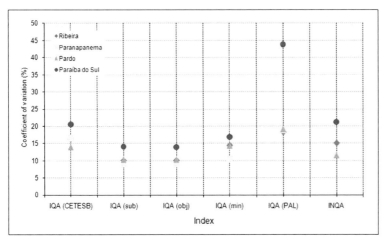

Fig. 12. Coefficients of variation of the indices.

Catchment area	Indices	AM deviation in relation to IQA (CETESB) %	GM deviation in relation to IQA (CETESB) %	HM deviation in relation to IQA (CETESB) %	AM deviation in relation to INQA %	GM deviation in relation to INQA %	HM deviation in relation to INQA %
Ribeira do Iguape river 'Conservation area'	IQA (CETESB)				5,5	5,5	5,4
	IQA (sub)	2,6	1,8	0,9	8,0	7,2	6,3
	IQA (obj)	-29,9	-30,9	-32,1	-22,7	-23,7	-25,0
	IQA (min)	-30,6	-30,9	-31,1	-23,4	-23,6	-24,1
	IQA (PAL)	-15,0	-14,5	-13,8	-8,7	-8,1	-7,7
	INQA	-5,8	-5,9	-5,7			
Paranapanema river 'Farming area'	IQA (CETESB)				0,5	1,3	2,3
	IQA (sub)	14,5	13,5	12,4	14,9	14,7	14,4
	IQA (obj)	-14,0	-15,3	-16,8	-13,5	-13,8	-14,1
	IQA (min)	-16,8	-17,9	-19,1	-16,2	-16,3	-16,4
	IQA (PAL)	0,4	1,1	2,2	0,9	2,4	4,4
	INQA	-0,5	-1,4	-2,3			
Pardo river 'Industrializing area'	IQA (CETESB)				5,6	5,9	6,2
	IQA (sub)	5,6	5,2	4,8	10,9	10,8	10,8
	IQA (obj)	-25,8	-26,3	-26,9	-18,8	-18,9	-19,0
	IQA (min)	-21,4	-21,3	-21,1	-14,6	-14,1	-13,6
	IQA (PAL)	-10,4	-9,0	-7,1	-4,2	-2,6	-0,4
	INQA	-5,9	-6,3	-6,6			
Paraiba do Sul river 'Industrial Area'	IQA (CETESB)				7,0	6,5	5,5
	IQA (sub)	3,8	2,8	1,8	10,5	9,1	7,2
	IQA (obj)	-27,8	-29,2	-30,6	-19,0	-20,9	-23,4
	IQA (min)	-24,9	-25,6	-26,0	-16,2	-17,4	-19,1
	IQA (PAL)	18,1			23,8		
	INQA	-7,5	-6,9	-5,8			

were:

AM - Aritmetic mean

GM - Geometric mean

HM - Harmonic mean

Table 9. Relative differences between the means of the indices and IQA$_{CETESB}$ and INQA.

The frequency histograms of the indices for the four watersheds are shown in Figure 13 and correspond to a visual representation of the frequency distribution tables. For analysis and interpretation of these graphs, see Lermontov (2009).

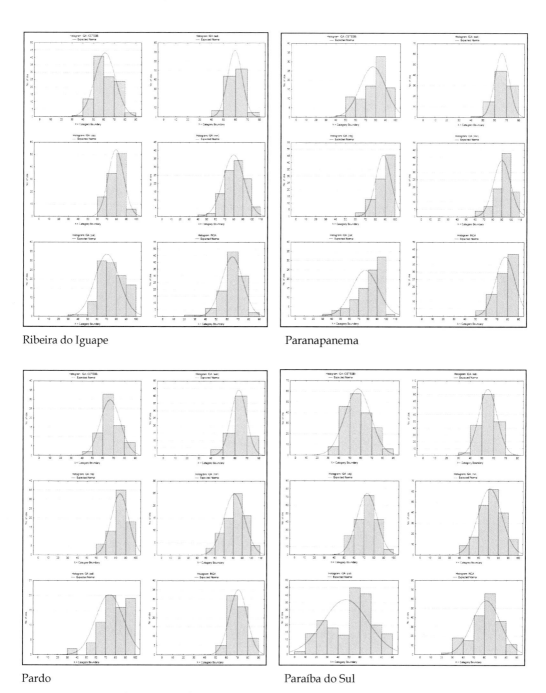

Ribeira do Iguape   Paranapanema

Pardo   Paraíba do Sul

Fig. 13. Frequency histograms for the four watersheds.

Figures 14 and 15 show box & whiskers plots for all indices and watersheds. These plots are a convenient way to visualize the main trend and the data scatter and to show, in the same graph, the main results of a sampling.

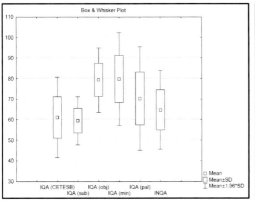

Ribeira do Iguape

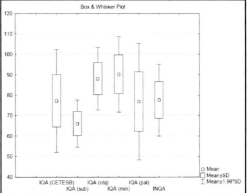

Paranapanema

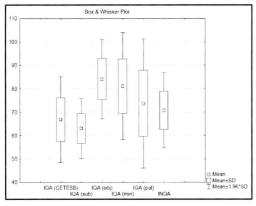

Pardo

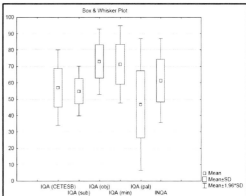

Paraíba do Sul

Fig. 14. Box & Whiskers plots of the mean, mean ± standard deviation and mean ± 1,96 times standard deviation for the four watersheds.

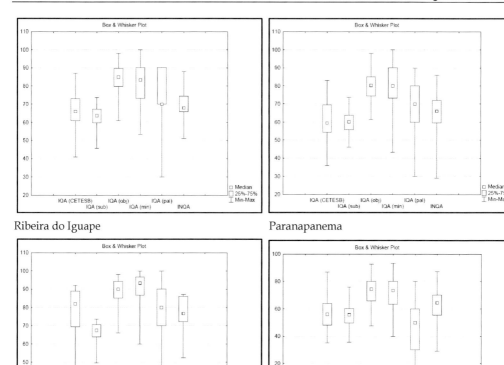

Ribeira do Iguape   Paranapanema

Pardo   Paraíba do Sul

Fig. 15. Box & Whiskers plots of the median, upper and lower quartile and maximum and minimum value for the four watersheds.

Table 10 shows the correlations between the fuzzy index (INQA) and the other indices. The best correlation, 0.8527 (a strong correlation), between the INQA and the IQA$_{CETESB}$ for the Paranapanema River, is illustrated in Figure 16. The worst correlation, 0.3740, between the INQA and the IQA$_{PAL}$ for the Ribeira do Iguape River, is illustrated in Figure 17.

	Corelations - Pearson's **r**			
	Ribeira do Iguape	Paranapanema	Pardo	Paraíba do Sul
INQA x IQA$_{CETESB}$	0.79381	0.8527	0.8206	0.7943
INQA x IQA$_{sub}$	0.57937	0.7710	0.7107	0.8127
INQA x IQA$_{obj}$	0.57937	0.7710	0.7107	0.8742
INQA x IQA$_{min}$	0.59937	0.6444	0.6520	0.7483
INQA x IQA$_{PAL}$	0.37406	0.3924	0.4025	0.5191

Table 10. Correlations between the INQA and the other indices for the four watersheds.

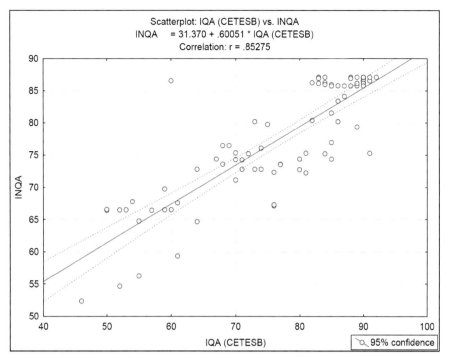

Fig. 16. Best correlation – INQA x IQA$_{CETESB}$ – r = 0.8527 – Paranapanema River

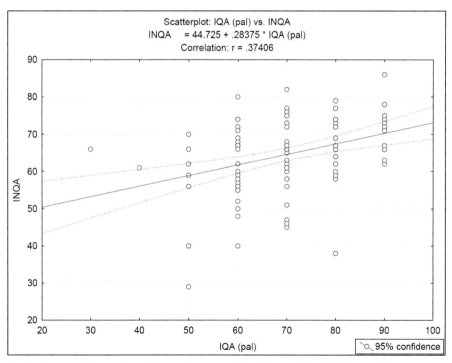

Fig. 17. Worst correlation – INQA x IQA$_{pal}$ – r = 0.3740 – Ribeira do Iguape River

4.2 Statistical discussion

The statistical data that were collected and presented in this work provide a rich field for discussion and analysis. However, our purpose here was only to validate the use of the fuzzy index (INQA). A simplified statistical analysis was implemented and fulfilled its purpose.

In the case of the Ribeira do Iguape River, we could compute all indices from the available data, except the IQA_{CETESB}, that was taken directly from reports.

In the case of the Paraíba do Sul River, since there was a minimum equal to zero, the geometric and harmonic means could not be computed.

For all watersheds and all indices, the geometric mean was lower than the arithmetic mean and the harmonic mean was lower than the arithmetic mean.

The geometric mean and the harmonic mean of the IQA_{PAL} could not be computed for the Paraíba do Sul River because, in the case, the minimum value was 0.

The coefficients of variation shown in the last column of Table 8 were plotted in Figure 12. In this kind of analysis, the statistical results are presented though a parameter that reflects the scattering of the data points. The worst coefficient of variation was that of the IQA_{PAL} and the best were those of the IQA_{sub} and the IQA_{obj}. When the results for the INQA and the IQA_{CETESB} are compared, one notices that the coefficient of variation of the INQA was smaller than that of the IQA_{CETESB} in three watersheds: Ribeira do Iguape, Paranapanema and Pardo. Only in the industrial area of the Paraíba do Sul River the coefficient of variation of the IQA_{CETESB} was smaller than that of the INQA. This is probably due to the fact that the Paraíba do Sul watershed is more polluted than the others, with low quality water.

The relative differences more relevant to our study, i.e. those between means of the other indices and the IQA_{CETESB} and the INQA means, were computed using Equation 6 and the results are shown in Table 9. In the case of the difference between the IQA_{CETESB} and the INQA, the main focus of our study, all the differences were smaller than 10%. The largest difference, 7.5%, was for the Paraíba do Sul watershed, an industrial area, and the smallest, 0.5%, was for the Paranapanema watershed, a farming area.

Examining the box and whiskers plots of Figures 14 and 15 along with the data from Table 9, one can draw the following conclusions:

- IQA_{obj} and IQA_{min} are the indices that diverge more sharply from the others, especially from IQA_{CETESB}, calculated using a well accepted method;
- INQA yielded satisfactory results when compared to a traditional method such as IQA_{CETESB};
- The results obtained using INQA and IQA_{CETESB} were closest for a farming region and were farthest for an industrial region.

The correlation data are shown in Table 10. The correlation coefficient r, or "Pearson's r", as it is also called, is used in this study to measure the degree of correlation between INQA and the other indices for each watershed. Values between 0.7 and 1.0 (positive or negative) indicate a strong correlation between two parameters. Examining the correlation data, one can draw the following conclusions:

- The worst correlation with INQA was that of IQA_{PAL} in all four watersheds. This is probably due to the fact that this indicator is based on only two parameters;
- The best correlation with INQA was that of IQA_{obj} in the industrial region (Paraíba do Sul watershed), but the correlation of IQA_{obj} with INQA was much weaker in the other regions;

- The best global correlation with INQA was that of IQA$_{CETESB}$, a widely accepted index;
- The best individual correlation between INQA and IQA$_{CETESB}$ was in the farming region (Paranapanema watershed).

4.3 Statistical conclusions

The main conclusions of the statistical analysis are the following:

- There is a strong correlation between the proposed fuzzy index (INQA) and a widely accepted, traditional index (IQA$_{CETESB}$);
- The relative differences between the means of INQA and IQA$_{CETESB}$ were less than 8% for all four watersheds;
- The box and whiskers plots for the two indices are reasonably similar;
- The other statistical results for the two indices also were reasonably similar;
- The coefficients of variation of the INQA were smaller than those of the IQA$_{CETESB}$ for all four watersheds.

5. General conclusions

The use of several water quality indices and the development, application and evaluation of a new indexing method to assess river water quality using fuzzy inference is discussed. A new index, called Fuzzy Water Quality Index (INQA) is developed to correct perceived deficiencies in environmental monitoring, water quality classification and management of water resources in cases where the conventional, deterministic methods can be inaccurate or conceptually limited. This methodology differs from other fuzzy water quality indexing methodologies by incorporating the weight factor in qualitative sphere throughout the rules in the inference engine. This is only possible due to a high variety of rules inserted in the inference system. The practical applications of the new index is tested in a realistic case study carried out in Ribeira do Iguape River in São Paulo State, Brazil, showing that the proposed index is reliable and consistent with the traditional qualitative methods.

Most institutional players are not familiar with fuzzy logic concepts, therefore being unaware of the potential of this technique for the transfer of expert knowledge in a qualitative sphere into a   formal system of environmental assessment. We think that this approach can and should be used as an alternate tool for the analysis of river water quality and for strategic planning and decision making in the context of integrated environmental management.

For this doctoral study, the same nine parameters used by CETESB State Organ to calculate its IQA were chosen for the methodology validation by statistical comparison. The authors also worked in the development of an index with additional parameters, such as heavy metals, organoleptic metals and toxic compounds, for a more realistic evaluation of the hydric bodies (Lermontov, 2009).

6. References

Balas, C.E., Ergin, A., Williams, A.T., Koc, L. (2004). Marine litter prediction by artificial intelligence. Mar. Poll. Bull. 48, 449–457.

Bárdossy, A., Duckstein, (1995). *Fuzzy rule-based modeling with applications to geophysical, biological and engineering systems.* CRC Press, Boca Raton, New York, London, Tokyo.

Barreto, J.M (2001). *Inteligência Artificial no Limiar do Século XXI.* 3ª Edição – Florianópolis; O Autor. 379p

Bhargava, D. S. (1983). Use of a water quality index for river classification and zoning of Ganga River, *Environmental Pollution Series B: Chemical and Physical,* 6, pp. 51-67.

Bolton, P. W., Currie, J. C., Tervet, D. J. and Welsh, W. T. (1978). An index to improve water quality classification, *Water Pollution Control,* 77, pp. 271-284.

Bordalo A. A., Nilsumranchit W., Chalermwat, K. (2001). Water quality and uses of the Bangpakong river. *Water Research* 35, 15, pp. 3635-3642.

Caldeira, A. M., Machado, M. A. S., Souza, R. C., Tanscheit, R. (2007). *Inteligência Computacional aplicada a administração, economia e engenharia em Matlab.* São Paulo, Thomson Learning.

Chang, N. B., Chen, H. W. and Ning, S. K. (2001). Identification of river water quality using the fuzzy synthetic evaluation approach, *Journal of Environmental Management,* 63, pp. 293-305.

Chau, K. (2006). A review on integration of artificial intelligence into water quality modeling. *Marine Pollution Bulletin* 52, pp.726-733.

Companhia de Tecnologia de Saneamento Ambiental (CETESB). (2004, 2005 and 2006) *Relatório de Qualidade das Águas Interiores do Estado de São Paulo,* São Paulo.

Conesa Fernandes-Vitora V. (1995). In: *Methodological Guide for Environmental Impact Evaluation,* 3nd ed., p.412. Mundi-Prensa, Madrid, Spain.

Cruz, A. J. de O. (2004). *Lógica Nebulosa. Notas de aula,* Universidade Federal do Rio de Janeiro, Rio de Janeiro.

Cude, C.O. (2001). Water quality index: a tool for evaluating water quality management effectiveness, *J. Am. Water Resour. Assoc.* 37, pp.125–137.

Dahiya S., Singh B., Gaur S., Garg V.K., Kushwaha H.S. (2007). Analysis of groundwater quality using fuzzy synthetic evaluation. *Journal of Hazardous Materials* 147, pp. 938–946

Horton, R. K. (1965). An index number system for rating water quality. *Journal of Water Pollution Control Federation* 37 (3), p.300-305.

House, M. A.; Newsome, D. H. (1989). A water quality index for river management. *Journal of the Institution of Water and Environmental Management,* 3, 1989, pp.336-344

Icaga, Y. (2007). Fuzzy evaluation of water classification. *Ecological Indicators* 7, pp.710-718.

Jornal da ASEAC. (2001). Paraíba do Sul: um Rio no curso da morte. *Informativo Mensal da Associação dos Empregados de Nível Universitário da CEDAE.* Edição de Maio/Junho de 2001, Acessed on 15 dez 2008, Available from: <http://www.aseac.com.br/ jorn34_9.htm>

Liou, S.; Lo S.; Wang, S. (2004). A generalized water quality index for Taiwan. *Environmental Monitoring Assessment* 96, pp. 35–52.

Lermontov, A. (2009). *Novo Índice de Qualidade das Águas com uso da Lógica e Inferência Nebulosa,* Rio de Janeiro: Escola de Química/UFRJ, 2009. Doctoral Tesis.

Lermontov, A., Yokoyama, L., Lermontov. M., Machado. M. A. S. (2009). River quality analysis using fuzzy water quality index: Ribeira do Iguape river watershed, Brazil. *Ecological Indicators,* Volume 9, p.1188-1197

Matlab® 6.0; 2006. Packaged software for technical computing, Release 14, The Math works, Inc.

Mitchell, M.K., Stapp, W.B. (1996). *Field Manual for Water Quality Monitoring: an Environmental Education Program for Schools,* Thomson-Shore Inc., Dexter, Michigan, pp. 277.

Nasiri, F., Maqsood, I., Huang, G. and Fuller, N. (2007). Water quality index: A fuzzy river-pollution decision support expert system, *Journal of Water Resources Planning and Management,* 133, pp. 95-105.

[NSF] National Sanitation Foundation International. (2007). Acessed on October of 2007, Available from: <http://www.nsf.org>

Ocampo-Duque W., Ferré-Huguet N., Domingo J. L., Schuhmacher M. (2006). Assessing water quality in rivers with fuzzy inference systems: A case study. *Environment International* 32, pp. 733–742.

Pesce, S. F., Wunderlin, D. A. (2000). Use of water quality indices to verify the impact of Córdoba city (Argentina) on Suquía river. *Water Research* 34, pp.2915-2926.

Ramesh, S., Sukumaran, N., Murugesan, A.G., Rajan, M.P. (2010). An innovative approach of Drinking Water Quality Index – A case study from Southern Tamil Nadu, India, *Ecological Indicators* 10, p.857-868.

Ross, T. J., (2004). *Fuzzy logic with engineering applications.* New York: John Wiley & Sons.

Said, A, Stevens, D, Selke, G. (2004). An innovative index for evaluating water quality in streams. *Environ Manage,* 34, pp.406–14.

SDD (1976). *Development of a Water Quality Index.* Scottish Development Department, Report ARD3, Edinburgh, p.35.

Silva, G. S.; Jardim, W. de F. (2006). Um novo índice de qualidade de águas para proteção de vida aquática aplicado ao rio Atibaia, região de Campinas/Paulínea – SP. *Química Nova* 29, No. 4, pp. 689-694.

Silvert, W. (1997). Ecological impact classification with fuzzy sets. *Ecological Modeling* 96, pp.1–10.

Silvert, W. (2000). Fuzzy indices of environmental conditions. *Ecological Modeling* 130, pp.111–119.

Stambuk-Giljanovic N. (1999). Water quality evaluation by index in Dalmatia, *Water Research* 16, pp. 3423-3440.

Taner, M. Ü., Üstün, B. Erdinçler, A. (2011). A simple tool for the assessment of water quality in polluted lagoon systems: A case study for Küçükçekmece Lagoon, Turkey, *Ecologigal Indicators,* Volume 11, Issue 2, p.749-756

Yager, R. R.; Filvel, D.P. (1994). *Essentials of Fuzzy Modeling and Control,* New York: John Wiley & Sons.

Yen, J.; Langari, R. (1999). *Fuzzy logic: intelligence, control, and information*, Prentice-Hall, Inc.

Zadeh, L.A. (1965). Fuzzy Sets, *Information and Control* 8, pp. 338-353.

21

Environmental Management of Wastewater Treatment Plants – the Added Value of the Ecotoxicological Approach

Elsa Mendonça[1], Ana Picado[1], Maria Ana Cunha[2] and Justina Catarino[1]
[1] Laboratório Nacional de Energia e Geologia (LNEG), Lisboa,
[2] Agência Portuguesa do Ambiente (APA), Amadora,
Portugal

1. Introduction

Pollution control has been changed by advances in scientific knowledge, because there is a connection of environmental contamination with the ability to measure it. With greater understanding of the impact of wastewater on the environment and more sophisticated analytical methods, advanced treatment is becoming more common (Lofrano & Brown, 2010).

The assessment of biological effects of wastewater discharges in the ecosystems is today considered relevant and ecotoxicological tests identifying the ecological hazard are useful tools for the identification of environmental impacts. Direct toxicity assessment, making use of ecotoxicological tests, can play an important role in supporting decision-making, either regulatory driven or on a voluntary basis.

Within the Integrated Pollution Prevention and Control Directive - IPPC, 2008/1/EC (European Commission [EC], 2008), the Direct Toxicity Assessment concept has been included as a suitable monitoring tool on effluent in several Best Available Techniques (BAT) Reference Documents. Also, in Water Framework Directive – WFD, 2000/60/EC (EC, 2000), direct toxicity assessment of Wastewater Treatment Plant (WWTP) effluents can contribute to attain or keep ecological quality objectives in water masses. So, for EU countries to comply with good ecological status, ecotoxicity evaluation of WWTP effluents is extremely relevant.

In many countries ecotoxicity tests are already in use for wastewater management (Power & Boumphrey, 2004; Tinsley et al., 2004; United States Environmental Protection Agency [USEPA], 2004; Vindimian et al., 1999). Bioassays are also used for wastewater surveillance and BAT compliance by authorities in Germany (Gartiser et al., 2010a). A global evaluation of wastewaters should include ecotoxicological tests to complement the chemical characterization, with advantages especially in the case of complex wastewaters (Mendonça et al., 2009). This approach has advantages particularly to protect biological treatment plants from toxic influents (Hongxia et al., 2004), to monitor the effectiveness of WWTP (Cěbere et al., 2009; Daniel et al., 2004; Emmanuel et al., 2005; Libralato et al., 2006; Metcalf & Eddy, 2003) and in the impact assessment of complex wastewaters. Bioassays are considered a suitable tool for assessing the ecotoxicological relevance of complex organic mixtures (Gartiser et al., 2010b).

As it is often referred (e.g. Metcalf & Eddy, 2003; Movahedian et al., 2005; Teodorović et al., 2009), physico-chemical parameters alone are not sufficient in obtaining reliable information on treated wastewater toxicity and toxicity tests must be performed in combination with routine chemical analysis. The prediction of toxicity from chemical data is considered limited and the better coincidence between the toxicity and chemical-based assessments were achieved when information from all tests in a test-battery was assembled (Manusadžianas et al., 2003).

In the framework of Life Cycle Assessment (LCA) comprehensive analysis of WWTP is evaluated for the physico-chemical characterization of the wastewaters as well as the inventory of inputs and outputs associated with the global process (Hospido et al., 2004). In a recent work Life Cycle Impact Assessment was done using emerging pollutants quantification to rank potential impacts in urban wastewater (Muñoz et al., 2008). A step forward in this approach would be to use ecotoxicological indicators.

In the last ten years and in the framework of European and National contracts developed in Lisbon area (Portugal) studies were conducted on the integrated evaluation of the ecotoxicological and physicochemical parameters of wastewaters from treatment plants receiving domestic and industrial effluents. The evaluation of ecotoxicological data from four of these WWTP was the main aim of this study. Data from acute tests with different species (bacteria, algae, crustaceans and plants) are discussed.

2. Material and methods

2.1 Wastewater treatment plants

The characteristics of the four WWTP that receive domestic and industrial wastewaters are presented in Table 1. These systems differ from each other, namely in the magnitude of flows (the daily flow goes from 16 000 m³/day to 155 000 m³/day), the treatment level implemented (from preliminary treatment to tertiary treatment) and the site of discharge (river, estuary or coastal area).

	WWTP 1	WWTP 2	WWTP 3	WWTP 4
Population equivalent	130 000	700 000	800 000	250 000
Flow (m³/day)	16 000	70 000	155 000	54 500
Treatment type	secondary	tertiary	preliminary	tertiary
Discharge	River	River	Sea	Estuary

Table 1. General information on the Wastewater Treatment Plants (WWTP)

2.2 Wastewater sampling

Wastewater samples were collected with different strategies and periodicities in the different Treatment Plants:

- WWTP1 and WWTP2 – Influent and effluent 24h-composite samples collected seasonally in November, March, September and December 2003/2004;
- WWTP3 – Effluent 24h-composite sample collected monthly from 2006 to 2009;
- WWTP4 – Influent and effluent 1h-composite samples collected in different days of the week (Monday, Tuesday and Friday) at 10 h, 14h and 23h in April 2010.

As presented in Figure 1, sampling point for WWTP1 was after secondary treatment, for WWTP2 after tertiary treatment, for WWTP3 after preliminary treatment and for WWTP4 after primary treatment.

Each sample was divided into subsamples, kept frozen (-20°C) for ecotoxicological analysis for no more than 1 month.

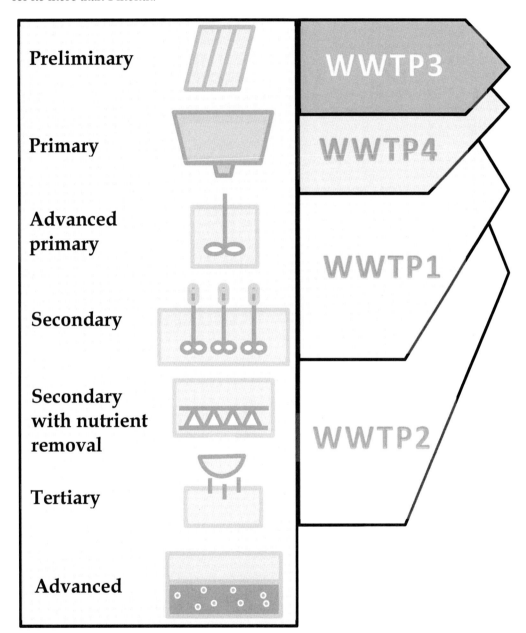

Fig. 1. General Scheme of WWTP treatment process and identification of the level of treatment analyzed in each Treatment Plant.

2.3 Ecotoxicity tests

Ecotoxicological evaluation of the samples was performed using *Vibrio fischeri*, *Pseudokirchneriella subcapitata*, *Thamnocephalus platyurus*, *Daphnia magna* and *Lemna minor* as test organisms, to assess acute aquatic toxicity, according to the following methods:

- Microtox test: Bacterial toxicity was assessed by determining the inhibition of the luminescence of *Vibrio fischeri* (strain NRRL B-11177) exposed for 15 minutes (Microtox® Test, Microbics, Carlsbad, U.S.A.). The test was performed according to the basic test procedure (Microbics, 1992);

- AlgalTox test: Algal toxicity was assessed by measuring the growth inhibition of *Pseudokirchneriella subcapitata* exposed for 72 hours, according to AlgalToxKit F™ test procedure (Microbiotests, 2004) that follow the OECD guideline 201 (Organisation for Economic Co-operation and Development [OECD], 1984). Optical density (OD 670 nm) of algae suspensions was determined;

- ThamnoTox test: Crustacean toxicity was assessed by determining the mortality of *Thamnocephalus platyurus* exposed for 24 hours according to ThamnoToxKit F™ test procedure (Microbiotests, 2003);

- Daphnia test: Crustacean toxicity was also assessed by determining the inhibition of the mobility of *Daphnia magna* (clone IRCHA-5) exposed for 48 hours, according to ISO 6341:1996 (International Organization for Standardization [ISO], 1996). Juveniles for testing were obtained from cultures maintained in the laboratory;

- Lemna test: Plant toxicity was assessed by determining the growth inhibition of *Lemna minor* (clone ST) exposed for 7 days, according to ISO 20079: 2005 (ISO, 2005). Plants for testing were obtained from cultures maintained in the laboratory. Total frond area was used as growth parameter, quantified by an image analysis system – Scanalyzer (LemnaTec, Würselen, Germany).

All samples were tested with Microtox, Daphnia and Lemna tests. For WWTP1, WWTP2 and WWTP4 samples, AlgalTox and ThamnoTox tests were also performed.

2.4 Data analysis

For each toxicity test EC_{50}-t or LC_{50}-t, the effective concentration (% v/v) responsible for the inhibition or lethality in 50% of tested population after the defined exposure period (t), was calculated:

- EC_{50}-72h for AlgalTox test, LC_{50}-24h for ThamnoTox test and EC_{50}-48 h for Daphnia test by using Tox-Calc™ software (version 5.0, Tidepool Scientific software, 2002);

- EC_{50}-7d for Lemna test by using Biostat 2.0 software (LemnaTec 2001);

- EC_{50}-15 min for Microtox test by using Microtox Omni™ software (Azur Environmental, 1999).

To obtain a direct interpretation between values and toxicity, ecotoxicity test results are in this work presented in Toxic Units (TU), calculated as TU=1/ EC_{50}*100. Aiming to include all raw data for TU calculation and for statistical analysis, EC_{50} values not determined due to low effect levels were considered as 100%. For data analysis, values lower than 1 TU were considered as 0.5 TU.

The tests sensitivity was assessed by Slooff's index (Slooff, 1983): each single test result (expressed as EC_{50} or LC_{50}) is divided by the arithmetic mean of all test results for each sample, and the geometric mean of these ratios for each test is calculated. The smaller value stands for the more sensitive test. The Slooff's index was calculated for Microtox, AlgalTox, ThamnoTox, Daphnia and Lemna tests.

Pearson correlations were determined for WWTP3 using statistical analysis software (JMP®
5.0.1) for the 48 samples on the following 4 variables:

- Wastewater flow (pers. comm.);
- Ecotoxicological data from Microtox, Daphnia and Lemna tests.

3. Results and discussion

Aiming to assess direct toxicity of samples from four WWTP we evaluated data from acute
tests with different species: bacteria, algae, crustaceans and plants. The results are presented
in Tables 2 to 5.

Results obtained for WWTP1 (Table 2) show clearly that influent and effluent samples have
different toxicity levels to the species tested, except for Lemna that shows no toxicity both
for influent and effluent samples.

	Sample	Microtox	AlgalTox	ThamnoTox	Daphnia	Lemna
Influent	Nov 03	27.0		3.8	<1	<1
	Mar 04	19.2	5.0	2.3	1.4	
	Sep 04	5.6	<1	7.1	4.8	<1
	Dec 04	11.5	1.8	1.7	2.4	<1
Effluent	Nov 03	<1		<1	<1	<1
	Mar 04	1.9	<1	2.2	<1	<1
	Sep 04	<1	<1	<1	<1	<1
	Dec 04	<1	<1	<1	<1	<1

Table 2. Values for ecotoxicological tests in Toxic Units (TU) obtained for WWTP1 influent
and effluent samples

For WWTP2 (Table 3), influent and effluent samples have also different toxicity levels to the
species tested, except for AlgalTox that shows no toxicity both for influent and effluent
samples. The effluent samples show in this case no toxicity in all the tests performed.

	Sample	Microtox	AlgalTox	ThamnoTox	Daphnia	Lemna
Influent	Nov 03	17.2		3.7	1.2	1.1
	Mar 04	62.5	<1	3.0	1.4	1.4
	Sep 04	47.6	<1	2.0	1.8	1.1
	Dec 04	83.3	<1	1.6	2.5	<1
Effluent	Nov 03	<1		<1	<1	<1
	Mar 04	<1	<1	<1	<1	<1
	Sep 04	<1	<1	<1	<1	<1
	Dec 04	<1	<1	<1	<1	<1

Table 3. Values for ecotoxicological tests in Toxic Units (TU) obtained for WWTP2 influent
and effluent samples

For WWTP3 (Table 4), effluent samples have different toxicity levels to the species tested, with Microtox having the higher TU values along the four years. No significant correlations were obtained between toxicity test results and corresponding daily discharge flow.

	Microtox				Daphnia				Lemna			
	2006	2007	2008	2009	2006	2007	2008	2009	2006	2007	2008	2009
Jan	16.3	14.5	5.9	33.3	3.2	1.4	2.4	1.5	1.6	<1	<1	<1
Feb	4.6	13.2	6.4	10.8	2.9	1.0	1.3	<1	1.2	<1	1.6	<1
Mar	2.2	10.4	15.6	11.6	1.4	2.0	2.9	1.8	<1	<1	1.3	1.0
Apr	8.1	8.4	14.9	10.9	1.4	1.9	2.6	2.5	1.4	<1	<1	<1
May	27.8	14.7	14.5	12.5	4.6	3.1	4.8	1.7	1.6	1.1	<1	1.0
Jun	32.3	16.4	13.2	10.3	7.1	2.6	2.1	1.2	<1	1.4	<1	1.0
Jul	13.5	25.0	19.2	22.2	6.6	2.2	1.2	<1	<1	1.1	1.1	1.0
Aug	14.5	12.2	19.2	4.1	3.2	3.1	3.6	2.2	<1	1.2	1.0	1.1
Sep	25.6	12.7	20.4	5.1	8.1	3.2	1.6	1.5	<1	1.4	<1	<1
Oct	17.5	7.8	31.3	10.0	2.6	1.5	1.5	1.3	1.1	<1	<1	<1
Nov	18.9	13.0	83.3	15.4	3.4	3.1	2.9	4.3	<1	1.3	1.0	1.1
Dec	16.7	4.7	71.4	9.4	3.2	1.4	3.2	<1	1.2	1.4	<1	<1

Table 4. Values for ecotoxicological tests in Toxic Units (TU) obtained for WWTP3 effluent samples.

No time pattern for effluent toxicity was observed in WWTP3. Between October 2008 and January 2009, the effluent samples were particularly toxic to the bacteria, with 83.3 TU in November 2008 (Figure 2).

For WWTP4 (Table 5), the difference in toxicity levels is not so clear between untreated and treated wastewater samples although for Microtox the range of values is higher for the untreated samples [5.8 TU - 93.5 TU] versus treated samples [2.3 TU – 35.8 TU].

During the week monitoring, the highest TU value was obtained on Friday night for Microtox. A peak in toxicity was obtained for Microtox in all samples collected at 23h. This is in line with Chapman (2007) that concludes that difficulties in obtaining representative samples arise in WWTP effluents, whose composition is highly variable, and repeated testing is required.

Analyzing the mean TU values obtained in the different tests, Microtox test shows higher values in all WWTP, followed by the crustacean tests. Low toxicity values were obtained in the plant and algae tests (Figure 3).

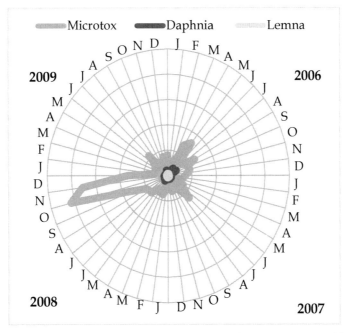

Fig. 2. Distribution of sample toxicity in Toxic Units (TU) for WWTP3 monthly samples from 2006 to 2009.

	Sample	Microtox	AlgalTox	ThamnoTox	Daphnia	Lemna
Influent	Mon-10h	5.8	<1	2.8	<1	1.3
	Mon-14h	19.4	<1	3.0	<1	<1
	Mon-23h	32.7	<1	3.6	1.5	1.1
	Tues-10h	13.9	<1	2.7	<1	1.3
	Tues-14h	12.6	<1	2.8	<1	<1
	Tues-23h	46.5	<1	3.4	1.9	<1
	Fri-10h	17.9	<1	2.6	3.6	<1
	Fri-14h	43.9	<1	2.5	1.9	<1
	Fri-23h	93.5	<1	2.4	1.4	<1
Effluent	Mon-14h	2.3	<1	2.8	<1	<1
	Mon-23h	11.1	<1	3.0	1.1	1.1
	Tues-10h	2.9	1.1	1.8	<1	1.3
	Tues-14h	4.8	<1	2.8	<1	1.3
	Tues-23h	17.8	<1	2.4	1.5	<1
	Fri-10h	16.6	<1	2.1	1.5	<1
	Fri-14h	11.4	<1	2.2	1.1	<1
	Fri-23h	35.8	<1	2.3	<1	<1

Table 5. Values for ecotoxicological tests in Toxic Units (TU) obtained for WWTP4 influent and effluent samples

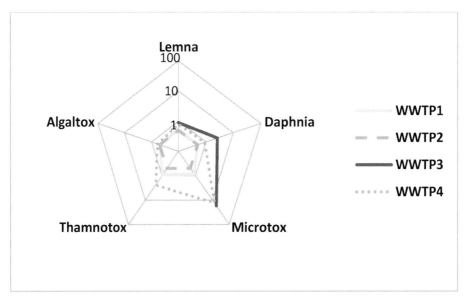

Fig. 3. Mean Toxic Units (TU) values for the tested species and for all effluent samples.

The acute toxicity is dependent on the treatment level of the studied WWTP and the species tested (Figure 3). TU values for Microtox and ThamnoTox are higher in the case of WWTP3 and 4, with preliminary and primary levels of treatment, respectively. The used tests are able to distinguish the different levels of treatment, with the exception of AlgalTox.

From data presented in Figure 4, toxicity removal was obtained for all the WWTP where input and output wastewaters were monitored. For WWTP4 – primary treatment – removal values were in the range 15-60%. For the WWTP with secondary (WWTP1) and tertiary (WWTP2) levels of treatment toxicity removal evaluated by both crustaceans is similar, only the bacteria achieve to detect higher efficiency (100%) with the tertiary treatment. Tyagi et al. (2007) found that the mean percentage removal in toxicity for *D. magna* after primary, secondary and tertiary treatment were 29%, 76% and 100%, respectively. Also Movahedian et al. (2005) reinforces that toxicity removal increases with the level of treatment (e.g. 8% for preliminary treatment and 38% for primary treatment).

A wastewater classification adapted from Tonkes et al. (1999) to the TU values, is as follows: samples with less than 1 TU are considered non toxic; between 1 and 10 TU are considered slightly toxic; with more than 10 TU are considered toxic. Values higher than 10 TU were obtained for Microtox test in 69% of the samples tested. Values between 1 and 10 TU were obtained for 79% of the samples for ThamnoTox and 74% of the samples for Daphnia. No toxicity to the alga and to the plant was registered for the majority of samples, respectively 90% and 65%.

Slooff's sensitivity index calculated for this group of acute test results shows that the bacterium *Vibrio fischeri* is the most sensitive species, and allows to establish the following gradient of test sensitivity, Microtox > ThamnoTox > Daphnia > AlgalTox > Lemna, from the corresponding Slooff's index values 0.2 < 0.7 < 1.0 < 1.4 < 1.6.

The sensitivity of Microtox test and the reliability of this test in monitoring toxicity of treatment plant wastewaters have also been observed by other authors (Araújo et al., 2005; Libralato et al., 2006; Lundström et al., 2010b). Related to the crustacean toxicity several authors concluded that *Daphnia magna* acute test can be a useful analytical tool for early warning system to monitor the different operational units of wastewater treatment plants (Movahedian et al., 2005; Tyagi et al., 2007) or to use in toxicity identification evaluation procedures (Hongxia et al., 2004). Also a study with a copepod as test organism showed that conventionally treated sewage effluent resulted in the most negative effects leading to the conclusion that additional treatments created effluents with less negative impacts (Lundström et al., 2010a).

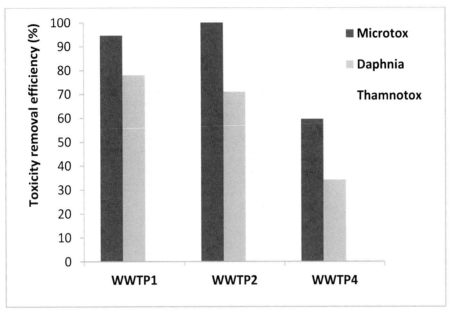

Fig. 4. Toxicity removal efficiency evaluated in WWTP 1, 2 and 4, for Microtox, Daphnia and ThamnoTox tests.

Though we found low sensitivity of *Lemna minor* in WWTP toxicity evaluation, the ecotoxicological assessment of pharmaceutical and food industries effluents using *Lemna minor* as a test organism was considered suitable by Radić et al. (2010) that demonstrated the relevance of *Lemna* as a sensitive indicator of water quality. In nutrient rich wastewaters, although the algae test can be sensitive, it might not be the most appropriate test because of the complex relationship of inhibition and promotion of algae growth often observed (Gartiser et al., 2010a).

When using the wastewater classification for the most sensitive species, in this study the bacteria *V. fischeri* used in the Microtox test, and considering all the WWTP under study, the distribution of toxicity level of treated samples in percentage is in accordance with the treatment process level implemented (Figure 5). For a tertiary treated effluent 100% samples are non toxic and for a preliminary treated effluent 75% are toxic.

Concerning WWTP systems and considering the relative sensitivity of the organisms used in wastewater testing and the importance to consider effects at different trophic levels, the test battery proposed in a previous work (Mendonça et al., 2009) for characterization of WWTP discharges included tests with a bacterium, an alga and a crustacean to monitor this type of wastewaters. For a screening only one test with the most sensitive species, Microtox, was proposed.

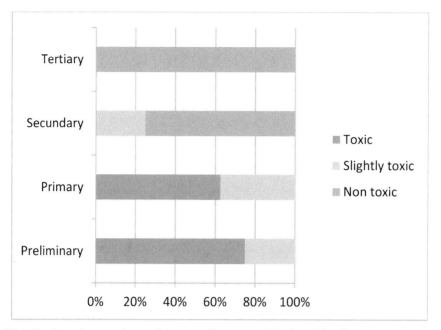

Fig. 5. Distribution of treated samples according to toxicity level for the more sensitive species - Microtox, and Wastewater Treatment Plant process level.

Once secondary and tertiary treatment are employed, the prevention of eutrophication became the next goal for wastewater treatment, requiring the removal of nitrogen, phosphorous or both (Lofrano & Brown, 2010).

On the other hand, little is known about the potential interactive effects of organic wastewater contaminants, namely steroids and hormones present in municipal effluents, when in complex mixtures that may occur in the environment and about their effect on human health (Filby et al., 2007). Chronic toxicity test and endocrine disruption assay of WWTP effluent samples indicated that, in a long term, potential population effects could arise in the receiving waters (Mendonça et al., 2009). Kontana et al. (2008) in an ecotoxicological assessment of municipal wastewater using several test organisms including *Vibrio fischeri* and *Daphnia magna*, observed a decrease of ecotoxicological responses for all bioassays but also the induction of immune response after tertiary treatment, pointing to the need of using sensitive biomarkers if wastewaters are intended for reuse.

Considering ecotoxicity testing as an integral part of the toolbox to investigate the environmental impacts of effluents but knowing that it can be complex, time consuming and expensive, a tiered approach is recommended when defining a realistic assessment strategy (European Centre for Ecotoxicology and Toxicology of Chemicals [ECETOC], 2004; OSPAR Convention for the Protection of the marine Environment of the North-East Atlantic [OSPAR], 2007). The validity of the use of acute tests to drive environmental improvement has been demonstrated, but methodologies for chronic toxicity need further development.

4. Conclusion

This work shows that wastewater acute toxicity is dependent on the treatment level of the WWTP and the species tested. The bacterium *Vibrio fischeri*, the test organism in Microtox test, proved to be the most sensitive species in wastewater ecotoxicological evaluation.

The distribution of treated samples according to the toxicity level to the most sensitive species clearly reveals the treatment process level implemented. All the used tests, with the exception of AlgalTox test, are able to distinguish the different levels of treatment and to assess toxicity removal efficiency.

The ecotoxicological approach proves to have an added value to hazard and risk assessment of discharges to the receiving waters and environmental management of the Wastewater Treatment Plant can use this tool with advantages. Even if a preliminary treatment in the WWTP is associated with the discharge in a submarine outfall, environmental monitoring including toxicological parameters proves to be important.

The inclusion of these ecological relevant data in the assessment of the grey water footprint for point sources of water pollution, like WWTP, can be the next step to have good indicators of the degree of water pollution.

5. Acknowledgment

Research data were obtained under programs supported by the EU LIFE Environment Program (LIFE02 ENV/P/000416 and LIFE08 ENV/P/000237) and a contract with a public enterprise.

6. References

Araújo, C.V.M., Nascimento, R.B., Oliveira, C.A., Strotmann, U.J. & da Silva, E.M. (2005). The use of Microtox® to assess toxicity removal of industrial effluents from the industrial district of Camaçari (BA, Brazil), *Chemosphere* 58, pp. 1277-1281.

Cēbere, B., Faltina, E., Zelčāns, N. & Kalnina, D. (2009). Toxicity tests for ensuring successful industrial wastewater treatment plant operation, *Environmental and Climate Technologies* 3, pp. 41-47.

Chapman, P.M. (2007). Determining when contamination is pollution - Weight of evidence determinations for sediments and effluents, *Environment International* 33, pp. 492-501.

Daniel, M., Sharpe, A., Driver, J., Knight, A.W., Keenan, P.O., Walmsley, R.M., Robinson, A., Zhang, T. & Rawson, D. (2004). Results of a technology demonstration project to compare rapid aquatic toxicity screening tests in the analysis of industrial effluents, *Journal of Environmental Monitoring* 6, pp. 855-865.

EC (2000). *Water Framework Directive* (WFD), Directive 2000/60/EC.

EC (2008). *Integrated Pollution Prevention and Control Directive* (IPPC), Directive 2008/1/EC.

ECETOC (2004). *Whole Effluent Assessment*, Technical Report No. 94, European Centre for Ecotoxicology and Toxicology of Chemicals, Brussels, Belgium.

Emmanuel, E., Perrodin, Y., Keck, G., Blanchard, J.-M. & Vermande, P. (2005). Ecotoxicological risk assessment of hospital wastewater: a proposed framework for raw effluents discharging into urban sewer network, *Journal of Hazardous Materials* A117, pp. 1-11.

Filby, A.L., Neuparth, T., Thorpe, K.L., Owen, R., Galloway, T.S. & Tyler, C.R. (2007). Health Impacts of Estrogens in the Environment Considering Complex Mixture Effects. *Environmental Health Perspectives*, 115, pp. 1704-1710.

Gartiser, S., Hafner, C., Hercher, C., Kronenberger-Schäfer, K. & Paschke, A. (2010a). Whole effluent assessment of industrial wastewater for determination of BAT compliance. Part 1: paper manufacturing industry, *Environmental Science and Pollution Research* 17, pp. 856-865.

Gartiser, S., Hafner, C., Hercher, C., Kronenberger-Schäfer, K. & Paschke, A. (2010b). Whole effluent assessment of industrial wastewater for determination of BAT compliance. Part 2: metal surface treatment industry, *Environmental Science and Pollution Research* 17, pp. 1149-1157.

Hongxia, Y., Jing, C., Yuxia, C., Huihua, S., Zhonghai, D. & Hongjun, J. (2004). Application of toxicity identification evaluation procedures on wastewaters and sludge from a municipal sewage treatment works with industrial inputs, *Ecotoxicology and Environmental Safety* 57, pp.426-430.

Hospido, A., Moreira, M.T., Fernández-Couto, M. & Feijoo, G. (2004). Environmental Performance of a municipal wastewater treatment plant, *The International Journal of Life Cycle Assessment* 9, pp. 261-271.

ISO (1996). *Water Quality – Determination of the inhibition of the mobility of Daphnia magna Straus (Cladocera, Crustacea) - Acute toxicity test*, ISO 6341, International Standard Organization.

ISO (2005). *Water Quality – Determination of toxic effect of water constituents and wastewater to duckweed (Lemna minor) – Duckweed growth inhibition test*, ISO 20079, International Standard Organization.

Kontana, A., Yiangou, M., Papadimitriou, C.A., Samaras, P. & Zdragas, A. (2008). Bioassays and biomarkers for ecotoxicological assessment of reclaimed municipal wastewater, *Water Science and Technology* 57, pp. 947-953.

Libralato, G., Losso, C., Arizzi Novelli, A., Avezzù, F., Scandella, A. & Volpi Ghirardini, A. (2006). Toxicity bioassays as effective tools for monitoring the performances of wastewater treatment plant technologies: SBR and UF-MBR as case studies, *Proceedings of 4th MWWD and 2nd IEMES*, Antalya, Turkey, 2006.

Lofrano, G. & Brown, J. (2010). Wastewater management through the ages: A history of mankind, *Science of the Total Environment* 408, pp. 5254-5264.

Lundström, E., Björlenius, B., Brinkmann, M., Hollert, H., Persson, J.-O. & Breitholtz, M. (2010a). Comparison of six sewage effluents treated with different treatment technologies – Population level responses in the harpacticoid copepod Nitroca spinipes, *Aquatic Toxicology* 96, pp. 298-307.

Lundström, E., Adolfsson-Erici, M., Alsberg, T., Björlenius, B., Eklund, B., Lavén, M. & Breitholtz, M. (2010b). Characterization of additional sewage treatment technologies: Ecotoxicological effects and levels of selected pharmaceuticals, hormones and endocrine disruptors, *Ecotoxicology and Environmental Safety* 73, pp. 1612-1619.

Manusadžianas, L., Balkelytė, L., Sadauskas, K., Blinova, I., Põllumaa, L. & Kahru, A. (2003). Ecotoxicological study of Lithuanian and Estonian wastewaters: selection of the biotests, and correspondence between toxicity and chemical-based indices, *Aquatic Toxicology* 63, pp. 27-41.

Mendonça, E., Picado, A., Paixão, S.M., Silva, L., Cunha, M.A., Leitão, S., Moura, I., Cortez, C. & Brito, F. (2009). Ecotoxicity tests in the environmental analysis of wastewater treatment plants: Case study in Portugal, *Journal of Hazardous Materials* 163: 665-670

Metcalf & Eddy (revised by Tchobanoglous, G., Burton, F.L. & Stensel, H.D.) (2003). *Wastewater Engineering, Treatment and Reuse*, 4th edition, McGraw-Hill, New York.

Microbics (1992). *Microtox Manual – A Toxicity Handbook*, Vols.I-IV, Microbics Corporation Inc., Carlsbad, CA/USA.

MicroBioTests (2003). *ThamnoToxKit FTM – Freshwater Toxicity Screening Test*. Standard Operational Procedure, MicroBioTests Inc., Nazareth, Belgium.

MicroBioTests (2004). *AlgalToxKit FTM - Freshwater Toxicity Test with Microalgae*. Standard Operational Procedure, MicroBioTests Inc., Nazareth, Belgium.

Movahedian, H., Bina, B. & Asghari, G.H. (2005). Toxicity Evaluation of Wastewater Treatment Plant Effluents Using *Daphnia magna. Iranian Journal of Environmental Health, Science and Engineering* 2, pp. 1-4.

Muñoz, I., Gómez, M.J., Molina-Diáz, A., Huijbregts, M.A.J., Fernández-Alba, A.R. & García-Calvo, E. (2008). Ranking potential impacts of priority and emerging pollutants in urban wastewater through life cycle impact assessment, *Chemosphere* 74, pp. 37-44.

OECD (1984). *Alga Growth Inhibition Test*. Guidelines for the testing of Chemicals, Test Guideline 201, OECD, Paris, France.

OSPAR (2007). *Practical Guidance Document on Whole Effluent Assessment*. Ospar Comission, Publication Number 316/2007, ISBN 978-1-905859-55-9.
http://www.ospar.org/documents/dbase/publications/p00316_WEA%20Guidance%20Document.pdf

Power, E.A. & Boumphrey, R.S. (2004). International Trends in Bioassay Use for Effluent Management, *Ecotoxicology* 13, pp. 377-398.

Radić, S., Stipaničev, D., Cvjetko, P., Mikelić, I.L., Rajčić, M.M., Širac, S., Pevalek-Kozlina, B. & Pavlica, M. (2010). Ecotoxicological assessment of industrial effluent using duckweed (*Lemna minor L.*) as a test organism, *Ecotoxicology* 19, pp. 216-222.

Slooff, W. (1983). Benthic macroinvertebrates and water quality assessment: some toxicological considerations, *Aquatic Toxicology* 4, pp. 73-82.

Teodorović, I., Bečelić, M., Planojević, I., Ivančev-Tumbas, I. & Dalmacija, B. (2009). The relationship between whole effluent toxicity (WET) and chemical-based effluent quality assessment in Vojvodina (Serbia), *Environmental Monitoring and Assessment* 158, pp. 381-392.

Tinsley, D., Wharfe, J., Campbell, D., Chown, P., Taylor, D. & Upton, J. (2004). The use of Direct Toxicity Assessment in the assessment and control of complex effluents in the UK: a demonstration programme, *Ecotoxicology* 13, pp. 423-436.

Tonkes, M., de Graaf, P.J.F. & Graansma, J. (1999). Assessment of complex industrial effluents in the Netherlands using a whole effluent toxicity (or WET) approach, *Water Science and Technology* 39, pp. 55-61.

Tyagi, V.K., Chopra, A.K., Durgapal, N.C. & Kumar, A. (2007). Evaluation of *Daphnia magna* as an indicator of toxicity and treatment efficiency of municipal sewage treatment plant, *Journal of Applied Sciences and Environmental Management* 11, pp. 61-67.

USEPA (2004). *NPDES Compliance Inspection Manual*, Environmental Protection Agency, EPA 305-X-03-004.

Vindimian, E., Garric, J., Flammarion, P., Thybaud, E. & Babut, M. (1999). An index of effluent aquatic toxicity designed by partial least squares regression, using acute and chronic tests and expert judgments, *Environmental Toxicology and Chemistry* 18, pp. 2386-2391.

22

Technology Roadmap for Wastewater Reuse in Petroleum Refineries in Brazil

Felipe Pombo, Alessandra Magrini and Alexandre Szklo
Federal University of Rio de Janeiro, Energy Planning Program
Brazil

1. Introduction

Because of the planned expansion of Brazil's refining capacity called for in the government's energy policy and the scenario of stress on water resources, it is necessary to design the country's new refineries so as to minimize water consumption and maximize reuse of effluents.

Existing refineries are large water consumers. In 2009, Brazilian refineries consumed 254,093 m^3 / day of water (estimated from the water consumption index of Petrobras refineries, of 0.9 m^3 water/ m^3 of oil) (Amorim, 2005). *Empresa de Pesquisa Energética* - EPE ("Energy Research Company"), a federally owned company that is part of the Ministry of Mines and Energy, forecasts an increase of 79% in Brazilian refining capacity with the construction of new refineries by 2030 (EPE, 2007). Some of them are planned for the Northeast region, which suffers from water shortage. While Brazil as a whole is blessed with water, having roughly 13% of the planet's freshwater reserves (Mierzwa & Hespanhol, 2005), these resources are very unevenly distributed, with some regions plagued by shortages (arid and semi-arid regions) and others blessed with abundant water. Finally, although the country's industrial heartland, the state of São Paulo, and the center of its oil industry, the state of Rio de Janeiro, both are in the country's semi-tropical region, they still face problems of water shortages due to high demand, causing conflicts among watershed users.

The methods to reduce water consumption are conservation, recycling and reuse. Among the three, water conservation requires the least effort and investment costs. It involves the rational use of water by industry, incorporating measures to prevent physical losses and improve operations (Matsumura & Mierzwa, 2008). Recycling (with regeneration) refers to the use of treated wastewater at the place of origin. Finally, water reuse can occur in the following forms: a) direct reuse of wastewater in other processes, when the level of contamination does not interfere in the next process; and b) with regeneration, which is reuse of treated effluent in different processes than the original one (Wang & Smith, 1994).

An important energy efficiency program was launched in 1992 by the U.S. Environmental Protection Agency, called Energy Star. As part of this program, a guide was issued focused on the refinery industry (Worrell & Galitsky, 2005). However, this document only covers energy use by refineries. There is a need for a similar document on efficient water use by refineries. Therefore, against the backdrop depicted above of unevenly distributed and locally insufficient water resources, a technology roadmap for Brazilian refineries is important.

There is a need to differentiate between treatment of refinery wastewater for discharge into water bodies and for reuse in other refinery units. The second case requires more advanced treatment systems, because the quality requirements are higher. Some examples of treatment techniques are reverse osmosis and reverse electrodialysis, with cost being the main barrier to widespread adoption of both (see Section 3). The first case requires more rudimentary treatment systems, as presented in Section 2.

This chapter addresses the problem identified above by presenting a technology roadmap for reuse of the effluents produced by Brazilian oil refineries, which have a great need to minimize water use, a need that can be met through the significant recent technological advances. Section 2 presents the conventional treatment of refinery wastewater while Section 3 lays out the proposed technology roadmap for wastewater treatment for reuse by refineries, analyzing the following technologies: membranes, membrane bioreactors (MBRs), reverse osmosis, reverse electrodialysis, ion exchange and advanced oxidative processes. Section 4 presents estimates of the costs and perspectives for application of these technologies in Brazil. Finally, Section 5 presents the conclusions of this chapter.

2. Conventional treatment of oil refinery effluents

The main contaminants in wastewater from refineries are oils and greases, which can exist in three forms: free (droplets with diameters larger than 150 μm), dispersed (droplets in the range of 20 to 150 μm) and emulsified (droplets smaller than 20 μm) (Cheryan & Rajagopalan, 1998).

The conventional methods to treat oily wastewater include (Cheryan & Rajagopalan, 1998):

- Gravity separation;
- Dissolved air flotation;
- Demulsification;
- Coagulation;
- Flocculation;
- Biological treatment.

Gravity separation is an efficient and low-cost method to remove free oil from wastewater (Cheryan & Rajagopalan, 1998). It is the first step of treatment of oily effluents at refineries. API (American Petroleum Institute) separators are the main such devices. This category also includes parallel and corrugated plate separators.

The process for oil/water separation by gravity includes two mechanisms: decantation and coalescence. The first mechanism occurs according to Stokes' Law (Equation (1)), while the second occurs through interactions at the interfaces of the dispersed oil droplets with the surrounding water (Jaworski, 2009). According to Equation (1), the smaller the oil droplet diameter, the more time it will take to separate the oil from the water.

$$Vr = gDo^2 (\rho w - \rho o) / 18\mu a \qquad (1)$$

Here Vr is the velocity of rise, g is the acceleration of gravity, ρw and ρo are the density of water and oil, respectively, Do is the oil droplet diameter and μa is the absolute viscosity of water.

In API separators, part of the oil accumulates at the liquid's surface because of its lower specific gravity than water, but oil in emulsion and small oil droplets (with diameters under 150 μm) are not separated. The part that rises is skimmed off, while another fraction, consisting of oil-soaked solids, settles to the bottom of the separator, where it is also removed. To prevent the formation of very small particles that cannot be separated by this method, it is important that the wastewater in the outlet pipes and drainage systems be carefully conveyed, to avoid generating turbulence, such as that caused by pumps or sudden falls. It is also important to avoid the presence of emulsifiers (Braile, 1979).

In general, refineries rely on the design standards of the manual entitled "Disposal of Refinery Wastes", according to which API separators can be installed to work in series with parallel plate interceptors (PPI) or corrugated plate interceptors (CPI), the last of which are more modern and besides separating oil from the water, can also remove part of the solid material. With PPI or CPI separators, it is possible to remove oil droplets with sizes down to 75 μm, representing an additional recovery of from 10 to 30 mg of oil per liter (Braile, 1979).

PPIs and CPIs improve the gravity separation because this process is based on the droplets reaching the continuous phase before leaving the separator, which is enhanced by increasing the specific surface area and reducing the height through which the oil droplets must rise before reaching the surface. Both of these devices accomplish this improvement (Jaworski, 2009).

Flotation is a technique initially used in ore processing for selective separation of one type of solid from another, through the different specific gravities of the desired and undesired solids. But with recent advances, flotation devices are increasingly being used for treatment of industrial effluents. According to Rubio et al. (2002), these advances include the higher efficiency of modern equipment, new separation schemes, selective recovery of valuable ions (such as gold, palladium and silver) and lower generation of sludge.

Dissolved air flotation (DAF) is the technique most often used to treat industrial effluents, particularly oil refinery wastewater. It works through the formation of micro-bubbles, by pre-saturating the effluent with air at pressures of 3 to 6 atm and then rapidly reducing this pressure to 1 atm. By this process, the solution first becomes oversaturated under pressure and then when the pressure drops the air forms micro-bubbles with diameters of between 50 and 100 μm through nucleation/cavitation, rupturing the fluid's structure (Rubio et al., 2002; Luz et al., 2002).

Since oil is hydrophobic, with weak affinity for water, it tends to join with the air micro-bubbles and is carried to the top of the device. This process can be enhanced by the addition of surfactants, which work by controlling the surface properties of the oil droplets, making them more hydrophobic and easier to separate out selectively (Luz et al., 2002; Al-Shamrani et al., 2002). The most important factors in designing and dimensioning industrial DAF systems are the characteristics of the saturator, the air/solids ratio, the hydraulic discharge and the micro-bubble generation system (Luz et al., 2002).

Conventional biological treatment is not able to remove all organic compounds to satisfy wastewater discharge standards. Therefore, pretreatment through biological purification is necessary. Among these processes, dissolved air flotation is the most common (Hami et al., 2007). These authors studied the effect of adding powdered activated carbon on the removal of pollutants in terms of BOD (biological oxygen demand) and COD (chemical oxygen demand) in a pilot-scale dissolved air flotation unit with a conical bottom, aiming to improve efficiency in adsorption of pollutants. They found that BOD and COD declined considerably with the addition of the activated carbon to the wastewater, and that increasing the quantity of activated carbon enhanced the pollutant removal efficiency (in %) for both BOD and COD.

Primary separators are used to break oil-water emulsions, allowing the demulsified oil to be separated from the water. Chemical methods (mainly addition of ferric and aluminum salts) are most commonly utilized. In this case, the process in general consists of rapid mixture of chemical coagulants with the wastewater, followed by flocculation and flotation/decantation. In turn, physical methods include heating, centrifugation, ultrafiltration and membrane processes (Yang, 2007).

There are various methods of breaking down emulsions and promoting coalescence of the oil droplets, after which they can be separated by gravity differential methods (Braile, 1979). Heating is used to reduce viscosity, accentuate density differences and weaken the interfacial films that stabilize the oil phase (Cheryan & Rajagopalan, 1998). Distillation is employed in some particularly resistant emulsions. Adjustment of the pH can destroy the protective colloid and permit sedimentation, which in some cases can also be achieved by aeration or chemical coagulation. Centrifugation increases the sedimentation force and can be used alone or together with heat or addition of chemical products. Filtration with diatomaceous earth or another element to assist filtration normally works well (Braile, 1979). In the case of chemical treatment, it is important to choose the right mixture of chemicals and optimize the process to reduce operating costs and enhance effectiveness (Cheryan & Rajagopalan, 1998).

Yang (2007) explained the mechanism of breaking down water-oil emulsions with electrochemical methods (electrochemical coagulation). This consists of an electrochemical reactor formed by iron electrodes (negative cathode and positive anode). During electrolysis, a DC voltage is applied to the electrodes, dissolving ferrous ions (Fe(II)) at the anode. These ions are in turn oxidized into ferric ions (Fe(III)), destabilizing the emulsion:

$$Fe_{(s)} \rightarrow Fe_{(aq)}^{2+} + 2e^- \rightarrow Fe_{(aq)}^{3+} + 3e^-, \tag{2}$$

$$2H_2O + 2e^- \rightarrow 2H_{2(g)} + 2OH_{(aq)}^-, \tag{3}$$

$$Fe_{(aq)}^{3+} + 3OH_{(aq)}^- \rightarrow Fe(OH)_{3(s).} \tag{4}$$

The coagulation is promoted by the addition of inorganic multivalent electrolytes, in general containing hydrosoluble cations, such as Al^{3+} and Fe^{3+} (Luz et al., 2002), and occurs when the attractive surface forces overcome the repulsive forces, allowing clots to form. The DLVO theory, named after the scientists who developed it independently (Derjaguin & Landau, 1941 and Verwey & Overbeek, 1948), explains the stability of colloid systems. This theory is based on the energy variations observed due to the aggregation of particles, considering only the Van der Waals attraction and electrostatic repulsion (Luz et al., 2002). The potential interaction energy (V_T) is obtained by the balance of attractive (V_A) and repulsive (V_R) interactions, as shown in Equation (5),

$$(V_T = V_A + V_R) \tag{5}$$

Aggregation occurs when $V_A > V_R$, while dispersion occurs when $V_A < V_R$ (Luz et al., 2002). In the case of two identical spherical particles, Equations (6) and (7) hold:

$$V_A = -Aa \ / \ 12d \tag{6}$$

$$V_R = 2\Pi\epsilon a\zeta^2 exp \ (-\kappa d), \tag{7}$$

where A is the Hamaker constant, a is the radius of the particles, ϵ is the permittivity of the solution, ζ is the zeta potential and κ is the Debye-Huckel parameter, or the inverse of the double electric layer thickness.

Flocculation involves the addition of a polymer, called a flocculant, which promote the aggregation of fine particles to form flakes. The polymers can be classified in three ways: by origin (natural, modified or synthetic), molecular weight (low or high molecular weight) and electrical charge (neutral, anionic or cationic). The aggregates can be formed independently of the structural forces involved. The efficiency of the process depends, among other factors, on the choice of the proper flocculant, the way it is applied, the chemical environment, the system's hydrodynamics and the sizes of the particles (Luz et al., 2002).

Biological treatment is particularly useful to remove biodegradable organic matter from refinery wastewater. The main techniques are aerated lagoons, activated sludge and biodiscs.

Aerated lagoons are artificial basins built to hold large volumes of effluents. They can be built above or below the original land surface. The aeration is not strictly natural; it is enhanced by the artificial introduction of oxygen, required by the organisms that decompose the soluble organic and fine particulate matter (Matos, 2005).

In aerated lagoons, the aeration energy defines whether the liquid mass will be held in total or partial suspension. These lagoons can be classified as *facultative aerated lagoons* or *suspension mixed lagoons*. In the first case, the formation and separation of biological flakes occurs in the lagoon itself, because the energy supplied to the aeration equipment is limited, ranging between 0.75 and 1.5 W/m³, which is insufficient to keep the sludge in suspension, so that solids settle in the lagoon. In the second case, the objective is to convert the soluble biodegradable organic material into biomass that can settle as sludge, which is done in secondary sedimentation ponds. The formation of biological flakes also occurs in the lagoon, but the aeration energy is greater than or equal to 3.0 W/m³, preventing the sedimentation of solids, which as stated, occurs in a secondary sedimentation pond. The removal rate in aerated lagoons is in general between 80 and 90% for total suspended solids (TSS), 65 and 80% for COD and 50 and 95% for BOD, depending on the type of setup (Matos, 2005).

The activated sludge process is carried out in two main compartments: the aeration tank and the clarification tank (Figure 1). Microorganisms (specific types of bacteria) are used for biological degradation of the effluent. Some bacteria need an environment rich in oxygen (aerobic), while others need one poor in oxygen (anaerobic). The conversion products are water, carbon dioxide, nitrogen and dead microorganisms (called surplus sludge). In the aeration tank the wastewater and activated sludge are mixed so that the conversion reaction can occur. Then the activated sludge is separated out of the liquid in the other compartment by sedimentation. Most of the sludge precipitated out is returned to the aeration tank to repeat the process, but an excess portion is purged. Without this purge, the activated slugde concentration would increase too much, reducing the sedimentation efficiency in the clarification tank (Oever, 2005).

In general treatment in a series of aerated lagoons is less expensive in terms of initial investment in equipment, but requires sufficient space. An activated sludge separation unit requires less area, but has higher operating cost and performs better. More demanding clean-up standards regarding removal of certain recalcitrant pollutants, mainly biomass, are only attained with units that enable extended residence times. Through knowledge of the phenomena that govern the transformations of the biodegradable and oxidizable compounds is important to assure good performance of new biological treatment units or to improve the performance of existing ones. Modeling these complex phenomena in advance is an important step in this sense (Piras, 1993).

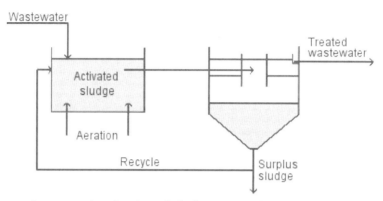

Fig. 1. Diagram of a conventional activated sludge process (Oever, 2005).

Biodiscs are cylindrical structures of plastic discs supported by a central axis. These structures are mounted horizontally above tanks so that about 30 to 40% of each disc is submersed in the liquid during rotation. The most common configuration is a disc diameter of 3.6 m (12 ft) by 8.2 m in length (27 ft). A typical biodisc system is in operation at the REFAP refinery in Brazil. It consists of four sets of discs. In the first set, the microorganisms, with adequate conditions in terms of oxygen, substrate, pH, ammonia and phosphate, attach themselves to the discs and start to grow, forming a biofilm. This biofilm uses the oxygen and organic carbon dissolved in the wastewater, removing the organic load by the action of heterotrophic bacteria. In the second set, the biofilm promotes nitrification by the action of nitrosomonas and nitrobacter bacteria. In the third set, the biofilm promotes denitrification by the action of specific bacteria. Finally, in the fourth set the process works as in the first set, to remove the residual organic load from the addition of methanol in the denitrification process (Ferreira et al., 2000).

3. Technological roadmap for wastewater treatment at oil refineries aiming at reuse

The objective of this chapter is to study the best available techniques (BATs) for treatment of oil refinery wastewater for purposes of reuse.

The expression "best available techniques" is defined in Section 5 of the U.S. Environmental Protection Agency Acts, 1992 and 2003, and Section 5(2) of the Waste Management Acts, 1996 to 2005, as the "most effective and advanced stage in the development of an activity and its methods of operation, which indicate the practical suitability of particular techniques for providing, in principle, the basis for emission limit values designed to prevent or eliminate or, where that is not practicable, generally to reduce an emission and its impact on the environment as a whole, where *best* in relation to techniques means the most effective in achieving a high general level of protection of the environment as a whole, *available techniques* means those techniques developed on a scale which allows implementation in the relevant class of activity under economically the technically viable conditions, taking into consideration the costs and advantages, whether or not the techniques are used or produced within the State, as long as they are reasonably accessible to the person carrying out the activity, and *techniques* includes both the technology used and the way in which the installation is designed, built, managed, maintained, operated and decommissioned" (EPA, 2008).

In designing an advanced treatment unit for secondary wastewater, the following aspects should be considered (Teodosiu et al., 1999):

- complete characterization of the effluent;
- the level of dissolved solids that can be reduced by coagulation-flocculation, sedimentation and/or filtration with sand, microfiltration or ultrafiltration;
- the dissolved organic matter that can be removed by adsorption with activated carbon, chemical oxidation, reverse osmosis, and ultrafiltration for solid organic matter;
- the dissolved solids that can be removed by reverse osmosis, ion exchange and electrodialysis;
- the possibility of integrating the proposed unit with existing installations; and
- the capital and operating costs.

The wastewater treatment methods for reuse at refineries can be classified as primary, secondary and tertiary. The primary methods are the simplest, including techniques such as oil/water separation and dissolved air flotation. These are considered conventional treatment techniques (see Section 2). Secondary treatment at refineries is used to remove a substantial part of the biodegradable organic matter. Tertiary treatment aims to remove ions (dissolved salts), to bring the quality up to the level required for reuse, mainly to feed cooling towers or boilers.

3.1 Membranes for micro, ultra and nanofiltration

Membrane processes are used to treat stable oil/water emulsions, especially water-soluble oily wastes, rather than oil floating in unstable emulsions, for which other methods are more suitable (Cheryan, 1998, as cited in Cheryan & Rajagopalan, 1998). Membranes are effective in removing oil droplets with micrometric size, usually smaller than 10 μm, and when the oil concentration is very low (Chakrabarty et al., 2008). These cases cannot be resolved by conventional techniques such as gravity separation, addition of chemical agents, thermal demulsification and biological treatment. The porous membrane matrix promotes coalescence of the micrometric and sub-micrometric oil droplets, which then can be easily removed by gravity (Hlavacek, 1995).

Membrane processes have several advantages, among them lower capital cost, no need to add chemicals and no subsequent generation of oily sludge (Ohya et al., 1998); operational simplicity, lower energy costs than for thermal treatment (Cheryan & Rajagopalan, 1998) and the capacity to produce a permeate with acceptable quality for discharge (Chakrabarty et al., 2008).

A membrane is a barrier that serves to separate two phases by selectively restricting the passage of chemical agents. A membrane can be homogeneous or heterogeneous, with a symmetric or asymmetric structure, and solid or liquid. It can selectively conduct a positive or negative charge or be neutral or bipolar. The transport through the membrane can be by convection or diffusion of individual molecules, by induction by an electrical field or by pressure or temperature gradient. The membrane's thickness can range from tens of microns to a few hundreds of micrometers (Ravanchi et al., 2009).

The pores of the membrane act as a physical barrier to impurities while permitting the passage of water molecules. A driving force must be applied to promote transport of the solution through the membrane. The main driving forces are pressure difference, concentration (or activity) difference – including difference in chemical potential (μ) – or difference in electrical potential between the two sides of the membrane (Ravanchi et al., 2009).

The permeate flux (Jp) and the selectivity of the membrane to a determined component of the feed solution are important properties for operation of membrane systems (Habert et al., 2006). The permeate flux in processes that use pressure difference as the driving force (microfiltration, ultrafiltration, nanofiltration and reverse osmosis) is given by Equation (8). The membrane's selective capacity can be calculated by the retention coefficient (R), defined as the fraction of the solution retained (retentate) by the membrane for a given feed concentration (Equation (9)):

$$J_P = L_P (\Delta P - \Delta \pi), \tag{8}$$

where L_P is the hydraulic permeability (in L/m²h bar); ΔP is the pressure difference (in bar); and $\Delta \pi$ is the osmotic pressure difference (in bar). J_P is therefore given in L/m²h. In turn, the retention coefficient is given by the following formula:

$$R\ (\%) = [(C_f - C_p)/C_a] \times 100, \tag{9}$$

where C_f is the feed solute concentration (ppm) and C_p is the solute concentration of the permeate (ppm).

Figure 2 presents the range of pore diameters and retention efficiencies of micro, ultra and nanofiltration membranes and of the reverse osmosis process (Perry & Green, 2007).

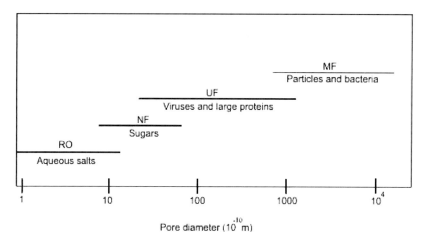

Note: RO - Reverse osmosis; NF - Nanofiltration; UF - Ultrafiltration; MF - Microfiltration.

Fig. 2. Range of pore diameters and removal efficiencies of micro, ultra and nanofiltration membranes and the reverse osmosis process (Perry & Green, 2007).

3.1.1 Microfiltration

Microfiltration and ultrafiltration membranes are used after conventional treatment techniques and as pretreatment just before reverse osmosis, to prolong the useful life of the

RO membrane and reduce incrustation (fouling) and operational costs of this process. They can also be used as part of a membrane bioreactor, to retain biomass, as will be discussed shortly. Microfiltration membranes are operated at a pressure of under 2.0 bar (Wagner, 2001).

Fouling is one of the main problems reducing the efficiency of membrane filters. It is caused by various factors, such as clogging of the pores, adsorption of solute by the membrane and formation of a gel on the membrane surface, among others. Fouling causes a gradual decline in the permeate flux when all the other parameters are constant (pressure, flow, temperature and feed concentration). Fouling can be either reversible or irreversible. The distinction is a consequence of the characteristics of the deposit formed on the membrane surface (temporary or permanent) and the possibilities of restoring the initial flux by backwashing or chemical cleaning. It also raises operating costs because of the higher pressure required to maintain the retention rate and the need to clean the membrane or to replace it in cases of irreversible fouling (Teodosiu et al., 1999).

3.1.2 Ultrafiltration

Ultrafiltration membranes are operated at a pressure range of 1.0 to 10.0 bar (Wagner, 2001). Teodosiu et al. (1999) studied the use of ultrafiltration (dual filtration with membranes made of polyethersulphone and polyvinylpirollidone) as pretreatment for reverse osmosis, for the purpose of recycling secondary refinery wastewater to feed cooling towers. An average efficiency of 98% was obtained for turbidity, meaning almost complete removal of suspended solids and colloids, along with efficiency of 30% for COD in the tests.

In a system with ultrafiltration followed by reverse osmosis, the ultrafiltration can remove the suspended and colloidal material, bacteria, viruses and organic compounds, while the reverse osmosis removes dissolved salts, as will be discussed shortly. The quality requirements for cooling water are related to the limits established for substances that can cause scaling, corrosion, fouling and growth of microorganisms, all of which reduce the performance of cooling towers. Scaling is caused by the presence of carbonates and calcium and magnesium sulfates, which precipitate as scales in heat exchangers. Corrosion is related to the presence of large quantities of dissolved solids, including chloride and ammonia. Microorganisms grow because of the presence of high concentrations of nutrients or organic substances. And fouling occurs mainly due to the presence of high levels of suspended solids, although organic fouling via adsorption of dissolved organic compounds is also a problem (Teodosiu et al., 1999).

Chakrabarty et al. (2008) used modified polysulfone membranes with the objective of attaining higher porosity and hydrophobicity through the use of additives such as polyvinylpirollidone and polyethylene glycol to remove oil from wastewater. The experiments were conducted in 12 different membranes in a semi-batch filtration cell made of Teflon. The authors evaluated the influence of feed properties such as initial oil concentration and pH of the solution on membrane performance. They concluded that these characteristics significantly affect the permeate flux and oil separation. With increasing concentration the flux diminished and the retention increased due to the formation of an oil layer on the membrane surface, leading to an increase in total resistance. With relation to pH, increased acidity or alkalinity of the feed solution caused greater oil retention for the four membranes selected in this analysis by the authors. The permeate flux varied according to the chemical composition of the membrane studied, and was highest under normal pH condition (of 6.12) in some cases, and at slightly alkaline pH (8.00) and slightly acid (5.00) conditions in other cases.

3.1.3 Nanofiltration

Nanofiltration membranes are operated at a pressure varying from 5 to 35 bar (Wagner, 2001). Nanofiltration membranes are generally used to separate multivalent ions and organic compounds with relatively low molecular weights (250 -1000 g/mol) from water. The treatment removes between 60 and 80% of the water hardness, over 90% of the color and all the turbidity (Bessarabov & Twardowski 2002).

In aqueous solutions, the nanofiltration membranes become charged, permitting the separation of ionic species. It is believed that steric hindrance is the dominant retention mechanism in these membranes for colloids and large molecules, while physico-chemical interactions between the solute and membrane are more important for ions and organic materials with lower molecular weights. Figure 3 shows a hypothetical polymeric nanofiltration membrane with carboxyl groups linked at the membrane surface, which are produced in contact with an aqueous solution of an electrolyte. The presence of the carboxyl groups dissociated at the membrane surface (R-COO⁻) causes the occurrence of membrane charging (Bessarabov & Twardowski, 2002).

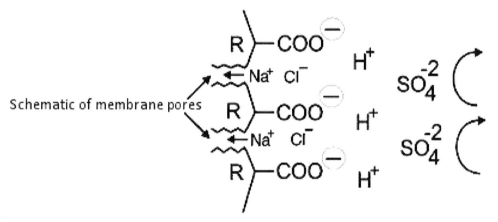

Fig. 3. Hypothetical polymeric nanofiltration membrane containing carboxyl groups. The presence of these groups dissociated at the membrane surface (R-COO⁻) causes membrane charging. This charge repels large SO_4^{2-} ions and permits the passage of smaller Cl⁻ ions through the membrane (Bessarabov & Twardowski, 2002).

3.2 Membrane bioreactors (MBR)

Membrane bioreactors (MBR) remove a large amount of biodegradable material (measured as BOD and COD) from oil refinery wastewater.

MBR systems consist of a combination of the activated sludge biological process (see Section 2) with the membrane separation process. The reaction occurs like it does in the activated sludge process, with the added advantage of being able to operate without the need for clarification or steps like sand filtration (Melin et al., 2006). These systems use micro or ultrafiltration to separate the effluent from the activated sludge. The two main MBR configurations involve submerged or external separation membranes, as depicted in Figure 4.

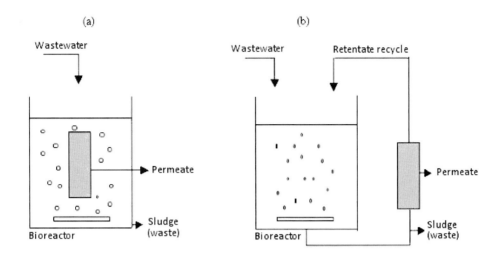

Fig. 4. Configuration of MBR systems. (a) Submerged MBR. (b) Lateral flow MBR (Melin et al., 2006).

The first option is more often applied to treat municipal wastewater (Melin et al., 2006), and can use both hollow fiber membranes (horizontal or vertical) and flat plate membranes (vertical). In side flow MBR systems, tubular membranes (horizontal or vertical) are placed outside the bioreactor and are fed by it. This system operates by cross-flow. Both systems are aerated at the lower part of the bioreactor, and the permeate is removed by suction (Oever, 2005).

As in regular membrane processes, fouling is a problem of membrane bioreactors, by hindering the permeate flux during filtration. This problem is influenced by the characteristics of the biomass, the operating conditions and characteristics of the membrane (Chang et al., 2002). The cost of periodically replacing the membrane because of aging and fouling raises the operating costs and reduces the competitiveness of the MBR technology (Buetehorn et al., 2008). Fouling is also influenced by the hydrodynamic conditions, type of membrane and configuration of the unit, as well as by the presence of compounds with high molecular weight, which can be produced by microbial metabolism or introduced by the sludge growth process (Melin et al., 2006).

Viero et al. (2008) evaluated the treatment of oil refinery wastewater using a submerged membrane bioreactor (SMBR), operating at a constant permeate flux. During the operation, high organic loading rates were applied to the unit by feeding mixtures of the effluent stream with another effluent having high phenolic strength, also generated by oil refineries. The influence of the loading rate on the filtration was assessed, including the effects on the production of soluble microbial products (polysaccharides and proteins) and the retention of these compounds by the membrane. The membrane played a key role in the process, since it improved the COD and TOC (total organic carbon) removal efficiencies by 17 and 20%, respectively, in comparison with the results obtained with biomass alone. The authors observed that good efficiencies in removing organic matter, indicated by the COD and TOC results, were achieved considering the complexity of the wastewater stream processed. Additionally, the tested system was highly effective in removing phenols.

Scholz & Fuchsm (2000) reported tests of a MBR with high activated sludge concentration (above 48 g/L) and showed that oily wastewater also containing surfactants was biodegraded with high efficiency. During the different loading stages, a removal rate of 99.99% was attained for fuel oil as well as for lubricating oil, at a hydraulic retention time of 13.3 hours. The maximum biodegradation of the fuel oil was 0.82g of hydrocarbons degraded per day. The average removal of COD and TOC during the experiments was 94-96% for fuel oil and 98% for lubricating oil, respectively. Because of the high efficiency in removing oily pollutants and complete retention of suspended solids by the ultrafiltration system, the authors stated the MBR system has good potential for industrial applications aiming to recycle effluents. The MBR removed 93-98% of the COD and 95-98% of TOC in a hydraulic retention time of 7-14 h and oil loading rates of 3-5 g/L/day (Scholz & Fuchsm, 2000).

3.3 Reverse osmosis

Along with the reverse electrodialysis process, described next, reverse osmosis is used to remove ions (dissolved salts) from oil refinery wastewater, as part of the tertiary treatment cycle.

Reverse osmosis is by far the most common membrane process used for desalination. It can reject nearly all the colloidal or dissolved material in an aqueous solution, producing concentrated salty water and a permeate of virtually pure fresh water. Reverse osmosis is based on the property of certain polymers called semi-permeability. While semi-permeable membranes are highly permeable to water, they have low permeability to dissolved substances. When a pressure difference is applied across the membrane, the water molecules contained in the feed stream are forced to permeate through the membrane. This pressure must be high enough to overcome the osmotic pressure working against the feed (Fritzmann et al., 2007). This pressure is generally in the range of 15 to 150 bar (Wagner, 2001).

The osmosis process occurs when a semi-permeable membrane (permeable to water but not to the solute) separates the feed liquid into two aqueous solutions with different concentrations. At equal temperature and pressure on both sides of the membrane, the water will diffuse (permeate) through the membrane, resulting in an overall flow of the diluted solution to the more concentrated one until the concentrations on both sides of the membrane are equal. If the pressure differential (Δp) is greater than the osmotic pressure ($\Delta \pi$), the flow is reversed and the water flows from the concentrated to the diluted side. This process is called reverse osmosis. In water desalination, the feed side is operated under high pressure and the concentration of the solute on the permeate side (diluted) is negligible when compared to the feed concentration. In this case permeate flux occurs because the Δp exceeds the $\Delta \pi$ of the feed solution (Fritzmann et al., 2007).

According to Nazarov et al. (1979), reverse osmosis can be employed to desalt waste streams from crude oil electric desalting units, where the salt content of these streams is very high (above 5,000 mg/L, including 75-85% sodium chloride, 4-5% magnesium chloride and 10-15% calcium chloride). They also mentioned the following aspects as advantages of reverse osmosis: the components (salts and water) are separated at ambient temperature without any phase conversion of the water (heating or cooling); the osmotic module is simple to design and operate; and the process can be fully automated. As disadvantages, they mentioned the difficulty of manufacturing reverse osmosis membranes, the low capacity of these membranes and the need to pre-treat the effluent to remove solid and emulsified contaminants or dissolved organic and inorganic substances.

In reverse osmosis, a dynamic layer of water and solutes is formed on the membrane surface. Only molecules of a strictly determined size will penetrate through this layer and through the membrane. Larger molecules do not pass through the membrane and are removed from the membrane surface under the influence of repulsive forces and longitudinal displacement of the liquid. Therefore, two streams are moving at the same time, a flow of liquid (water) and substances with low molecular weights through the layer of the membrane due to the difference in concentrations of these substances on either side of the membrane, and a flow of liquid and substances with high molecular weights from the surface of the membrane to within the solution, with subsequent carry-off (by purging) from the separation zone (Nazarov et al., 1979).

3.4 Reverse electrodialysis

The reverse electrodialysis process is also used to remove ions (dissolved salts) from oil refinery wastewater.

Electrodialysis can be used to concentrate or remove charged species in aqueous solutions. The process is based on the movement of charged species in an electrical field. Dissolved anions, such as Cl^- and NO_3^{3-}, move towards the anode while cations, such as K^+ and Na^+, are attracted by the cathode. The movement of the ions is controlled by ion-selective membranes placed between the anode and cathode. Anion-exchange membranes (AEMs) are permeable to anions but not to cations, which are thus retained. Cation-exchange membranes (CEMs) work analogously but in the opposite way. The electrolysis device is divided into various cells by an alternating sequence of AEMs and CEMs. In this way, the concentration of ionic species is reduced in the diluted compartments and increased in the concentrate compartments. The basic unit of a device consists of a diluted compartment and a concentrate compartment in tandem (Fritzmann et al., 2007).

Figure 5 shows a diagram of the reverse electrodialysis process. The electrodes' polarity is

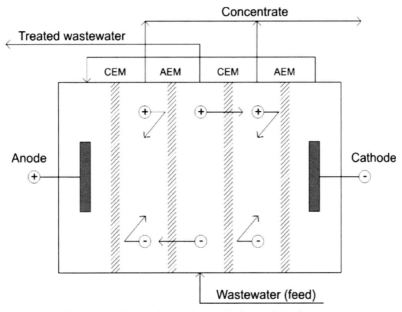

Note: CEM - Cation Exchange Membrane; AEM - Anion Exchange Membrane.

Fig. 5. The principle of reverse electrodialysis.

periodically reversed, so that the direction of the ion movement is also reversed. Therefore, the concentrate streams become diluted streams and vice versa. The periodic switching of polarity works as a self-cleaning mechanism, reducing the surface fouling of the ion-exchange membrane. Reverse electrodialysis systems are physically and chemically more durable than reverse osmosis systems and can support effluent flows with higher loads of organic matter, colloid particles and microorganisms than can reverse osmosis systems (Chao & Liang, 2008).

3.5 Ion exchange

Ion exchange processes occur with the substitution of the undesirable ions of a liquid (such as wastewater) with ions like H^+ and OH^- from a solid material in which the ions are sufficiently mobile, usually a synthetic resin. Eventually the resin becomes exhausted and needs to be regenerated by contact with a small quantity of a solution with a high content of the desired ion. Resins can be tailored to have selective affinities for particular types of ions, such as mercury, boron, ferrous ions or copper in the presence of iron (Couper et al., 2010). An important property of these ion-exchange resins is their capacity to retain ions in their structure.

There are specific resins for each ion species: cationic, with the capacity to retain cations, and anionic, specific for retention of anions. Within these two groups of resins there is a further subdivision, summarized below. Each of these is suitable to remove specific ions and has particularities in its regeneration processes (Mierzwa & Hespanhol, 2005).

- *Strongly acidic cation-exchange resin:* This type of resin has a chemical structure formed by styrene and divinylbenzene. Its functional groups are sulfonic acid radicals (R-SO$_3^-$ H$^+$). It can operate in a broad pH range and can be conditioned to operate in a sodium or hydrogen cycle, depending on the application: water softening or demineralization.
- *Weakly acidic cation-exchange resin:* Its functional groups are carboxylated (R-COOH), which are not ionized at low pH values. Therefore, this type of resin operates at pH values varying from neutral to alkaline. These resins are used to treat industrial water with high hardness, exclusively for calcium bicarbonate and carbonate.
- *Strongly basis anion-exchange resin:* Its functional group is quaternary amine (R-N(CN$_3$)$_3^+$). There are two sub-groups: Type I and Type II. The difference between these is basicity. Type I resins have a stronger basicity than Type II resins, and for this reason produce better output water, with less anion leakage principally of silica.
- *Weakly basic anion-exchange resin:* This type of resin is employed in water treatment systems designed mainly to remove anions from strong acids, among them chloride, sulfate and nitrate, because this type of resin is not able to remove weakly ionizable anions, among them bicarbonate and silica.

Except in very small-scale applications, ion exchangers are used in cyclical operations, involving sorption and desorption steps. A typical ion-exchange cycle used in water treatment applications involves: (a) backwashing: to remove accumulated solids and to fluidize the exchanger bed; (b) regeneration: a regenerant passes slowly through the exchanger to restore its original ionic form; (c) rinsing: water passes through the exchanger to remove the resin regenerant (in the case of porous exchangers, from the resin's pores); and (d) loading: the solution to be treated passes through the exchanger until the leakage starts to occur. Water softening occurs in this way, with a cation-exchange column containing sodium. At the low ionic strength used in the loading step, calcium and magnesium are strongly preferred over sodium, permitting nearly all of it to be removed.

Since the selectivity for divalent cations diminishes sharply with ionic concentration, the regeneration is performed effectively with a concentrated sodium chloride solution. Removal of sulfates from boiler feed water is carried out by similar means with anion exchangers in chloride form (Perry & Green, 2007).

Therefore, the ion-exchange process can treat effluents that contain dissolved ionic species, such as metals (Al^{3+}, Pb^{2+}, Sr^{2+}, etc.), inorganic anions (F^-, NO_3^-, SO_4^{2-}, CN^-, etc.) and organic acids (carboxylic, phenolic, etc.), among others. The advantages of using ion exchange are: (i) the generation of an outflow with higher quality than produced by other processes; (ii) the selective removal of undesired species; (iii) the fact that the process and equipment have been widely tested; (iv) the availability of automatic and manual systems in the market; and (v) the possibility of using them to treat small and large volumes of wastewater. In contrast, the disadvantages are: (i) the chemical products involved in the regeneration process; (ii) the relatively high concentration of contaminants and other compounds in the outflow; (iii) the possibility that organic substances, microorganisms, suspended particles and other substances will degrade or reduce the treatment capacity of the resins; and (iv) the possible impairment of the process by small variations in the feed stream characteristics (Mierzwa & Hespanhol, 2005).

3.6 Advanced oxidative processes

Advanced oxidative processes are characterized by producing OH radicals, an extraordinarily reactive chemical species that attacks the majority of organic molecules. These processes can be used in pre- or post-treatment in a biological process, contributing to the degradation of toxic or refractory substances (Coelho, 2004). Table 1 summarizes the existing advanced oxidative processes (Andreozzi et al., 1999).

Advanced oxidative processes	
H_2O_2 / Fe^{2+}	Fenton
H_2O_2 / Fe^{3+}	Fenton-like
H_2O_2 / Fe^{2+} (Fe^{3+}) / UV	Photo / Fenton
H_2O_2 / Fe^{3+} - Oxalate	Photo / Fenton –like
Mn^{2+} / Oxalic Acid / Ozone	
TiO_2 / UV / O_2	Photocatalysis
O_3 / H_2O_2	Peroxidation
O_3 / UV	Oxidation by O_3 / UV
H_2O_2 / UV	Oxidation by H_2O_2 / UV

Table 1. Advanced oxidative processes (Andreozzi et al., 1999).

Some of the processes cited above are described in more detail below (Castro, 2004). The Fenton, photo-Fenton, ozone and H_2O_2/UV processes act in the following form (Reactions (10), (11), (12), (13), (14), respectively - Reactions (12) and (13) refer to the process with ozone):

$$H_2O_2 + Fe^{2+} \rightarrow Fe^{3+} + OH^- + \cdot OH \tag{10}$$

$$Fe^{3+} + H_2O + h\nu \rightarrow Fe^{2+} + \cdot OH + H^+ \tag{11}$$

$$O_3 + OH^- \rightarrow O_2 + O_2 \qquad (12)$$

$$O_3 + H_2O \rightarrow 2OH \cdot + O_2 \qquad (13)$$

$$H_2O_2 \rightarrow (hv)\ 2\ OH \qquad (14)$$

Equations (15) to (19) represent the reactions between organic substances and the hydroxyl radical (Castro, 2004):

- Addition

$$Ar-H + OH \rightarrow Ar-OH + H \cdot \qquad (15)$$

- Abstraction of hydrogen:

$$R-H + OH \rightarrow H_2O + R \cdot \qquad (16)$$

- Electron transfer:

$$R \cdot + O_2 \rightarrow ROO \cdot \qquad (17)$$

- Termination (interaction of radicals):

$$R \cdot + R \cdot \rightarrow R-R \qquad (18)$$

$$OH + OH \rightarrow H_2O_2 \qquad (19)$$

Coelho et al. (2006) investigated the performances of various advanced oxidative processes to remove organic pollutants from sourwater from oil refineries. The preliminary experiments were conducted using the H_2O_2, H_2O_2/UV, UV, photocatalysis, ozonization, Fenton and photo-Fenton processes. Only the Fenton and photo-Fenton processes produced satisfactory results, considered to be reduction of the dissolved organic carbon (DOC) of the sourwater by 35%. For this reason, these two techniques were analyzed in more detail.

The authors observed that the photo-Fenton process was very rapid, taking only a few minutes to attain a final DOC removal of 13-27% due to the formation of iron complexes. Radiation for an additional period of 60 minutes was found to increase the DOC removal to above 87%. DOC removal rates above 75% were achieved when the reaction system was operated at hydraulic retention times longer than 85 min. In the batch experiments, the maximum DOC removal was 87%, using 4 and 0.4 g/L of ferrous sulfate and hydrogen peroxide, respectively. The Fenton reaction was also very fast, but lower DOC removal rates were attained, depending on the ferrous sulfate concentration used. The photo-Fenton process, meanwhile, was able to improve the DOC removal in a short interval (50 min), leading to high overall performance levels. The highest DOC removal (94%) was achieved with continuous operation of the combined processes (Fenton and photo-Fenton), when the system was operating with a hydraulic retention time of 1200 min. However, appreciable DOC removal rates (greater than 75%) were also obtained with hydraulic retention times in the range of 60 to 120 min. (Coelho et al., 2006).

4. Assessment of the costs and applications in Brazil

Wagner (2001) indicated the costs of membrane processes. According to him, the cost if installing a plant with spiral filters is between US$ 300 and 500 per m² of membrane area, while tubular systems are sold for more than US$ 1,000 per m². The price of a flat plate system ranges from US$ 200 to 300 per m². The cost of units with a fiber membrane configuration is US$ 1,700 per m², while ceramic systems are the most expensive, at US$ 10,000 per m². These costs refer to complete systems, that is, membranes, internal pipes, pumps and control equipment.

Spiral membranes were originally made for water desalination, but their compact configuration and low cost make them attractive for industrial applications. Tubular systems are simple and have the advantage of tolerating suspended solids and fibers. Flat plate systems are robust and compact. Fiber membrane systems are mechanically more fragile and thus are used only for determined ultrafiltration applications and oil emulsions. Finally, ceramic systems can be very effective for microfiltration (Wagner, 2001).

Depending on the capacity, a membrane filtration system can cost around US$ 1300-5300/m³/day, while the operating costs are between US$ 0.79-3.96/m³ of treated wastewater (micro and ultrafiltration technologies) (Cheryan & Rajagopalan, 1998).

Another source (CostWater, 2010) mentions the costs of membrane technology for microfiltration to remove particulate matter according to treatment capacity. According to this source, the costs are considerably lower than those mentioned above, ranging from US$ 400/m³/day for treatment capacity of 38,000 m³/day to around US$ 600/m³/day for a capacity of 3,800 m³/day.

Membranes are a promising technology for treatment of refinery wastewater for reuse. They are generally used for pretreatment before reverse osmosis or reverse electrodialysis (micro and ultrafiltration technologies). Figure 6 shows a diagram of an advanced wastewater treatment system for reuse at oil refineries, considering ultra and microfiltration membranes and reverse osmosis or reverse electrodialysis as tertiary treatment.

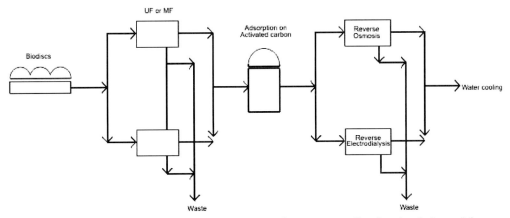

Fig. 6. Diagram of a wastewater treatment process for reuse at oil refineries (adapted from CENPES, 2004).

For MBR systems, the costs of membrane bioreactors fell from US$ 400/m² to around US$ 50/m² in the 1990s. Figures from the EPA show an operating cost of US$ 0.47/m³ of treated wastewater, including electricity, membrane exchange and chemical inputs but not amortization of the initial outlay. Other estimates show the operating cost of MBR unit with capacity of 3,785 m³/day is around US$ 0.11-0.15 per m³ of treated effluent. These estimates are much lower than that of the EPA. The operating cost per volume treated appears not to very much with the system's capacity (CostWater, 2010).

Oever (2005) mentioned the AirLift MBR system, which uses air to create turbulence and keep the membrane surface clean, with specific energy consumption of approximately 0.4 to 0.7 kWh/m³. This consumption would mean a cost of R$ 0.0965 to 0.1689/m³ at the industrial electricity tariff in the Southeast region of Brazil (where more than half of the country's refining capacity is located), at the rate in effect in December 2009 (R$ 241.25/MWh) (ANEEL 2010). (US$ 1.00 = R$ 1.75228 on December 31, 2009.)

Figure 7 shows a diagram of an advanced refinery wastewater treatment system considering membrane bioreactors for secondary treatment and reverse osmosis or reverse electrodialysis as tertiary treatment (Torres at al., 2008).

As can be observed, the effluent system passes through the primary treatment processes and then the oil polishing process, which can be by sand filtration, as shown in Figure 7, or nutshell filtration (for protection of the membrane) (CENPES, 2005). Nutshells are highly effective in absorbing free oil and suspended solids, due to their characteristic of promoting the coalescence of oil droplets. Activated carbon filters help remove refractory organic compounds from the biological process, allowing the treated effluent to be reused as industrial water.

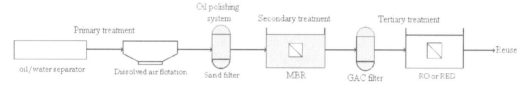

Note: GAC - Granulated Activated Carbon; RED - Reverse electrodialysis.

Fig. 7. Advanced oil refinery wastewater treatment (adapted from Torres et al., 2008).

Membrane bioreactors for wastewater reuse have been or are being installed at various existing Petrobras refineries or will be at new refineries. Table 2 presents these projects (Santiago, 2009).

Refinery	Description	Capacity (m³/h)	Start of Operation
REVAP	New Industrial Waste Treatment Station	300	2009
CENPES*	New Industrial Waste Treatment Station	65	2010
REPAR	New Industrial Waste Treatment Station	400	2011
COMPERJ	New Refinery	1100	2012
RENEST	New Refinery	600	2012
REGAP	New Biological Treatment Unit	750	-
LUBNOR	New Industrial Waste Treatment Station	66	-

Note: * CENPES is a pilot project at the Petrobras Research Center.

Table 2. Membrane bioreactor units at refineries under construction (Santiago, 2009).

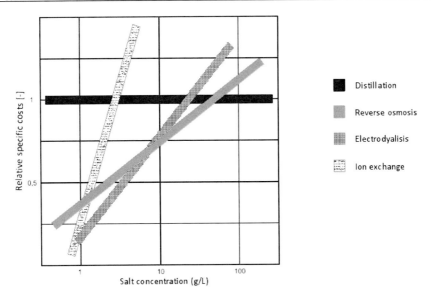

Fig. 8. Costs of wastewater treatment with ion exchange and competing technologies (Rautenbach & Melin, 2003, as cited in Fritzmann et al., 2007).

The capital cost of the reverse osmosis technology in Brazil is from US$1454 to $4483/m^3/day$, while the operating cost ranges from US$ 0.12 to $0.37/m^3$ (including amortization of the investment, operation and maintenance and membrane substitution) (OAS, 2010).

According to Fritzmann et al. (2007), electricity consumption of the reverse osmosis process is between 0.4 and 7 kWh/m^3 of treated effluent. That consumption range would mean a cost of R$ 0.0965 to $1.6888/m^3$, considering the industrial electricity tariff in the Southeast region of Brazil in December 2009 (R$ 241.25/MWh) (ANEEL, 2010).

In treatment of refinery wastewater for reuse, reverse osmosis is used as tertiary treatment to remove ions (such as chlorides), as already mentioned. The competing technology is reverse electrodialysis.

According to Fritzmann et al. (2007), electrodialysis consumes 1 kWh of electricity per m^3 of treated wastewater. At the average industrial energy rate in the Southeast region in December 2009 (R$ 241.25/MWh), this would cost R$ $0.2413/m^3$ (ANEEL, 2010).

Chao & Liang (2008) also estimated the operating cost of a mini reverse electrodialysis plant. According to their calculations, the electricity consumption by electrodes and pumps is 0.85 kWh/m^3 of treated effluent, which works out to R$ $0.205/m^3$ at the same industrial rate applied above (ANEEL, 2010). They estimated the total operating costs, including electricity and chemicals, at US$ $0.146/m^3$.

The reverse electrodialysis process is promising for removal of ions (such as chlorides) from refinery wastewater, as mentioned. In a test program to analyze technologies to remove ions for reuse of wastewater (reverse osmosis and reverse electrodialysis) at pilot units at the REGAP refinery, reverse electrodialysis was the most promising. The advantage of this technology was its greater operational continuity. Both the reverse osmosis and reverse electrodialysis pilot plants were fed with effluent from the microfiltration unit, after filtration by activated charcoal. There was no fouling of the reverse electrodialysis membranes, while this was a serious problem with the reverse osmosis membranes, causing increased pressure and frequent need for chemical cleaning (CENPES, 2004).

With respect to the costs of the ion exchange process, Figure 8 presents these costs in comparison with those of competing technologies (Rautenbach & Melin, 2003, as cited in Fritzmann et al., 2007).

It can be seen from the figure that for low salt concentrations, ion exchange is a competitive technology. This indicates that ion exchange can be used for the polishing step for reverse osmosis for treatment of wastewater for reuse at refineries in Brazil and the rest of the world.

Table 3 shows the operating costs of treatment to remove nitrophenols with advanced oxidative processes, for 90% reduction (initial concentration of 0.04 mM) (Goi & Trapido, 2002).

Treatment Process	Compound	$[H_2O_2]o$ (mM)	$[Fe^{2+}]o$ (mM)	Energy required (kWh/m³)	Energy cost (US$/m³)	Total cost (US$/m³)
UV	4,6-DN-0-CR	0	0	901	63.10	63.10
	2,6-DNP	0	0	658	46.10	46.10
	4-NP	0	0	872	61.10	61.10
UV/H_2O_2	4,6-DN-0-CR	10	0	21.9	1.53	1.82
	2,6-DNP	10	0	16.3	1.14	1.43
	4-NP	10	0	5.15	0.36	0.65
Fenton	4,6-DN-0-CR	4	0.4	0	0	0.13
	2,6-DNP	4	0.4	0	0	0.13
	4-NP	2	0.1	0	0	0.06
Photo-Fenton	4,6-DN-0-CR	4	0.4	2.39	0.17	0.30
	2,6-DNP	4	0.1	2.06	0.14	0.26
	4-NP	2	0.1	2.00	0.14	0.20

Note: DN - dinitro; CR - cresol; DNP - dinitrophenol; NP - nitrophenol.

Table 3. Operating cost for treatment to remove nitrophenols with advanced oxidative processes, for 90% reduction (initial concentration of 0.04 mM) (Goi & Trapido, 2002).

Advanced oxidative processes can be used to treat sourwater from oil refineries containing low biodegradability compounds and toxic substances that prevent use of biological treatment (Coelho et al., 2006). Sourwater is an industrial effluent that should be segregated and treated by combined processes because of its complex chemical composition (see Table 4), containing emulsified oil, phenols, sulfides, mercaptans, ammonia, cyanide and other micro-pollutants.

Despite its complex composition, sourwater can be considered a candidate for industrial reuse when submitted to efficient treatment processes. It is produced when steam is injected in some refinery processing units to reduce the initial steam pressures of hydrocarbons, permitting operation at lower temperatures. After separation at the top of the tower, the sourwater can be fed into a rectification tower to remove ammonia and hydrogen sulfide. Besides being highly polluting, sourwater is very corrosive. The amount of sourwater generated by a refinery depends on various factors, including the process configuration and type and characteristics of the crude oil being processed. Typical production of sourwater at large refineries ranges from 0.2 to 0.5 m³/tonne (metric ton) of crude oil (Coelho et al., 2006).

Parameter	Range or average
COD (mg / L)	850-1020
DOC(mg / L)	300-440
BOD$_5$	570
Phenol (mg/L)	98-128
Ammonia (mg/L)	5.1-21.1
TSS (mg/L)	n.d[a]
VSS (mg/L)	n.d[a]
pH	8-8.2
Turbidity (NTU)	22-52
Sulfide (mg/L)	15-23
Toluene (µg/L)	1.1
Ethylbenzene (µg/L)	3.7
m,p-Xylene (µg/L)	15.4
o-Xylene (µg/L)	3.7
Oil and grease (mg/L)	12.7

Note: a - not detected; TSS - Total Suspended Solids; VSS – Volatile Suspended Solids.

Table 4. Average characteristics of sourwater (Coelho et al., 2006).

5. Conclusion

Brazil is currently expanding its refining capacity and faces problems of localized water shortage, both in semi-arid regions and intensely urbanized ones (such as the metropolitan areas of Rio de Janeiro and São Paulo), in the latter case because of high water demand. This chapter presented conventional wastewater treatment technologies and those aimed at improving the quality sufficiently for reuse. In the second case, the costs and perspectives for application in Brazil were presented.

The conventional wastewater treatment methods at oil refineries include gravity separation (mainly in API separators), dissolved air flotation, demulsification, coagulation, flocculation and biological treatment (aerated lagoons, activated sludge systems and biodiscs).

For treatment of refinery wastewater for reuse, the technologies include membranes (micro and ultrafiltration), membrane bioreactors (MBRs), reverse osmosis and reverse electrodialysis. These technologies work in series with conventional treatment techniques.

Some technologies, not yet applied in large scale for treating refinery effluents aiming at reuse, are promising and should be tested further. Among these are nanofiltration, which presents removal efficiency levels between those of ultrafiltration and reverse osmosis; ion exchange, which as shown in this chapter would be useful for the polishing step of reverse osmosis; and advanced oxidative processes, which are effective for treating sourwater. Despite the expensive investigations summarized here, further studies are necessary to assess the feasibility of these technologies for large-scale application to treat oil refinery wastewater for reuse.

6. Acknowledgments

We thank the National Research Council (CNPq) and the Rio de Janeiro State Research Foundation (FAPERJ) for funding.

7. References

Agência Nacional de Energia Elétrica - ANEEL. Retrieved on: August 26, 2010. Available from: <www.aneel.gov.br/arquivos/PDF/informacoes_gerenciais_novo.pdf>.

Al-Shamrani, A.A., James, A., Xiao, H. (2002) Destabilisation of oil-water emulsions and separation by dissolved air flotation. *Water Research*, Vol. 36, No. 6, (March 2002), pp. 1503-1512, ISSN 0043-1354.

Amorim, R.S. (2005). *Abastecimento de água em uma refinaria de petróleo - Caso Replan*. Master's dissertation in Management System, Universidade Federal Fluminense.

Andreozzi, R.; Caprio, V., Insula, A. Marotta, R. (1999). Advanced oxidation processes (AOP) for water purification and recovery. *Catalysis Today*, Vol. 53, No.1, (October 1999), pp. 51-59, ISSN 0920-5861.

Bessarabov, D.; Twardowski, Z. (2002). Industrial application of nanofiltration - new perspectives. *Membrane Technology*, (September 2002), pp. 6-9.

Braile, P.M. (1979). *Manual de Tratamento de águas residuárias industriais*, CIA Estadual Tecnol. Saneamento Ambiental, São Paulo.

Buetehorn, S.; Koh, C.N.; Wintgens, T. Volmering, D. Vossenkaul, K.; Melin, T. (2008). Investigating the impact of production conditions on membrane properties for MBR applications. *Desalination*, Vol .231, No. 1-3, (October, 2008), pp. 191-199, ISSN 0011-9164.

Castro, A.V.S. (2004). *Processos Oxidativos Avançados para tratamento de águas ácidas de refinarias de petróleo*, Master's dissertation in chemical engineering, Instituto Alberto Luiz Coimbra de Pós-graduação e Pesquisa de Engenharia (COPPE/UFRJ).

Cenpes. (2004). *Efluentes hídricos: Resultados em P & D. Avaliação de tecnologias visando ao reúso de efluentes*, (June 2004), Cenpes, Rio de Janeiro.

Cenpes. (2005). *Efluentes hídricos: Resultados em P & D. Tratamentos avançados de efluentes hídricos - PROAMB 5. Unidade protótipo de biorreator a membrana*, (December 2005), Cenpes, Rio de Janeiro.

Chao, Y; Liang T.M. A feasibility study of industrial wastewater recovery using electrodialysis reversal. (2008). *Desalination*, Vol. 221, No. 1-3, (March 2008), pp. 433-439, ISSN 0011-9164.

Chakrabarty, B.; Ghoshal, A.K.; Purkait, M.K. (2008). Ultrafiltration of stable oil-in-water emulsion by polysulfone membrane. *Journal of Membrane Science*, Vol. 325, No. 1, pp. 427-437, ISSN 0376-7388.

Chang, I.S., Le Clech, P., Jefferson, B., Judd, S. (2002). Membrane fouling in membrane bioreactors for wastewater treatment. *Journal of Environmental Engineering*, Vol. 128, No. 11, pp. 1018-1029, ISSN.0733-9372.

Cheryan, M., Rajagopalan, N. (1998). Membrane processing of oily streams. Wastewater treatment and waste reduction. *Journal of Membrane Science*, Vol. 151, No. 1, (December 1998), pp. 13-28, ISSN 0376-7388.

Coelho, A.D. (2004). *Tratamento de águas ácidas de refinaria de petróleo pelos processos Fenton e Foto-Fenton*, Master's dissertation in chemical engineering, Instituto Alberto Luiz Coimbra de Pós-graduação e Pesquisa de Engenharia (COPPE/UFRJ).

Coelho, A.; Castro, A.V.; Dezotti, M.; Sant'Anna Jr., G.L. (2006). Treatment of petroleum refinery sourwater by advanced oxidation processes. *Journal of Hazardous Materials*, Vol. 137, No. 1, (September 2006), pp.178-184, ISSN 0304-3894.

CostWater.. Retrieved on: July 20, 2010. Available from: <http://www.costwater.com>.

Couper J.R., Penney W.R., Fair J.R., Walas S.M. (2010). *Chemical Process Equipment: Selection and Design*, Elsevier, London.

Empresa de Pesquisa Energética - EPE. (2007). *Plano Nacional de Energia 2030*, EPE, Rio de Janeiro.

Environmental Protection Agency - EPA. (2008). *BAT guidance note on best available techniques for oil and gas refineries*, 1. edition, ISBN: 1-84095-291-1, USA.

Ferreira, E.F.T., Almeida, J.H.C., Santiago, V.M.J., Wachburger, R.L. (2000). Ampliação da Estação de Tratamento de Despejos Industriais (ETDI) da Refinaria Alberto Pasqualini (REFAP) da Petrobras, *Proceedings of XXVII Congresso Interamericano de Engenharia Sanitária e Ambiental*.

Fritzmann, C; Löwenberg, J.; Wintgens, T.; Melin, T. (2007). State-of-the-art of reverse osmosis desalination. *Desalination*, Vol. 216, No. 1-3, (October 2007), pp. 1-76, ISSN 0011-9164.

Goi, A.; Trapido, M. (2002). Hydrogen peroxide photolysis, Fenton reagent and photo-Fenton for the degradation of nitrofenols: a comparative study. *Chemosphere*, Vol. 46, No. 6, (February 2002), pp. 913-922, ISSN 0045-6535.

Habert, A.C., Borges, C.P., Nóbrega, R. (Eds.). (2006). *Processos de separação por membranas*, Série Escola Piloto em Engenharia Química (COPPE/UFRJ), Rio de Janeiro.

Perry, R.H.; Green, D.W. (Eds). (2007). *Perry's Chemical Engineers' Handbook*, McGraw Hill, New York.

Hami, M.L., Al-Hashimi, M.A., Al-Doori, M.M. Effect of activated carbon on BOD and COD removal in a dissolved air flotation unit treating refinery wastewater. (2007). *Desalination*, Vol. 216, No. 1-3, (October 2007), pp. 116-122, ISSN 0011-9164.

Hlavacek, M. (1995). Break-up of oil-in-water emulsions induced by permeation through a microfiltration membrane. *Journal of Membrane Science*, Vol. 102, No. 15, (June 1995), pp. 1-7, ISSN 0376-7388.

Jaworski, A.J. (2009). On-line measurement of separation dynamics in primary gas/oil/water separators: Challenges and technical solutions - a review. *Petroleum Science and Engineering*, Vol. 68, No. 1-2, (September 2009), pp. 47-59, ISSN 0920-4105.

Luz, A.B., Sampaio, J.A., Monte, M.B.M., Almeida, S.L.M. (Eds.). (2002). *Tratamento de Minérios*, Centro de tecnologia mineral - CETEM, 3. edition, Rio de Janeiro.

Matos, O.S. (2005). *Avaliação do desempenho e caracterização de parâmetros em Lagoa seguida de Lagoa de sedimentação*, Master's dissertation in civil engineering, Instituto Alberto Luiz Coimbra de Pós-graduação e Pesquisa de Engenharia (COPPE/UFRJ).

Matsumura, E.M., Mierzwa, J.C. (2008). Water conservation and reuse in poultry processing plant - A case study. *Resources Conservation & Recycling*, Vol. 52, No. 6, (April 2008), pp. 835-842, ISSN 0921-3449.

Melin, T.; Jefferson, B.; Bixio, D.; Thoeye, C.; De Wilde, W.; De Koning, J.; Van der Graaf, J.; Wintgens, T. (2006). Membrane bioreactors technology for wastewater treatment and reuse. *Desalination*, Vol. 187, No. 1-3, (February 2006), pp. 271-282, ISSN 0011-9164.

Mierzwa, J.C. Hespanhol, I. (2005). *Água na Indústria - Uso racional e reúso*, Oficina de Textos, São Paulo.

Nazarov, V.I., Asylova, K.G., Lukinskaya, N.G. (1979) Refinery wastewater desalting by means of reverse osmosis. *Chemistry and Technology of Fuels and Oils*, Vol. 15, No. 4, pp. 278-281.

Oever, R.V. MBR focus: is submerged best? *Filtration + Separation*, (June 2005), pp. 24-27.

Ohya, H.; Kim, J.J.; Chinen, A.; Aihara, M.; Semenova, S.I.; Negishi, Y.; Mori, O.; Yasuda, M. (1998). Effects of pore size on separation mechanisms of microfiltration of oily water, sing porous glass tubular membrane. *Journal of Membrane Science*, v. 145, No. 1, (June 1998), pp. 1-14, ISSN 0376-7388.

Organization of American States - OAS. *Desalination by Reverse Osmosis*. Available at: http://www.oas.org/DSD/publications/Unit/oea59e/ch20.htm. Retrieved on: August 31, 2010.

Piras, P.R.F. (1993). *Tratamento biológico de efluentes de refinaria de petróleo em lagoas aeradas em série*, Master's dissertation in chemical engineering, Instituto Alberto Luiz Alberto Coimbra de Pós-graduação e Pesquisa de Engenharia (COPPE/UFRJ).

Ravanchi, M.T.; Kaghazchi, T.; Kargari, A. (2009). Application of membrane separation processes in petrochemical industry. *Desalination*, Vol. 235, No. 1-3, (January 2009), pp.199-244, ISSN 0011-9164.

Rubio, J. Souza, M.L., Smith, R.W. (2002). Overview of flotation as a wastewater treatment technique. *Minerals Engineering*, Vol.15, No. 3, (March 2002), pp. 139-155, ISSN 0892-6875.

Santiago, V.M.J. (2009). *Avaliação de Biorreator com membranas (MBR) no tratamento e reúso de efluentes da Petrobras*. Apresentação para o Simpósio de Processo de Separação com Membranas, (July 23, 2009).

Scholz, W., Fuchsm, W. (2000). Treatment of oil contaminated wastewater in a membrane bioreactor. *Water Research*, Vol. 34, No. 14, (October 2000), pp. 3621-3629, ISSN 0043-1354.

Teodosiu, C.; Kennedy, M.D.; Van Straten, H.A.; Schippers, J.C. (1999) Evaluation of secondary refinery effluent treatment using ultrafiltration membranes. *Water Research*, Vol. 33, No. 9, (June 1999), pp. 2172-2180, ISSN 0043-1354.

Torres, A.P.R.; Santiago, V.M.J.; Borges, C.P. (2008). Performance evaluation of submerged membrane bioreactor pilot units for refinery wastewater treatment. *Environmental progress*, Vol. 17, No. 2, (July 2008), pp.189-194, ISSN 1944-7442.

Viero, A.F.; Melo, T.M.; Torres, A.P.R.; Ferreira, N.R. Sant'Anna, G.L.; Borges, C.P.; Santiago, V.M.J. (2008). The effects of long-term feeding of high organic loading in a submerged membrane bioreactor treating oil refinery wastewater. *Journal of Membrane Science*, Vol. 319, No. 1-2, (July 2008), pp. 223 – 230, ISSN 0376-7388.

Wagner, J. (2001). *Membrane Filtration Handbook Practical tips and hints*, 2nd ed., Osmonics Inc, Minnetonka.

Wang, Y.P., Smith, R. (1994). Wastewater minimization. *Chemical Engineering Science*, Vol. 49, No. 7, (April 1994), pp. 981-1006, ISSN 0009-2509.

Worrell, E., Galitsky, C. (2005). *Energy Efficiency Improvement and Cost Saving Opportunities for Petroleum Refineries - An Energy Star Guide for Energy and Plant Managers*, Ernest Orlando Lawrence. Berkeley National Laboratory (February 2005).

Yang, C. (2007). Electrochemical coagulation for oily water demulsification. *Separation Purification Technology*, Vol. 54, No. 3, (May 2007), pp. 388-395, ISSN 1383-5866.

Made in the USA
Las Vegas, NV
13 November 2024

696aaf5a-4a01-46ce-932d-b92b6e192bc8R02